THE PROTEINS

CHEMISTRY, BIOLOGICAL ACTIVITY, AND METHODS

VOLUME I, PART B

The Proteins

CHEMISTRY, BIOLOGICAL ACTIVITY, AND METHODS

Edited by

HANS NEURATH

Department of Biochemistry
University of Washington
Seattle, Washington

KENNETH BAILEY

Department of Biochemistry
University of Cambridge
Cambridge, England

VOLUME I, PART B

ACADEMIC PRESS INC., PUBLISHERS

NEW YORK, 1953

Library of Congress Catalog Card Number: 52-13366

PRINTED IN THE UNITED STATES OF AMERICA

CONTRIBUTORS TO VOLUME I, PART B

JOHN T. EDSALL, *University Laboratory of Physical Chemistry Related to Medicine and Public Health, Harvard University, Boston, Massachusetts.*

IRVING M. KLOTZ, *Department of Chemistry, Northwestern University, Evanston, Illinois.*

R. R. PORTER, *National Institute for Medical Research, Mill Hill, London, England.*

FRANK W. PUTNAM, *Department of Biochemistry, University of Chicago, Chicago, Illinois.*

CONTENTS

CONTENTS OF VOLUME I, PART A

CONTENTS OF VOLUME II (TWO PARTS)

CHAPTER 7

The Size, Shape and Hydration of Protein Molecules

By JOHN T. EDSALL

I. Introduction

Protein molecules are large and unstable; they are also extraordinarily reactive, and in extremely diverse ways.   They form complexes, of varying stability, with almost all anions and cations, with lipides, with carbo-hydrates, and with one another.   In addition to the conjugated proteins of well-defined character, such as the hemoglobins, there are innumerable proteins with a specific affinity for molecules with particular configura-tions, notably the enzymes with their capacity to react with their sub-strates and with other molecules containing the same or similar groupings in the correct arrangement.   Some enzyme molecules are bound very tightly to particular coenzymes; others form very loose unstable enzyme–coenzyme complexes.   Proteins are generally obtained for study either from actively metabolizing tissues or from media such as blood plasma, which are in a constant state of dynamic interchange with such tissues. The lifetime of a protein molecule in its natural surroundings is commonly short, often a matter only of days or even hours; some, however, such as collagen or mammalian hemoglobin, may persist for months, being in relatively isolated structures, set apart from the constant flux of dynamic interchange proceeding in tissues such as liver.

This chapter will deal with studies on purified proteins, separated by various fractionation procedures from the complex systems of which they form a part in nature.   Such studies on separated proteins are funda-mental to the progress of this field.   However, the results so obtained must always be interpreted with due consideration of the natural origins of the separated protein molecules, and of their commonly great sensi-tivity to denaturation even when they are prepared and kept under con-ditions of maximum stability.   When the physical chemist makes a series of measurements on the properties of a particular protein prepara-tion, he may be studying a different kind of molecule in his last measure-ment from that which he studied in the first.   Moreover, even the freshly prepared substance may be something quite different from anything that was present in the original tissue from which the protein preparation had been extracted.

These considerations should not discourage the investigator of pro-teins from proceeding with his work, but they should cause him to proceed in constant awareness of the delicacy and complexity of the structures with which he deals, of the imperfections and dangers of all fractionation procedures, and of the frequent need for revising his methods and his conclusions as better methods become available.   The results presented in this chapter should be read in connection with Chap. 1 where methods of isolation are discussed in detail.

The values of molecular weight discussed in this chapter are commonly reliable to within 5 to 10 per cent; sometimes, in exceptionally favorable cases, to within 1 or 2 per cent.   The absolute values of molecular dimensions, on the other hand, are as a rule considerably more uncertain.

Estimates of molecular shape are generally complicated by the difficulty of resolving effects due to solvation of the protein from those due to molecular asymmetry. In many cases, also, the data on asymmetry permit description of the molecule only in terms of an equivalent ellipsoid of revolution having approximately the same physical constants as the actual molecule. Electron micrographs provide more specific pictures, but they are taken of dried proteins, which cannot be generally identical in size and shape with the same molecules in aqueous solution. Thus our present conceptions of the shapes of protein molecules give only a rather broad fuzzy outline, like a photograph considerably out of focus; the finer details of the geometry of the molecule as yet escape us. Deeper insight is beginning to be obtained from x-ray diffraction studies on protein crystals; for the discussion of that topic, and for the detailed structure of some amino acids and peptides, the reader should turn to Chap. 4.[1]

The studies to be presented here raise two important general questions, which deserve some discussion before the separate methods and data are considered. Just what is meant when we speak of a protein molecule? And how do we recognize a pure protein when we have prepared it, if indeed there is any such thing as a pure preparation?

1. What Is a Protein Molecule?

To many chemists the term "molecule" denotes a group of atoms linked together by covalent bonds. For the purposes of the protein chemist, such a definition is too restricted. Indeed even among very simple organic compounds, one finds structures which almost everyone would denote as molecules, but which do not obey this definition, for example, the dimers of formic acid and of the higher fatty acids.

$$
\begin{array}{ccc}
 & O \cdots H{-}O & \\
R{-}C & & C{-}R \\
 & O{-}H \cdots O &
\end{array}
$$

The two single molecules are held together in this structure by hydrogen

(1) Some general references on the problem of protein size and shape may be noted here.[2-5b]

(2) E. J. Cohn and J. T. Edsall, Proteins, Amino Acids and Peptides, Reinhold Publishing Corporation, New York, 1943.

(3) J. L. Oncley, Ann. N. Y. Acad. Sci. 41, 121 (1941).

(4) J. Wyman and E. N. Ingalls, J. Biol. Chem. 147, 297 (1943).

(5) J. T. Edsall, Fortschr. Chem. Forsch. 1, 119 (1949); a few portions of this article have, with the permission of the publishers (Springer-Verlag), been incorporated in some pages of the present chapter, especially in sec. XIX.

(5a) A. E. Alexander and P. Johnson, Colloid Science, Clarendon Press, Oxford, 1949.

(5b) C. Sadron, Progress in Biophys. and Biophys. Chem. (London and New York) 3, 237 (1953).

bonds only, and to form two molecules of monomer from the dim
requires the expenditure of only about 10 kcal. of energy per mole. Yet
in spite of the relative instability of this structure, it involves a pattern
with such a definite configuration that few chemists would hesitate to
call it a molecule. The analogy with protein molecules is actually very
close, since there is now strong evidence that the fundamental subunits
of protein structure are largely held together by hydrogen bonds.

A comparison between the chemistry of proteins and of high polymers
is perhaps instructive in this respect. The monomer units in synthetic
high polymers are almost always linked together through covalent bonds.
The same unit repeats itself throughout a long chain with a characteristic
free terminal group at each end. To the high-polymer chemist, the
molecule is, therefore, the structure which contains one such free terminal
group at each end; and one of the most satisfactory methods of molecular
weight determination for molecules that are not too large is to apply an
analytical technique that is specific for the particular end groups of a
particular polymer. Of course, aggregates of these primary molecular
units can and frequently do form; but they are, in general, loose and
unstable, of variable composition, and, therefore, without a precisely
defined molecular weight. Thus, the polyamino acids prepared by
Woodward and Schramm[6] were reported by them to give extremely high
molecular weights of over a million in certain solvents, as deduced from
osmotic pressure and viscosity measurements. However, studies in other
solvents[7] have shown that these large structures are aggregates which can
be dissociated into much smaller units by a suitable choice of solvent.
The true average molecular weight was considered to be that found in the
solvent giving the lowest value of all those tested, and proved to be of the
order of 40,000.

On the other hand, the protein chemist takes a different attitude
toward the molecule of such a substance as human or horse hemoglobin.
Here the molecular weight of 67,000, as determined from measurements
in water or dilute salt solutions, is taken to be a true unit, in spite of the
fact that hemoglobin from several animal species dissociates into two half
molecules, each with a molecular weight of 34,000, when dissolved in
concentrated urea solution.[8,9] According to the criterion applied by
most high-polymer chemists, the latter is the true molecule, and the
larger unit is an aggregation product. However, the latter is universally

(6) R. B. Woodward and C. H. Schramm, *J. Am. Chem. Soc.* **69**, 1551 (1947).
(7) F. Eirich, E. Katchalski, J. Reisman, and P. Spitnik, unpublished results;
     for a review of the whole situation, see E. Katchalski, *Advances in Protein
     Chem.* **6**, 123 (1951) especially p. 166.
(8) N. F. Burk and D. M. Greenberg, *J. Biol. Chem.* **87**, 197 (1930).
(9) J. Steinhardt, *J. Biol. Chem.* **123**, 543 (1938).

regarded by protein chemists as the native hemoglobin molecule, even though it consists of two halves which can be split by relatively mild reagents. The smaller unit is, of course, also a definite molecule. This point of view is justified by various facts: for instance, that native hemoglobin forms very perfect crystals, showing a high degree of internal regularity in molecular structure, as judged by x-ray diffraction patterns; and also by the fact that in its combinations with other molecules, such as oxygen, it functions not as a loose aggregate but as a highly integrated structure, in which the four heme groups present in the 67,000 molecular-weight unit show strong interactions indicating that they are closely coupled.[10]

Analysis of free end groups gives no simple correlation here with other findings; horse and donkey hemoglobin are reported to contain six terminal amino groups of valine per molecule of 66,000 molecular weight; human hemoglobin to contain five valine amino groups; and cow, sheep, and goat to contain two valine and two methionine.[11] As yet these data are not easy to correlate with other known properties of hemoglobin; presumably they indicate subunits of peptide chains within the larger molecular framework, but the subunits have never been isolated as such, and it is not particularly helpful at present to think of them as molecules.

For the purposes of the discussion in this chapter, we shall generally consider a molecule as a molecular kinetic unit in solution—the unit which is observed to move in a diffusion or sedimentation experiment, and which by its presence lowers the activity of the solvent and thereby determines the osmotic pressure of the system. The significance of such measurements for protein chemistry, however, lies in the fact that the molecular kinetic unit is also generally a structural unit with a definite pattern. This is not true, for instance, of a particle of gold in a gold sol; such particles are fragments, derived from the breakdown of a larger structure, and the exact number of gold atoms in a particle is arbitrary, depending on the conditions of preparation. The nearest analog in protein chemistry is gelatin, which consists of a heterogeneous mixture of breakdown products derived from the hydrolysis of collagen. Studies of the molecular-weight distribution of the breakdown products,[12] and of the x-ray diffraction patterns given by the native collagen,[13] suggest the existence of rather compact structural units in collagen, which may be

(10) J. Wyman, *Advances in Protein Chem.* **4**, 407 (1948).

(11) R. R. Porter and F. Sanger, *Biochem. J.* **42**, 287 (1948); also *in* F. J. W. Roughton and J. C. Kendrew, eds., Haemoglobin, Butterworths Scientific Publications, London, 1949, p. 121.

(12) G. Scatchard, J. L. Oncley, J. W. Williams, and A. Brown, *J. Am. Chem. Soc.* **66**, 1980 (1944).

(13) R. S. Bear, *Advances in Protein Chem.* **7**, 69 (1952).

called molecules. There are similar indications from x-ray studies on keratin.[14] These postulated molecules are elements in a fibrous structure and have never been identified as such in solutions derived from the fibers. However, the indications of their existence serve to broaden the possible significance of the term molecule as applied to proteins and may lead in time to the isolation and characterization of these units. In this chapter, however, the discussion will be restricted to protein molecules which can be studied in solution.

2. Criteria of Purity of Protein Preparations

It is extremely difficult to demonstrate the purity of a protein preparation. Many criteria can be applied, and a truly pure protein must satisfy all of them. Thus, when studied by electrophoresis (Chap. 6), such a protein should not only migrate with a single boundary, but the degree of boundary spreading should be no greater than corresponds to the diffusion constant of the protein, as independently determined. Moreover this should be true over the entire pH range within which the protein is stable.[15] The same is true of sedimentation measurements in the ultracentrifuge and of the rate of free diffusion. Not only should there be only a single sedimenting boundary, but the form of this boundary should possess the symmetry characteristic of a single component. A similar statement holds for diffusion. Likewise, the study of rotary diffusion, discussed later in this chapter, provides additional evidence; measurements of double refraction of flow on elongated molecules, for example, may show the presence of several components of differing length. Osmotic-pressure measurements, taken alone, give only a number-average molecular weight; but if light-scattering measurements, which give a weight average, are made on the same preparation, agreement between the two results provides evidence of uniformity with respect to molecular weight.

Each of these methods gives evidence only with respect to certain gross properties of the molecules in the preparation—general size and shape, and net electric charge. All the molecules may be indistinguishable in these general properties, and yet may differ greatly among themselves in their amino acid composition and in the finer details of their structure. The solubility test of purity, discussed in Chap. 1, is in this respect a more searching criterion. Even this, however, is limited in its

(14) R. S. Bear and H. J. Rugo, *Ann. N. Y. Acad. Sci.* **55**, 627 (1950).

(15) It should be pointed out that the pH stability range of a protein is usually determined by just such criteria as uniformity of electrophoretic mobility and sedimentation constant. The important thing here is that there is a pH range of significant width over which these criteria of uniformity are satisfied.

sensitivity; several per cent of a minor component might well be present without being detected with assurance, owing to the inherent errors of solubility measurements and the difficulty of making determinations when the amount of solid phase in equilibrium with the solution is very small.

Recent advances in the detailed study of the sequence of amino acid residues in the polypeptide chains of proteins have provided another important criterion of uniformity. If two protein molecules are identical, the sequence of amino acid residues in all the peptide chains present in both proteins must be identical. This criterion has been applied to the B-chain of the insulin molecule, which contains a terminal phenyl-alanyl amino group, by Sanger and Tuppy;[16] and to the A-chain of insulin, which contains a terminal glycyl amino group, by Sanger and Thompson.[16a] All breakdown products derived from the partial hydrolysis of both chains were found to have structures compatible with a unique sequence of amino acid residues in each of the two original total chains. In this fundamental respect, therefore, the insulin molecules in the original preparation appeared to be all alike. No similar data of this sort for other proteins are yet available. Fundamental as such studies are, however, it must be remembered that the unique structure of a native protein depends not only on the sequence of amino acid residues in the peptide chains, but also on the geometrical configuration of the chains and the pattern in which they are folded. A given sequence is compatible with many such configurations, so that a collection of molecules uniform with respect to sequence could still differ markedly among themselves in detailed structure. A mixture of native and denatured hemoglobin or serum albumin molecules, for example, might well exemplify such a system, if denaturation simply involves a disarrangement of peptide chains from their native configuration, without any actual splitting of covalent bonds.

An analytical proof of lack of purity may often be derived from amino acid analysis, or from the determination of any specific reactive group in the molecule. If the molecular weight is known by any of the methods to be described in this chapter, and if accurate analysis shows that on the average less than one group of a particular type is present per molecule of protein, then it is clear that more than one type of molecule is present in the preparation. Thus the tryptophan content[17] of crystallized

(16) F. Sanger and H. Tuppy, *Biochem. J.* **49**, 463, 481 (1951).

(16a) F. Sanger and E. O. P. Thompson, *Biochem. J.* **53**, 353, 366 (1953); F. Sanger, E. O. P. Thompson, and H. Tuppy, *in* Symposium sur les Hormones Protéiques et Dérivées des Protéines, Paris, 1952.

(17) E. Brand, B. Kassell, and L. J. Saidel, *J. Clin. Invest.* **23**, 437 (1944).

human serum albumin was found to be only 0.6 residue per molecule of molecular weight 69,000. Even more conclusive was the finding of Hughes[18] and of Benesch and Benesch[19] that the content of titratable sulfhydryl groups in these serum albumin preparations was only 0.6–0.7 per mole. In this case the sulfhydryl-containing mercaptalbumin was crystallized by Hughes as a mercury derivative; the albumin molecules which lacked a free sulfhydryl group remained in the supernatant liquid. Thus the test which demonstrated the lack of homogeneity in the preparation also served as a clue to a method of separating the components.

In general, one may separate a protein preparation into two or more fractions by any method that does not denature the protein. If the protein is a single substance, all the fractions should be identical in amino acid content, in absorption spectrum, and in any specific activity that the preparation may possess, such as enzymatic or hormonal activity. Here again, as with other criteria discussed above, the evidence is essentially negative. The separation of two fractions of significantly different properties is a proof that the original preparation was not pure, but the failure to achieve such a separation is no sure test of purity. However, if several different methods of fractionation all fail to achieve separation, and if the protein meets the other tests of purity already described, few chemists would hesitate to pronounce it pure.

Immunological assay is often a powerful tool for the investigation of protein purity, and has been well discussed by Kabat.[20]

Recently the purity of insulin has been examined by the method of countercurrent distribution.[21] The preparations studied showed definite evidence of resolution into two components, after 900 transfers, involving distribution between 2-butanol and 1 per cent aqueous dichloroacetic acid; but the proportions of the two components differed considerably in different preparations. It will probably be difficult to extend this method to most other proteins, because of the difficulty of finding suitable solvents giving a suitable distribution coefficient and the danger of denaturing most proteins during the long series of equilibrations involved. However, the method is so powerful where it is applicable that further exploration is certainly called for.

In the case of some of the smaller proteins, at least, separation on an ion-exchange resin may be employed as an effective means of obtaining the desired component free from accompanying impurities, and also as a

(18) W. L. Hughes, Jr., *Cold Spring Harbor Symposia Quant. Biol.* **14**, 79 (1950).

(19) R. Benesch and R. E. Benesch, *Arch. Biochem.* **19**, 35 (1948).

(20) E. A. Kabat, *J.Immunol.* **47**, 513 (1943), especially pp. 520–2.

(21) E. J. Harfenist and L. C. Craig, *J. Am. Chem. Soc.* **73**, 877 (1951); **74**, 3083 (1952).

sensitive technique for examining the purity of the separated component. Preliminary studies of this sort have been reported on cytochrome c,[21a] and on ribonuclease and lysozyme,[21b] using the cation-exchange resin Amberlite IRC-50. All of these proteins have molecular weights below 18,000. It remains to be seen whether larger proteins can be purified by similar methods without denaturation.

Closely related to this procedure is the fractionation of proteins by partition chromatography. Martin and Porter[21c] fractionated ox pancreas ribonuclease, using a two-phase system composed of ammonium sulfate, water, and ethylene glycol monoethyl ether (cellosolve). At suitable compositions this separates into a lighter phase containing chiefly water and cellosolve, and a denser phase composed chiefly of water and ammonium sulfate. The supporting column of kieselguhr held the lighter (stationary) phase, and the aqueous salt solution, containing the ribonuclease, flowed down through this. A sharp resolution into two enzymatically active fractions was obtained. More recently Porter[21d] has explored other two-phase systems containing water, various glycol ethers, and concentrated phosphate buffers or other salts. Very homogeneous insulin preparations could be obtained by chromatographic fractionation in such systems, even when the starting material was quite impure. Promising results were obtained with several other proteins.

It must be admitted that few, if any, of the proteins known today meet all the complex and exacting tests of purity here briefly summarized. For instance, the studies of Alberty, Anderson, and Williams[22,23] have demonstrated electrophoretic heterogeneity in preparations of proteins which had earlier been reported as pure even by the very rigorous solubility test.[24] This evidence of imperfect purity in even the best available protein preparations should not deter the chemist from studying them as

(21a) S. Paléus and J. B. Neilands, *Acta Chem. Scand.* **4**, 1024 (1950).

(21b) C. H. W. Hirs, W. H. Stein, and S. Moore, *J. Am. Chem. Soc.* **73**, 1893 (1951). A full report of the work on ribonuclease is given by C. H. W. Hirs, S. Moore, and W. H. Stein, *J. Biol. Chem.* **200**, 493 (1953) and on lysozyme by H. H. Tallan and W. H. Stein, *ibid.* **200**, 507 (1953).

(21c) A. J. P. Martin and R. R. Porter, *Biochem. J.* **49**, 215 (1951).

(21d) R. R. Porter, *ibid.* **53**, 320 (1953).

(22) R. A. Alberty, E. A., Anderson, and J. W. Williams, *J. Phys. & Colloid Chem.* **52**, 217 (1948).

(23) E. A. Anderson and R. A. Alberty, *J. Phys. & Colloid. Chem.* **52**, 1345 (1948).

(24) It would be desirable, to make such tests even more illuminating, to carry out the electrophoretic studies, the solubility measurements, and as many other kinds of studies as possible, on the identical preparation of protein in the same laboratory at the same time. The instability of protein molecules in general, and the difficulty of reproducing different preparations exactly, would suggest the desirability of this procedure.

they can now be obtained.   Progress will come by working with the best preparations available, bearing in mind their limitations as to purity, and constantly striving to develop better methods of purification, in conjunction with the characterization of the products.   The proteins to be discussed in this chapter are for the most part preparations which are fairly homogeneous with respect to size and shape, and generally also with respect to electrophoretic mobility.   Some have been found, at least in certain preparations, to satisfy the rigorous solubility test.   Other well-known and widely studied preparations, like zein or the γ-globulins, are certainly not chemical individuals at all, but families of closely related proteins.   The reader should bear these limitations in mind as the discussion proceeds.

II. The Binding of Water by Proteins

In most of this chapter we shall be concerned primarily with the properties of proteins in solution.   The major component of the solvent is almost always water,[25] generally containing some dissolved ions and often various organic solutes.   The molecular kinetic unit in solution is not the anhydrous protein molecule but the molecule with a considerable amount of water quite tightly bound.   Often the binding of other solute molecules and ions by the protein is very strong; such interactions are discussed elsewhere in this volume by Klotz (Chap. 8), and will be mentioned only incidentally here.   The binding of water by the protein, however, is of such major importance for the subject of this chapter that it requires more detailed consideration.

Several studies have now been made on the binding of water by dried proteins, as a function of the vapor pressure of water in the system.[26-30]

(25) The prolamines, such as zein, gliadin, and secalin, dissolve best in alcohol–water mixtures containing mostly alcohol, or in such organic solvents as propylene glycol.   Insulin is also soluble in propylene glycol–water mixtures.

(26) H. B. Bull, *J. Am. Chem. Soc.* **66**, 1499 (1944).

(27) E. F. Mellon, A. H. Korn, and S. R. Hoover, *J. Am. Chem. Soc.* **69**, 827 (1947); **71**, 2761 (1949); E. F. Mellon, A. H. Korn, E. L. Kokes, and S. R. Hoover, *J. Am. Chem. Soc.* **73**, 1870 (1951).

(28) H. J. Frey and W. J. Moore, *J. Am. Chem. Soc.* **70**, 3644 (1948).

(29) S. W. Benson, D. A. Ellis, and R. W. Zwanzig, *J. Am. Chem. Soc.* **72**, 2102 (1950).

(30) F. Haurowitz, *J. Biol. Chem.* **193**, 443 (1951).   This is a study of hemoglobin, and especially of the binding of water by the heme groups.   The term "dried protein" here denotes material which has been carefully dried *in vacuo*, so that the amount of water which can still be removed by heating in an oven at 105° or above is considerably less than 1% of the weight of the protein. Air-dried proteins may still contain 8 or 10% water; this is, of course, the strongly bound water which is under discussion here.

Some typical curves, taken from the work of Bull, are shown in Fig. 1. For all proteins studied, there is a very rapid increase of water uptake as the vapor pressure of water rises from zero to about one tenth of that for pure water at the same temperature. This is followed by a plateau, with another steep rise as 100 per cent humidity is approached. The amount

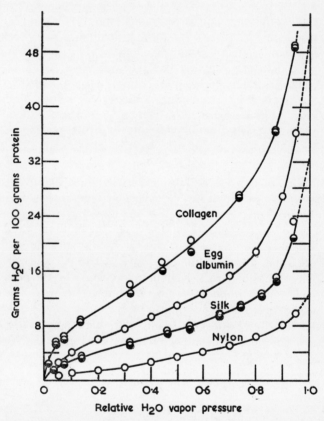

FIG. 1. Water adsorption curves for unstretched nylon, for wet (open circles) and dry (half circles) silk, for unlyophilized egg albumin, and for wet (open circles) and dry (half circles) collagen at 25°. From Bull.[26]

bound in the first steep portion of the curve varies for different proteins from about 4 to 10 g. per 100 g. dry protein. It is considerably less than the amount required to form a monolayer of water over the surface of the protein molecule. Pauling[31] has pointed out a correlation between the amount of water which is strongly bound and the number of ionic and polar groups in the amino acid side chains of the protein. Pauling con-

(31) L. Pauling, *J. Am. Chem. Soc.* **67**, 555 (1945).

cluded from Bull's data that there is little or no binding of water by the —CONH— groups of the peptide chain. However, the later work of Mellon, Korn, and Hoover[27] does provide direct evidence for the participation of peptide groups in water binding.

Further analysis of Bull's data showed that the water molecules bound in the first steep portion of the curve combine with the protein with a large liberation of heat, 3–6 kcal./mole water.[32] This is the (negative) value of ΔH for the isothermal transfer of 1 mole of water from the pure liquid state to its combination with the dried protein. The energy liberated in the binding of additional water is much smaller. Also, the binding of the first water molecules is accompanied by a marked volume contraction,[33,34] of the order of 0.05 cc./g. protein. These findings have recently been extended to several other proteins by McMeekin.[35] Neurath and Bull found that the density of dried ovalbumin actually increased on the binding of the first portions of water.

Recent studies by Richards[36] on crystals of β-lactoglobulin and of human serum mercaptalbumin mercury dimer indicate an even greater relative change of density when water is taken up by a thoroughly dried protein. X-ray diffraction measurements and composition studies on vacuum-dried crystals of both these proteins indicated a density close to 1.17. The measured density by a flotation method on the same crystals was near 1.25. However, the evidence clearly indicated that the latter method gave falsely high results due to the penetration of the surrounding liquid into the crystals, and that the value near 1.17 was the true density. The density increased to 1.27 in air-dried crystals containing 8 to 10 per cent moisture, and the uptake of this amount of moisture produced practically no change in the dimensions of the unit cell of the crystal. Thus it would appear that the first portions of water incorporated into the vacuum-dried crystal fitted into interstices between, or within, the protein molecules and did not increase the volume of the crystal at all. The fitting involved is, of course, much more than the mere geometrical filling of empty space; strong interactions between the water and the polar groups of the protein molecules are indicated by the large heat changes associated with the uptake of water in these systems.

The marked volume contractions are associated with the first portions of water added to the protein; the addition of further water involves

(32) M. Dole and A. D. McLaren, *J. Am. Chem. Soc.* **69**, 651 (1947).
(33) H. Chick and C. J. Martin, *Biochem. J.* **7**, 92 (1913).
(34) H. Neurath and H. B. Bull, *J. Biol. Chem.* **115**, 519 (1936).
(35) T. L. McMeekin, *J. Polymer Sci.*, in press (1953).
(36) F. M. Richards, Ph.D. Thesis, Harvard University, 1952.

practically no net volume change.   Thus the volume of a wet protein crystal containing 40–60 per cent by weight of water can be calculated from the chemical composition and the specific volumes of the components (see Chap. 4) using the same value of the partial specific volume of the protein that is derived from measurements in dilute aqueous solutions.[37]

In later portions of this chapter, we shall be concerned with the very complex question of the extent of hydration of proteins in solution, that is, the amount of water which is bound to the protein molecule tightly enough so that it travels with it in its motion through the solution.   This definition is to some extent ambiguous; any water molecule in the shell of water around the protein will in the course of time exchange with the unbound water of the surrounding medium.   However, if the water is tightly bound, the exchange rate will be very slow; if it is loosely bound, the exchange will be rapid.   We should like to know how this exchange rate varies as a function of the distance from the surface of the protein, and how it varies from one region of the protein surface to another.[38]   Of all this we are very ignorant.   The water which is tightly bound to the dry protein must certainly form part of the water of hydration in solution, and the figure for this hydration can hardly be less than this, that is, at least 0.04–0.10 g. water/g. protein.   An upper limit to hydration in solution would presumably be the amount of water per gram protein in a wet crystal in equilibrium with its mother liquor.   This is commonly of the order of 0.6–1.1 g. water/g. protein (see Chap. 4).   Some of the water in the crystal may serve simply to fill up interstices in the structure; such water would presumably not stick tightly to the protein molecules when they are free to move in the surrounding medium.   We shall consider later several lines of evidence, which will serve to narrow the range of possible values of hydration and to make this general concept somewhat more precise.

III. Partial Specific Volumes of Proteins in Solution

1. Definition and Measurement of Partial and Apparent Volumes

The determination of the hydration of proteins is a very difficult problem, as the discussion in the preceding section has indicated.   For many purposes, it is more helpful to consider a quantity which can be determined without ambiguity, namely, the volume increment resulting

(37) For a detailed discussion of protein crystals, see Chap. 4.

(38) For a study of the exchange rates of water bound to simple ions in solution, see J. P. Hunt and H. Taube, *J. Chem. Phys.* **19**, 602 (1951); R. A. Plane and H. Taube, *J. Phys. Chem.* **56**, 33 (1952).

from the addition of 1 g. of dried protein to a very large volume of solution. This quantity is known as the partial specific volume, $\bar{v}$, of the protein. The partial molal volume, $\bar{V}$, is equal to $\bar{v}$ multiplied by the molecular weight. The partial specific volumes of most simple proteins lie in the range 0.70–0.75 cc./g., although a few are slightly higher or lower. The values for lipoproteins are considerably higher, as a rule, than 0.75, depending on the amount of lipides present; those for glyco-proteins and mucoproteins are generally lower than 0.70. Extensive tables of values for partial specific volumes are given by Svedberg and Pedersen,[39] by Cohn and Edsall,[2] and by Lundgren and Ward.[40] Selected tables of such data are given later in this chapter.

The determination of partial specific volumes is fundamental for the evaluation of molecular weights from sedimentation studies in the ultra-centrifuge. The effective centrifugal force acting on the protein molecule is proportional to the density difference between the protein and the surrounding medium; and as a first approximation we may take the density of the dry protein in solution as the reciprocal of the partial specific volume. Correction factors depending on hydration will be considered later in sec. XIV. Here we shall discuss the determination of partial specific and molal volumes, and their correlation with chemical structure.

It is convenient to define a related quantity, the apparent molal (or specific) volume, which is closely related to the partial molal volume and is more readily measured.[41] Consider a system containing n_1 moles of solvent (component 1) and n_2 moles of solute (component 2); let the molal volume of the pure solvent be $v_1{}^0$, and let V be the volume of the whole system. Then the apparent molal volume of solute, $\Phi(v_2)$, is

$$\Phi(v_2) = (V - n_1 V_1{}^0)/n_2 \tag{1}$$

Thus Φ is the total volume increment, per mole of solute, above the volume of the pure solvent. Experimentally Φ is determined from density measurements on solvent and solution, and concentration determinations on the solution. If d_1 is the density of pure solvent and d that

(39) T. Svedberg, and K. O. Pedersen, The Ultracentrifuge. Clarendon Press, Oxford, 1940.

(40) H. P. Lundgren and W. H. Ward, in D. M. Greenberg, ed., Amino Acids and Proteins, C. C. Thomas, Publishers, Springfield, Illinois, 1951, Chap. VI.

(41) For a general discussion of apparent and partial molar and specific volumes, and other partial molal properties of solutions, see Lewis and Randall[42] and Glasstone.[43]

(42) G. N. Lewis and M. Randall, Thermodynamics, McGraw-Hill Company, New York, 1923.

(43) S. Glasstone, Thermodynamics for Chemists, D. Van Nostrand, Co., New York, 1947, Chap. XVIII.

of the solution, C_2 the concentration of solute in moles/l., and M_2 its molecular weight, then

$$\Phi(v_2) = \frac{1000}{C_2}\left(\frac{d_1 - d}{d_1}\right) + \frac{M_2}{d_1} \tag{2}$$

the partial molal volume of component 2, at any concentration is

$$\bar{V}_2 = (\partial V/\partial C_2)$$

at constant pressure, temperature, and mass of component 1 in the system. In very dilute solution $\bar{V}_2$ and $\Phi(v_2)$ become identical, and if Φ is independent of concentration over a given concentration range extending down to infinite dilution, then the two quantities are also equal over this entire range. In general, if solute concentration is expressed so that n_2 in Eq. (1) is given as moles of solute for a fixed quantity of solvent, n_1, then we obtain by differentiation

$$\bar{V}_2 = \frac{\partial V}{\partial n_2} = \Phi + n_2\frac{\partial \Phi}{\partial n_2} \tag{3}$$

If n_1 is chosen so that the system contains 1 kg. solvent, then n_2 in Eq. (3) becomes identical with the molality m_2. In the present discussion, however, we shall not consider the relatively small variations of $\Phi(v_2)$ and $\bar{V}_2$ with concentration,[44] but shall be concerned with the values in very dilute solutions, where apparent and partial molal (or specific) volumes are practically identical.

No attempt will be made here to discuss methods of density determination. Pycnometric methods have been the most widely used; these and other methods, for solids and liquids, are well presented by Bauer.[45] An extremely accurate flotation method, involving the motion in the liquid of a completely immersed magnetic float, has recently been described.[46,46a] The method appears to be accurate to less than 1 p.p.m. for the density values, but it requires rather large volumes of liquid, of the order of 300 cc.

(44) For studies of the variation of these quantities with concentration, for amino acids and peptides, see Cohn and Edsall,[2] Chap. 7, where a discussion of apparent molal heat capacities and compressibilities is also given. See also F. T. Gucker, Jr. and T W. Allen, *J. Am. Chem. Soc.* **64**, 191 (1942).

(45) N. Bauer, *in* A. Weissberger, ed., Physical Methods of Organic Chemistry, Interscience Publishers, New York, 1949, Vol. I., part I, p. 253.

(46) D. A. MacInnes, M. O. Dayhoff, and B. R. Ray, *Rev. Sci. Instruments* **22**, 642 (1951).

(46a) M. O. Dayhoff, G. E. Perlmann, and D. A. MacInnes, *J. Am. Chem. Soc.* **74**, 2515 (1952).

2. Relations to Chemical Composition; Electrostriction Due to Charged Groups

Traube[47] showed that the apparent molal volumes of most organic compounds could be expressed as the sums of molal volumes (in cubic centimeters) assigned to the constituent atoms: carbon 9.9, hydrogen 3.1, nitrogen 1.5, hydroxyl oxygen 2.3, sulfur 15.5, and so forth. Slightly revised values of these figures have been employed[48] to fit the data on amino acids and peptides: 16.3 cc. per CH_2 group, 20.0 cc. per CONH group, 7.7 cc. per NH_2 group, and 18.9 cc. per COOH group. A table of values of partial specific and molal volumes of amino acid residues has been given by Cohn and Edsall[2] on this basis.

Two correction factors must be considered before these values can be applied to actual specific or molal volumes of amino acids, peptides, and proteins. First, the actual value for an uncharged molecule in aqueous solution is larger than that calculated from the sum of the atomic volumes, the difference being of the order of 13 cc./mole. This term, called by Traube the covolume, must be added to the sum of the atomic volumes; for molecules as large as proteins, however, the covolume is a negligibly small fraction of the total molal volume. For dipolar ions, the partial molal volume is always smaller than that of an isomeric uncharged molecule: compare, for example, glycine with glycolamide, and α- or β-alanine with lactamide (Table I). The formation of an $-NH_3^+$ and a COO^- group from an uncharged $-NH_2$ and ^-COOH group in aqueous solution, involves a volume contraction of the order of 13 cc./mole if the amino group is alpha to the carboxyl, 15 cc./mole if it is in the β-position, and 18–20 cc./mole if the two groups are separated by a large distance. This contraction is known as electrostriction; it is due to orientation and close packing of water molecules around the ionic groups in the intense inhomogeneous electric field produced by the ionic charges. Thus the fact that the partial molal volume of glycine is smaller than that of glycolamide is not due to a smaller volume of the glycine molecule. Presumably the two molecules are of nearly the same size; it is the state of the surrounding water which is altered in the glycine solution.[49]

Electrostriction effects are also strikingly shown by studies of the heat capacities of solutions of ions and dipolar ions. The freedom of rotation of the water molecules held by the electrical attraction of the

(47) J. Traube, *Samml. Chem. u. Chem.-Tech. Vorträge* **4**, 255 (1899).

(48) E. J. Cohn, T. L. McMeekin, J. T. Edsall, and M. H. Blanchard, *J. Am. Chem. Soc.* **56**, 784 (1934); also Cohn and Edsall,[2] Chap. 16.

(49) Electrostriction also decreases the heat capacity and compressibility of solutions of dipolar ions as compared with their uncharged isomers. See Cohn and Edsall,[2] Chap. 7.

TABLE I

LIMITING APPARENT MOLAL VOLUMES, $\Phi(V)$, AND HEAT CAPACITIES, $\Phi(C_p)$, OF AMINO ACIDS AND THEIR UNCHARGED ISOMERS IN WATER AT 25°

	Apparent molal volume			Apparent molal heat capacity		
	$\Phi(V)_{c=0}$	$(\partial\Phi/\partial c)_{c=0}$	Volume electrostriction effect	$\Phi(C_p)_{c=0}$	$(\partial\Phi/\partial c)_{c=0}$	Heat capacity electrostriction effect
1. Glycolamide (CH$_2$OH.CONH$_2$)	43.20	0.160		35.76	0.62	
2. Glycine ($^+$H$_3$N.CH$_2$.COO$^-$)	56.16	0.861	12.96	8.83	4.58	26.93
3. Lactamide (CH$_3$CHOH.CO.NH$_2$)	73.51	0.0169		58.38	-0.48	
4. α-Alanine ($^+$H$_3$N.CH(CH$_3$).COO$^-$)	60.61	0.573	12.90	33.69	1.48	24.69
5. β-Alanine ($^+$H$_3$N.CH$_2$.CH$_2$.COO$^-$)	58.72	0.717	14.78	18.27	2.64	40.11
6. Methylhydantoic acid (H$_2$N.CONH.CH(CH$_3$).COOH)	94.2					
7. Glycylglycine ($^+$H$_3$N.CH$_2$.CONH.CH$_2$.COO$^-$)	76.8	1.30	17.4			

Values of $\Phi(V)$ in cc./mole, of $\Phi(C_p)$ in cal. deg.$^{-1}$ mole^{-1}. Limiting slopes, $(\partial\Phi/\partial c)_{c=0}$ expressed with respect to molar concentrations. Electrostriction effects are calculated by subtracting the value of Φ for the dipolar ion from that for its uncharged isomer.
References:

Nos. 1 and 2: from F. T. Gucker, Jr., W. L. Ford, and C. E. Moser, *J. Phys. Chem.* **43**, 153 (1939).
Nos. 3, 4, and 5: from F. T. Gucker, Jr., and T. W. Allen, *J. Am. Chem. Soc.* **64**, 191 (1942).
No. 6: from T. L. McMeekin, E. J. Cohn and J. H. Weare, *J. Am. Chem. Soc.* **57**, 626 (1935).
No. 7: from J. Daniel and E. J. Cohn, *J. Am. Chem. Soc.* **58**, 415 (1936). Compare Chap. 7 of Cohn and Edsall.[2]

charged groups is greatly inhibited, and this diminishes the heat capacity of the solution. The apparent molal heat capacity is defined similarly to the apparent molal volume (see reference 2, Chap. 7). Very accurate measurements of the apparent molal heat capacities of some dipolar ions and their uncharged isomers have been made by F. T. Gucker, Jr., and his collaborators at several temperatures. Some of their data at 25° are shown in Table I.

Although the covolume correction should be negligible in proteins, the electrostriction effect might be expected to be appreciable. The anionic side chains of free aspartic and glutamic acid residues, and the cationic groups of the histidine, arginine, and lysine residues, should exert such effects if the charges are free and not shielded by surrounding groups. Thus for human serum albumin the molecular weight[49a] is near 69,000 (Tables V, VI, and VIII), the partial specific volume is 0.733 (Table II), and the partial molal volume is thus 50.6 l. The titration data of Tanford[50] indicate that at the isoelectric point the molecule contains just over 100 cationic, and of course an equal number of anionic, groups. The electrostriction should thus be of the order of 100×18 cc. or 1.8 l.; i.e., about 3.5% of the observed partial molal volume. Nevertheless, from the available data on amino acid analysis, McMeekin[51] has calculated for this protein a partial specific volume that is in excellent agreement with the experimental value, using the specific volumes already indicated for the amino acid residues. He has also similarly found good agreement for a group of other proteins for which adequate amino acid analyses are available, as shown in Table II.

The success of these calculations suggests that it is correct to neglect electrostriction due to the charged side chains in computing the volume of a protein from that of its constituent amino acid residues. It is conceivable that these groups are so shielded in the native protein that they are unable to produce electrostriction of neighboring water molecules. However, the titration curves of native proteins show that many, if not all, of the acidic and basic groups are free to bind or release protons, and therefore presumably also to interact with water.[52] At present further

(49a) As pointed out on p. 721, some very recent and accurate measurements on serum albumin indicate a lower molecular weight, near 65,500; but this difference is actually irrelevant here, since we are concerned only with the number of charged groups per unit mass of protein, and any convenient unit may be chosen.

(50) C. Tanford, J. Am. Chem. Soc. **72**, 441 (1950).

(51) T. L. McMeekin and K. Marshall, Science **116**, 142 (1952).

(52) J. Steinhardt and E. M. Zaiser, J. Biol. Chem. **190**, 197 (1951), have shown that in hemoglobin there is a set of about 36 acidic and basic groups per molecule, nontitratable in the native but titratable in the denatured protein. These, however, represent only about one-fifth of the total acidic and basic groups in hemoglobin.

TABLE II
Specific Volume of Proteins

Protein	Specific volume observed (a) cc./g.	Specific volume calcd. from amino acid composition (b) cc./g.
Silk fibroin (suspended in water)	0.701(2)	0.689(3)
Ribonuclease	0.709(4)	0.703(3)
Wool (suspended in water)	0.716(5)	0.712(3)
Lysozyme	0.722(6)	0.717(7)
Fibrinogen (human)	0.725(8)	0.723(3)
α-Casein	0.728(9)	0.725(9)
Chymotrypsinogen	0.73(10)	0.734(3)
Casein (unfractionated)	0.731(9)	0.731(9)
Serum albumin (bovine)(c)	0.734(11)	0.734(12)
Insulin (Zn)	0.735(13)	0.724(3)(d)
D-Glyceraldehydephosphate dehydrogenase	0.737(11)	0.743(11)
Aldolase	0.740(11)	0.743(11)
β-Casein	0.741(9)	0.743(9)
Ovalbumin(c)	0.745(14)	0.738(3)
Hemoglobin (horse)	0.749(15)	0.741(3)(e)
β-Lactoglobulin	0.751(16)	0.746(17)
Botulinus toxin	0.75(18)	0.736(18)
Gelatin	0.682(19)	0.707(3)
Edestin	0.744(20)	0.719(3)

This table is taken with a few minor alterations from T. L. McMeekin and K. Marshall, *Science* **116**, 142 (1952).

(a) These values were determined at 20°C., or close thereto.

(b) With the exception of Refs. (9), (11) and (18), the specific volume values have been calculated from the amino acid compositions given in the cited reference. A value of 0.63 cc. was used for the volume of the cystine residue instead of 0.61 cc., as given in Cohn and Edsall(1).

(c) Recent very accurate measurements (22) give the partial specific volume of bovine serum albumin as 0.7343 and of ovalbumin as 0.7479.

(d) The specific volume of zinc is not included.

(e) The specific volume of hemin is not included.

(1) E. J. Cohn and J. T. Edsall, Proteins, Amino Acids and Peptides, Reinhold, New York, pp. 370–81.

(2) A. C. Goodings and L. H. Turl, *J. Textile Inst.* **31,** *T*69 (1940).

(3) G. R. Tristram, *Advances in Protein Chem.* **5,** 83 (1949).

(4) A. Rothen, *J. Gen. Physiol.* **24,** 203 (1940–1).

(5) A. T. King, *J. Textile Inst.* **17,** T53 (1926).

(6) L. R. Wetter and H. F. Deutsch, *J. Biol. Chem.* **192,** 237 (1951).

(7) H. L. Fevold, *Advances in Protein Chem.* **6,** 187 (1951).

(8) S. H. Armstrong, Jr. *et al., J. Am. Chem. Soc.* **69,** 1747 (1947).

(9) T. L. McMeekin, M. L. Groves, and N. J. Hipp, *J. Am. Chem. Soc.* **71, 3298** (1949).

(10) G. W. Schwert, *J. Biol. Chem.* **179,** 655 (1949).

(11) J. F. Taylor, *Federation Proc.* **9,** 237 (1950).

speculation along these lines must remain uncertain, especially as the estimated values for the specific volumes of the amino acid residues cannot be considered highly accurate. Further studies of densities and molal volumes, however, should lead to important information relating to protein structure.

IV. Minimum Molecular Weights from Analytical Data

Each protein molecule must possess an integral number of atoms or of amino acid residues, or of any prosthetic group that may be present in a conjugated protein. If the preparation is homogeneous, analysis for any such atom or group furnishes a minimum equivalent weight. The classical example is mammalian hemoglobin, for which the iron content is near 0.335 per cent.[53] The atomic weight of iron is 55.85; hence the equivalent weight of hemoglobin per iron atom is

$$55.85 \times 100/0.335 = 16,700$$

Osmotic pressure and ultracentrifugal data fix the number of iron atoms as 4; hence the actual molecular weight is 66,800—a much more accurate figure than could at present be obtained by physical measurements alone.

The calculation of minimum molecular weights from data of amino acid analysis was first extensively treated by Cohn,[54] who showed, for instance, that the tryptophan content of ovalbumin led to a minimum molecular weight of the order of 35,000. This and numerous other calculations by Cohn showed, at a time when considerable doubt on this point still prevailed, that protein molecules were large structures, and indicated the correct order of magnitude of their minimum sizes. However, the errors in the analytical data were then generally large, and most of the protein preparations available were inhomogeneous. In the last quarter century the errors of analysis have been much reduced, and more

(53) O. Zinoffsky, Z. physiol. Chem. **10**, 16 (1886).

(54) E. J. Cohn, Physiol. Revs. **5**, 349 (1925).

[References to Table II (continued)]

(12) W. H. Stein and S. J. Moore, J. Biol. Chem. **178**, 79 (1949).

(13) K. O. Pedersen, Cold Spring Harbor Symposia Quant. Biol. **14**, 140 (1949).

(14) G. S. Adair and M. E. Adair, Proc. Roy. Soc. (London), **B120**, 422 (1936).

(15) T. Svedberg and R. Fåhraeus, J. Am. Chem. Soc. **48**, 430 (1926).

(16) K. O. Pedersen, Biochem. J. **30**, 961 (1936).

(17) E. Brand et al., J. Am. Chem. Soc. **67**, 1524 (1945).

(18) F. W. Putnam, C. Lamanna, and D. G. Sharp, J. Biol. Chem. **176**, 401 (1948).

(19) K. Krishnamurti and T. Svedberg, J. Am. Chem. Soc. **52**, 2897 (1930).

(20) T. Svedberg and A. J. Stamm, J. Am. Chem. Soc. **51**, 2170 (1929).

(21) K. Linderstrøm-Lang, Cold Spring Harbor Symposia Quant. Biol. **14**, 117 (1949).

(22) M. O. Dayhoff, G. E. Perlmann, and D. A. MacInnes, J. Am. Chem. Soc. **74**, 2515 (1952).

carefully purified proteins are available.   Yet, the uncertainty in deducing molecular weights from the analytical data still remains.   If a given protein, of molecular weight M, contains n residues of a given amino acid, of residue molecular weight w, then the weight fraction, x, of residue in the protein is $x = nw/M$.   The value of w is known, and x is experimentally determined; the calculated equivalent weight is $w/x = M/n$. One may repeat the calculation for all the amino acid residues for which data are available and find the smallest value of M that makes n an integer for all the residues determined, within the limits of error of the method employed.   Vickery[55] examined the problem critically for several proteins.   Brand, Saidel, Goldwater, Kassell, and Ryan[56] in their classical paper on the complete analysis of β-lactoglobulin inferred a minimum molecular weight of 42,020 from the data; and Brand[57] made analogous calculations for several other proteins (human and bovine serum albumin, human γ-globulin, and insulin).   However, if n is large, for a given residue almost any plausible value of M will make n an integer within the limits of error; and if n is small, the percentage error in the analytical determination is likely to be increased by virtue of that very fact.   The later analyses of β-lactoglobulin and serum albumin by Moore and Stein,[58] using a very different analytical method, showed generally good agreement with Brand's values; but for certain amino acid residues deviations of 10 or even 20 per cent were observed.   When the uncertainties concerning homogeneity of the preparations are also taken into account, it would appear that at present no great reliance can be placed on such minimum molecular-weight calculations for the larger proteins.   For small molecules and highly pure preparations, such as insulin and perhaps also lysozyme and ribonuclease, amino acid analysis should fix the molecular weight and composition of the molecule with high precision.   The reader interested in pursuing this topic further should turn to Chap. 3.

The criticisms offered here do not, of course, diminish in any way the importance of knowledge of the amino acid composition of proteins, knowledge which is indispensable in giving a picture of the general character of the proteins, and as a first step toward the determination of structure.

A new type of approach to analytical molecular weight determinations has recently been introduced by Battersby and Craig.[59]   It involves

(55) H. B. Vickery, *Ann. N. Y. Acad. Sci.* **41**, 87 (1941).
(56) E. Brand, L. J. Saidel, W. H. Goldwater, B. Kassell, and F. J. Ryan, *J. Am. Chem. Soc.* **67**, 1524 (1945).
(57) E. Brand, *Ann. N. Y. Acad. Sci.* **47**, 187 (1946).
(58) S. Moore and W. H. Stein, *J. Biol. Chem.* **178**, 53 (1949).
(59) A. R. Battersby, and L. C. Craig, *J. Am. Chem. Soc.* **73**, 1887 (1951).

treating the compound under study—specifically a peptide or protein—
with a substance capable of reacting with certain free groups; for instance,
the dinitrofluorobenzene reagent of Sanger,[11] which combines with amino
groups to form dinitrophenyl (DNP) derivatives.   If the peptide contains n amino groups, $n + 1$ different classes of compounds can be
formed, containing respectively 0, 1, 2 . . . n DNP amino groups per
molecule.   These can be separated by countercurrent fractionation.[60]
In general, all compounds containing a given total number of substituted
groups will tend to have nearly the same distribution coefficient and will
stay together as a group on fractionation, if not too many transfers are
employed.   If the molar extinction coefficient of a DNP amino group is
nearly the same for each of the groups in the molecule, then the ratio of
extinction to weight in the different fractions is proportional to the
number of DNP amino groups per molecule.   The compound with the
lowest value of this ratio should then be the one with only a single substituted group, and the determination of the weight to extinction ratio
for this compound thus gives the molecular weight.   This method was
applied by Battersby and Craig[59] to a relatively small peptide grami-
cidin-S($n = 2$), but it should have real importance for more complex
peptides and perhaps also for some of the smaller proteins.   The assumptions made in employing the method require, of course, critical examination in each case.   Sanger's reagent, for instance, reacts with imidazole
and phenolic hydroxyl groups as well as with amino groups.   Battersby
and Craig[59] mention partial esterification as another method being
employed for the same type of analysis.   For certain substances, this
type of method should be a powerful tool; the principles of the method
and the experimental procedures are discussed in detail by Craig and
Craig.[60]

Recently Harfenist and Craig[60a] have reported the application of this
method to insulin, for which they deduce a molecular weight near 6500.
The two-phase system employed for the countercurrent fractionation in
this case consisted of 2-butanol and 1 per cent aqueous dichloroacetic
acid.   This molecular weight is of great interest, since studies by other
methods on insulin in acid solution point to a molecular weight approximately twice as great.   (Compare the discussion on p. 717.)

V. Electron Microscope Studies on Size and Shape of Proteins

The best way of learning about the size and shape of proteins is to
look at them directly, if that be possible.   To an important degree, this

(60) L. C. Craig and D. Craig, *in* A. Weissberger, ed., Physical Methods of
    Organic Chemistry, Interscience Publishers, New York, 1950, Vol. III,
    Chap. IV.
(60a) E. J. Harfenist and L. C. Craig, *J. Am. Chem. Soc.* **74**, 3087 (1952).

possibility has been realized by the use of the electron microscope.   The
electron wavelengths used in microscopy today are very short—less than
0.05 A., according to Wyckoff[61]—far smaller than the diameters of
individual atoms.   However, other factors limit the resolving power at
present attainable to about 20 A.   This should be sufficient for observation of the general size and form of even the smaller protein molecules.
However, it remains very difficult to distinguish such small structures
from the background material on which they are deposited, and to distinguish between accidental impurities and the structures of real interest.
Up to the present time, it appears that no detailed study has been
reported of a protein with molecular weight less than 200,000.   However, studies of smaller molecules should now be feasible and should
yield important results.

The gravest limitation of the technique of electron microscopy lies in
the fact that the specimen must be studied in a high vacuum, and therefore the specimen is completely dry.   Hence no protein can be studied
in its natural hydrated state.   In spite of this drawback, the information
gained from electron microscopy is of prime importance.

The molecules most accurately studied hitherto[62] include several
plant viruses, several hemocyanins, and a few smaller molecules, such as
fibrinogen, edestin, and catalase.   There also have been extended studies
on such fibrous proteins as collagen,[8] and on the structure of muscle[63]
and its component structural proteins, myosin and actin.[62,64,65]   Actin-
free myosin consists of very long thin fibrils, "globular" actin of corpuscular units, which aggregate reversibly to form the long chains of fibrous
actin.   These phenomena and the interaction of actin and myosin to form
the actomyosin complex will be discussed by Bailey in Vol. II and will
not be treated further here.

Data for some well-characterized proteins and viruses are presented
in Table III, and photographs of the crystals of edestin and catalase,
showing individual molecules, are reproduced in Figs. 2 and 3.   Some
brief comments on the data are given in the table, and a few more may be

(61) No attempt will be made here to discuss the theory of electron microscopy,
     or the details of experimental technique.   The excellent book by R. W. G.
     Wyckoff, Electron Microscopy, Interscience Publishers, New York, 1949,
     provides a general, and relatively nontechnical, introduction to the subject,
     with extensive references, as well as a superb series of photographs of macro-
     molecules and biological structures.

(62) R. W. G. Wyckoff, Advances in Protein Chem. 6, 1 (1951).

(63) C. E. Hall, M. A. Jakus, and F. O. Schmitt, Biol. Bull. 90, 32 (1946).

(64) G. Rozsa, A. Szent-Györgyi, and R. W. G. Wyckoff, Biochim. et Biophys.
     Acta 3, 561 (1949); idem, Exptl. Cell Research 1, 194 (1950).

(65) O. Snellman and B. Gelotte, Exptl. Cell Research 1, 234 (1950).

added here.   The organization of the large molecular units from smaller subunits is strongly indicated by many of the observations.   Four short rods appear to be packed together into a cube in *Busycon* hemocyanin; and in preparations from alkaline solutions the cubes were found to have broken up completely into the component rods.   This corresponds with

FIG. 2.   Electron micrograph showing edestin molecules about 80 A. in diameter. The crystals were grown on a collodion film which is covered with an amorphous layer of edestin.   From Hall.[65b]

the dissociation phenomena noted also in sedimentation experiments with the ultracentrifuge (secs. XIV and XXI).   The molecules of fibrinogen appear to be built of small subunits, not far from spherical or cubic in shape, strung together like beads.   Catalase, with a molecular weight near 250,000, appears to consist of a cluster of smaller globular units, with particle weights estimated by Hall[65a] at 25,000 ± 10,000.   Hall also noted evidence for the presence of similar subunits in edestin and several other proteins.   It is worth noting in this connection that edestin, with a molecular weight near 300,000, dissociates into about six subunits in

(65a) C. E. Hall, *J. Biol. Chem.* **185**, 749 (1950).

(65b) C. E. Hall, *J. Biol. Chem.* **185**, 45 (1950).

TABLE III

SOME PROTEINS AND VIRUSES STUDIED IN THE ELECTRON MICROSCOPE

Substance	Shape	Major axis	Minor axis	Comments	Ref.
Tomato bushy stunt virus	Spherical	ca. 250	ca. 250	Particles very uniform in size and shape	(1)
Tobacco necrosis virus	Spherical	ca. 250	ca. 250	Two varieties studied appear alike	(1)
Southern bean mosaic virus	Spherical	ca. 250	ca. 250	May not be accurately spherical	(1)
Squash mosaic virus	Spherical	ca. 250	ca. 250		(2)
Turnip yellow virus	Spherical	ca. 200	ca. 200	Virus particles pack in crystal in diamond lattice. Wet-virus diameter 280–300 A.	(3)
Tobacco mosaic viruses[a]	Rodlike	2800	152	Considerable distribution in lengths observed; several different strains appear alike	(4)
Cucumber mosaic viruses	Rodlike	3000	135	Several strains studied	(4)
Hemocyanin, *Limulus*	Spherical	160	160	Some random variation in size, perhaps due to denaturation	(5, 6)
Hemocyanin, *Busycon*	Cubelike	(ca. 300?)	(ca. 300?)	Cubes composed of bundle of four short rods; only the rods are observed in alkaline solution	(7)
Rothamstead tobacco necrosis protein }	Spherical	140	140		(8)
Bovine fibrinogen	Rodlike	700	ca. 40	Many different lengths found (300–1100 A.); molecules appear built of subunits strung together	(9)
Edestin	Spherical	80	80	Some indications that molecular subunits are present	(5, 10)
Catalase	Small blocks	80	64	Molecules approx. 80 × 64 × 64 A., appear to contain small subunits, about ten per molecule.	(11)

[a] R. C. Williams and R. L. Steere, *J. Am. Chem. Soc.* **73**, 2057 (1951) have analyzed the length distribution in tobacco mosaic virus particles, and concluded that in their original suspension before drying the particles were present almost entirely as monomers or dimers, the monomer length being 2980 ± 10 A. The most accurate values for the cross section of the tobacco mosaic virus come from the X-ray studies of J. D. Bernal and I. Fankuchen, *J. Gen. Physiol.* **25**, 111, 147 (1941).

(1) W. C. Price, R. C. Williams, and R. W. G. Wyckoff, *Arch. Biochem.* **9**, 175 (1946).

(2) W. N. Takahashi and T. E. Rawlins, *Am. J. Botany* **34**, 271 (1947).

(3) V. E. Cosslett and R. Markham, *Nature* **161**, 250 (1948).

(4) C. A. Knight and G. Oster, *Arch. Biochem.* **15**, 289 (1947); G. Oster, C. A. Knight, and W. M. Stanley, *ibid.* **15**, 279 (1947).

(5) W. M. Stanley and T. F. Anderson, *J. Biol. Chem.* **146**, 25 (1942).

(6) R. C. Williams and R. W. G. Wyckoff, *Nature* **156**, 68 (1945).

(7) A. Polson and R. W. G. Wyckoff, *Nature* **160**, 153 (1947).

(8) F. C. Bawden and N. W. Pirie, *Brit. J. Exptl. Path.* **23**, 314 (1942); *ibid.* **26**, 277 (1945).

Value quoted in the Table is from Wyckoff, Chap. IX.

(9) C. E. Hall, *J. Biol. Chem.* **179**, 857 (1949).

(10) C. E. Hall, *J. Am. Chem. Soc.* **71**, 2951 (1949); *idem J. Biol. Chem.* **185**, 45 (1950).

(11) C. E. Hall, *J. Biol. Chem.* **185**, 749 (1950).

See also other references cited by R. W. G. Wyckoff, Electron Microscopy, Interscience Publishers, New York, 1949, Chap. VIII.

concentrated urea solutions, as judged by osmotic pressure measurements (sec. VII).

Some of the electron microscope data have an important bearing on the problem of hydration, when taken in conjunction with other information. Thus from small-angle x-ray scattering in solution (sec. X), Beeman and his co-workers[66] have calculated a radius of 149 ± 3.3 A. for southern bean mosaic virus (SBMV) and of 150 ± 2.8 A. for tobacco

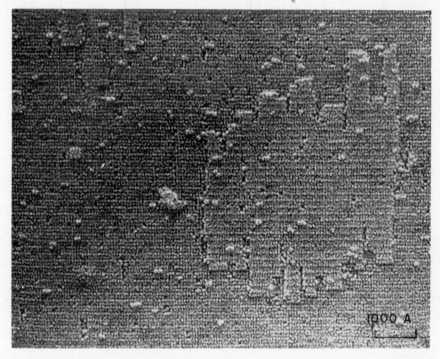

1000 A

FIG. 3. Electron micrograph of the surface of a catalase crystal showing molecules in a rectangular pattern. The large patch at the right is one molecular step above the surrounding layer. From Hall.[65a]

necrosis virus (TNV); electron micrographs of the dried viruses gave radii very near 130 A., corresponding closely to the radius calculated for anhydrous SBMV from sedimentation, diffusion, viscosity, and partial specific volume data by Miller and Price.[67] Thus the molecules actually shrink in going from the wet to the dry state, indicating an internal hydration calculated by Beeman et al.[66] at 0.55 g. water/g. protein. The

(66) B. R. Leonard, Jr., J. W. Anderegg, P. Kaesberg, S. Shulman, and W. W. Beeman, J. Chem. Phys. 19, 793 (1951).
(67) G. L. Miller and W. C. Price, Arch. Biochem. 10, 467 (1946).

data of Miller and Price were taken as indicating a total hydration of 0.83; on this basis the external hydration of these viruses should be 0.28 g. water/g. protein, corresponding to a layer of water 7 A. thick around the virus particle.

The arrangement of the edestin molecules in the dried crystal (Hall[65b]) indicates that they are arranged in a face-centered cubic lattice, the axis a_0 of the unit cell being 114 A. (4 molecules per cell, molecular weight 290,000–300,000, taking the crystal density as 1.30–1.35). The studies of Bailey[68] indicate that wet edestin crystals contain approximately 0.64 g. water/g. protein. R. S. Bear, as reported by Hall,[65b] determined x-ray powder patterns of wet edestin crystals and found the spacing to be 140 A. The increase over the value of 114 for the dry crystals was almost exactly what would be calculated from the water content, assuming that the bound water has a density of unity and that the spherical molecules remain spherical, but increase in size owing to the water bound. These data give no evidence as to whether the water of hydration is internal or external to the edestin molecule.

In a structure built up of close-packed spheres, the spheres themselves occupy only about 74 per cent of the space. If such a model really described the dry edestin crystal correctly, one might expect that on hydration some of the water would be used to fill up the empty space, and therefore that the increase in the length of the lattice spacing would be less than that actually observed. However, it is probably an oversimplification to consider the dried edestin molecules as spheres; they are indeed roughly spherical, but they might actually be more like little cubes. It is important to know how the water of hydration distributes itself between, around, or within the protein molecules; but the data as yet are not revealing enough to justify a discussion of this point.

VI. Molecular Weights by Direct Particle Counting

Electron microscopy has been employed by Williams and Backus[69] to count directly the number of particles of bushy stunt virus in a known volume of solution. A determination of the dry weight of virus per unit volume then permitted direct calculation of the molecular weight. In order to know the volume of solution corresponding to a given number of particles in the fields seen under the electron microscope, the virus preparations were quantitatively mixed with an aqueous suspension of spherical Dow polystyrene latex particles, containing a known number of latex particles per milliliter. The latex particles were very uniform in

(68) K. Bailey, *Trans. Faraday Soc.* **38**, 186 (1942).
(69) R. C. Williams and R. C. Backus, *J. Am. Chem. Soc.* **71**, 4052 (1949).

size, with an average diameter[70] close to 2600 A. The mixed suspension was then sprayed[71] onto collodion-coated microscope screens, forming small circular patterns which were observed in the electron microscope. Counts of a very large number of such patterns led to an estimated molecular weight of the tomato bushy stunt virus of 9.4 (± 0.7) $\times$ 10^6.

A later study, by essentially the same method, of tobacco mosaic virus[72] gave an estimated molecular weight of 49 $\times$ 10^6. This paper also gives a more detailed critical discussion of the sources of error in the method, especially as regards the detectability of contaminating impurities of various sizes and their influence on the calculated molecular weights. The presence of a few large particles, such as bacteria, would lead to serious errors. The mass of one bacterium (say 10^{-11}–10^{-12} g.) is equivalent to 10^4–10^6 virus particles; yet the number of bacteria present might be so small that their presence would be overlooked in the electron microscope, even if many fields were examined. The visual microscope and turbidity measurements can be used as controls here. A critical discussion of the pitfalls that may be encountered in this method of molecular-weight determination has been given by Lauffer.[72a]

Although this method of direct counting has hitherto been applied only to virus molecular weights, it should in principle be applicable to any type of particles that can be seen and counted in the electron microscope; hence, proteins with molecular weights down to 70,000, and perhaps smaller, could be studied. We may note that the values reported by Williams and Backus for the two viruses are well within the range of molecular weights found by other investigators for the same materials, using the more indirect methods of determination to be discussed later in this chapter.

VII. Osmotic Pressure of Proteins

1. PRELIMINARY CONSIDERATIONS

The study of osmotic pressure, apart from its great importance in determining the flow of liquids in living organisms, is significant to the physical chemist for determining the molecular weights of large molecules and in studying the interactions between them.

When two solutions are separated by a membrane, at constant temperature and pressure, the chemical potential (or activity) of every com-

(70) R. C. Backus and R. C. Williams, *J. Applied Phys.* **20**, 224 (1949). A careful investigation of the size of these particles by light-scattering measurements has been reported by W. B. Dandliker, *J. Am. Chem. Soc.* **72**, 5110 (1950).

(71) R. C. Backus and R. C. Williams, *J. Applied Phys.* **21**, 11 (1950).

(72) R. C. Williams, R. C. Backus, and R. L. Steere, *J. Am. Chem. Soc.* **73**, 2062 (1951).

(72a) M. A. Lauffer, *J. Am. Chem. Soc.* **73**, 2370 (1951).

ponent which can pass through the membrane must be the same on both sides, if equilibrium is to exist. For a volatile component, such as water, the vapor pressure is a convenient measure of the activity. If one or more components are present which cannot pass through the membrane— we shall speak of these generally as nondiffusible components—and if their concentration on one side is higher than on the other, then equilibrium cannot exist if the total pressure is the same on both sides. The potentials (or vapor pressures) of the diffusible components must in general be higher in the solution containing the lower concentration of the nondiffusible components. Hence, the diffusible components flow across the membrane, toward the solution in which their potentials are lower. However, this tendency can be counteracted by applying an excess hydrostatic pressure on the solution which would otherwise receive the inflow. Increase of hydrostatic pressure increases the molal chemical potential of any component, in direct proportion to its partial molal volume. When a sufficient pressure difference is applied to make the potentials of the diffusible components equal on both sides, equilibrium is restored. The pressure necessary to achieve this is the osmotic pressure. If the nondiffusible solute is present at sufficiently low concentration, the osmotic pressure can be written as RT times the concentration of the solute in moles per liter; it is then numerically equal to the pressure which the same number of solute molecules, in the same volume, would exert on the walls of the container if present as a gas. This is van't Hoff's law, which is the basis for the determination of molecular weights from osmotic pressure measurements. However, many actual solutions of proteins deviate greatly from van't Hoff's law, and the molecular weights can be determined only by a suitable extrapolation. The deviations are generally most pronounced when the protein molecules carry a large net charge, and the ionic strength of the solution is low; the law of the effects involved was stated in general form by Gibbs, and later more explicitly by Donnan. Apart from the general Gibbs-Donnan effect, many deviations from ideal behavior in protein solutions arise from interactions of proteins with small ions and with one another. Some of these are general electrostatic interactions which can be described by the theory of Debye and Hückel, or some extension of it; others are highly specific, differing from protein to protein and from one small ion to another. Osmotic-pressure measurements furnish a powerful tool for studying such interactions; it will be seen in sec. IX that light-scattering measurements can also be used to furnish equivalent information, often over a wider range of conditions.

The term "osmotic pressure" is often used by physical chemists to designate a colligative property of any solution, determined not directly by osmotic measurements but by some thermodynamically equivalent procedure, such as measurement of the freezing point depression or the boiling point elevation of the solvent, produced by the solute; or by iso-piestic vapor-pressure measurements against some standard set of solutions. The osmotic pressure deduced from such measurements is the *total* pressure that would be required to produce equilibrium, in the presence of a (real or hypothetical) membrane impermeable to all components but the solvent. In the study of proteins and other large molecules, however, the term osmotic pressure is used to denote the pressure difference at equilibrium, in the presence of a membrane that will let through the small molecules and ions present, and hold back the large ones.[73] This definition is vague in its use of the terms "large" and "small," but in practice it is generally not difficult to give meaning to these terms. It is relatively easy to prepare or obtain membranes, usually of collodion or cellophane, which are impermeable to protein molecules with a molecular weight of about 12,000 or above, while readily allowing small molecules, with a molecular weight below 500, to pass through. Osmotic-pressure measurements are generally most useful in the molecular-weight range from about 30,000 to 100,000; smaller molecules are likely to leak through the membranes used, while very large ones give a low ratio of osmotic pressure to weight concentration, so that the probable error of the measurements is larger. However, in some cases, molecular weights of the order of a million have been determined with reasonable accuracy.

2. SOME ASPECTS OF GENERAL THEORY

The Gibbs free energy, F, of a system is defined by the equation

$$F = E + PV - TS \qquad (4)$$

where E denotes total energy, P the pressure on the system, V its volume, T the absolute temperature, and S the entropy.[74] F, during any process at constant temperature and pressure, is a measure of the maximum "useful" work—that is, work not arising from volume changes in the system—which could be derived from that process. Spontaneous processes involve a total decrease of F, and are denoted as exergonic processes. Endergonic processes, in which F increases, can occur in nature only if coupled with exergonic ones, so that the over-all value of ΔF is negative.

On differentiating Eq. (4) we obtain, in general, for a phase of constant composition:

$$dF = dE + PdV + VdP - SdT - TdS \qquad (5)$$

(73) Some authors have termed this the "oncotic pressure" to distinguish it from the total osmotic pressure calculated from freezing point depression; but we shall not follow this usage here.

(74) For detailed discussion of the significance and uses of the function F, on a fairly elementary level, see, for instance, Lewis and Randall[42] or Glasstone.[43] Note that Lewis and Randall use the symbol $\bar{F}$ to denote the chemical potential, whereas here, following Gibbs and later authors, the symbol μ is used.

On the other hand, for a variation of the energy, dE, regarded as a function of the entropy and volume:

$$dE = TdS - PdV \tag{6}$$

Here TdS is the heat absorbed, and $-PdV$ is the pressure–volume work done by the system, so that Eq. (6) is simply an expression of the first law of thermodynamics. On substituting (6) in (5) we obtain

$$dF = -SdT + VdP \tag{7}$$

If we consider F also, for a system of variable composition, as a function of the masses, n_i, n_j, etc. of the various components i, j, Eq. (7) is expanded to become

$$dF = -SdT + VdP + \mu_1 dn_1 + \mu_2 dn_2 + \cdots$$
$$\equiv -SdT + VdP + \Sigma \mu_i dn_i \tag{8}$$

The μ's, which are known as the chemical potentials of the components, are discussed further below.

Also, since F is a function of T, P, and the various n's, we may write

$$dF = \left(\frac{\partial F}{\partial T}\right)_{p,n} dT + \left(\frac{\partial F}{\partial P}\right)_{T,n} dP + \sum \left(\frac{\partial F}{\partial n_i}\right)_{T,p,n_j} dn_i \tag{9}$$

The subscripts denote in each case the variables held constant during the differentiation; the subscript n denotes that all the masses of the components are held constant, the subscript n_j that the masses of all components except component i are held constant.

Equating the coefficients of dT, dP, and the various n's, as they appear in Eqs. (8) and (9), respectively, we obtain immediately

$$\left(\frac{\partial F}{\partial T}\right)_{P,n} = -S \tag{10}$$

$$\left(\frac{\partial F}{\partial P}\right)_{T,n} = V \tag{11}$$

$$\left(\frac{\partial F}{\partial n_i}\right)_{T,Pn_j} = \mu_i \tag{12}$$

Thus the chemical potential of component i is the differential increment of the free energy of the system with respect to that component, at constant pressure, temperature, and mass of all the other components. We shall choose to express the masses of the components in moles. In what follows we shall omit the subscripts after the differential coefficients if it seems clear which variables are being held constant. If F is differentiated twice, with respect to P and to n_i, we obtain:

$$\frac{\partial^2 F}{\partial P \partial n_i} = \frac{\partial}{\partial P}\left(\frac{\partial F}{\partial n_i}\right) = \frac{\partial}{\partial n_i}\left(\frac{\partial F}{\partial P}\right) = \frac{\partial \mu_i}{\partial P} = \overline{V}_i \tag{13}$$

Thus the rate of change of the potential of any component with pressure, at constant temperature and composition, is equal to the partial molal volume of that component.

We cannot measure the absolute value of the chemical potential of any component, but we can measure the differences between its potentials in different states. In general, we choose a standard state, define the potential of component i in that state as $\mu_i{}^0$ and determine other values of μ_i with reference to this.   For a solvent such as water, it is convenient to take the standard state as the pure substance and denote the corresponding activity as unity.   For substances present in dilute solution we also define the standard state as one of unit activity, but fix this unit by the convention that activity is equal to concentration (or molality, or mole fraction) in a very dilute solution.   One may choose the standard state of any component in any way that is convenient, but once this state is chosen, it must be consistently adhered to.

Whatever the choice, the relation between activity a_i and chemical potential μ_i, for any component i, is:

$$\mu_i - \mu_i{}^0 = RT \ln a_i \tag{14}$$

where R is the gas constant.

Moreover, if component i is volatile, we may set a_i proportional to p_i, the vapor pressure[75] of component i.   For the solvent, if $p_i{}^0$ is the vapor pressure of the pure component, we can write

$$a_i = p_i/p_i{}^0 \tag{15}$$

This fulfills the condition that the activity of the pure component is defined as unity.

The essential condition for equilibrium, in a system of two or more phases, is that the chemical potential of each component that is free to move between the phases shall be the same throughout the system.   In case this condition for equilibrium does not exist, any component tends to pass from a phase where its potential is higher to one where it is lower.   In an osmotic-pressure experiment, there is at least one component which is prevented by a membrane from passing freely between the phases.

3. Elementary Theory for a Two-Component System

The simplest type of system to consider consists of two components: a solvent, component 1, present at high concentration, which flows freely across the membrane; and a solute, component 2, present in low concentration, to which the membrane is impermeable.   The essential condition for equilibrium is that the chemical potential of the solvent, μ_i, be the same on both sides of the membrane.

For the solvent we shall take the standard state as pure solvent at the temperature of the experiment and at atmospheric pressure.   Under these circumstances the activity (a_1) of the solvent is unity.   Its activity in a solution is related to its potential by Eq. (14) above.

Consider now a solution, containing solute (component 2), at mole fraction N_2,

(75) This statement implies that the vapor is so dilute that it behaves like a perfect gas.   For aqueous solutions at ordinary temperatures the vapor pressure is so low that this assumption is correct unless extreme refinement of measurements and calculations is required.   Where there are significant departures from the perfect gas laws, it is necessary to compute the fugacity of the vapor (see Lewis and Randall,[42] Chap. XVII, or Glasstone,[43] Chap. XII).

inside the membrane, and pure solvent outside. The activity of the solvent outside is 1; inside it is $a_1 < 1$ since the addition of any solute lowers the vapor pressure of the solvent. To obtain equilibrium the hydrostatic pressure on the inside solution must be increased until a_1 is increased to unity. From Eqs. (13) and (14) we see that

$$\frac{\partial \mu_1}{\partial P} = RT \frac{\partial \ln a_1}{\partial P} = \bar{V}_1 \tag{16}$$

Integrating at constant temperature and composition, we have:

$$RT \int_{a_1}^{1} d \ln a_1 = \int_{P_o}^{P_o + \text{II}} \bar{V}_1 dP \cong \bar{V}_1 \text{II} \tag{17}$$

Here P_o denotes atmospheric pressure, and II denotes the osmotic pressure, which is thus the pressure required to raise a_1 to its value in the outer solution. In carrying out the integration we assume that $\bar{V}_1$ is not affected by the applied pressure, that is, that the liquid is incompressible. This is of course not exactly true, but the error in making this assumption is ordinarily negligible.

On this basis, integration of Eq. (17) gives

$$\text{II}\bar{V}_1 = -RT \ln a_1 \tag{18}$$

This is the fundamental equation of osmotic pressure which connects the pressure with the activity of the solvent.

Equation (18) shows little obvious relation to van't Hoff's law. In order to derive this we limit the discussion to dilute solutions in which the mole fraction of solvent (N_1) is not far from unity. In such solutions we may apply Raoult's law, which states that in general a_1 and N_1 approach identity as N_1 approaches unity. (Note that by definition $N_1 = n_1/(n_1 + n_2)$ and $N_2 = 1 - N_1 = n_2/(n_1 + n_2)$ for a two-component system.)

Thus if N_2 is small we may write Eq. (18) in the form:

$$\text{II} V_1 = -RT \ln N_1 = -RT \ln (1 - N_2) \tag{19}$$

Here we may use the general series expansion:

$$- \ln (1 - N_2) = N_2 + N_2^2/2 + N_2^3/3 + \cdots \tag{20}$$

Even for a molal solution of a solute in water, the second term in this expansion is less than 1 per cent of the first; in most dilute solutions, therefore, we may disregard the higher terms and write, from Eqs. (19) and (20):

$$\text{II} = \frac{RTN_2}{\bar{V}_1} = \frac{RT}{\bar{V}_1} \frac{n_2}{n_1 + n_2} \cong \frac{RTn_2}{\bar{V}_1 n_1} \tag{21}$$

The last approximation in (21) is justified if $n_2 \ll n_1$.

Now if we choose the number of moles (n_1) of component 1 so that $\bar{V}_1 n_1 \cong 1$ l., then n_2 is the number of moles of component 2 per liter of solvent, which in very dilute solution is the same as the concentration in moles per liter of solution. Hence

$$\lim_{m_2 \to 0} \frac{\text{II}}{m_2} = RT \tag{22}$$

which is van't Hoff's law.

584   JOHN T. EDSALL

If c_2 is the weight concentration[76] of component 2 in g./cc. solution, and M_2 is its molecular weight, then van't Hoff's law may be written:

$$\lim_{c_2 \to 0} \frac{\Pi}{RTc_2} = \frac{1}{M_2} \tag{23}$$

If Π is expressed in atmospheres, then the appropriate value of R in Eq. (23) is 82.07 cc.-atm./deg. Since Π, T, and c_2 are all determinable by experiment, this gives a basis for determination of the molecular weight. However, the ratio of Π to c_2 that is needed for this calculation is a limiting value, to be determined in general by a suitable extrapolation. Often this ratio, even at relatively small finite concentrations, deviates greatly from the limiting ratio at zero concentration. Serious errors in calculated molecular weights have been made, even by careful investigators, owing to the failure to extrapolate the measurements properly to zero concentration. In general, the best procedure is probably to express Π/RTc_2 as a power series in c_2:

$$\frac{\Pi}{RTc_2} = \frac{1}{M_2} + Bc_2 + Cc_2{}^2 + \cdots \tag{24}$$

The coefficients B, C, . . . of the successive powers of c_2 may be determined by experiment.[79] Thus if the experimental values of Π/RTc_2 are plotted as ordinates against c_2 as abscissa, the intercept on the ordinate axis gives the reciprocal of the molecular weight, and the initial slope at low c_2 values gives the factor B. In general the factors B, C, . . . are functions of molecular interactions.

Of these the first term, B, which we may call the interaction constant,

(76) Different units of weight concentration have been used by different authors. Commonly it has been expressed as grams protein (or other high molecular weight solute) per 100 cc. solution. The more recent convention is to use a unit 0.01 times as large, that is g./cc. solution. Scatchard[77,78] employs the unit w_2, expressed as grams protein/kg. solvent (component 1), which has the great advantage of being independent of temperature.

(77) G. Scatchard, *J. Am. Chem. Soc.* **68**, 2315 (1946).

(78) G. Scatchard, A. C. Batchelder, and A. Brown, *J. Am. Chem. Soc.* **68**, 2320, (1946).

(79) Some authors have employed the equation $\Pi/RTc_2 = 1/M_2(1 - B'c_2)$, where B' is an empirical constant, to describe their data; several related forms of this equation, which are more or less equivalent, have been used. For a review of the work up to 1936, with extensive references, see D. M. Greenberg, in Schmidt,[80] pp. 347–73, incl.

(80) C. L. A. Schmidt, The Chemistry of Amino Acids and Proteins, C. C Thomas, Publishers, Springfield, Illinois, 1938.

is the most important and is the only one that need be considered in dilute solution. B may be regarded as a measure of the "effective volume" of the molecules, that is, of the size of the region around the center of a given molecule into which other molecules cannot penetrate. If the molecules can be described as hard elastic spheres, which do not attract or repel one another, B is four times the molecular volume. Attractive forces tend to diminish B, repulsive forces to increase it. If the attractive forces are sufficiently strong to more than counterbalance the steric factors, B may become negative. Large negative values, however, are almost never found, because phase separation of the solute molecules generally occurs when the value of B becomes large and negative. On the other hand, if the molecules are very asymmetrical—long rods or thin disks—the effective (excluded) volume becomes much larger than the actual volume of the molecules, and the values of B become large and positive. The effect of molecular shape on the value of B has been considered by Zimm,[81] Schulz,[82] and Onsager[83] for rigid molecules; and by P. J. Flory, M. L. Huggins, A. Munster, G. V. Schulz, A. R. Miller and others for flexible molecules.[84] Electrostatic repulsions also increase the value of B, so that under otherwise comparable conditions the value of this coefficient for a protein increases with the net charge on the protein. This charge effect is computed in the next section in the discussion of the Donnan equilibrium.

The absolute magnitude of the pressure experimentally obtainable in actual protein solutions is an important consideration in relation to the accuracy of the results. One mole of a perfect gas, confined in 1 l., would exert a pressure of 22.4 atm. at 0°C. (273.1°K.). This is therefore the "ideal osmotic pressure" of a molar solution at this temperature. Thus a solution of a protein of molecular weight 100,000, at a concentration of 10 g./l. and at 0°C., if it obeys van't Hoff's law, gives an osmotic pressure of 0.00224 atm., or 1.70 mm. Hg, or 23.2 mm. H_2O. Thus if the reading were made with a column of water, and the error in reading the position of the top of the column and of the base line corresponding to atmospheric pressure were ± 0.1 mm., the total error of the reading would be ± 0.2 mm., or approximately 1 per cent of the total reading. Other errors of course are involved in the actual measurements; but it may be seen that the errors from this source alone are likely to introduce serious errors into the determination of molecular weights, if the latter are of the order of a million.

(81) B. H. Zimm, *J. Chem. Phys.* **14**, 164 (1946).
(82) G. V. Schulz, *Z. Naturforsch.* **2a**, 348 (1947).
(83) L. Onsager, *Ann. N. Y. Acad. Sci.* **51**, 627 (1949).
(84) For a critical review of this work, with references, see P. J. Flory and W. R. Krigbaum, *Ann. Rev. Phys. Chem.* **2**, 383 (1951).

4. Gibbs-Donnan Equilibrium and the Distribution of Diffusible Ions

The discussion up to this point has tacitly implied that the protein molecules in the system are uncharged and at their isoionic point. If they carry a net charge, through the addition or removal of protons, or binding of other ions, other free diffusible ions must be retained inside the membrane to balance the charge on the protein. Thus the *concentrations* of diffusible *ions* will in general be different outside and inside the membrane; however, it is a fundamental condition of equilibrium that the *potentials* of diffusible *components* must be the same inside and outside at equilibrium. This point involves the definition of what may be considered a component. If many diffusible ions are present, any combination of those ions that would yield an electrically neutral compound may be taken as a component. For instance, if the solution contains Mg^{++}, Na^+, Cl^-, and SO_4^{--}, then $NaCl$, $MgCl_2$, Na_2SO_4, and $MgSO_4$ are all possible choices in defining the components. The potential of a salt is taken as the sum of the potentials of its ions: thus, $\mu_{Na_2SO_4}$ is equal to $2\mu_{Na} + \mu_{SO_4^{--}}$, and μ_{MgSO_4} is equal to $\mu_{Mg^{++}} + \mu_{SO_4^{--}}$. Correspondingly, for the activities we may set a_{MgSO_4} equal to $(a_{Mg^{++}})(a_{SO_4^{--}})$ and

$$a_{Na_2SO_4} = (a_{Na^+})^2(a_{SO_4^{--}})$$

Since a salt like Na_2SO_4 or $MgSO_4$ is a neutral and diffusible component, its activity at equilibrium must be the same inside and outside the membrane. Hence the corresponding product of ion activities must also be the same inside and outside.

For instance, consider a system containing the four ions mentioned above. We shall follow Scatchard[77] in denoting quantities referring to the solution outside the membrane by primes, while unprimed quantities refer to the solution inside the membrane. Also, for the present, we shall assume that the activities of the ions can be replaced by their concentrations. Then the requirement of equal potentials at equilibrium gives

$$(Na^+)(Cl^-) = (Na^+)'(Cl^-)' \tag{25}$$
$$(Mg^{++})(Cl^-)^2 = (Mg^{++})'(Cl^-)'^2 \tag{26}$$
$$(Na^+)^2(SO_4^{--}) = (Na^+)'^2(SO_4^{--})' \tag{27}$$
$$(Mg^{++})(SO_4^{--}) = (Mg^{++})'(SO_4^{--})' \tag{28}$$

Also, since an aqueous solution always contains H and OH ions, we may write similar equations for such possible components as HCl and $NaOH$:

$$(H^+)(Cl^-) = (H^+)'(Cl)' \tag{29}$$
$$(Na^+)(OH^-) = (Na^+)'(OH)' \tag{30}$$

Such equations as these may be combined into a series to yield the quantity generally known as the Donnan ratio, r:

$$r = \frac{(Cl^-)}{(Cl^-)'} = \frac{(OH^-)}{(OH^-)'} = \frac{(H^+)'}{(H^+)} = \frac{(Na^+)'}{(Na^+)} = \left[\frac{(Mg^{++})'}{(Mg^{++})}\right]^{\frac{1}{2}} = \left[\frac{(SO_4^{--})}{(SO_4^{--})'}\right]^{\frac{1}{2}} \quad (31)$$

In applying these equations, at least three points must be remembered:

(a) It has been assumed valid to replace activities by concentrations; where this assumption fails, Eq. (31) fails also.

(b) The concentrations are those of the *free* ions in the system; ions bound to the protein are not to be counted.

(c) All the ions are assumed to pass through the membrane freely; the equalities of Eq. (31) cannot hold for any ion that does not pass. Thus the normal mammalian red cell membrane is nearly impermeable to cations other than H^+ ion; hence Na^+ and Mg^{++} (also Ca^{++} and other cations) would have to be omitted from the equation defining r for the equilibrium between red cells and plasma. On the other hand, the equation for this equilibrium includes other ions not mentioned here, such as HCO_3^-, $H_2PO_4^-$, and HPO_4^{--}. (For a fuller discussion, see Henderson.[85])

In general a diffusible ion, I, of valence Z would enter into Eq. (31) by the ratio $(I'/I)^{1/Z}$, where Z is taken positive for a cation, negative for an anion.

We shall consider in more detail the special case of a single type of protein ion, denoted by the subscript 2, and a single uni-univalent salt, such as Na^+Cl^-. Let the net charge on the protein, per mole, be Z_2. Assuming that the concentration of H^+ and OH^- ions is negligible compared to that of Na^+ and Cl^-, the equation of electrical neutrality inside the membrane becomes:

$$(Na^+) + Z_2 m_2 = (Cl^-) \quad (32)$$

Outside the membrane we have simply

$$(Na^+)' = (Cl^-)' \quad (33)$$

The Gibbs-Donnan equations require that

$$[(Na^+) + Z_2 m_2](Na^+) = (Na^+)'(Cl^-)' = (Na^+)'^2 = (Cl^-)'^2 \quad (34)$$

We shall consider in this section only solutions where van't Hoff's law may be applied. In such cases, to calculate Π we count up all the moles of solute particles—whether protein ions or diffusible ions—inside the membrane, per unit volume; then we make a similar count outside

(85) L. J. Henderson, Blood: A Study in General Physiology, Yale Univ. Press, New Haven, 1928.

the membrane, then subtract the latter figure from the former, and multiply by RT.

$$\Pi = \frac{RT}{1000}\,[m_2 + (\text{Na}^+) + (\text{Cl}^-) - (\text{Na}^+)' - (\text{Cl}^-)'] \tag{35}$$

The factor 1000 occurs in the denominator, since we have taken $R = 82.07$ [see Eq. (23)].

From Eqs. (32), (33) and (34) we obtain

$$(\text{Cl}^-)' = (\text{Cl}^-)\left[1 - \frac{Z_2 m_2}{(\text{Cl}^-)}\right]^{\frac{1}{2}} \tag{36}$$

The protein concentration, c_2, in g./cc. solution, is equal to $m_2 M_2/1000$. Thus we may rewrite Eq. (35) as

$$\frac{\Pi}{RTc_2} = \frac{RT}{M_2}\left[1 + \frac{(\text{Na}^+) + (\text{Cl}^-) - (\text{Na}^+)' - (\text{Cl}^-)'}{m_2}\right] \tag{37}$$

For brevity we shall write (Cl^-) as y. Then from Eqs. (36) and (37):

$$
\begin{aligned}
\frac{\Pi}{RTc_2} &= \frac{1}{M_2}\left[1 + \frac{2y - Z_2 m_2 - 2y\sqrt{1 - \dfrac{Z_2 m_2}{y}}}{m_2}\right] \\
&= \frac{1}{M_2}\left[1 + \frac{y}{m_2}\left(2 - \frac{Z_2 m_2}{y} - 2\sqrt{1 - \frac{Z_2 m_2}{y}}\right)\right] \\
&= \frac{1}{M_2}\left[1 + \frac{y}{m_2}\left(1 - \sqrt{1 - \frac{Z_2 m_2}{y}}\right)^2\right]
\end{aligned} \tag{38}
$$

If the expression under the square root sign is expanded by means of the binominal theorem, we obtain (resubstituting (Cl^-) for y):

$$\sqrt{1 - \frac{Z_2 m_2}{(\text{Cl}^-)}} = 1 - \frac{Z_2 m_2}{2(\text{Cl}^-)} - \frac{Z_2{}^2 m_2{}^2}{8(\text{Cl}^-)^2} \cdots \tag{39}$$

$$\frac{\Pi}{RTc_2} = \frac{1}{M_2}\left[1 + \frac{Z_2{}^2 m_2}{4(\text{Cl}^-)} + \cdots\right] = \frac{1}{M_2}\,1 + \frac{1000\,Z_2{}^2 c_2}{4M_2{}^2(\text{Cl}^-)}$$
$$+ \cdots \simeq \frac{1}{M_2} + \frac{1000 Z_2{}^2 c_2}{4M_2{}^2 m_3} \tag{40}$$

Thus a plot of Π/RTc_2 against c_2 should yield the reciprocal of the molecular weight as the intercept on the ordinate axis, regardless of the charge on the protein. The interaction coefficient, B [compare Eq. (24)], on the other hand, is proportional to the square of the net charge and inversely proportional to the concentration of diffusible ions inside the membrane. If $(\text{Cl}^-) \gg Z_2 m_2$ then we may write the molar concentration of sodium chloride, m_3, instead of (Cl^-) in this equation.[86]   The higher terms in the expansion of Eqs. (39) and (40) have been neglected here; they are generally negligible unless $Z_2 m_2$ is of the same order of magnitude as (Cl^-).

It is clear that the Donnan effect always increases the observed osmotic pressure above that due to the protein ions alone; an increase of the ratio of protein to salt increases the Donnan term; to get rid of the influence of this term, we must therefore increase the salt in the system, or extrapolate the measurements to zero protein concentration.

For a unibivalent electrolyte, such as calcium chloride, the factor $4m_3$ in the denominator of Eq. (40) is replaced by $12m_3$; in either case, the factor is equal to four times the ionic strength contributed by component 3.

5. Definition of the Protein Component in Multicomponent Systems

The formulation of the equations for the Donnan effect given above assumes the validity of van't Hoff's law.   Apart from the unequal distribution of diffusible ions, determined by the charge on the protein ion, each particle of solute present is given the same weight in counting the total contribution to the osmotic pressure, and no correction has been made for activity coefficients.

Moreover, no exact definition of the protein component has been given for cases in which the protein ion carries a net charge.   For a more rigorous discussion, such a definition is essential.   Many definitions could be chosen, but in any case we should employ a definition that makes the net charge on the protein component equal to zero.   Otherwise, it would be impossible to add or remove protein component from the system without leaving a net charge.   This means that the protein component must be defined so as to include some of the diffusible ions.

It is also advantageous to define the protein component in such a way that when it is added to the system, the total number of solute particles introduced is equal to the number of protein ions added.   A suitable definition that meets all these requirements was first proposed by Scatchard.[77]   For illustration consider a solution of serum albumin, (component 2) carrying a net charge of Z_2 proton units per molecule, where Z_2 may be positive, zero, or negative.   If the other components of the system are water (component 1) and sodium chloride (component 3), then 1 mole

(86) The derivation given here follows closely that of Scatchard, Batchelder, and Brown.[87]

(87) G. Scatchard, A. C. Batchelder, and A. Brown, *J. Clin. Invest.* **23**, 458 (1944); see especially footnote 77 on p. 460.

of the protein component contains 1 mole of the protein ion, $Z_2/2$ moles of chloride ion, and $-Z_2/2$ moles of sodium ion. This means that, as we add protein component to the system, we add protein ion of net charge Z_2. If the charge is positive, we must also add half the number of chloride ions needed to balance the charge on the protein, and at the same time *take away* an equal number of sodium ions. If the net charge on the protein is negative with numerical value Z_2, then we must add $Z_2/2$ moles of sodium ion along with the protein and take away $Z_2/2$ moles of chloride ion. In either case, the net addition of diffusible ions is zero. The molarity, m_3, of the salt component is then defined, by the following equation, in terms of the total concentration of sodium and of chloride ions present in the protein solution:

$$m_3 = [(Na^+) + (Cl^-)]/2 \tag{41}$$

Suppose that the concentration of serum albumin ion is 10^{-4} molar (approximately 7 g./l.) in a solution to which 20×10^{-4} mole per liter of HCl has been added to the isoelectric protein, so that $Z_2 = -20$, and $Z_2m_2 = 0.002$. Suppose also that 0.010 mole per liter of NaCl has been added to the solution. Thus the total concentration of diffusible ions, in moles per liter, is $(Na^+) = 0.010$, $(Cl^-) = 0.012$, and the molarity of component 3 is $(0.010 + 0.012)/2 = 0.011$. If we make up a solution with double the concentration of protein ion, keeping $Z_2 = +20$, we have $Z_2m_2 = 0.004$. This, as before, represents the amount of chloride ion needed to balance the charge on the protein. To make $m_3 = 0.011$ in this solution, as in the previous one, we add 0.009 mole per liter of NaCl, giving $(Na^+) = 0.009$ and $(Cl^-) = 0.013$. The same procedure may be followed at other protein concentrations.

The same type of procedure may be employed when the solution contains diffusible ions of higher valence. The necessary equations are given by Scatchard,[77] and are discussed in more detail by Edsall, Edelhoch, Lontie, and Morrison.[88]

This definition has the advantage that, as protein component is added to the system, the total number of diffusible ions present remains constant. Hence the change in the activity of the solvent, as protein component is added, is determined only by the increase in the number of protein ions in the system, if all activity coefficients can be taken as unity.

6. Effects of Variation of Activity Coefficients on Osmotic Pressure Equations

In general, the activity coefficients of the components are not unity, and any variation in the composition of the system may be expected to

(88) J. T. Edsall, H. Edelhoch, R. Lontie, and P. R. Morrison, *J. Am. Chem. Soc.* **72**, 4641 (1950).

modify the activities and activity coefficients of all the components. These variations are not independent but are connected by certain thermodynamic equations. If a_j is the activity of component j, and m_j its molarity, then we may write for any pair of components j and k, in a multicomponent system, the relation:

$$\frac{\partial \ln a_j}{\partial m_k} = \frac{\partial \ln a_k}{\partial m_j} \tag{42}$$

that is, the rate of change in the logarithm of the activity of j per mole of k added, in unit volume, is equal to the rate of change of the logarithm of the activity of k per mole of j added in unit volume. In either case we start from the same initial system.[88a] Consider now the three-component system discussed in sec. VII-5 above. For the activity of the protein, of net charge Z_2, we may write

$$\ln a_2 = \ln m_2 + \frac{Z_2}{2} \ln (\text{Cl}^-) - \frac{Z_2}{2} \ln (\text{Na}^+) + \beta_2 \tag{43}$$

the terms involving the concentration of sodium and chloride ions appear because these ions must be added to the system—or withdrawn from it— when we add protein component. For the activity of sodium chloride (component 3) we write:

$$\ln a_3 = \ln (\text{Na}^+) + \ln (\text{Cl}^-) + \beta_3 \tag{44}$$

the β's are related to the activity coefficients, γ_2 and γ_3—following Scatchard's notation—by the definition:

$$\beta_2 = \ln \gamma_2 \tag{45}$$
$$\beta_3 = \ln \gamma_{\text{Na}^+} + \ln \gamma_{\text{Cl}^-} = 2 \ln \gamma_3 \tag{46}$$

Likewise, by definition:

$$\beta_{22} = \frac{\partial \ln \gamma_2}{\partial m_2} \tag{47}$$

$$\beta_{23} = \frac{\partial \beta_3}{\partial m_2} = \beta_{32} \tag{48}$$

$$\beta_{33} = \frac{\partial \beta_3}{\partial m_3} \tag{49}$$

moreover, the concentrations of the sodium and chloride ions are related to m_2 and m_3 by the equations:

$$(\text{Na}^+) = m_3 - \frac{Z_2 m_2}{2} \tag{50}$$

$$(\text{Cl}^-) = m_3 + \frac{Z_2 m_2}{2} \tag{51}$$

(88a) Equation 42 could obviously be written using logarithms to the base 10 instead of natural logarithms, but the natural logarithm is more convenient if we wish to consider chemical potentials as well as activities.

These equations are readily generalized for systems containing several protein components, or several salts, including ions of higher valence types, or neutral molecules of any sort. The general equations are given by Scatchard[77] in very compact form; for a more extended discussion see, for instance, Edsall et al.[88] or Doty and Edsall.[89]

For the particular case of the three-component system just discussed, Scatchard's equations[77,78] give the intercept and the initial slope of the curve for Π/RTc_2 as a function of c_2 [compare Eq. (24)] as:

$$\frac{\Pi}{RTc_2} = \frac{1}{M_2} + \frac{1000}{2M_2{}^2}\left(\frac{Z_2{}^2}{2m_3} + \beta_{22} - \frac{\beta_{23}{}^2 m_3}{2 + \beta_{33}m_3}\right) c_2 \qquad (52)$$

thus the factor multiplying c_2 in Eq. (52) is equal to the interaction constant B in (24). This equation resolves B into three terms, all containing the constant factor $1000/2M_2{}^2$. The first term in the parentheses, $Z_2{}^2/2m_3$, is the Donnan term already given in Eq. (40). If all activity coefficients are unity, this is the only term which does not vanish. It vanishes if the net charge on the protein is zero, and is diminished by increasing the salt concentration (m_3). The second term, β_{22}, depends on the variation of the activity coefficient of the protein component with its own concentration. For an isoionic protein in salt-free water this is the only term which would remain. It is this term which becomes large and positive for very asymmetrical molecules (rods or disks).[81-83] Finally, the third term in the parentheses depends on the protein–salt and (to a lesser degree) the salt–salt interaction. It is always negative, except in the very unlikely case that $2 + \beta_{33}m_3$ is negative. This term is generally relatively small, but may be important if the protein–salt interactions are particularly strong.

7. Experimental Data on Osmotic Pressure

A number of experimental molecular weight values from osmotic-pressure measurements are given in Tables IV and V. The outstanding early investigations in this field were those of Sørensen[90] on ovalbumin and serum albumin, and of Adair[91] on hemoglobin. The molecular weights estimated by Sørensen were less reliable than the data from which they were derived, and required some revision in the light of later work. Adair's work was of particular importance, as it established for

(89) P. Doty and J. T. Edsall, Advances in Protein Chem. 6, 35 (1951).
(90) S. P. L. Sørensen, Compt. rend. trav. lab. Carlsberg 12, 262 (1917).
(91) G. S. Adair, Proc. Roy. Soc. (London) A108, 627 (1925); ibid. A109, 292 (1925).

the first time that the molecular weight of mammalian hemoglobin was in the neighborhood of 67,000 with four iron atoms per molecule, a result soon after confirmed by ultracentrifugal studies. In later studies, Adair[92] reported further data and developed in detail the theoretical interpretation of his findings, in terms of fundamental thermodynamic equations. The more recent papers of Scatchard[77] and of Güntelberg and Linderstrøm-Lang[93] have carried the theoretical development still further.

Most of the data of Table IV concern proteins of molecular weights below 100,000, where osmotic-pressure data are generally most significant. The values for the proteins of higher molecular weight are generally more uncertain and often show considerable discrepancies from values obtained for the same proteins from sedimentation and diffusion measurements. The value given for myosin, however, appears to be more reliable than most of these; the probable error is estimated by Portzehl[94] as ±30,000 in 840,000, and the reported figure agrees closely with the values obtained by Portzehl from sedimentation and diffusion measurements.

The work of Scatchard, Batchelder, and Brown[78] on bovine serum albumin represents the most systematic study yet made of the variation of the interaction constant, B, with change in the valence of the protein. They showed that the Donnan term alone is quite inadequate to describe the observed effects; in 0.15 M sodium chloride, at the isoelectric point, the value of B is large and positive, and it decreases toward zero as the valence of the protein—defined as the mean number of protons bound per albumin molecule, referred to the isoionic point as zero—increases to values between +10 and +20. The data pointed strongly to binding of chloride ions by the protein as a major reason for the observed discrepancy; and determinations of total chloride inside and outside the membrane also indicated considerable chloride binding. Nevertheless, the plot of Π/RTc_2 against c_2, at any given pH and ionic strength, was linear; and the molecular weight of 69,000, as determined by extrapolation, was the same at all values of Z_2, as would be predicted from Eq. (52). Related data on light scattering are discussed in the next section (p. 606).

The geometrical dissymmetry of the serum albumin molecule is rather low, so that the contribution to the factor B, due to this cause, should be small compared to that of the Donnan term. Rabbit myosin—L-myosin in the terminology of H. H. Weber—is, on the other hand, a highly asymmetric molecule. The work of Portzehl[94] has shown that the

(92) G. S. Adair, *Proc. Roy. Soc.* (London) **A120**, 573 (1928); *ibid.* **A126**, 16 (1929).
(93) A. V. Güntelberg and K. Linderstrøm-Lang, *Compt. rend. trav. lab. Carlsberg*, *Sér. chim.* **27**, 1 (1949).
(94) H. Portzehl, *Z. Naturforsch.* **5b**, 75 (1950).

TABLE IV

MOLECULAR WEIGHT OF CERTAIN PROTEINS FROM OSMOTIC PRESSURE
MEASUREMENTS

Protein	Molecular weight $\times 10^{-3}$
Insulin (in acid solution)(1)	12.0
Lysozyme (egg white)(2)	17.5
Trypsin inhibitor, soybean(3, 4)	24.0
Prolactin(5)	26.5
Erythocruorin ("hemoglobin"), *Gastrophilus*(6)	34.0
β-Lactoglobulin, cow(7)	35.0
Trypsin(8)	36.5
Pepsin(9)	36.0
Chymotrypsin(10)	41.0
Chymotrypsinogen(10)	36.0
Metakentrin, sheep(11)	40.0
Ovalbumin(12, 13, 14, 15, 16)	40.0–46.0
Ovalbumin(17)	44.9–45.1
Plakalbumin(17)	44.6–44.8
Growth hormone, anterior pituitary, ox(18)	43.6–44.2
Hemoglobin(19)	67.0
Hemoglobin or carboxyhemoglobin, human(20)	67.0
Albumin, serum, bovine(21)	69.0
Albumin, serum, horse(22)	73.0
Albumin, serum, human(21, 23)	69.0
Amandin(24)	206.0
Excelsin(24)	214.0
Hemocyanin, king crab (*Limulus*)(25)	544.0
Hemocyanin, crab (*Carcinus*)(26)	550.0
Hemocyanin, octopus(26)	710.0
Hemocyanin, snail (*Helix*)(26)	1800.0
Fibrinogen, plasma, human(23)	580.0
Myosin (L-myosin)(27)	840.0

(1) H. Gutfreund, *Biochem. J.* **50**, 564 (1952).

(2) G. Alderton, W. H. Ward, and H. L. Fevold, *J. Biol. Chem.* **157**, 43 (1945).

(3) M. Kunitz, *J. Gen. Physiol.* **30**, 291 (1947).

(4) B. Katchman and A. D. McLaren, *J. Polymer. Sci.* **3**, 138 (1948).

(5) C. H. Li, W. R. Lyons, and H. M. Evans, *J. Biol. Chem.* **140**, 43 (1941).

(6) G. S. Adair, A. G. Ogston, and J. P. Johnson, *Biochem. J.* **40**, 867 (1946).

(7) H. B. Bull and B. T. Currie, *J. Am. Chem. Soc.* **68**, 742 (1946).

(8) M. Kunitz and J. H. Northrop, *J. Gen. Physiol.* **18**, 433 (1934–35).

(9) J. H. Northrop, *J. Gen. Physiol.* **13**, 767 (1929–30).

(10) M. Kunitz and J. H. Northrop, *J. Gen. Physiol.* **18**, 433 (1935); *ibid.* **20**, 575 (1937).

(11) C. H. Li, M. E. Simpson, and H. M. Evans, *J. Am. Chem. Soc.* **64**, 367 (1942); *idem Science* **92**, 355 (1940).

(12) G. S. Adair, *Ann. Rev. Biochem.* **6**, 163 (1937),

osmotic-pressure data on this protein can be described by the equation (II in atm., c_2 in g./cc.):

$$\Pi/RTc_2 = 1.19 \times 10^{-6} + 8.9 \times 10^{-5}c_2$$
$$= 1.19 \times 10^{-6} (1 + 75c_2) \tag{53}$$

The measurements were made in 0.5 M potassium chloride, and the protein was not far from its isoelectric point, so that the Donnan term in B must have been very small, and the large observed slope is thus to be explained in terms of molecular asymmetry. The theoretical calculations of Zimm[81] and Onsager[83] lead to an equation, which for cylindrical rod-shaped molecules of length l and diameter d, can be written:

$$\Pi/RTc_2 = M_2^{-1}(1 + \bar{v}c_2l/d) \tag{54}$$

where $\bar{v}$ is the partial specific volume of the protein, found by Portzehl to be 0.74. Comparison of Eqs. (53) and (54) gives the axial ratio, l/d for myosin as 101. Portzehl herself used a similar equation to (54), derived by Schulz,[82] from which the axial ratio was given as 128. It is clear that myosin is extremely asymmetric, and these findings from osmotic pressure are in accord with all the other available evidence. The molecular length calculated from these data, assuming a rod-shaped molecule, is between 2300 and 2400 A. The evidence from sedimentation and diffu-

[References to Table IV (continued)]
   (13) H. B. Bull, *J. Biol. Chem.* **137**, 143 (1941).
   (14) J. Marrack and L. F. Hewitt, *Biochem. J.* **23**, 1079 (1929).
   (15) G. L. Taylor, G. S. Adair, and M. E. Adair, *J. Hyg.* **32**, 340 (1932).
   (16) S. P. L. Sörensen, *Compt. rend. trav. lab. Carlsberg* **12**, 262 (1917).
   (17) A. V. Güntelberg and K. Linderstrøm-Lang, *Compt. rend. trav. lab. Carlsberg* **27**, 1 (1949).
   (18) C. H. Li, *J. Phys. & Colloid Chem.* **51**, 218 (1947).
   (19) G. S. Adair, *Proc. Roy. Soc.* (London) **A120**, 573 (1928).
   (20) G. S. Adair, *Proc. Roy. Soc.* (London) **A108**, 627 (1925); *ibid.* **A120**, 573 (1928); N. F. Burk and D. M. Greenberg, *J. Biol. Chem.* **87**, 197 (1930).
   (21) G. Scatchard, A. C. Batchelder, and A. Brown, *J. Am. Chem. Soc.* **68**, 2320 (1946); G. Scatchard, A. C. Batchelder, A. Brown, and M. Zosa, *J. Am. Chem. Soc.* **68**, 2610 (1946).
   (22) G. S. Adair and M. E. Robinson, *Biochem. J.* **24**, 1864 (1930). See also J. L. Oncley, *Ann. N. Y. Acad. Sci.* **41**, 121 (1941).
   (23) J. L. Oncley, G. Scatchard, and A. Brown, *J. Phys. & Colloid Chem.* **51**, 184 (1947).
   (24) N. F. Burk, *J. Biol. Chem.* **120**, 63 (1937).
   (25) N. F. Burk, *J. Biol. Chem.* **133**, 511 (1940).
   (26) J. Roche, A. Roche, G. S. Adair, and M. E. Adair, *Biochem. J.* **29**, 2576 (1935).
   (27) H. Portzehl, *Z. Naturforsch.* **5b**, 75 (1950).

sion indicated that these preparations were very homogeneous in the size and shape of the molecules.

The measurements on proteins in concentrated urea solutions (Table V) show that some proteins are readily split into smaller units in such solutions; while others, such as serum albumin, do not split, although other evidence indicates that the molecules swell and partially unfold

TABLE V

MOLECULAR WEIGHTS OF VARIOUS PROTEINS FROM MEASUREMENTS OF THEIR OSMOTIC PRESSURE IN ISOELECTRIC UREA SOLUTIONS

Amandin(1)	30.0
Casein(2)	33.6
Egg albumin(2, 3)	34.0
Pepsin(4)	36.0(a)
Edestin(2)	49.0
Serum albumin(5)	73.8
Serum globulin(6)	173.0
Hemoglobin, horse(2)	34.3
Methemoglobin, sheep(3)	66.2
Methemoglobin, dog(7)	65.9
Methemoglobin, ox(7)	39.2
Oxyhemoglobin, sheep(7)	65.6
Oxyhemoglobin, dog(7)	65.9
Oxyhemoglobin, ox(7)	37.7
Globin, sheep(7)	63.0
Globin, dog(7)	67.5
Globin, ox(7)	34.3

(a) This value was derived from the ultracentrifuge experiments of Steinhardt(4), who found that urea caused no dissociation of pepsin.

(1) N. F. Burk, *J. Biol. Chem.* **120**, 63 (1937).
(2) N. F. Burk and D. M. Greenberg, *J. Biol. Chem.* **87**, 197 (1930).
(3) T. C. Huang and H. Wu, *Chinese J. Physiol.* **4**, 221 (1930).
(4) J. Steinhardt, *J. Biol. Chem.* **123**, 543 (1938).
(5) N. F. Burk, *J. Biol. Chem.* **98**, 353 (1932).
(6) N. F. Burk, *J. Biol. Chem.* **121**, 373 (1937).
(7) H. Wu and E.-F. Yang, *Chinese J. Physiol.* **6**, 51 (1932).

under the influence of the urea. Some hemoglobins dissociate into half molecules of molecular weight near 34,000; others are unchanged in molecular weight. Edestin, of molecular weight near 300,000 in aqueous salt solution—as judged by sedimentation and diffusion measurements, and by the electron microscope data given in Table III—appears to dissociate into about six subunits under the influence of urea. Presumably the linkages holding the subunits together are hydrogen bonds or other similarly weak linkages (Chap. 9).

8. METHODS OF DETERMINATION OF OSMOTIC PRESSURE

An excellent discussion of osmotic-pressure methods has been given by Wagner.[95] Here we shall make no attempt to give a comprehensive survey of methods, but shall mention only a few typical illustrations of procedure. Precision in the determination of the pressure difference between the two liquid phases at equilibrium is obviously fundamental, but it is of almost equal importance that the apparatus be so designed that the approach to equilibrium is rapid. The latter condition requires, among other things, that the surface of the membrane be large in relation to the volume of the liquid on either side of it. The pioneer investigators in this field, such as Sørensen[90] and Adair,[91] used osmometers that required many days to come to equilibrium. The risk of bacterial contamination or protein denaturation is considerable in such experiments, but this risk was minimized in Adair's work by carrying out the measurements at 0°. Later workers, however, designed apparatus of equal accuracy but far more rapid in approach to equilibrium, such as that of Oakley[96] and Bourdillon,[97] the latter requiring only 3 or 4 hr. to attain equilibrium at room temperature. Some still more recent types of apparatus are discussed in more detail below.

The choice of materials for the membranes has been well discussed by Wagner.[95] Satisfactory membranes for many purposes can be made from cellophane or sausage casing of suitable grades, which are readily available commercially. Collodion membranes, prepared by the experimenter himself, can be made however with different degrees of permeability, according to the conditions of preparation; and the advantage of using such membranes often justifies the extra labor involved. For example, Gutfreund,[98] in his recent work on insulin, prepared collodion membranes which were impermeable to molecules of molecular weight 12,000, using Adair's[91] method of preparation and applying five coats of collodion.

Not only the material of the membrane, but also its shape, is important. Generally membranes are either bags or flat sheets. Bag membranes have been used by most investigators in the field of protein chemistry, beginning with Sørensen[90] and Adair.[91] A simple apparatus, successfully employed by Bull,[99] is shown in Fig. 4. The sack containing the protein solution is made from Visking sausage casing. The stopcock seen on the left of the diagram is left open until temperature equilibrium is reached. It is then closed, and the position of the toluene in the capillary on the right is marked. The level of the protein in the protein solution column is then adjusted as the experiment proceeds, so as to maintain the level of the toluene nearly constant. When equilibrium is reached, the levels of the liquid in the protein solution and in the outer solution are measured with a cathetometer; the difference, multiplied by the density of the protein solution, gives the osmotic pressure of the solution in centimeters of water, after correction for the small pressure difference due to the displacement of the toluene column from its original position.

An apparatus employing similar principles, but more elaborately designed to give higher precision, has been described by Scatchard, Batchelder, and Brown.[78] Like Oakley,[96] they designed the apparatus so that the protein solution is at atmospheric pressure, while the pressure on the outer solution is below atmospheric pressure.

(95) R. H. Wagner, *in* A. Weissberger, *Physical Methods of Organic Chemistry*, 2nd Ed., Interscience Publishers, New York, 1949, Vol. I, part I, p. 487.

(96) H. B. Oakley, *Trans. Faraday Soc.* **31**, 136 (1935).

(97) J. Bourdillon, *J. Biol. Chem.* **127**, 617 (1939).

(98) H. Gutfreund, *Biochem. J.* **50**, 564 (1952).

(99) H. B. Bull and B. T. Currie, *J. Am. Chem. Soc.* **68**, 742 (1946).

A very useful type of osmometer, employing a flat membrane and requiring only very small quantities of liquid, was originally designed by Hepp,[100] and further much improved by Peters and Saslow[101] and by Rehm.[102]   Still further improvements have been made by Scatchard, who has recently given a brief description of his model of

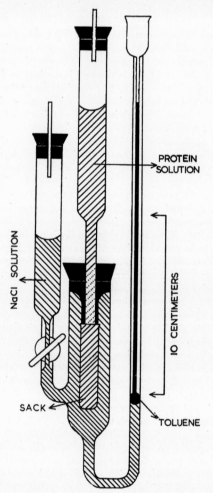

PROTEIN
SOLUTION

NaCl SOLUTION

10 CENTIMETERS

SACK

TOLUENE

FIG. 4.   Osmotic-pressure apparatus.   From Bull and Currie.[99]

this instrument,[103] which is shown in Fig. 5.   The outer solution is held in the pores of a circular piece of filter paper, which is placed under the flat horizontal membrane and supported by a flat Lucite disk.   The membrane is fastened tightly over the disk,

(100) O. Hepp, *Z. ges. exptl. Med.* **99,** 709 (1936).
(101) E. Peters and G. Saslow, *J. Gen. Physiol.* **23,** 177 (1939).
(102) W. S. Rehm, *Science* **100,** 364 (1944).
(103) G. Scatchard, *Am. Scientist* **40,** 61 (1952).

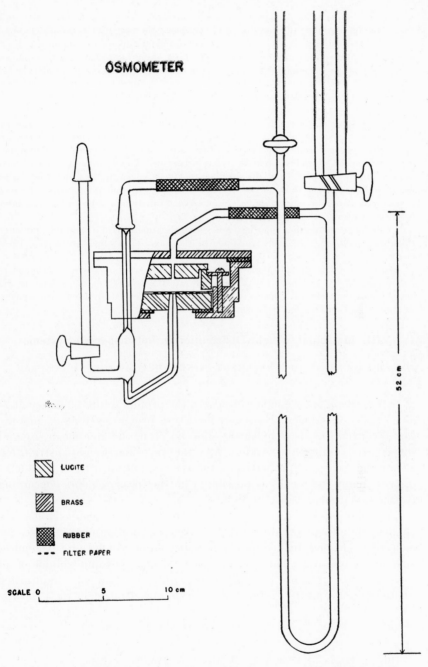

FIG. 5.   Modified Hepp osmotic-pressure apparatus.   From Scatchard.[103]

and the protein solution is placed over the membrane. Only 1.5–2.0 cc. of this solution is required, and equilibrium is rapid because of the very high ratio of membrane surface to the volume of either solution. The capillary tube below the filter paper is filled with outer solution, and the adjoining bulb is about half filled with this solution also. Toluene or decane fills the upper part of the bulb and part of the capillary above it, the level being adjusted by opening the stopcock in the side arm shown on the left of the diagram, and setting the manometer to the desired level. The rate of movement of the liquid in this capillary, at a given pressure level in the osmometer, indicates the rate of approach to equilibrium. Thus the osmometer is well adapted to measurements of the static pressure at equilibrium, or of the dynamic pressure when the system is displaced from equilibrium and the rate of liquid movement is determined as a function of the applied pressure. The latter type of measurement is particularly valuable in the study of a polydispersed system such as gelatin, in which the smaller components may leak through the membrane as the experiment proceeds. In such cases the dynamic pressure may be measured as a function of time and extrapolated back to zero time.

Cellophane membranes may be used with this apparatus, but suitably prepared collodion membranes give flow rates across the membrane which are several times faster.

Finally, mention should be made of the osmotic balance, devised by Jullander[104] and improved by Enoksson.[105] This is the most precise form of osmometer yet devised, but for technical reasons it has not yet been successfully used with aqueous solutions and therefore has not been applied to proteins.

VIII. Molecular Weight Distribution in Polydispersed Systems

1. Evaluation of Different Kinds of Average Molecular Weight

Up to this point we have considered the protein solute (component 2) as a single substance. However, in nature protein systems commonly contain several kinds of molecules differing from one another in size and shape. It is important to know how the molecular-weight distribution affects the measured properties of the system, and in turn to be able to draw as many inferences as possible from the measurements concerning the molecular weight distribution.

In osmotic-pressure studies, in the region where van't Hoff's law applies, the measured value of Π/RT gives the total number of moles (or molecules) of nondiffusible solutes in unit volume of solution. Chemical analysis, on the other hand, yields the total mass per unit volume of all these solutes. Suppose that there are p different kinds of nondiffusible solute molecules in the system, the weight concentration of the i'th type of molecule being c_i and its molecular weight M_i. Let $c = \sum_{i=1}^{p} c_i$ denote

(104) I. Jullander, *Arkiv Kemi, Mineral. Geol.* **21A**, No. 8 (1945).
(105) B. Enoksson, *J. Polymer Sci.* **3**, 314 (1948).

the total weight concentration of these solutes. The contribution to the total value of Π/RT, made by the i'th component, is c_i/M_i, and the total contribution of all components is $\sum_{i=1}^{p} (c_i/M_i)$. Thus, for the total osmotic pressure, divided by RT times the total concentration of solute, we have:

$$\frac{\Pi}{RTc} = \frac{\Pi}{RT\Sigma c_i} = \frac{\Sigma(c_i/M_i)}{\Sigma c_i} = \frac{1}{\bar{M}_n} \qquad (55)$$

the number-average molecular weight, defined by this equation, is thus:

$$\bar{M}_n = \frac{\Sigma c_i}{\Sigma(c_i/M_i)} = \frac{\Sigma(m_i M_i)}{\Sigma m_i} \qquad (56)$$

The chief contribution to the number-average molecular weight is obviously made by the smallest molecules in the system to which the membrane is impermeable. One gram per liter of molecules of weight 40,000 contributes three times as much to the number average as 1 g./l. of molecules of weight 120,000.

Certain other types of measurements, such as light scattering (sec. IX), when carried out on polydispersed systems, give another form of average molecular weight known as the weight average, $\bar{M}_w$. This is equal to the sum of the squares of the masses of the molecules divided by the total mass.

$$\bar{M}_w = \frac{\Sigma m_i M_i^2}{\Sigma m_i M_i} = \frac{\Sigma c_i M_i}{\Sigma c_i} \qquad (57)$$

Sedimentation equilibrium measurements on polydispersed systems have led to the consideration of a still different type of average known as the Z-average molecular weight, $\bar{M}_z$. This equals the sum of the cubes of the masses of the molecules divided by the sum of their squares. Even more than the weight average, the Z-average weights most heavily the largest molecules in the system in the calculation of the average.

$$\bar{M}_z = \frac{\Sigma m_i M_i^3}{\Sigma m_i M_i^2} = \frac{\Sigma c_i M_i^2}{\Sigma c_i M_i} \qquad (58)$$

It is obvious that we can extend this series of definitions and obtain an infinite series of different kinds of averages, each of an order one higher than the preceding. What we may call the $(Z + 1)$ average molecular weight, for example, would be equal to:

$$\bar{M}_{z+1} = \frac{\Sigma m_i M_i^4}{\Sigma m_i M_i^3} = \frac{\Sigma c_i M_i^3}{\Sigma c_i M_i^2} \qquad (59)$$

The use and determination of such an average, and of averages of higher orders, have been discussed by Wales;[106] see also Wales, Williams, Thompson, and Ewart.[107]

One may illustrate the significance of these averages by considering a particular system, for instance a hypothetical solution containing molecules of molecular weight (in thousands) 50, 100, 200, and 400, the weight concentration of all four species being the same. Calculation from the equations given above shows readily that the various average molecular weights, in thousands, are: $\bar{M}_n = 107$; $\bar{M}_w = 187.5$; $\bar{M}_z = 284$; $\bar{M}_{z+1} = 320$. This shows clearly the increased weight given to the larger molecules as we proceed to the average of higher order.

IX. Light Scattering: Its Relation to Molecular Shape and Molecular Dimensions[108]

1. SCATTERING FROM SOLUTIONS OF SMALL MOLECULES; RELATION OF LIGHT SCATTERING AND OSMOTIC PRESSURE

All material media which refract light also scatter it. Hence a beam of light passing through any medium, even if no substance present absorbs the light, suffers a diminution in intensity as it proceeds, because a fraction of the light is scattered in all directions by the molecules of the medium. The scattering is due to the electronic oscillations set up in the molecules by the rapidly alternating electric field of the light wave. The molecules thus become oscillating electric dipoles, which send out radiation in all directions. The intensity of this scattered radiation increases with the size of the molecules and with their electric polarizibility, that is, with the magnitude of the dipole moment induced by an electric field of given intensity. Experimentally the polarizability is inferred from the magnitude of the refractive index. If the molecules are very small, less than about one-twentieth of the wavelength of the light, the scattering from them may be calculated as if they were point dipoles; if they are considerably larger than this, the light scattered from one portion of the molecule may be out of phase with that coming from another portion, and the resulting internal interference diminishes the

(106) M. Wales, *J. Phys. & Colloid Chem.* **52**, 976 (1948).
(107) M. Wales, J. W. Williams, J. O. Thompson, and R. H. Ewart, *J. Phys. & Colloid Chem.* **52**, 983 (1948).
(108) Optical aspects of the phenomenon of light scattering are discussed by Doty and Geiduschek in Chap. 5. Several reviews of the subject have appeared in recent years, of which a few are cited here.[89,109,110]
(109) G. Oster, *Chem. Revs.* **43**, 319 (1948); *idem, Progr. Biophys. and Biophys. Chem.* **1**, 73 (1950).
(110) J. T. Edsall and W. B. Dandliker, *Fortschr. chem. Forsch.* **2**, 1 (1951).

intensity, as compared with the ideal value that would be attained if interference were absent.   Here we discuss systems of small molecules where internal interference is absent; the effects of such interference are treated below, in sec. IX-2.

However in a liquid or solid the molecules are so close together that the light scattered from any one molecule is partially destroyed by interference due to the scattering from its neighbors which are out of phase with it.   This *intermolecular* interference would reduce the scattering to zero if the molecules were arranged in a perfectly regular array, as in a perfect crystal at the absolute zero of temperature.   In an actual solution, however, the concentration of solute molecules in any given small region of the solution fluctuates constantly from moment to moment, although the average concentration, taken over a long period of time, must be the same as in the solution as a whole.   It is these fluctuations that determine the observed scattering, and the method of evaluating their influence was first developed by Smoluchowski[111] and by Einstein.[112] The probability of a fluctuation in concentration depends on the molar free energy change that would be involved in producing the same concentration change in a volume of solution containing 1 mole of solute.   This is closely correlated with the change in osmotic pressure that would be produced by a change in concentration of solute.   On the other hand, the magnitude of the scattering effect produced depends on the rate of change of polarizability of the system with the change in the solute concentration produced by the fluctuation.   This depends both on the refractive index, n, of the medium and on the refractive index increment, dn/dc, of the solute, where c is the solute concentration in g./cc.   Calculation shows that the observed effects are proportional to the squares of both these quantities.

We may study the scattering either by measuring the intensity of the scattered light directly, or by determining the diminution in intensity of the transmitted beam as it passes through the medium.   In the former case, what must be determined is the reduced intensity, R_θ—also known as Rayleigh's ratio—of the light scattered at angle θ with respect to the forward direction of the incident beam.   This is defined by the equation:

$$R_\theta = \frac{i_\theta r^2}{I_0} \tag{60}$$

Here I_0 is the intensity of the incident beam at the point where the scattering is being observed, i_θ is the scattered intensity per unit volume of scattering medium in the direction θ, and r is the distance from the

(111) M. Smoluchowski, *Ann. Physik* **25**, 205 (1908).

(112) A. Einstein, *Ann. Physik* **33**, 1275 (1910).

scattering region to the observer. If the incident light is unpolarized, and the solute molecules are isotropic, and small compared to the wavelength of the light, then it is found that the angular dependence of R is given by the simple equation:

$$R_\theta = R_{90}(1 + \cos^2 \theta) \tag{61}$$

where R_{90} is the reduced intensity in the direction perpendicular to the incident beam. For isotropic molecules, the scattered light at 90° is completely plane-polarized, the electrical vector being vertical if the plane determined by the incident beam and the direction from the scattering center to the observer is horizontal. In the direction of the forward incident beam (R_0) and in the backward direction (R_{180}) the light is completely unpolarized, and the total intensity in either of these directions is twice as great as at 90°. Calculations, due particularly to Debye,[113] give for R_{90} the following equation:

$$R_{90} = \frac{2\pi^2}{N_0 \lambda_0{}^4} n^2 \left(\frac{dn}{dc_2}\right)^2 \frac{RTc_2}{\left(\dfrac{\partial \Pi}{\partial c_2}\right)} = \frac{KRTc_2}{\dfrac{\partial \Pi}{\partial c_2}} \tag{62}$$

Here N_0 is Avogadro's number, λ_0 the wavelength of the light *in vacuo*, n the refractive index of the medium (practically equal in a dilute solution to the value for the solvent, n_0), and dn/dc_2 the refractive index increment of the solute. K is defined by the equation. Moreover we can write from Eq. (24) that:

$$\frac{\partial \Pi}{\partial c_2} = RT \left(\frac{1}{M_2} + 2Bc_2 + 3Cc_2{}^2 + \cdots\right) \tag{63}$$

Using this value of $\partial \Pi / \partial c_2$ in Eq. (62), and dropping all the interaction terms of higher order than that involving B, we may rearrange (62) to give:

$$\frac{Kc_2}{R_{90}} = \frac{1}{M_2} + 2Bc_2 \tag{64}$$

Here the coefficient B is identical with that appearing in the osmotic-pressure equation (24). The intercept of the curve, when either Kc_2/R_{90} or Π/RTc_2 is plotted against c_2, is equal to the reciprocal of the molecular weight of the solute; but the slope of the former curve is just twice that of the latter.

Alternatively, we may express the scattering in terms of the decrease in intensity of the incident beam as it progresses through the medium. If this intensity has diminished from I_0 to I_d after the light has traversed

(113) P. Debye, *J. Phys. & Colloid Chem.* **51**, 18 (1947).

a distance d in the medium, the turbidity (τ) of the medium is defined by the equation:

$$\tau = \frac{1}{d} \ln \frac{I_0}{I_d} \tag{65}$$

If the reduced intensity can be described by Eq. (61), then it is easy to show that τ and R_{90} are related by the equation:

$$\tau = 16\pi R_{90}/3 \tag{66}$$

and hence that:

$$Hc_2/\tau = 1/M_2 + 2Bc_2 \tag{67}$$

where $H = 16\pi K/3$. Either Eq. (64) or (67) may be used in evaluating molecular weights from light-scattering data. In practice, it is generally the reduced intensity, or a quantity proportional to it, that is measured, for the turbidity of most dilute protein solutions is so low that the decrease in intensity of the transmitted beam cannot be determined very accurately. On the other hand, the extreme sensitivity of modern photomultiplier phototubes permits the recording of scattered light intensity with high accuracy, even when it is extremely faint; for instance, the light scattered by pure, dust-free organic liquids. It is, of course, of the utmost importance to remove all traces of dust and large particles of any sort; in protein solutions this is generally done by filtering through very fine filters, or by high-speed centrifuging, or by a combination of both operations.

Equations (64) and (67) must generally be employed with two corrections. A small part of the observed scattering arises from the solvent; in a very dilute protein solution the solvent contribution becomes comparable with that of the dissolved protein. Therefore the scattering of the solvent should always be separately determined and subtracted from that of the solution. Moreover, it was assumed in deriving Eqs. (64) and (67) that the scattering molecules are isotropic; if this is not the case the light scattered at 90° will not be completely polarized, but will contain a small horizontally polarized component in addition to the major vertically polarized component. The depolarization factor ρ, which gives the ratio of these components, is discussed in Chap. 5 in its relation to the molecular anisotropy. The values of ρ for most protein solutions lie between 0.005 and 0.03; this involves a small correction factor in calculating the molecular weight from the observed intensity of scattering.

Scattering in multicomponent systems at finite concentrations is affected by the thermodynamic interactions of all the components in the system. The general equations for such systems have been formulated by Brinkman and Hermans,[114] by Kirkwood and Goldberg,[115] and by Stockmayer;[116] for reviews see articles by Doty and Edsall[89] and Edsall and Dandliker.[110] In a mixed solvent, it is not in general true that Kc_2/R_{90}, extrapolated to $c_2 = 0$, yields the reciprocal of the molecular weight of the solute. If the solute selectively binds one component of the mixed solvent, and if this has a different refractive index from the other component, the limiting value of Kc_2/R_{90} may be either greater or

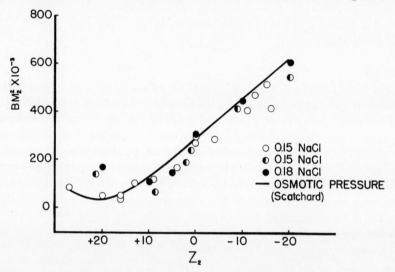

FIG. 6. Comparison of the interaction constant B [Eqs. (24) and (52)] for bovine serum albumin, from osmotic-pressure and from light-scattering measurements. Slopes are expressed as $BM_2^2/1000$, where M_2 is the molecular weight of the protein. The abscissa gives Z_2, the net proton charge per molecule of albumin. Solid line from osmotic-pressure data of Scatchard, Batchelder, and Brown.[78] Points from light-scattering measurements [Edsall et al.[88]].

less than in a two-component system.[117] The application of the general equations to the system: water (component 1), protein of valence Z_2 (component 2), and salt (component 3), has been treated in detail by Edsall et al.[88] For moderate protein concentrations, if the ionic strength is not very low and the net charge on the protein not too high, it is found that the data can be described by Eq. (64) or (67), the limiting value of B being the same as that derived by Scatchard for osmotic-pressure measurements [Eq. (52)]. An experimental comparison is shown in Fig. 6 for

(114) H. C. Brinkman and J. J. Hermans, J. Chem. Phys. **17**, 574 (1949).
(115) J. G. Kirkwood and R. J. Goldberg, J. Chem. Phys. **18**, 54 (1950).
(116) W. H. Stockmayer, J. Chem. Phys. **18**, 58 (1950).
(117) R. H. Ewart, C. P. Roe, P. Debye, and J. R. McCartney, J. Chem. Phys. **14**, 687 (1946).

bovine serum albumin; the points, determined from light scattering, lie mostly a little below the line which describes the osmotic-pressure measurements, but the agreement is on the whole quite satisfactory.

The study of light scattering can be carried out over a much wider range of conditions than is possible with osmotic-pressure measurements, since only a single solution is studied, and it is not necessary to equilibrate across a membrane with an outer solution.   This permits the study of proteins under conditions of high net charge and low ionic strength.

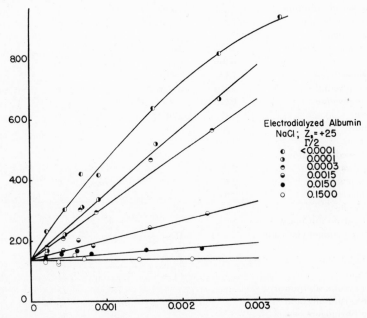

Fig. 7.   Values of Kc_2/R_{90} as a function of c_2, for bovine serum albumin with a net proton charge of $+25$, at several different concentrations of sodium chloride. From Edsall et al.[88]

Figure 7 shows measurements on bovine serum albumin with a net proton charge of $+25$, and sodium chloride concentrations ranging from below 0.0001 to 0.15 M.   The curves all extrapolate to the same limiting intercept, giving a molecular weight near 77,000, and the curves are linear at low protein concentrations.   The values of B decrease with increasing m_3, as would be predicted from Eq. (52).   However, B does not fall to zero when the net proton binding is zero, but does approach a minimum value very close to zero at more acid pH values.   The numerical value of the net proton charge at which this minimum occurs increases with the salt concentration.   The results are explainable in terms of the binding of anions of the salt by the serum albumin; detailed studies of the

TABLE VI

MOLECULAR WEIGHTS OF PROTEINS DETERMINED BY LIGHT SCATTERING

Molecular weight in thousands from scattering at indicated wavelengths

Protein	5780 A.	5461 A.	4358 A.	Calibration method (b)	Observers
Insulin (acid solution)	....	....	12	D, H	(12)
Ovalbumin	38.2	37.6	...	A	(1)
Horse serum albumin	76.5	72.2	...	A	(1)
Bovine serum albumin	77.7	76.6	...	A	(1)
Pig serum albumin	72.1	71.9	...	A	(1)
Hemocyanins:					
Palinurus vulgaris	461	464	...	A	(1)
Homarus vulgaris (A)	630	617	...	A	(1)
H. vulgaris (B)	733	689	...	A	(1)
Sepia officinalis	3210	3150	...	A	(1)
Helix pomatia	6340	....	...	A	(1)
Excelsin	281	276	...	A	(1)
(Amandin)	(330)	(330)	...	A	(2)
Edestin(a)	335	....	...	A	(2)
Prunus seed globulins:					
P. avium(a)	286–316	....	...	A	(3)
P. cerasus(a)	295	....	...	A	(3)
P. domestica(a)	290	....	...	A	(3)
Yeast enolase	....	66	...	B	(4)
Rabbit serum antibody (anti-p-azophenylarsonic)	....	158	...	C	(5)
Ovalbumin	....	45.7	...	D	(6)
β-Lactoglobulin	....	35.7	...	D	(6)
Lysozyme	....	14.8	...	D	(6)
Bovine serum albumin(a)	....	....	73	D	(6)
Bovine serum albumin	....	....	77	E	(7)
Bovine fibrinogen	....	....	540	E	(8)
Bovine fibrinogen	....	....	340	D	(13)
Tobacco mosaic virus	....	40,000	...	F	(9)
Bushy stunt virus	....	9,000	...	G	(10)
Influenza virus	....	322,000	...	G	(10)

(a) Denotes preparations which were somewhat unstable and showed a perceptible tendency to aggregate on standing.

(b) Calibration methods:

A. Molecular weights given relative to amandin as a standard protein which is taken as having a molecular weight of 330,000.

B. Calibration with reference to edestin as a standard protein; assumed molecular weight of edestin 300,000.

C. Calibration with reference to pure carbon disulfide as a standard.

D. Calibration made on an absolute scale; for details of calibration, see Brice, Halwer, and Speiser(11). Molecular weights reported in reference (6) were determined also at 4358 A. with results in close agreement with those at 5461 A.

E. Calibration with reference to pure benzene as a standard scatterer; reduced intensity of benzene assumed as 49×10^{-6} at 4358 A.

effects involved, for chloride and thiocyanate solutions, have been reported by Edsall *et al.*[88] These effects are important as a means of studying the interaction of proteins with other molecules and ions; they must also be allowed for in extrapolating experimental data to zero concentration in order to obtain correct values of molecular weight.

Most of the molecular-weight values hitherto obtained for proteins by light scattering are listed in Table VI, which also indicates briefly the methods used by the various investigators for calibrating their data. This can be done by comparing the scattering from the solution under study with that from another solution of known turbidity, or containing a solute of known molecular weight at a known concentration. Alternatively, the scattered light intensity may be determined in absolute terms; this involves numerous special precautions; discussions of the methods involved, with references, have been previously given.[89,110]

It is difficult to estimate the magnitude of the probable error in the data of Table VI. Even the best values from light scattering are probably uncertain within ±4–5 per cent at present, and the error is generally likely to be somewhat greater. The range of molecular weights that can be covered is far greater than for osmotic-pressure measurements. The lower limit hitherto obtained for proteins—about 12,000 for acid insulin—

F. Reduced intensity measurements at 90° calibrated by direct turbidity measurements and corrected for angular dissymmetry of scattering.

G. Determination by direct turbidity measurements.

H. Calibration in terms of "ludox" colloidal silica as standard; silica calibrated by absolute turbidity measurements.

(1) P. Putzeys and J. Brosteaux, *Mededeel. Koninkl. Vlaam. Acad. Wetenschap, Belg. Klasse Wetenschap.* **3**, No. 1 (1941).

(2) M. L. Beeckmans and R. Lontie, *Bull. soc. chim. biol.* **28**, 509 (1946).

(3) P. Putzeys and M. L. Beeckmans, *Bull. soc. chim. biol.* **28**, 503 (1946).

(4) T. Bücher, *Biochim. et Biophys. Acta* **1**, 467 (1947).

(5) D. H. Campbell, R. H. Blaker, and A. B. Pardee, *J. Am. Chem. Soc.* **70**, 2496 (1948).

(6) M. Halwer, G. C. Nutting, and B. A. Brice, *J. Am. Chem. Soc.* **73**, 2786 (1951).

(7) J. T. Edsall, H. Edelhoch, R. Lontie, and P. R. Morrison, *J. Am. Chem. Soc.* **72**, 4641 (1950).

(8) R. F. Steiner and K. Laki, *Arch. Biochem. and Biophys.* **34**, 24 (1951).

(9) G. Oster, P. Doty, and B. H. Zimm, *J. Am. Chem. Soc.* **69**, 1193 (1947).

(10) G. Oster, *Science* **103**, 306 (1946); *Chem. Revs.* **43**, 319 (1948).

(11) B. A. Brice, M. Halwer, and R. Speiser, *J. Optical Soc. Am.* **40**, 768 (1950).

(12) F. Tietze and H. Neurath, *J. Biol. Chem.* **194**, 1 (1952).

(13) S. Katz, K. Gutfreund, S. Shulman and J. D. Ferry, *J. Am. Chem. Soc.* **74**, 5706 (1952).

See also D. A. I. Goring and P. Johnson, *Trans. Faraday Soc.* **48**, 267 (1952). (Values for bovine serum albumin, arachin, edestin, legumin and turnip yellow virus); S. Y. Frenkel, *Biockhimiya* **17**, 535 (1952); *Chem. Abstracts* **47**, 3660 (1953) (ovalbumin, horse serum albumin, chymotrypsinogen, α-chymotrypsin, edestin, trypsin).

is about the same for both methods, but light scattering can give fair results with even smaller molecules, which would pass through any osmometer membrane. For very high molecular weights light scattering is vastly superior to osmotic pressure, since the intensity of scattering goes up with increasing molecular weight whereas osmotic pressure goes down. For the very large molecules, the direct readings of R_{90} must be corrected for internal interference effects (see below) in order to obtain correct molecular weights, but these corrections are readily applied if the angular dependence of the scattering is known.

In a polydispersed system the extrapolated value of Kc/R_{90} gives the reciprocal of the weight-average molecular weight. This may be readily seen by considering the limiting form of Eq. (64) as c_2 approaches zero, which may be written: $R_{90} = Kc_2M_2$. If the solute consists of a series of components, the contribution of the ith component, of concentration c_i and molecular weight M_i, to R_{90} is Kc_iM_i, and:

$$\lim_{c \to 0} R_{90} = K \Sigma c_i M_i \tag{68}$$

On the other hand, the total weight concentration of all the solute molecules is $c = \Sigma c_i$. Multiplying both sides of Eq. (68) by $\Sigma c_i/R_{90}\Sigma c_iM_i$, we obtain:

$$\lim_{c \to 0} \frac{Kc}{R_{90}} = \frac{K\Sigma c_i}{R_{90}} = \frac{\Sigma c_i}{\Sigma c_iM_i} = \frac{1}{M_w} \tag{69}$$

Comparison with Eq. (57) shows immediately that the reciprocal of the weight-average molecular weight is obtained. Thus, in a polydispersed system, light scattering always gives a higher average molecular weight than osmotic pressure. If both methods give the same value, this is strong proof that the molecules are alike with respect to molecular weight.

2. Effects of Internal Interference upon Scattering; Evaluation of Molecular Dimensions

If a molecule is longer than about one-twentieth of the wavelength of the light which it is scattering, the oscillating electric dipoles in different parts of the molecule are no longer in phase; the light radiated from one portion of the molecule interferes, to a greater or less extent, with that radiated from other portions. Hence the scattered intensity R_θ, at the angle θ to the forward direction of the incident beam, is less than would be calculated from Eqs. (61) and (64). Moreover, the magnitude of the interference effect varies greatly with the angle of scattering. For scattering in the forward direction ($\theta = 0°$), there is no interference at all if the refractive index of the solute particles is not very different from that of the solvent medium. As the angle of scattering increases, the interference increases also, the reason being illustrated in Fig. 8.   The effect of the internal interference, when the protein solution is very dilute, can be described by inserting a factor denoted as $P(\theta)$ into the limiting form of Eqs. (61) and (64) combined:

$$\lim_{c_2 \to 0} R_\theta = Kc_2 M_2 (1 + \cos^2 \theta) P(\theta) \qquad (70)$$

$P(\theta)$ is equal to unity at all angles if the molecules are very small compared to the wavelength λ of the light in the medium.[118]   If this condition does not hold, $P(0°)$ is still unity, but $P(\theta)$ decreases more and more

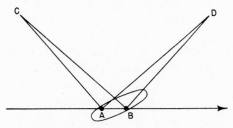

FIG. 8.   Illustration of the dependence of destructive interference on the scattering angle.   Note the larger path length difference for light scattered in the backward angle $(AB + BC - AC)$ than in the forward angle $(AB + BD - AD)$.   From Doty and Edsall.[89]

at higher angles.   Formulas for $P(\theta)$ for a uniform sphere of diameter D and for a uniform rod of length L were derived by Rayleigh[119] and by Neugebauer:[120]

Sphere:

$$P(\theta) = \left[\frac{3}{x^3} (\sin x - x \cos x) \right]^2 ; \; x = \frac{ksD}{2} \qquad (71)$$

Rod:

$$P(\theta) = \frac{1}{x} \int_0^{2x} \frac{\sin w}{w} \, dw - \left(\frac{\sin x}{x} \right)^2 ; \; x = \frac{ksL}{2} \qquad (72)$$

Here k is equal to $2\pi/\lambda$ and s is equal to $2 \sin (\theta/2)$.   The integral in Eq. (72) is known as the integral sine function; numerical values are given in various tables.   Debye[113] has also derived a formula for a randomly coiled chain, a model which fits well the behavior of nonpolar synthetic polymers like polystyrene.   Figure 9, taken from the work of Doty and

(118) Note that $\lambda = \lambda_0/n$, when λ_0 is the wavelength *in vacuo*, and n the refractive index of the solution.

(119) J. W. S. Rayleigh, *Proc. Roy. Soc.* (London) **A84**, 25 (1911).

(120) T. Neugebauer, *Ann. Physik* **42**, 509 (1943).

Steiner,[121] shows the variation of $P(\theta)$ with x (or with $\sqrt{x}$ in the case of the random coil[122]) for spheres, rods, and random coils. Formulas for $P(\theta)$ have also been derived for ellipsoids of revolution,[123] for cylinders of revolution,[124] and for disks of negligible thickness.[125] In the derivation of the equations for all these models, as for rods and random coils, the molecular axes are assumed to be randomly oriented in the solution.

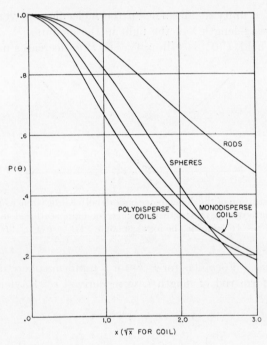

Fig. 9. Particle scattering factors for spheres, rods, and monodisperse and polydisperse randomly kinked coils. From Doty and Steiner.[121]

In practice, these equations have been used in two ways. Some types of apparatus are so designed that the cell containing the liquid under study is semioctagonal, with plane windows in the path of the incident beam and also at three other angles, generally 45, 90, and 135 degrees to

(121) P. Doty and R. F. Steiner, *J. Chem. Phys.* **18**, 1211 (1950).
(122) For a random coil, $x = K^2s^2R^2/6$, where R^2 is the mean square value of the distance between the ends of the coil.
(123) C. C. Shull and L. C. Roess, *J. Applied Phys.* **18**, 295 (1947); L. C. Roess and C. C. Shull, *ibid.* **18**, 308 (1947). P. Debye has also derived an equivalent formula, which is somewhat simpler in appearance; it is given by Edsall and Dandliker[110] (p. 38) and by Doty and Edsall[89] (p. 76).
(124) G. Fournet and A. Guinier, *J. phys. radium* **11**, 516 (1950).
(125) O. Kratky and G. Porod, *J. Colloid Sci.* **4**, 35 (1949).

the incident beam.   It is then convenient to measure R_θ at these three angles.   The ratio $z = R_{45°}/R_{135°}$ is commonly known as the dissymmetry; assuming a given type of model, z is then a calculable function of the ratio of some absolute dimension of the model to the wavelength (λ) of the light.   This function is plotted for spheres, rods, and random coils in the right half of Fig. 10, also taken from Doty and Steiner.[121]   The ordinate of this figure is D/λ, where D for a sphere is the diameter, for a rod is the length, and for a coil is the root mean square distance between the ends.   If the wavelength of the light in the medium is known the determination of z immediately fixes the value of D for any given model. For a given angle of scattering, knowledge of D fixes the value of x in Eq. (71) or (72), or in analogous equations for other models. $P(\theta)$ can then be calculated for the given angle; if, in particular, $\theta = 90°$, one obtains values which are plotted in the left half of Fig. 10 for $P^{-1}(90)$ as a function of z.

Thus the measurement of z, assuming a given type of model, gives a characteristic length of the model; then, from the observed z value, $P^{-1}(90)$ is computed. If R_{90} and K are known from experiment, the molecular weight may be computed from Eq. (70), rewritten in the form, for $\theta = 90°$:

$$M_2 = \lim_{c \to 0} \frac{R_{90}P^{-1}(90)}{Kc_2} \tag{73}$$

This method was used by Oster, Doty, and Zimm[126] to determine the length and the molecular weight of tobacco mosaic virus.   From electron microscopy, the virus was known to be rod-shaped, so that Eq. (72) is applicable.   They determined the ratio $R_{49°}/R_{131°}$, and plotted a curve similar to the lower half of Fig. 10.   From the limiting value (1.94) of this ratio at infinite dilution they calculated L/λ as 0.66.   The light used was the mercury green line, for which $\lambda_0 = 5461$ A. and

$$\lambda = 5461/1.33 = 4090 \text{ A.}$$

This gave the molecular length $L = 2700$ A., in satisfactory agreement with electron microscope determinations.   The uncorrected value of Kc_2/R_{90} would have corresponded to a molecular weight near 24,000,000; but multiplication by $P^{-1}(90)$, which was 1.65–1.7, gave a final molecular weight value of 40,000,000.

More information can be obtained if R_θ is determined over a wide variety of angles.   It is not practicable at present to make measurements at θ less than about 20°, but with a properly designed cell for the liquid under study measurements are readily made from this lower limit up to about 150°.   A suitable apparatus was described, for instance, by

(126) G. Oster, P. Doty, and B. H. Zimm, *J. Am. Chem. Soc.* **69**, 1193 (1947).

614   JOHN T. EDSALL

Zimm.[127] To analyze the data, Zimm plots the measured relative values of $P^{-1}(\theta)$ against $\sin^2(\theta/2) + Kc_2$, where K is an arbitrary constant chosen for convenience in plotting the data.   The observed data are thus represented in the form of a grid, the points for any given angle being extrapolated to zero concentration, and the resultant curve for zero concentration being extrapolated to zero angle of scattering.   Since the internal interference vanishes at $\theta = 0°$, the value of R_0/c_2 as $c_2 \to 0$ permits directly the calculation of the molecular weight.   The limiting

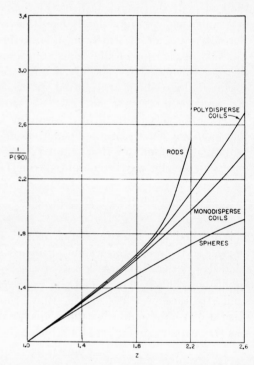

Fig. 10.   Correction factors and particle dimensions relative to the wavelength

slope of the curve for $P^{-1}(\theta)$ against $\sin^2(\theta/2)$ permits the evaluation of a characteristic molecular length; for a rod of length L, for instance, Zimm[127] gives the equation:

$$P^{-1}(\theta) = 1 + x^2/9 + 7x^4/2025 + \cdots \tag{74}$$

where $x = (2\pi L/\lambda)\sin(\theta/2)$ as in Eq. (72).   A plot of this function, and of analogous functions for spheres and coils, is given by Edsall and Dandliker (Ref. 110, p. 39).

(127) B. H. Zimm, *J. Chem. Phys.* **16**, 1099 (1948).

Often it is uncertain what model is most suitable to represent a given protein.   Determination of the molecular weight, however, may rule out certain possibilities.   Thus Edsall and Dandliker (Ref. 110, p. 40) studied a pathological serum globulin, and found that the angular-dependence data could be accounted for equally well by thin rods 563 A. long or by spheres 414 A. in diameter.   Such spheres, however, would have a molecular weight near 30,000,000, while the molecular weight actually

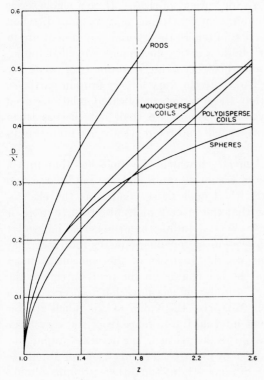

λ', as a function of the dissymmetry $(R_{45°}/R_{135°})$.   From Doty and Steiner.[121]

determined was 1,160,000.   Therefore the rod model could be used to fit all these data—a suitably chosen ellipsoid would also be an applicable model—and the possibility of spherical shape was ruled out.

Zimm's extrapolation method, involving determinations over a wide range of angles of scattering, is particularly valuable in the study of polydispersed systems.   Small amounts of very large particles are readily revealed by the intense scattering at low angles to which they give rise, whereas they may contribute relatively little to scattering at higher angles.   If measurements are made only at 45, 90, and 135 degrees, such large particle impurities may fail to be detected, and misleading apparent values of molecular weight and length may be obtained.

In all of this discussion it has been assumed that the relative refractive index, m, of the protein and the surrounding medium is not very far from unity. The general case, for scattering from spherical molecules of any radius and any value of m, was worked out by Mie.[128] Mie's general equations have been applied by La Mer and his associates[129] to monodispersed sulfur sols of a wide variety of sizes. Here a whole series of secondary maxima and minima of scattering may be found, when scattering is studied as a function of angle; theory and experiment are in excellent agreement. Other characteristic phenomena are also found, different in many respects from those occurring in proteins of relatively small size and m values. It is only in the very largest protein particles, such as influenza virus,[130] that these more complicated relations need be considered in protein systems. Hence we shall not discuss them further here; the interested reader will find references to the literature in several reviews.[89,109,110]

"Reversed dissymmetry" effects, in which z becomes less than unity, have been found in solutions of serum albumin at large net charge and extremely low ionic strengths.[131] Under these conditions the electrostatic repulsions are so strong that the protein molecules behave more or less like spheres of much larger effective radius than the actual molecular size. Calculation for such a system of repelling spheres indicates that just such effects are to be expected. Increase of the concentration of diffusible ions, or decrease of the net charge on the protein, causes the value of z to return to unity. Similar effects have been observed with tobacco mosaic virus;[126,132] in this case the value of z is much greater than unity at $c = 0$, because of internal interference from the very large molecules; but in the absence of salt, at pH near 7, z decreases rapidly as protein concentration increases, owing to the same type of repulsive intermolecular interactions. Similar studies on other proteins should throw much light on the intermolecular forces in these systems.

X. Low-Angle X-Ray Scattering from Protein Solutions

The laws governing the scattering of visible light by solutions of large molecules, as a function of angle, are directly applicable to the scattering

(128) G. Mie, *Ann. Physik* **25**, 377 (1908).
(129) See, for instance, I. Johnson and V. K. LaMer, *J. Am. Chem. Soc.* **69**, 1184 (1947); M. Kerker and V. K. LaMer, *ibid.* **72**, 3516 (1950).
(130) G. Oster, *Science* **103**, 306 (1946). See also Ref. 109.
(131) P. Doty and R. F. Steiner, *J. Chem. Phys.* **20**, 85 (1952); see also Ref. 89, pp. 96–107, incl.
(132) G. Oster, *J. Gen. Physiol.* **33**, 445 (1950).

of x-rays by such systems.   Indeed, since the refractive index of x-rays is practically unity in any medium, equations such as (71) and (72) for rods and spheres, respectively, hold more rigorously for x-rays than for visible light.   Many of the theoretical calculations cited in sec. IX-2 were carried out with their application to x-ray scattering in mind.

The major difference lies in the fact that for x-rays, with λ of the order of 1 A., and with proteins having dimensions of the order of 40 or 50 A. up to several thousand angstroms, the values of D/λ, or L/λ, in Eqs. (71) and (72) are very large.   Hence the whole scattering curve lies at very small angles, extremely close to the primary beam.   At such angles, $\sin \theta = \theta$ to a very close approximation, if θ be expressed in radians, and this permits a simplification in the form of the equations.

The absolute intensity of x-ray scattering at zero angle depends on the electron density of the scattering material and on the number of scattering particles in unit volume.   It must be remembered that equations such as (71) and (72), and similar equations for ellipsoids or cylinders, are derived on the assumption that the scattering macromolecule is of uniform electron density throughout; the actual inhomogeneities within the molecular structure are replaced by an average value.   The electron density within a protein molecule is greater than that of the surrounding water.   Hence the structure which contributes to the scattering may be considered as the protein molecule, including any *internal* water of hydration, but excluding the water of hydration on the outer surface. Strongly bound ions or molecules attached to the protein also contribute to the scattering.   Closely packed water molecules on the surface, due to electrostriction of the solvent, have a higher electron density than free water further away from the protein, but the difference is probably not great enough to affect the scattering greatly.

The first important theoretical treatment of the general problem was that of Guinier.[132a]   At very low angles, and in solutions of particles dilute enough to be considered independent, the angular distribution of scattered intensity can be written:

$$P(\theta) = \exp\left(-4\pi R_g^2 \theta^2 / 3\lambda^2\right) \tag{75}$$

Here R_g is the radius of gyration of the macromolecule.   For a sphere of radius R, R_g is $\sqrt{\tfrac{3}{5}}\, R = 0.774R$.   Formulas for the radii of gyration of ellipsoids of revolution were given by Guinier;[132a] and values have also been given graphically, as a function of molecular weight and of axial ratio, for ellipsoids of revolution and for right-circular cylinders, by

(132a) A. Guinier, *Ann. phys.* **12**, 161 (1939).

Ritland, Kaesberg, and Beeman.[133] A plot of the logarithm of the scattered intensity as a function of the square of the angle of scattering, at very low angles, can then be used to compute the radius of gyration. If the molecular weight is known, this permits a calculation of the axial ratio of the unhydrated molecule, assuming it to be an ellipsoid of revolution. However, on this basis alone it is impossible to distinguish an oblate from a prolate ellipsoid; an axial ratio can be given for either. Alternatively, the molecules may be described as cylindrical rods or disks, the calculated axial ratio being very similar to that for ellipsoids. Neither model, of course, is to be considered as more than a very rough approximation to the actual shape of a protein molecule.

At higher angles, the scattered intensity becomes a function of the absolute molecular dimensions, as indicated by Eq. (71) or (72), or similar equations for ellipsoids or cylinders. From such measurements, combined with the radius of gyration determined from measurements at very low angles, it should be possible to evaluate both the molecular weight and the axial ratio independently of other data. However, the form of the scattering curve at higher angles cannot as yet be determined with high precision, so that the reliability of axial ratios so obtained is not very great. It is also important, if trustworthy results are to be obtained from such measurements, that the protein preparation studied should be of high purity. Even a moderate degree of contamination with other molecules of different size and shape from the one under study can give very misleading results.

The data available by this method are still few. Kratky[134] reported preliminary studies on edestin, insulin, hemocyanin, and tobacco mosaic virus. The most clear-cut results were obtained with edestin, for which the scattering curve coincided closely with that to be expected for a spherical molecule of molecular weight 300,000, in good agreement with the results obtained from electron microscopy (sec. V). Dervichian, Fournet, and Guinier[135] studied horse hemoglobin, serum albumin, and the hemocyanin of the snail *Aspersa*. For both hemoglobin and serum albumin, they obtained a radius of gyration of 23 A., corresponding to a sphere 59 A. in diameter, or to an ellipsoidal model of rather low asymmetry, with an axial ratio of less than 2 to 1. The scattering curve for the hemocyanin was more difficult to interpret, but it clearly corresponded to a much larger molecule; the authors concluded the major

(133) H. N. Ritland, P. Kaesberg, and W. W. Beeman, *J. Chem. Phys.* **18**, 1237 (1950).

(134) O. Kratky, *J. Polymer Sci.* **3**, 195 (1948).

(135) D. G. Dervichian, G. Fournet, and A. Guinier, *Bull. soc. chim. biol.* **31**, 101 (1949).

dimension was probably several times as great as 220 A., and might be an exact multiple of this figure.

The most detailed study of proteins by this method is that of Ritland, Kaesberg, and Beeman.[133] Their results are compactly summarized in Table VII, which lists radii of gyration and the calculated axial ratios.

TABLE VII

ESTIMATED SHAPES AND HYDRATIONS OF PROTEINS FROM LOW-ANGLE X-RAY SCATTERING(a)*

Protein	Radius of gyration, A.	Assumed mol. wt. $\times 10^{-3}$	Frictional ratio	Axial ratios	Hydration, g. water/g. protein
Lysozyme	16.0	18	1.20	2.3 prolate $(2.8)^{-1}$ oblate	0.32 prolate 0.25 oblate
β-Lactoglobulin	24.6	35.4	1.25	3.6 $(5.5)^{-1}$	0.20 0.00
Ovalbumin	24.0	44	1.16	2.9 $(4.0)^{-1}$	0.15 0.00
Bovine hemoglobin	23.9	66.7	1.16	2.1 $(2.4)^{-1}$	0.28 0.20
Bovine serum albumin*	26.6	69	1.27	2.7 $(3.4)^{-1}$	0.42 0.30

(a) From H. N. Ritland, P. Kaesberg, and W. W. Beeman, *J. Chem. Phys.* **18**, 1237 (1950).

* Recent work in the same laboratory (J. Anderegg, Thesis, University of Wisconsin, 1952) indicates some need for revision in the figures of this table. More accurate radii of gyration have been obtained by making measurements as a function of concentration down to $c = 0.005$ g./cc., and extrapolating to $c = 0$. The revised value of R_g for bovine serum albumin is 29.8, instead of 26.6 A. as given above. The value for human serum mercaptalbumin (31 A.) is significantly higher than for bovine serum albumin. The value for human serum mercaptalbumin mercury dimer is 37.2 A.

It also gives frictional ratios, determined from sedimentation and diffusion measurements (sec. XIV), which give a measure of the combined effects of asymmetry and hydration. Since a dissymmetry factor is calculated directly from the x-ray measurements, the hydration factor can then be evaluated from the frictional ratio, and the resulting figures are given in the last column. The hydration values for β-lactoglobulin and ovalbumin would appear to be zero, if these molecules are taken to be oblate ellipsoids; this seems most unlikely, and may be taken as an argument against the oblate model for these molecules. If they are taken as prolate ellipsoids, the hydration values of 0.15–0.20 g. water/g. protein are in reasonable agreement with those found by other methods, though perhaps a little lower than most. The weight of other evidence, to be presented later, also favors the prolate shape for these proteins. The radius of gyration for bovine serum albumin found by these authors (26.6 A.) is considerably higher than 23 A., as given by Dervichian *et al.*,[135]

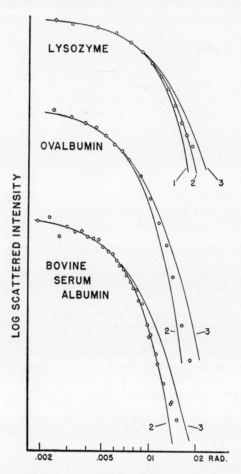

Fig. 11. The extended x-ray scattering curves of three proteins. The solid lines are theoretical curves for prolate ellipsoids of the indicated axial ratio. The experimental points span intensity ratios of about 6 for lysozyme, 35 for ovalbumin, and 17 for bovine serum albumin. From Ritland *et al.*[133]

and suggests a higher asymmetry, which is in accord with most of the evidence on this protein from other sources.

The scattering at higher angles for three of these proteins is shown in Fig. 11. Comparison of the experimental data with theoretical curves for prolate ellipsoids indicates axial ratios for serum albumin near 2.2, lysozyme 2.0, and ovalbumin 2.5. The corresponding values from Table VII are 2.7, 2.3, and 2.9. The differences are in the same direction in all three cases, and may be due to the effects of hydration in modifying the curves of Fig. 11; but the probable error of all the asymmetry and hydration values is large enough to make such conclusions very uncertain.

Recently Beeman et al.[66] have studied two spherical viruses by this method, and the results have already been discussed in sec. V, in connection with electron microscope studies. These data are of particular importance in indicating a large amount of internal hydration for these virus particles.

It is significant for experimental work that low-angle x-ray studies can be carried out at concentrations as high as 0.12–0.15 g. protein/cc. solution without significant evidence of interaction, if the molecules are small and not very asymmetrical, like hemoglobin[135] or serum albumin.[133] Riley and Herbert[136] carried out studies on solutions of much higher concentration—up to 0.58 g./cc. for human hemoglobin and 0.424 for ovalbumin—and have inferred from the presence of several Bragg diffraction spacings, the numerical values of which vary in a characteristic way with the concentration, that the molecules are packed in a semicrystalline array in these solutions. They have drawn inferences about molecular size and shape from these measurements, which agree reasonably well with those derived by other methods. Recently Riley and Oster[137] have given a more elaborate theoretical analysis of the molecular distribution in such concentrated solutions, and have deduced scattering curves for several model systems. From a study of bovine serum albumin solutions—0.33–0.51 g./cc.—they inferred that this protein could not be very far from spherical, and that their data could be fitted by a cylinder 45 A. in height and 49 A. in diameter. Such a model would have a radius of gyration of only 22 A., as against the value of 26.6 A. given in Table VII. There is also evidence, to be discussed later in this chapter, which indicates that serum albumin is considerably more asymmetrical than this, and may be roughly about 150 A. long, and around 40–45 A. in width at the middle (sec. XXI). Therefore the significance of the data of Riley and Oster is still not altogether clear.

XI. Molecular Weights from Solubility Determinations

It has been shown by Linderstrøm-Lang[138] that under certain conditions the molecular weight of a protein can be deduced from the variation

(136) D. P. Riley and D. Herbert, *Biochim. et Biophys. Acta* **4**, 374 (1950).
(137) D. P. Riley and G. Oster, *Discussions Faraday Soc.* No. 11, 107 (1951). For further calculations see also G. Oster and D. P. Riley, *Acta Cryst.* **5**, 1 (1952).
(138) K. Linderstrøm-Lang, *Arch. Biochem.* **11**, 191 (1946).

of its solubility with pH. If S is the solubility of the protein in grams per liter (or indeed in any other convenient unit) and $\bar{h}$ is the mean net proton charge per gram of protein—that is, $\bar{h} = Z_2/M_2$ in the terminology of sec. VIII, provided that no ions other than protons are bound to, or removed from, the isoionic protein—then the molecular weight M_2 is given by the equation:

$$M_2 = -\frac{1}{\bar{h}} \frac{d \log S}{d \text{ pH}} \qquad (76)$$

The conditions under which this equation is valid must be carefully noted: (a) The chemical potential of the protein must be fixed; hence the composition of the crystals must not vary with pH. (b) The molecular weight of the protein must be independent of pH. (c) The ionic strength of the medium must be constant over the entire pH range studied; it should also be large enough so that the contribution of added acid or alkali to the ionic strength, as the pH changes, is negligible compared to the ionic strength due to the salt present.

Very few of the solubility measurements yet reported fulfil these exacting requirements. Probably the most satisfactory are those of Grönwall[139] on β-lactoglobulin. From the slope of the log S vs. pH curve obtained by Grönwall near the isoionic point, in 0.005 M sodium chloride, Linderstrøm-Lang calculated a molecular weight near 36,000, in excellent agreement with the best values by other methods. However in 0.01 M sodium chloride the slope of the solubility curve was much higher. Even in this exceptionally favorable case, indeed, there are uncertainties concerning the purity and reproducibility of the protein preparation; moreover, the salt concentration is low enough so that it is doubtful whether condition (c) above is strictly fulfilled. Subject to this and the other stated conditions, Eq. (76) should be quite rigorous. It is to be hoped that more solubility data on pure proteins under well-defined conditions will be available in the future, to extend the range of applicability of this interesting treatment.

Fredericq and Neurath[139a] applied Eq. (76) to their measurements on the solubility of insulin in acid solution, in mixtures of sodium chloride and thiocyanate, at a total ionic strength of 0.1. Insulin shows a fairly strong interaction with thiocyanate ions, and its average molecular weight varies with pH. Therefore, it is doubtful whether the first two of the conditions indicated above are fulfilled in this case. Nevertheless, for any fixed ratio of chloride to thiocyanate, the form of the curve for log S as a function of pH could be approximately described by the equation:

$$\log S = \log S_0 - K(\text{pH} - \text{pH}_0)^2 \qquad (76a)$$

(139) A. Grönwall, *Compt rend. trav. lab. Carlsberg, Sér. chim.* **24,** 185 (1942).

(139a) E. Fredericq and H. Neurath, *J. Am. Chem. Soc.* **72,** 2684 (1950).

Here S_0 is the solubility at the pH ($=$pH$_0$) of minimum solubility; both S_0 and pH$_0$ are functions of the particular salt mixture used as solvent, but K was approximately 0.81 in all the solvents studied, at ionic strength 0.1. From these data, and the slope of the titration curve of insulin, Fredericq and Neurath calculated a molecular weight near 8000 for insulin from Eq. (76). This does not correspond exactly to any of the values found by other methods, which are discussed on pp. 717–19, but it is at least of the right order of magnitude.

XII. Molecular Weights of Proteins in Surface Films

Nearly all the methods of study with which we are concerned in this chapter deal with proteins in solution, or occasionally in the solid state. However, some interesting information has been derived from the study of surface films. If a film of protein is spread on a liquid surface, which is separated by a barrier from a clean surface of the same liquid with no surface film upon it, then it is found that a pressure is exerted upon the barrier, which tends to push it outward and expand the area of the film. Several investigators have reported that at very low film pressures protein films behave as so-called "gaseous" films; the first of these workers appears to have been Guastalla,[140] who studied ovalbumin, gliadin, and hemoglobin. Similar, but somewhat more precise, studies were made by Bull[141,142] on ovalbumin, β-lactoglobulin, and zein. There has been some controversy concerning the ability of proteins to form films of this type (see the review by Bull[143] for references), but their existence seems now to be well-established. As the surface concentration of protein approaches zero, a limiting relation appears to be approached, which is analogous to van't Hoff's law for osmotic pressure:

$$\lim_{n_2 \to 0} FA = n_2RT \tag{77}$$

Here F is the "surface pressure" in dynes/cm., A is the area of the film, and n_2 the number of moles of protein in the area A. If w_2 is the weight of protein then $n_2 = w_2/M_2$. Choosing w_2 as 1 mg., and expressing A in square meters, the molecular weight at 25° is given by the equation:

$$M_2 = 24.6 \times 10^2/FA \tag{78}$$

At higher film pressures this limiting equation must be expanded to include a second term which is linear in the surface pressure:

$$FA = n_2RT + \alpha F \tag{79}$$

(140) J. Guastalla, *Compt rend.* **208**, 973 (1939).
(141) H. B. Bull, *J. Am. Chem. Soc.* **67**, 4 (1945).
(142) H. B. Bull, *J. Am. Chem. Soc.* **68**, 745 (1946).
(143) H. B. Bull, *Advances in Protein Chem.* **3**, 95 (1947).

Bull[144] has given a derivation of this equation, which stresses the analogy between the surface pressure of a surface film and the osmotic pressure within a solution. He interprets the term α as a direct measure of the surface occupied by the spread protein.

In practice, the technique of spreading the film and the choice of the substrate on which the film is spread are of great importance. Bull[143,144] has found ammonium sulfate solutions, of various concentrations, to be suitable for the spreading of protein films. In a recent critical study,[144] he has noted that the plots of FA against F are not always linear at low F values, as Eq. (79) would imply, but that the curves may show sharp discontinuities in the neighborhood of $F = 0.1$ dyn./cm. or thereabouts. These may or may not appear, depending on the particular protein studied, the initial surface concentration of protein in the film, the time elapsed after spreading, and the presence of small amounts of substances such as glycerol in the substrate liquid. These phenomena greatly increase the difficulty of making a reliable extrapolation of the FA curves to zero F, but Bull concludes that the extrapolated molecular weights are probably reliable to about ± 10 per cent. He gives values near 45,000 for ovalbumin, 70,000 for bovine serum albumin, and near 35,000 for trypsin and insulin.[144] Earlier[142] he had reported a molecular weight of only about 17,000 for β-lactoglobulin spread on 20% ammonium sulfate—that is, only half the molecular weight found by osmotic pressure and other studies in solution—but stated that a normal value of about 34,000 was found if 0.00025 M $CuSO_4$ was added to the underlying liquid.

In the interpretation of surface-film measurements, it must be remembered that the protein after being spread in a film has undergone profound and usually irreversible changes as compared to the same protein in solution. These changes may involve splitting of the protein into subunits; it is perhaps remarkable that in most of the proteins hitherto studied such splitting does not occur. It may be expected that the shapes of the molecules in the films should generally bear very little relation to those in solution; the coiled peptide chains present in the native protein tend to uncoil, and the molecule in the surface film is less than 10 A. thick, far thinner than any native protein of the corpuscular type.

XIII. Translational Diffusion Coefficients

1. INTRODUCTORY DISCUSSION

Up to this point we have considered static methods for the determination of size and shape; nonequilibrium conditions have not been considered. Some of the most powerful methods for the study of large

(144) H. B. Bull, *J. Biol. Chem.* **185**, 27 (1950).

molecules, however, depend on the rate of their motion when subjected to an external force, or when they are returning to an equilibrium state after the equilibrium has been disturbed. All these methods involve the study of molecular diffusion—either free diffusion after a concentration or distribution gradient has been set up, or processes in which diffusion is opposed by an external force. Diffusion may be either translational or rotary; in either case it depends on the random Brownian movement of the molecules, which tends to distribute them in uniform concentration and random orientation throughout a solution.

We may consider translational diffusion first.[145,146] If a concentration gradient of solute is set up, for instance in a tube of uniform cross section containing the solution, the purely random thermal motion of the molecules tends to level out the gradient. Take the axis of the tube as the x-axis; the concentration c is then only a function of x, and of the time t from the beginning of the experiment. The net rate of transfer of solute from left to right at a given point, say $x = x_0$, is proportional to the concentration gradient at that point and to the cross section (A) of the tube. If dm is the net mass of solute transferred in the time increment dt, then

$$\left(\frac{dm}{dt}\right)_{x=x_0} = -DA\left(\frac{\partial c}{\partial x}\right)_{x=x_0} \tag{80}$$

the proportionality factor D is the diffusion coefficient of the solute. D has the dimensions $l^2 t^{-1}$; it is generally expressed in cm.^{2}/sec. The minus sign indicates that the direction of net transfer is opposite to that in which the concentration is increasing. Equation (80) was first stated by A. Fick, and is known as Fick's first law of diffusion. Fick's second law can in fact be derived from the first; it relates the rate of change of concentration with time, at any point in the solution, with the rate at which the concentration gradient is changing with x, at the same point:

$$\frac{\partial c}{\partial t} = D\,\frac{\partial^2 c}{\partial x^2} \tag{81}$$

Fick's second law is readily extended to the more general case in which the concentration may depend on y and z as well as on x. In this case, Eq. (81) becomes:

$$\frac{\partial c}{\partial t} = D\left(\frac{\partial^2 c}{\partial x^2} + \frac{\partial^2 c}{\partial y^2} + \frac{\partial^2 c}{\partial z^2}\right) = D\nabla^2 c \tag{82}$$

(145) J. W. Williams and L. C. Cady, *Chem. Revs.* **14**, 171 (1934).
(146) H. Neurath, *Chem. Revs.* **30**, 357 (1942).

The operator ∇^2 is known as the Laplacian operator. In Cartesian coordinates, from Eq. (82), it is obviously equal to

$$\nabla^2 = \partial^2/\partial x^2 + \partial^2/\partial y^2 + \partial^2/\partial z^2$$

It is readily expressed in terms of other coordinate systems;[147] the analog of Fick's second law, for rotary diffusion, is best expressed in spherical polar coordinates. (See sec. XV, Eq. 108.)

We are here concerned with the determination of diffusion coefficients as a tool for the study of molecular size and shape. The most important system in practice for such studies consists of a tube divided initially into two halves, the lower half containing a protein solution at uniform concentration, and the upper half containing pure solvent which has been equilibrated against the protein solution by dialysis. At a precisely defined time, the solution and solvent are brought into contact, the initial boundary which separates them being sharp. The concentration, or the concentration gradient, is then determined as a function of x at various times. Some of the experimental problems involved in forming a sharp boundary and in making the subsequent measurements are discussed below. If the solution may be considered ideal, so that the solute molecules do not interact, a straightforward solution of Fick's law can be obtained (see, for instance, Williams and Cady[145]) provided the tube can be considered as infinitely long. This condition is fulfilled for practical purposes if the initial concentration, c_0, remains unchanged at the very bottom of the tube throughout the experiment, and likewise if no protein reaches the very top of the tube during the same time. The concentration at level x and time t is then given by the equation:

$$c = \frac{c_0}{2} \{ 1 - P(z) \} \tag{83}$$

Here $z = x/\sqrt{4Dt}$, and P is the probability integral:

$$P(z) = \frac{2}{\sqrt{\pi}} \int_0^z e^{-z^2} dz \tag{84}$$

Numerical values of $P(z)$ are listed in many published mathematical tables. Differentiation of Eq. (83) gives immediately for the concentration gradient:

$$\frac{\partial c}{\partial x} = \frac{-c_0}{(4\pi Dt)^{\frac{1}{2}}} e^{-x^2/4Dt} \tag{85}$$

(147) See, for instance, L. Page, Introduction to Theoretical Physics, 2nd Ed., Van Nostrand, New York, 1935.

The rate of change of concentration with time, at given value of x, is:

$$\frac{\partial c}{\partial t} = \frac{c_0 X}{4\pi^{1/2}D^{1/2}t^{3/2}} \, e^{-x^2/4Dt} = D \, \frac{\partial^2 c}{\partial x^2} \tag{86}$$

These relations are illustrated in Fig. 12.   As the initially sharp boundary becomes progressively blurred by the diffusion process, the maximum

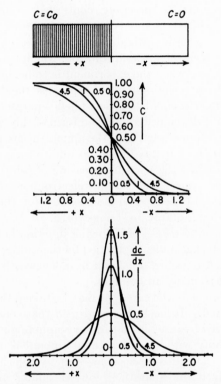

FIG. 12.   Relation between concentration and distance of migration in a diffusion column.   Top section: graphical illustration of the diffusion column; center section: relation between concentration and distance of migration; bottom section: relation between concentration gradient and distance of migration.   The curves as drawn refer to diffusion times of 0.5, 1, and 4.5 hr., respectively.   The whole diagram should be rotated counterclockwise about an angle of 90° in order to conform with the proper space directions.   From Neurath.[146]

value of dc/dx—which always coincides with the position of the original boundary—sinks more and more, being inversely proportional to the square root of the time, and, for a given time, being inversely proportional to the square root of the diffusion coefficient.   The ideal curve is always symmetrical about this maximum.

2. Experimental Methods in the Study of Translational Diffusion

a. Free Diffusion

The measurement of diffusion coefficients involves serious technical difficulties. Convection and vibration must be carefully avoided, and the temperature must be precisely controlled. The formation of a sufficiently sharp initial boundary between solution and solvent is a serious problem. Some investigators, such as Lamm,[148,149] have used a thin partition between solvent and solution, which can be withdrawn by the turning of a screw when the experiment is to begin. Others, such as Neurath,[146] have used a sliding joint to superpose the solvent on the solution, the two compartments being first filled separately and then superposed. Claesson[150] developed a modified form of this cell in which all the empty spaces in the upper section of the apparatus are filled with solvent. This diminishes somewhat the difficulties due to leakage of solvent from the cell, and minimizes the need for greasing of joints, which may give rise to troublesome films. The Tiselius electrophoresis cell, with certain modifications, has also been used successfully for the measurement of diffusion coefficients, notably by Longsworth.[150a,150b] The formation of the initial boundary by means of a flowing junction between solvent and solution, the flow being suddenly stopped by the sliding of a partition, has been described by Coulson et al.[156] and by Longsworth.[150c] This type of cell appears to have many advantages.

Usually, in spite of all the care that may be taken, the initial boundary is somewhat blurred. It has been found[151,152] that considerable sharpening may be achieved by inserting a capillary siphon, guided by a rack and pinion, and carefully withdrawing a small amount of liquid at the level of the boundary. Detailed discussions of many aspects of experimental procedure are given by Neurath,[146] by Alexander and Johnson,[5a] by Lundgren and Ward,[40] and by Geddes.[152a]

In the diffusing liquid system, either the concentration or its gradient

(148) O. Lamm, Nova Acta Regiae Soc. Sci. Upsaliensis [4], 10, No. 6 (1937).
(149) O. Lamm and A. Polson, Biochem. J. 30, 528 (1936).
(150) S. Claesson, Nature 158, 834 (1946).
(150a) L. G. Longsworth, Anal. Chem. 23, 346 (1951).
(150b) L. G. Longsworth, J. Am. Chem. Soc. 74, 4155 (1952).
(150c) L. G. Longsworth, Rev. Sci. Instruments 21, 524 (1950).
(151) D. S. Kahn and A. Polson, J. Phys. & Colloid Chem. 51, 816 (1947).
(152) L. J. Gosting, E. M. Hanson, G. Kegeles, and M. S. Morris, Rev. Sci. Instruments 20, 209 (1949).
(152a) A. L. Geddes, in A. Weissberger, Physical Methods of Organic Chemistry, 2nd Ed., Interscience Publishers, New York, 1949, Vol. I, part I, p. 551.

or both may be measured.   Tiselius and Gross[153] determined the concentration directly by measuring the light absorption as a function of distance in the cell, using light of a wavelength absorbed by the protein but not by the solvent.   The most widely used method, however, has been that of Lamm[148,149] in which the image of a uniformly ruled, transparent scale is photographed after the light has passed through the diffusing liquid.   The displacement of the scale lines on the photograph gives a direct measure of the refractive index gradient at various levels.   This is a linear function of the concentration gradient, and for most purposes the refractive index gradient may be used directly to compute the diffusion coefficient, making due allowance for the magnification factor in the optical system employed.   Several methods of analyzing the data have been employed; these are well presented by Lamm[148,149] and by Neurath[146] and will not be discussed here.   All these methods involve the assumption that the gradient curve is symmetrical and Gaussian—that is, the concentration distribution is given by Eqs. (83) and (84).   This can be true only if the solute is monodispersed with respect to diffusion coefficient, and if the molecules do not interact.   Polydispersed solutions give curves which may be symmetrical but are non-Gaussian, while interaction may lead to markedly skewed curves; good examples of such curves are shown in Neurath's review.[146]   It is therefore always desirable to evaluate diffusion coefficients, from a given set of curves, by at least two methods; if both give the same value of D within a few per cent, this gives added assurance that the values are significant.   In general the values reported by different investigators, of comparable care and skill, on the same protein, differ by several per cent.   Some of this variation may be due to differences between one sample of protein and another; but in considerable part it appears to arise from the uncertainties of the method itself.   A useful critical discussion, together with carefully evaluated data on several proteins and other large molecules, has been given by Bevilacqua et al.[153a]

Recently two methods have come into use, both involving the use of interference phenomena.   One depends on a phenomenon noted by Gouy[154] in 1880 and then long forgotten; the method was revived by Longsworth,[155] and independently by Coulson et al.,[156] and a general

(153) A. Tiselius and D. Gross, Kolloid-Z. 66, 11 (1934).
(153a) E. M. Bevilacqua, E. B. Bevilacqua, M. M. Bender, and J. W. Williams, Ann. N. Y. Acad. Sci. 46, 309 (1945–1946).
(154) Gouy, Compt rend. 90, 307 (1880).
(155) L. G. Longsworth, J. Am. Chem. Soc. 69, 2510 (1947).
(156) C. A. Coulson, J. T. Cox, A. G. Ogston, and J. St. L. Philpot, Proc. Roy. Soc. (London) A192, 382 (1948).

theory of the effect was given by Kegeles and Gosting.[157] Monochromatic light from a horizontal slit is collected by a lens and passes through the solution, which contains the diffusing boundary. In the focal plane beyond the solution, the image of the slit is spread out into a pattern of interference fringes. The upper edge of this rectangular pattern is formed by light that passes, without being deflected, through the upper and lower layers of liquid in the cell, in which there is no refractive index gradient. The bottom of the pattern is formed by light which has suffered a maximum deflection at the boundary. The intervening region, at any instant, consists of a pattern of dark and light fringes, the dark bands representing the points for which there is interference between the pencils of light coming from corresponding positions on the two sides of the boundary. As diffusion proceeds and the boundary becomes more blurred, the whole interference pattern contracts upward, and the spacing between successive fringes diminishes. This simple qualitative picture was found to require some modification in the quantitative theory developed by Kegeles and Gosting;[157] this supplied a precise basis for the calculation of D from the spacing of the fringes and the variation of this spacing with the time. A detailed description of the apparatus used has been given by Gosting et al.[152] The method has been used to obtain extremely precise values of D for sucrose[157a] and for glycine[158] as a function of concentration at two different temperatures (1° and 25°). As an example of the accuracy of the method, the equations given by Lyons and Thomas[158] to describe their data for glycine may be given:

At 1.00°: $D = 5.200(1 - 0.0303c + 0.0014c^2)10^{-6}$ cm.^{2}/sec.
At 25.00°: $D = 10.63_5(1 - 0.0241c)10^{-6}$ cm.^{2}/sec.

These values are believed reliable to $\pm 0.08\%$ for values of c (in g./100 cc. solution) up to about 5.

No data of comparable accuracy have yet been reported for proteins by the Gouy method. Longsworth[155] studied ovalbumin and serum albumin but the results were unsatisfactory owing to various technical difficulties. Even a small degree of polydispersity in the system tends to disturb the system of fringes, and makes the theoretical treatment difficult to apply.

Coulson et al.[156] developed the method with particular attention to its use for making rapid determinations of diffusion coefficients. Ogston[159]

(157) G. Kegeles and L. J. Gosting, J. Am. Chem. Soc. **69**, 2516 (1947). A more general and rigorous theoretical treatment has been given by L. J. Gosting and L. Onsager, ibid. **74**, 6066 (1952).

(157a) L. J. Gosting and M. S. Morris, J. Am. Chem. Soc. **71**, 1998 (1949).

(158) M. S. Lyons and J. V. Thomas, J. Am. Chem. Soc. **72**, 4506 (1950).

(159) A. G. Ogston, Proc. Roy. Soc. (London) **A196**, 272 (1949).

has treated the use of the method for two diffusing solutes, and has applied it to the systems β-lactoglobulin and sucrose in water, and β-lactoglobulin and potassium chloride in water, with reasonably satisfactory results for the diffusion coefficients of the two solute components in each case. Very recently Creeth[308] has obtained measurements of apparently high accuracy with bovine serum albumin, using essentially the techniques of Coulson et al.[156] and of Ogston,[159] but with some modifications of procedure which proved important in practice. Creeth's final value for $D_{20,w}°$ for this protein was $6.14_8 \pm 0.02_2 \times 10^{-7}$ cm.^{2}/sec. (see also p. 721).

The other type of interference method involves the use of a Rayleigh interferometer,[159a,160] the effective light source being a vertical or diagonal slit illuminated by monochromatic light, in conjunction with a horizontal cylindrical lens beyond the diffusion cell. By adjustment of the experimental arrangement, it is possible to determine either the concentration (refractive index) or its gradient as a function of distance within the cell. Measurements by Svensson[160] on sucrose indicate that the method should give results of accuracy at least comparable to those obtained by the Gouy method. Recent studies by Longsworth[150b] on a number of amino acids, peptides, and sugars, using this method, in water at 1°, have indeed given values that are precise to less than 0.1 per cent in all cases. All these substances were studied at one concentration only; but Longsworth's value for glycine agreed within considerably less than 0.1 per cent with that found by Lyons and Thomas[158] for a comparable concentration using the Gouy method. Longsworth found that the product of diffusion coefficient (D) by the cube root of the apparent molal volume (V), for most of the substances he studied, was a linear function of D, the relation being described by the equation

$$DV^{\frac{1}{3}} = 10.772 \times 10^{-6} + 1.450D$$

However, phenylalanine, tryptophan, proline, and hydroxyproline gave distinctly higher values of $DV^{\frac{1}{3}}$ than would be predicted by the equation.

Still another method for the determination of diffusion coefficients has been described by Scheibling.[160a] This involves measuring, by means of a Jamin interferometer, the concentration difference between two fixed levels in the diffusion cell as a function of time, one level being above

(159a) J. St. L. Philpot and G. H. Cook, Research (London) 1, 234 (1948).

(160) H. Svensson, Acta Chem. Scand. 3, 1170 (1949); 4, 399 (1950); 5, 72 (1951). An important technique for obtaining multifringe interference patterns of high intensity has been described by H. Svensson, Acta Chem. Scand. 5, 1301 (1951).

(160a) G. Scheibling, J. chim. phys. 47, 688 (1950).

the initial boundary between solution and solvent, the other being preferably at an equal distance below it. Let us denote the distance from the boundary to either of these levels as a; then the two levels are separated by the distance $2a$. The concentration *difference*, c', between the two levels is measured optically by the interference between two light beams passing through the cell at the levels $+a$ and $-a$. What must be known is the time derivative of c' as a function of time. From Eqs. (83) and (84)—compare also Eq. (86)—this is deduced to be:

$$\frac{dc'}{dt} = \frac{ac_0'}{2\sqrt{\pi}} D^{-1/2} t^{-3/2} e^{-a^2/4Dt} \tag{86a}$$

where c_0', the concentration difference at the beginning of the experiment, is equal to the initial concentration of solution below the boundary. The results are conveniently analyzed by plotting $\log [t^{3/2}(dc'/dt)]$ against $1/t$. The negative slope of the resulting curve is equal to $a^2(\log e)/4D$, from which D is immediately determined. The intercept, at $1/t = 0$, is $ac_0'/2\sqrt{\pi D}$, which gives an additional check on the value of c_0'. If D varies with the concentration, or if two or more solutes of different diffusion coefficients are present, the curves become nonlinear. This method appears to give results of considerable accuracy, although it can hardly attain the very great precision of which the interferometric methods described above are capable. This method has been applied to ovalbumin by Champagne,[160b] who has obtained a value $(D_{20,w} = 7.63 \times 10^{-7})$ in good accord with those found by other observers.

b. Diffusion Through a Porous Disk

Another method, which has been widely applied on account of its great simplicity, involves the use of a sintered-glass plate between solution and solvent. Diffusion takes place through the pores of the plate; these pores must therefore be large in comparison with the size of the diffusing molecules, but small enough to prevent streaming of the liquid in bulk. Disturbances due to vibration are not harmful in this method; indeed stirring is helpful, in order to maintain uniform composition of the liquid on the two sides of the plate. Analysis of the amount of material which has diffused through the plate in a given time may be carried out by any suitable method; if an enzyme or hormone is under study, its rate of diffusion may be determined by assays of specific activity in the outer liquid, even though the active substance has not yet been isolated in pure form. This method was first described by Northrop and Anson;[161] it has

(160b) M. Champagne, *J. chim. phys.* **47**, 693 (1950).
(161) J. H. Northrop and M. L. Anson, *J. Gen. Physiol.* **12**, 543 (1929).

been further developed by McBain and Liu[162] and by Hartley and Runnicles.[163] A detailed and careful, critical discussion has been given by Gordon.[163a]

This method can give only relative diffusion coefficients; it must be calibrated by measuring the rate of diffusion of some standard substance, of known diffusion coefficient, through the same sintered-glass disk. Calibration has proved a rather difficult problem; this is due primarily to the fact that the diffusion coefficients of most substances change with concentration, and there is a considerable concentration difference between the two sides of the glass disk.   The problem has been discussed, and treated experimentally, by James, Hollingshead, and Gordon,[164] and by Hartley and Runnicles,[163] who have defined what appears to be a satisfactory system of calibration, employing the diffusion of 0.1 M KCl into water as the process taken as a standard of reference.   The analysis of the problem by Gordon[163a] should be studied in this connection.

Mehl and Schmidt[165] have measured the diffusion coefficients of several amino acids in water by this method; their values, and others for amino acids and peptides, have been tabulated by Edsall and Mehl (Ref. 2, p. 412).   The method has also been applied to a number of proteins, but the accuracy attained has generally not been equal to that achieved by the method of free diffusion, and the latter has been increasingly used in recent years for proteins.   Nearly all the diffusion coefficients recorded in Table VIII were obtained by the latter method.

3. Diffusion Coefficients in Relation to Brownian Movement and Molecular Shape. The Frictional Ratio

The work of Einstein[166] and of Smoluchowski[167] first clearly related diffusion to Brownian movement.   If a particle is free to move at random, its thermal energy causes it to follow an irregular zigzag path in the medium.   With respect to any axis fixed in space—say the x-axis—it is on the average just as likely to move in the positive as in the negative direction.   The most probable value of its mean net displacement with respect to the x-axis, at the end of a time t, is therefore zero.   However,

(162) J. W. McBain and T. H. Liu, *J. Am. Chem. Soc.* **53**, 59 (1931).

(163) G. S. Hartley and D. F. Runnicles, *Proc. Roy. Soc.* (London) **A168**, 401 (1938).

(163a) A. R. Gordon, *Ann. N. Y. Acad. Sci.* **46**, 285 (1946).

(164) W. A. James, E. A. Hollingshead, and A. R. Gordon, *J. Chem. Phys.* **7**, 89 (1939).

(165) J. W. Mehl and C. L. A. Schmidt, *Univ. Calif. (Berkeley) Pubs. Physiol.* **8**, 165 (1937).

(166) A. Einstein, *Ann. Physik* [4], **17**, 549 (1905); **19**, 371 (1906).

(167) M. v. Smoluchowski, *Ann. Physik* [4], **21**, 756 (1906).

TABLE VIII

MOLECULAR WEIGHTS AND FRICTIONAL RATIOS OF PROTEINS*
INCLUDING PARTIAL SPECIFIC VOLUMES, SEDIMENTATION AND DIFFUSION CONSTANTS
Note that all molecular weights are given in thousands

Protein	V_{20}	$s_{20,w} \times 10^{13}$	$D_{20,w} \times 10^7$	$M_{s,d} \times 10^{-3}$	$M_e \times 10^{-3}$	f/f_0	References(p) to V_{20}	$s_{20,w}$	$D_{20,w}$	$M_{s,d}$	M_e
Insulin (monomer)(k)	0.749	1.6	15	12.0			1	175	175	175	
	0.735	1.95	7.3	24.5			171	171	171	171	
	0.71–0.72	1.2(n)	16(n)	6.3		1.1	174	164	9	9	
		1.75(n)						9			
		1.65						10			
		1.85						174			
Insulin (trimer, or tetramer)		3.5	8.2	41.0	35.0	1.13		1	2	3	1
		3.55	7.53	46.0				7	7	7	
		3.68(a)	7.45(a)	47.8		1.18		8	8	8	
		3.34						4			
		3.47						6			
		4.06						174			
		3.12	8.2	34.8				163	163	163	11
		3.34(n)						5			
Ribonuclease	0.709(d)	1.85(d)	13.6(d)	12.7	13.0	1.04	11	11	11	11	11
	0.73–0.74	2.15	10.2	17.0			162	162	162	162	
Cytochrome c	0.707	1.9	10.1	15.6		1.29	13	14	2	15	
"		1.83	11.3	13.2		1.22		182	182	182	
(cow heart)		2.5	13.3	15.6		1.00		181	181	181	
(horse heart)		2.1	13.0	13.4		1.01		181	181	181	
(pig heart)		2.3	12.3	15.5				181	181	181	
Myoglobin	0.741	2.04	11.3	16.9	17.5	1.11	16	2	2	15	2
Bacillus phlei protein	0.748	1.8	10.2	17.0		1.22	17	17	17	17	
Erythrocruorin (Lampetra)	0.751	1.87	10.7	17.1	19.0	1.17	18	18	2	3	18
Lysozyme (chicken)	(0.70–0.75)	1.9	11.2	14.0–17.0				159	159	159	
	0.75	1.8	8.6				160	161	160		
Lactalbumin (cow)	0.722	2.11(a)	10.2–11.2	17.2		1.14–1.21	19	19	19	19	
	(0.751)	1.9	10.6	17.4				20	2	3	

Protein	$\bar{V}$			M		f/f_0	References
Adrenocorticotropic hormone (sheep)	(0.75)	2.1	10.5	20.0			21, 21, 21
Adrenocorticotropic hormone (pig)		2.00(a)	9.0(a)	20.0			22, 22, 22
		2.04		20.0			23
		2.11					23
Chymotrypsin							
α-(monomer)	0.736	2.4	7.1	21.6			25, 24, 25, 25
α-(dimer)	0.731	3.5	10.2(n)	42.9			25, 25, 26
γ-(dimer)		3.2	7.4				26
δ-		$2.5_a(n)$					27
β-		2.6	9.9	23.6		1.13	28, 28, 28, 28
(cryst.)		2.52–2.65					29
Chymotrypsinogen		2.74(a)	4.14(a)	64.5		1.9	8, 8, 8
		3.1	7.9	38.0			30, 30, 30
		2.7(n)	(7.9)	30.0			27, 26
α-		2.54(n)	9.5(n)	23.2		1.19	31, 31, 31
β-		2.5	10.2	22.0		1.13	28, 28, 28
		2.5	10.4	21.6		1.11	28, 28, 28
Trypsin		1.69(a)	10.95(a)	15.1		1.2	8, 8, 8
		2.5(n)					32
DFP trypsin(c)	(0.73)	$2.5_0(n)$	9.5(n)	23.7		1.18	33, 32, 32, 32
Trypsinogen	0.73_7	$2.4_8(n)$	9.7(n)	23.7		1.15	33, 33, 33
Toxin, scarlet fever	(0.736)	2.7	9.5	27.0			34, 34, 34
Carbonic anhydrase	(0.749)	2.8	9.0	30.0			35, 35, 35
		3.80(d)					36
Crotoxin	0.704	3.14	8.6	30.0	30.5	1.22	37, 37, 37, 37
Oxytocic, pressor hormone	(0.749)	2.61	8.5	30.0		1.15	38, 38, 38
		1.2–1.8					39
Carboxypeptidase	(0.75)	1.87(e)	4.4(e)	31.0		1.18	40, 40, 40
		3.07	8.68			1.16	41, 42
Human tuberculosis bacillus protein	0.70	3.3	8.2	32.0		1.25	17, 17, 17, 17
Prolactin		3.3	7.5	32.0			44, 44, 43, 44
Pepsin	(0.750)	2.65	9.0	35.5	39.0	1.08	2, 45, 45, 45
		3.3	9.0				46, 46
Peroxidase	0.699	3.0	9.69	39.8		1.36	48, 49, 50, 50
		3.48(a)	7.05(a)				50, 50
β-Lactoglobulin	0.751_4	3.12	7.30	41.5	38.0	1.26	51, 52, 51, 51
		3.2					53
		3.05(n)					54
		2.83(n)	7.34			1.30	56, 55
		2.91(n)					5

47

51

TABLE VIII. (Continued)

Protein	V_{20}	$s_{20,w} \times 10^{13}$	$D_{20,w} \times 10^{7}$	$M_{s,d} \times 10^{-3}$	$M_e \times 10^{-3}$	f/f_0	References(p) to V_{20}	$s_{20,w}$	$D_{20,w}$	$M_{s,d}$	M_e
Concanavalin B	0.73	3.5	7.4				57	57	57	57	
Plakalbumin	0.749	3.55(f)	7.76	42.0	40.5	1.16	59	63	60	58	61
Ovalbumin	0.747$_9$	3.66(n)	3.96–4.14(g)	43.7	43.5		62	5	65	60	64
		3.34(n)	7.63	44.0					66		
			7.3						173		
Growth hormone, pituitary	0.76	3.60(n)	7.15	49.0		1.31	67	70	67	69	
			7.36	49.2					70	70	
Zein	0.776	1.9	4.0	50.0			178	179	179	180	
L-Amino acid oxidase (moccasin)	(0.749)	6.91(a)	11.0(a)	61.6		2.17		71	71	71	
Pyrophosphatase	(0.75)	4.4(n)	6.8(h)	63.0				72	8	72	
Enolase	0.735	5.59(a)	8.08(a)	63.7		1.01	8	8	73	8	
Follicle-stimulating hormone	0.71$_8$–0.72$_4$	4.7(n)	6.0	67.0		1.33	73	73	84	73	
Serum albumin (cow)	0.730	4.73(n)	6.0(a)	65.4		1.30	82	83	85	85	
	0.734$_3$	4.27(n)	6.15				62	63			
	(0.74)	4.31						85			
		4.49(a)						81			
		4.30(n)						5			
		4.22(n)						81			
		4.32(n)						86			
Serum albumin (horse)	0.748	4.46(i)	6.1	70.0	68.0	1.27	74	75	75	75	74
		4.50(n)	6.11					54	76		
			6.14			1.21–1.25			172		
			6.1–6.5						77		
			6.5						173		
Serum albumin (man)	0.748	4.58(a)	6.42(a)	68.9		1.21	8	8	8	8	
	0.733	4.6	6.1	69.0		1.28	78	78	78	78	
	0.736	4.67		72.3			79	79		79	
Carbonylhemoglobin (cow)	0.729	4.28(a)	5.93	61.5		1.30	80	81	79	81	
	0.749	4.6	6.32(a)			1.30	80	171	81		

Protein	$\bar{v}$			M		f/f_0				
Carbonylhemoglobin (horse)		4.4	6.9	63.0						
Ferrihemoglobin (horse)		4.6(a)	6.7	76.0						
Hemoglobin or carbonylhemoglobin (man)	(0.749)	4.46 / 5.3 / 4.31(n) / 4.5				1.16		61 / 87 / 63 / 171	171, 176	60 / 87 · 60 / 87
Diphtheria toxin	0.736	4.6	6.0	74.0		1.22	88	88	88	88
Luteinizing hormone (pig)	(0.749)	5.39 / 6.65	5.9	90.0				89, 90	89, 90	89, 90 · 90
Diphtheria antitoxin	0.749	5.5	5.76	90.5		1.23	91, 92	91, 92	91, 92	91, 92
Tropomyosin	0.71	2.51(a)–2.60	2.22(a)–2.43	92.7		3.1	93	93	93	93
Concanavalin A	0.73	6.0	5.6	96.0		1.25	57	57	57	57
Hexokinase	0.740	3.1	2.9	96.6		2.37	94	94	94	94
Glyceraldehyde phosphate dehydrogenase										
Yeast	(0.74)	6.8(n)	5.19	122		1.24	95	95	95	95
Rabbit muscle	0.74	7.0(n)	5.46	120		1.19		95	95	95
Mercuric albumin dimer	(0.75)	6.5(a)	4.6	146				96	97	97
Ascorbic acid oxidase	(0.749)	6.9	5.77	152				97	98	98
β-Amylase (sweet potato)		8.9						98		
γ-Globulin, serum (cow)	0.725	7	4.1 (j, a)				82	99		
(cow)	0.720₀	6					62	100		
(horse)		7.28–7.31(n) / 7.4(a) / 7						83 / 101 / 99 / 54		
(man)	0.739	6.90(n) / 7.2	3.84	176			118	118 / 102 / 103	102	102
(pig)	(0.745)	7.1 / 7.28					82	104	104	104
(rabbit)	0.744	7.05 / 6	4.1	160				100		
Aldolase	0.74	8.27(a)	4.29	180		1.03	95	105	105	105
Fumarase	(0.75)	7.3(n)	4.63	147		1.31		95	95	95
Catalase	0.73	8.51 / 11.3(a) / 11.0(a)	4.05 / 4.1 / 4.5	204 / 250	270	1.25	107	106 / 107 / 108	106 / 107 / 109	106 / 107
Phycocyan (Ceramium, main component)	(0.746)	11.4	4.05	270	275			110	111	15

TABLE VIII. (Continued)

Protein	V_{20}	$s_{20,w} \times 10^{13}$	$D_{20,w} \times 10^{7}$	$M_{s,d} \times 10^{-3}$	$M_e \times 10^{-3}$	f/f_0	References (p) to				
							V_{20}	$s_{20,w}$	$D_{20,w}$	$M_{s,d}$	M_e
Phycoerythrin (*Ceramium*)	0.746	12.0	4.00	290	290	1.21	59	110	111	46	110
Phosphorylase (rabbit muscle)	(0.74)	13.7	3.2–3.8	340–400				112	112	112	
Fibrinogen (cow)	0.706	7.9(n) 6.6–9.6 8.43–8.62(n) 8.4(n) 7.89(a)	2.02	330		2.34	82	113 114 83 115 116	68	68	
(man)	0.725	9 8.5					117	118 156			
Hemocyanin (*Palinurus*)	(0.740)	16.4	1.1–1.3	670(b)	450	1.23		119	156	46	119
Apoferritin	(0.747)	17.6	3.4	450				120	2	120	
Urease	0.73	18.6	3.61	467			121	121	120	121	
Thyroglobulin (pig)	0.72	19.2	3.46	630	650	1.31	122	122	121		122
Hemocyanin (*Homarus*)	(0.740)	22.6	2.65 2.78	760	800			119	2 2	3	119
Myosin	0.74	7.2(n) 7.1(n) 6.7(n) 5.2(a)	0.87(n) 0.34(a) 0.5	829–880		4.0	165	165, 166 167 130 131	168 8 165	168	
Toxin (*Clostridium botulinum*)	0.755 0.736	17.3	2.14 2.10	900		1.60	123 125	124, 125	124 123 125	124, 125, 126	
Glutamic acid dehydrogenase	0.75	26.6	1.87	1,000		1.26	127	127	127	127	
β1-Lipoprotein, serum (man)	0.97(o) 0.950(o)	5.9(o) 2.9(o)	2.54 1.7	2,600(o) 1,300(o)		1.7	128 118	128 118	128	128	
Erythrocruorin (*Planorbis*)	(0.745)	33.7	1.96	1,630	1,540			18, 132	60	60	47
Erythrocruorin (*Lumbricus*)	0.740	60.9	1.81	3,150	2,950		133	133	2	3	47
Pyruvic oxidase	(0.74)	40.4(l)	0.91(l, a)	4,000		1.51		134	134	134	
Hemocyanin (*Helix pomatia*)	0.738	103	1.07 1.06(a)	8,900	6,700	1.24	135	135	136 8	136	119
Actomyosin	(0.75)	12.0	0.30	3,900				129	129	129	

Virus	V_{10}	$s_{20,w}$	$D_{20,w}$	$M_{s,d}$	M_e	f/f_0	References
yellow fever	0.87	~200(n); >90- >>280		2,500(m)			137; 137; 137; 169, 167
tobacco necrosis		27–45; 49; 76–91					137, 138, 139
poliomyelitis							
turnip yellow mosaic	0.666	106	1.55	4,970		1.25	170; 170; 170; 170
southern bean mosaic	0.696	115(n); 123.5	1.39(n)	6,630		1.25	177; 140, 177; 177; 177
potato latent mosaic	0.73				7,600		12; 12; 12; 141
tomato bushy stunt	0.739	146; 132	1.15	10,600		1.09; 1.27	141; 141; 142, 143; 144; 144; 144
tobacco mosaic (ordinary strain from tobacco)	0.727	174; 185	0.3; 0.53	59,000; 31,600		2.9; 1.94	157; 158, 157; 158; 158; 157
tobacco mosaic (strain TM58, from tobacco)	0.743	198(n); 253	0.46	40,700		2.0	145; 145, 146; 145; 145
equine encephalitis	0.756	280		47,100		1.65	147; 147; 147; 147
rabbit papilloma	0.761	297	0.51				148; 148
Chicken sarcoma		550; 700					149, 150; 151; 152
influenza (PR8)		660					153
T2 bacteriophage	0.665–0.669	700					153; 154, 139; 155
polyhedral (silkworm)	0.770	1871	0.215	916,000			155; 155; 155; 155

* This table was prepared by W. B. Dandliker. Many of the data cited were taken from similar tables by E. J. Cohn and J. T. Edsall, Proteins, Amino Acids and Peptides, Reinhold Publishing Corp., New York, 1943; and J. M. Greenberg, ed., Amino Acids and Proteins, C. C Thomas, Springfield, Ill., 1951. Molecular weights from sedimentation and diffusion should not be accepted without comparison with values obtained by other methods. See Tables IV, V, VI, VII, IX, X, and XI in this chapter. In some instances disagreement in sedimentation data from different laboratories may be explained by differences in experimental technique, especially in the measurement of cell temperature. This point is fully discussed in the text. Occasionally footnotes have been inserted to indicate whether s and D values have been extrapolated to zero concentration. When no indication is given, the original sources should be consulted.

Explanatory Notes:

V_{10} is partial specific volume of the protein. The values in brackets are assumed values.

$s_{20,w}$ is sedimentation constant in c.g.s. units reduced to water at 20°.

$D_{20,w}$ is diffusion constant in c.g.s. units reduced to water at 20°.

$M_{s,d}$ is molecular weight calculated from sedimentation and diffusion.

M_e is molecular weight by sedimentation equilibrium.

f/f_0 is frictional ratio.

Footnotes for Table VIII, continued:

(a) Not extrapolated to zero concentration.

(b) This value is probably far too high. Oncley, Scatchard, and Brown (78) give $M = 400,000$ from sedimentation and viscosity measurements. See asterisked footnote. The recent measurements of Shulman (68) for bovine fibrinogen are probably still more reliable ($M = 330,000$).

(c) Modified by treatment with diisopropyl fluorophosphate (DFP).

(d) Values at 25°.

(e) Sedimentation constant at 6.3°. Diffusion constant at 0.3°.

(f) Mean value obtained by a number of different observers in Uppsala.

(g) Referred to water at 0°. This confirmed Polson's values for 20°.

(h) Data of Kunitz by porous-disk method; cited by Schachman (72).

(i) Mean values for the A and B fractions prepared by Kekwick (75).

(j) Value of Kahn and Polson quoted in Ref. (101).

(k) The values for V_{20} are arbitrarily listed under *Insulin* (monomer).

(l) For 7°C.

(m) Estimate from sedimentation constant.

(n) Extrapolated to zero concentration.

(o) Oncley, Scatchard and Brown (78) calculate $f/f_0 = 1.7$ for β-lipoprotein (human) correcting for the partial specific volume of the hydrated protein (0.97), using an equation of Kraemer (see Svedberg and Pedersen "The Ultracentrifuge" equation 124, p. 65). A solvation of 0.6 g. H_2O/g. protein was used for the calculation, and the molecule was assumed spherical. The sedimentation constant of 2.9×10^{-13} was obtained in 0.5 M sodium chloride solution, corrected to standard conditions in the usual manner.

The molecular weight of 2,600,000 for this protein (X-protein) as reported by Pedersen(128) is a value for the hydrated protein; the corresponding value for the anhydrous protein is 1,900,000, assuming the molecule spherical. Note that the value of $\bar{V} = 0.97$ is also for the hydrated protein; 0.95 is the value for the anhydrous protein.

The measured value of the sedimentation rate of β-lipoprotein is very sensitive to small variations in the density of the medium, because the partial specific volume of the protein is so close to that of water. The original papers should be consulted for details.

(p) References to Table VIII:

(1) B. Sjögren and T. Svedberg, *J. Am. Chem. Soc.* **53**, 2657 (1931).

(2) A. G. Polson, Thesis, University of Stellenbosch, 1937.

(3) T. Svedberg, *Nature* **139**, 1051 (1937).

(4) H. Gutfreund and A. G. Ogston, *Biochem. J.* **40**, 432 (1946).

(5) G. L. Miller and R. H. Golder, *Arch. Biochem. and Biophys.* **36**, 249–58 (1952).

(6) H. Gutfreund, *Biochem. J.* **42**, 544–8 (1948).

(7) G. L. Miller and K. J. I. Andersson, *J. Biol. Chem.* **144**, 459–64 (1942).

(8) G. Bergold, *Z. Naturforsch.* **1**, 100–08 (1946).

(9) E. Fredericq and H. Neurath, *J. Am. Chem. Soc.* **72**, 2684–91 (1950).

(10) H. Gutfreund, *Biochem. J.* **50**, 564–9 (1952).

(11) A. Rothen, *J. Gen. Physiol.* **24**, 203 (1940–1).

(12) M. A. Lauffer and T. E. Cartwright, *Arch. Biochem. and Biophys.* **38**, 371–5 (1952).

(13) H. Theorell, *Biochem. Z.* **285**, 207 (1936).

(14) K. O. Pedersen and K. J. I. Andersson, unpublished. See Ref. (171).

References to Table VIII, continued:
(15) T. Svedberg, *Chem. Revs.* **20**, 81 (1937).
(16) H. Theorell, *Biochem. Z.* **268**, 46 (1934).
(17) F. B. Seibert, K. O. Pedersen, and A. Tiselius, *J. Exptl. Med.* **68**, 413 (1938); *idem, Am. Rev. Tuberc.* **38**, 399 (1938).
(18) T. Svedberg and I.-B. Eriksson-Quensel, *J. Am. Chem. Soc.* **56**, 1700 (1934).
(19) L. R. Wetter and H. F. Deutsch, *J. Biol. Chem.* **192**, 237–42 (1951).
(20) R. A. Kekwick unpublished.
(21) C. H. Li, H. M. Evans, and M. E. Simpson, *J. Biol. Chem.* **149**, 413 (1943).
(22) C. H. Li and K. O. Pedersen, *Arch. Biochem. and Biophys.* **36**, 462–7 (1952).
(23) G. Sayers, A. White, and C. N. H. Long, *J. Biol. Chem.* **149**, 425 (1943).
(24) M. Kunitz and J. H. Northrop, *J. Gen. Physiol.* **18**, 433 (1935); *cf.* J. L. Oncley, *Ann. N. Y. Acad. Sci.* **41**, 121 (1941).
(25) G. W. Schwert and S. Kaufman, *J. Biol. Chem.* **190**, 807–16 (1951).
(26) G. W. Schwert, *J. Biol. Chem.* **179**, 655–64 (1949).
(27) G. W. Schwert and S. Kaufman, *J. Biol. Chem.* **180**, 517–23 (1949).
(28) E. L. Smith, D. M. Brown, and M. Laskowski, *J. Biol. Chem.* **191**, 639–50 (1951).
(29) E. L. Smith and D. M. Brown, *J. Biol. Chem.* **195**, 525–30 (1952).
(30) E. L. Hess and J. W. Williams, cited by J. L. Oncley, *Ann. N. Y. Acad. Sci.* **41**, 121 (1941).
(31) G. W. Schwert, *J. Biol. Chem.* **190**, 799–806 (1951).
(32) L. W. Cunningham, F. Tietze, N. M. Green, and H. Neurath, *Discussions Faraday Soc.* No. 13, 58 (1953).
(33) F. Tietze and H. Neurath, unpublished.
(34) L. E. Krejci, A. H. Stock, E. B. Sanigar, and E. O. Kraemer, *J. Biol. Chem.* **142**, 785 (1942).
(35) M. Petermann and N. Hakala, *J. Biol. Chem.* **145**, 701–5 (1942).
(36) F. Eirich and E. Rideal, *Nature* **146**, 541 (1940).
(37) N. Gralén and T. Svedberg, *Biochem. J.* **32**, 1375 (1938).
(38) H. B. Van Dyke, B. F. Chow, R. O. Greep, and A. Rothen, *J. Pharmacol. Exptl. Therap.* **74**, 190 (1942).
(39) M. Rosenfeld, *Bull. Johns Hopkins Hosp.* **66**, 398 (1940).
(40) H. B. Van Dyke, B. F. Chow, R. O. Greep, and A. Rothen, *Am. J. Physiol.* **133**, 473 (1941).
(41) E. L. Smith, D. M. Brown, and H. T. Hanson, *J. Biol. Chem.* **180**, 33–6 (1949).
(42) F. W. Putnam, H. Neurath, E. Elkins, and S. Segal, *J. Biol. Chem.* **166**, 603 (1946).
(43) A. White, H. R. Catchpole, and C. N. H. Long, *Science* **86**, 82 (1937).
(44) C. H. Li, W. R. Lyons, and H. M. Evans, *J. Biol. Chem.* **140**, 43 (1941).
(45) J. St. L. Philpot, *Biochem. J.* **29**, 2458 (1935); J. St. L. Philpot and I.-B. Eriksson-Quensel, *Nature* **132**, 932 (1933).
(46) T. Svedberg and I.-B. Eriksson-Quensel, *Tab. Biol.* **11**, 351 (1936).
(47) I.-B. Eriksson-Quensel, cited in T. Svedberg and K. O. Pedersen, The Ultracentrifuge. Oxford Univ. Press, New York, 1940; *cf.* T. Svedberg and I.-B. Eriksson-Quensel, *Tab. Biol.* **11**, 351 (1936).
(48) J. Steinhardt, *J. Biol. Chem.* **123**, 543 (1938).
(49) J. H. Northrop, *J. Gen. Physiol.* **13**, 739 (1930).
(50) R. Cecil and A. G. Ogston, *Biochem. J.* **49**, 105–6 (1951).

References to Table VIII, continued:

(51) K. O. Pedersen, *Biochem. J.* **30**, 961 (1936).

(52) A. Polson, *Kolloid-Z.* **87**, 149 (1939); *ibid.* **88**, 51 (1939).

(53) J. A. Bain and H. F. Deutsch, *Arch. Biochem.* **16**, 221–9 (1948).

(54) J. P. Johnston and A. G. Ogston, *Trans. Faraday Soc.* **42**, 789–99 (1946).

(55) A. G. Ogston, *Proc. Roy. Soc.* (London) **A196**, 272–85 (1949).

(56) R. Cecil and A. G. Ogston, *Biochem. J.* **43**, 592–8 (1948).

(57) J. B. Sumner, N. Gralén, and I.-B. Eriksson-Quensel, *J. Biol. Chem.* **125**, 45 (1938).

(58) N. Eeg-Larsen, K. Linderstrøm-Lang, and M. Ottesen, *Arch. Biochem.* **19**, 340–4 (1948).

(59) T. Svedberg and N. B. Lewis, *J. Am. Chem. Soc.* **50**, 525 (1928).

(60) O. Lamm and A. Polson, *Biochem. J.* **30**, 528 (1936).

(61) K. O. Pedersen, cited in T. Svedberg and K. O. Pedersen, The Ultracentrifuge. Oxford Univ. Press, New York, 1940.

(62) M. O. Dayhoff, G. E. Perlmann, and D. A. MacInnes, *J. Am. Chem. Soc.* **74**, 2515–17 (1952).

(63) G. Kegeles and F. J. Gutter, *J. Am. Chem. Soc.* **73**, 3770–7 (1951).

(64) G. Kegeles, *J. Am. Chem. Soc.* **69**, 1302–5 (1947).

(65) L. G. Longsworth, *Ann. N. Y. Acad. Sci.* **41**, 267–85 (1941).

(66) M. Champagne, *J. chim. phys.* **47**, 693–7 (1950).

(67) C. H. Li, *J. Phys. & Colloid Chem.* **51**, 218 (1947).

(68) S. Shulman, in press.

(69) A. E. Wilhelmi, J. B. Fishman, and J. A. Russell, *J. Biol. Chem.* **176**, 735–46 (1948).

(70) E. L. Smith, D. M. Brown, J. B. Fishman, and A. E. Wilhelmi, *J. Biol. Chem.* **177**, 305–10 (1949).

(71) T. P. Singer and E. B. Kearney, *Arch. Biochem.* **29**, 190–209 (1950).

(72) H. K. Schachman, *J. Gen. Physiol.* **35**, 451–4 (1952).

(73) C. H. Li and K. O. Pedersen, *J. Gen. Physiol.* **35**, 629–37 (1952).

(74) T. Svedberg and B. Sjögren, *J. Am. Chem. Soc.* **50**, 3318 (1928).

(75) R. A. Kekwick, *Biochem. J.* **32**, 552 (1938).

(76) G. R. Cooper and H. Neurath, cited by H. Neurath, *Chem. Revs.* **30**, 357 (1942).

(77) H. Neurath, G. R. Cooper, and J. O. Erickson, *J. Biol. Chem.* **138**, 411 (1941).

(78) J. L. Oncley, G. Scatchard, and A. Brown, *J. Phys. &. Colloid Chem.* **51**, 184 (1947).

(79) K. O. Pedersen, Ultracentrifugal Studies on Serum and Serum Fractions. Almqvist and Wiksell, Boktryckeri AB, Uppsala, 1945.

(80) G. S. Adair and M. E. Adair, *Proc. Roy. Soc.* (London) **A190**, 341–56 (1947).

(81) P. A. Charlwood, *Biochem. J.* **51**, 113–18 (1952).

(82) V. L. Koenig, *Arch. Biochem.* **25**, 241–5 (1950).

(83) V. L. Koenig and K. O. Pedersen, *Arch. Biochem.* **25**, 97–108 (1950).

(84) K. G. Stern, S. Singer, and S. Davis, *J. Biol. Chem.* **167**, 321 (1947).

(85) J. M. Creeth, *Biochem. J.* **51**, 10–17 (1952).

(86) J. F. Taylor, *Arch. Biochem. and Biophys.* **36**, 357–64 (1952).

(87) D. H. Moore and L. Reiner, *J. Biol. Chem.* **156**, 411 (1944).

(88) M. L. Petermann and A. M. Pappenheimer, Jr., *J. Phys. Chem.* **45**, 1 (1941); see also A. Tiselius and O. Dahl, *Arkiv Kemi, Mineral. Geol.* **14B**, No. 31, 7 (1941).

References to Table VIII, continued:

(89) K. Meyer, R. Thompson, J. W. Palmer, and D. Khorazo, *J. Biol. Chem.* **113**, 303 (1936).

(90) T. Shedlovsky, A. Rothen, R. O. Greep, H. B. Van Dyke, and B. F. Chow, *Science* **92**, 178 (1940).

(91) J. H. Northrop, *J. Gen. Physiol.* **25**, 465 (1941-2).

(92) A. Rothen, *J. Gen. Physiol.* **25**, 487 (1941-2).

(93) K. Bailey, H. Gutfreund, and A. G. Ogston, *Biochem. J.* **43**, 279-81 (1948).

(94) M. Kunitz and M. R. McDonald, *J. Gen. Physiol.* **29**, 393 (1946).

(95) J. F. Taylor, "Phosphofructokinase and Aldolase," *in* McElroy and Glass, eds., Phosphorus Metabolism I, The Johns Hopkins Press, Baltimore, Md., 1951.

(96) W. L. Hughes, Jr., *Cold Spring Harbor Symposia Quant. Biol.* **14**, 79-84 (1950).

(97) F. J. Dunn and C. R. Dawson, *J. Biol. Chem.* **189**, 485-97 (1951).

(98) S. Englard and T. P. Singer, *J. Biol. Chem.* **187**, 213-19 (1950).

(99) E. L. Smith and D. M. Brown, *J. Biol. Chem.* **183**, 241-9 (1950).

(100) J. R. Cann, R. A. Brown, S. J. Singer, J. B. Shumaker, Jr., and J. G. Kirkwood, *Science* **114**, 30-3 (1951).

(101) E. L. Hess and H. F. Deutsch, *J. Am. Chem. Soc.* **70**, 84-8 (1948).

(102) E. A. Kabat, *J. Exptl. Med.* **69**, 103 (1939).

(103) V. L. Koenig, *Arch. Biochem.* **23**, 229-35 (1949).

(104) J. C. Nichol and H. F. Deutsch, *J. Am. Chem. Soc.* **70**, 80-3 (1948).

(105) M. V. Glikina and P. A. Finogenov, *Biokhimiya* **15**, 457-64 (1950).

(106) V. Massey, *Biochem. J.* **51**, 490-4 (1952). Addendum by R. Cecil and A. G. Ogston.

(107) J. B. Sumner and N. Gralén, *Science* **87**, 284 (1938); *idem J. Biol. Chem.* **125**, 33 (1938).

(108) R. Cecil and A. G. Ogston, *Biochem. J.* **43**, 205-6 (1948).

(109) J. B. Sumner, A. L. Dounce, and V. L. Frampton, *J. Biol. Chem.* **136**, 343 (1940).

(110) I.-B. Eriksson-Quensel, *Biochem. J.* **32**, 585 (1938).

(111) A. Tiselius and D. Gross, *Kolloid-Z.* **66**, 11 (1934).

(112) A. A. Green and G. T. Cori, *J. Biol. Chem.* **151**, 21 (1943).

(113) P. Ehrlich, S. Shulman, and J. D. Ferry, *J. Am. Chem. Soc.* **74**, 2258-65 (1952).

(114) V. L. Koenig and J. D. Perrings, *Arch. Biochem. and Biophys.* **36**, 147-57 (1952).

(115) S. Shulman and J. D. Ferry, *J. Phys. & Colloid Chem.* **55**, 135-44 (1951).

(116) K. Laki, *Arch. Biochem. and Biophys.* **32**, 317-24 (1951).

(117) S. H. Armstrong, Jr., M. J. E. Budka, K. C. Morrison, and M. Hasson, *J. Am. Chem. Soc.* **69**, 1747-53 (1947).

(118) J. L. Oncley, G. Scatchard, and A. Brown, *J. Phys. & Colloid Chem.* **51**, 184-98 (1947).

(119) I.-B. Eriksson-Quensel, *Biol. Bull.* **71**, 498 (1936).

(120) A. Rothen, *J. Biol. Chem.* **152**, 679 (1944).

(121) J. B. Sumner, N. Gralén, and I.-B. Eriksson-Quensel, *J. Biol. Chem.* **125**, 37 (1938).

(122) M. Heidelberger and K. O. Pedersen, *J. Gen. Physiol.* **19**, 95 (1935).

(123) G. Kegeles, *J. Am. Chem. Soc.* **68**, 1670 (1946).

References to Table VIII, continued:

(124) F. W. Putnam, C. L. Lamanna, and D. G. Sharp, *J. Biol. Chem.* **165**, 735 (1946).

(125) F. W. Putnam, C. L. Lamanna, and D. G. Sharp, *J. Biol. Chem.* **176**, 401 (1948).

(126) H. J. Buehler, E. J. Schantz, and C. L. Lamanna, *J. Biol. Chem.* **169**, 295–302 (1947).

(127) J. A. Olson and C. B. Anfinsen, *J. Biol. Chem.* **197**, 67–79 (1952).

(128) K. O. Pedersen, *J. Phys. & Colloid Chem.* **51**, 156 (1947); see also ref. (79).

(129) M. Ziff and D. H. Moore, *J. Biol. Chem.* **153**, 653 (1944).

(130) W. F. H. M. Mommaerts and R. G. Parrish, *J. Biol. Chem.* **188**, 545–52 (1951).

(131) V. Kessler and S. S. Spicer, *Biochim. et Biophys. Acta* **8**, 474–6 (1952).

(132) T. Svedberg and A. Hedenius, *Biol. Bull.* **66**, 191 (1934).

(133) T. Svedberg and I.-B. Eriksson, *J. Am. Chem. Soc.* **55**, 2834 (1933).

(134) R. S. Schweet, B. Katchman, R. M. Bock, and V. Jagannathan, *J. Biol. Chem.* **196**, 563–7 (1952).

(135) T. Svedberg and E. Chirnoaga, *J. Am. Chem. Soc.* **50**, 1399 (1928).

(136) S. Brohult, *J. Phys. & Colloid Chem.* **51**, 206 (1947).

(137) E. G. Pickels and J. H. Bauer, *J. Exptl. Med.* **71**, 703 (1940).

(138) A. G. Ogston, *Brit. J. Exptl. Path.* **26**, 286 (1945).

(139) H. S. Loring, L. Marton, and C. E. Schwerdt, *Proc. Soc. Exptl. Biol. Med.* **62**, 291 (1946).

(140) G. L. Miller, E. S. Eitelman, and R. H. Golder, *Arch. Biochem. and Biophys.* **34**, 162–8 (1951).

(141) A. S. McFarlane and R. A. Kekwick, *Biochem. J.* **32**, 1607 (1938).

(142) W. M. Stanley and T. F. Anderson, *J. Biol. Chem.* **139**, 325 (1941).

(143) M. A. Lauffer and W. M. Stanley, *J. Biol. Chem.* **135**, 463 (1940).

(144) H. Neurath and G. R. Cooper, *J. Biol. Chem.* **135**, 455 (1940).

(145) G. Schramm and G. Bergold, *Z. Naturforsch.* **2b**, 108–12 (1947).

(146) A. R. Taylor, D. G. Sharp, D. Beard, and J. W. Beard, *J. Infectious Diseases* **71**, 110, 115 (1942).

(147) H. Neurath, G. R. Cooper, D. G. Sharp, A. R. Taylor, D. Beard, and J. W. Beard, *J. Biol. Chem.* **140**, 293 (1941).

(148) D. G. Sharp, A. R. Taylor, and J. W. Beard, *J. Biol. Chem.* **163**, 289 (1946).

(149) A. Claude, *Science* **91**, 77 (1940).

(150) A. Pollard, *Brit. J. Exptl. Path.* **20**, 429 (1939).

(151) W. M. Stanley and M. A. Lauffer, *J. Phys. & Colloid Chem.* **51**, 148–56 (1947).

(152) S. Gard and P. von Magnus, *Arkiv Kemi, Mineral. Geol.* **24B**, No. 8, 1–4 (1947).

(153) D. G. Sharp, A. E. Hook, A. R. Taylor, D. Beard, and J. W. Beard, *J. Biol. Chem.* **165**, 259 (1946).

(154) A. E. Hook, D. Beard, A. R. Taylor, D. G. Sharp, and J. W. Beard, *J. Biol. Chem.* **165**, 241 (1946).

(155) G. Bergold, *Z. Naturforsch.* **2b**, 122–43 (1947).

(156) C. G. Holmberg, *Arkiv Kemi Mineral. Geol.* **17A**, No. 28 (1944).

(157) M. A. Lauffer and W. M. Stanley, *Chem. Revs.* **24**, 303 (1939); M. A. Lauffer, *J. Am. Chem. Soc.* **66**, 1188 (1944); M. A. Lauffer, *Science* **87**, 469 (1938).

(158) H. Neurath and A. M. Saum, *J. Biol. Chem.* **126**, 435 (1938).

(159) G. Alderton, W. H. Ward, and H. L. Fevold, *J. Biol. Chem.* **157**, 43 (1945).

if we repeat the experiment many times, and tabulate each time the *square* of the displacement at the end of the same time interval t, it will naturally be found that the mean value of x^2—denoted by $\bar{x}^2$—is positive, since every term that contributes to this mean is positive or zero. Furthermore, Einstein showed that $\bar{x}^2$ is proportional to t and that the ratio of these two quantities is equal to twice the diffusion coefficient of the particle:

$$D = \bar{x}^2/2t \qquad (87)$$

The statistical nature of this concept should be noted. We must make a very large number of measurements on the same particle, each over the same period t, and take an average of the squares of the x-coordinates found each time; or in principle we can take a very large number of

References to Table VIII, continued:

(160) A. G. Passynskii and V. Plaskeyev, *Compt. rend. acad. sci. U. R. S. S.* **48,** 579 (1945).

(161) E. P. Abraham, *Biochem. J.* **33,** 622 (1939).

(162) C. F. Vilbrandt, H. G. Tennent, and N. V. Hakala, quoted in W. B. Bridgman and J. W. Williams, *Ann. N. Y. Acad. Sci.* **43,** 195–210 (1942).

(163) J. M. Creeth, *Nature* **170,** 210 (1952).

(164) F. Tietze and H. Neurath, *J. Am. Chem. Soc.* (to be published).

(165) O. Snellman and T. Erdös, *Biochim. et Biophys. Acta* **2,** 650–9 (1948).

(166) P. Johnson and H. R. Landolt, *Discussions Faraday Soc.* No. 11, 179–94 (1951).

(167) H. Portzehl, G. Schramm, and H. H. Weber, *Z. Naturforsch.* **5b,** 61–74 (1950).

(168) H. Portzehl, *Z. Naturforsch.* **5b,** 75–8 (1950).

(169) O. Snellman and T. Erdös, *Biochim. et Biophys. Acta* **3,** 523–6 (1949).

(170) R. Markham, *Discussions Faraday Soc.* No. 11, 221–7 (1951).

(171) K. O. Pedersen, *Cold Spring Harbor Symposia Quant. Biol.* **14,** 140–52 (1949).

(172) I. Kojiro and I. Wanatabe, *Repts. Radiation Chem. Research Inst., Tokyo Univ.* No. 4, 7–8 (1949); from *C. A.* **44,** 6455 (1950).

(173) M. Champagne, *J. chim. phys.* **48,** 627–31 (1951); from *C. A.* **46,** 5624 (1952).

(174) J. L. Oncley, E. Ellenbogen, D. Gitlin, and F. R. N. Gurd, *J. Phys. Chem.* **56,** 85–92 (1952).

(175) L. S. Moody, Ph. D. Dissertation, Univ. of Wisconsin, 1944; quoted by J. W. Williams, *Ann. Rev. Phys. Chem.* **2,** 412 (1951).

(176) H. Gutfreund, unpublished, 1946; cited by J. Boyes-Watson, E. Davidson, and M. F. Perutz, *Proc. Roy. Soc.* (London) **A191,** 83–132 (1947).

(177) G. L. Miller and W. C. Price, *Arch. Biochem.* **10,** 467–77 (1946).

(178) J. F. Foster and D. French, *J. Am. Chem. Soc.* **67,** 687–8 (1945).

(179) C. C. Watson, S. Arrhenius, and J. W. Williams, *Nature* **137,** 322 (1936); and unpublished.

(180) J. F. Foster and J. T. Edsall, *J. Am. Chem. Soc.* **67,** 617–25 (1945).

(181) S. M. Atlas, E. Farber, and K. G. Stern, 122nd Meeting of the American Chemical Society, Atlantic City, Sept. 1952, p. 23C.

(182) K. O. Pedersen, unpublished work, quoted by K.-G. Paul in "The Enzymes" Vol. II Part 1, p. 375 (Academic Press, New York, 1951).

identical particles, start them all off at the same time, find the distribution of x-values for the whole system, and take the average of their squares after time t.

Einstein and Smoluchowski introduced still another way of looking at the problem, which directly relates the diffusion coefficient to the molecular size and shape. The rate of diffusion is directly proportional to the thermal energy (kT) of the molecule. On the other hand, diffusion is retarded by the viscous resistance which the particle experiences as it moves through the medium; this may be characterized by a frictional coefficient f. For a spherical particle of radius r, moving with velocity v through a medium of viscosity η, the resisting force is equal to $6\pi\eta rv$, provided that the rate of motion is relatively slow; the frictional coefficient for such a particle is simply the factor $6\pi\eta r$. For a sphere, then, we may write for the diffusion coefficient:

$$D \text{ (sphere)} = kT/6\pi\eta r \tag{88}$$

and, in general, for a particle of any shape:

$$D = kT/f \tag{89}$$

Here f is for the moment undetermined; it will, however, in general be proportional to the viscosity of the medium and to a factor having the dimensions of a length, which is some function of the size and shape of the particle.

Consider the hypothetical special case of a spherical protein molecule of anhydrous molecular weight M; suppose that it binds no solvent when dissolved in water or other media, and that the density of the anhydrous particle is given by the reciprocal of the partial specific volume $\bar{v}$. The molar volume is $M\bar{v}$, and the volume of the individual molecule is $M\bar{v}/N$; the latter is also equal to $4\pi r_0^3/3$, where r_0 is the radius. The frictional coefficient for such an anhydrous sphere is denoted by the symbol f_0:

$$f_0 = 6\pi\eta r_0 = 6\pi\eta(3M\bar{v}/4\pi N)^{1/3} = \eta(162\pi^2 M\bar{v}/N)^{1/3} \tag{90}$$

For any molecule of known molecular weight and partial specific volume, moving in a medium of known viscosity, a value of f_0 may be calculated from Eq. (90). On the other hand, if the diffusion coefficient D is known, the actual frictional coefficient f is immediately given by Eq. (89). Thus horse hemoglobin ($M = 67,000$, $\bar{v} = 0.749$) should have a radius r_0 equal to 27 A. (27×10^{-8} cm.) if it were an anhydrous sphere. In water at 20° ($\eta = 0.01$ poise, very nearly) the value of $D_0 = kT/f_0$ should be 7.9×10^{-7} cm.^{2}/sec. The observed value of D (Table VIII) is 6.3×10^{-7}. Hence $f/f_0 = D_0/D = 1.24$.

The ratio f/f_0 is known as the *frictional ratio*. Its value is in practice always found to be greater than unity, from which we may conclude that no protein molecule in water can be treated as an anhydrous sphere. Deviations of f/f_0 from unity may arise because the molecule is solvated, or because its shape deviates from that of a sphere, or from both causes.

Consider first the effect of solvation, specifically, the binding of a uniform shell of water around the protein molecule. Suppose that the protein binds w grams of water per gram protein, and that the density of the bound water has the same value (ρ) as that of the free solvent. Then the molar volume of the hydrated protein is $M\bar{v} + Mw/\rho$ and the frictional ratio due to hydration is:

$$(f/f_0) \text{ hydration} = \left(1 + \frac{w}{\bar{v}\rho}\right)^{\frac{1}{3}} \tag{91}$$

If w is 0.3 g. water/g. protein—a plausible value which has often been assumed in such calculations—and if $\bar{v}$ is 0.75, then f/f_0 is found to be 1.12. If w is equal to 1—an improbably high value for most proteins—then f/f_0 would be 1.325. For many proteins, however, f/f_0 values considerably greater than this have been found; some of the values (see Table VIII) are as high as 2 or more. Such values can be explained only if the molecules are not spherical.

Exact calculations for f/f_0 have been made for ellipsoids of revolution by Perrin[168] and by Herzog, Illig, and Kudar.[169] In making such calculations, it is necessary to consider the resistance of such a particle to motion through a viscous medium, for any given orientation, and then to calculate an average resistance, assuming that all orientations are equally probable.

Perrin's[168] equations—those of Herzog, Illig, and Kudar are equivalent—give f/f_0 as a function of the ratio $\rho = b/a$, where b is the equatorial semiaxis of the ellipsoid, and a is the semiaxis of revolution.[170] For a prolate ellipsoid ($\rho < 1$):

$$\frac{f}{f_0} = \frac{(1 - \rho^2)^{\frac{1}{2}}}{\rho^{\frac{2}{3}} \ln [1 + (1 - \rho^2)^{\frac{1}{2}}]/\rho} \tag{92}$$

and for an oblate ellipsoid ($\rho > 1$):

$$\frac{f}{f_0} = \frac{(\rho^2 - 1)^{\frac{1}{2}}}{\rho^{\frac{2}{3}} \tan^{-1} (\rho^2 - 1)^{\frac{1}{2}}} \tag{93}$$

(168) F. Perrin, *J. phys. radium* [7], **7**, 1 (1936).
(169) R. O. Herzog, R. Illig, and H. Kudar, *Z. physik. Chem.* **A167**, 329 (1934).
(170) The use of the symbol ρ to denote a/b in these equations should not be confused with its use to denote the density of the solvent elsewhere in this chapter.

Numerical values of f/f_0 for various values of ρ, calculated from these equations, are listed by Svedberg and Pedersen[39] (p. 41) and by Cohn and Edsall[2] (p. 405). A very useful method of considering the combined effects of hydration and asymmetry is by means of the graph designed by Oncley,[3] which is reproduced in Fig. 13. Here any contour line denotes a value of f/f_0, which is a quantity that can be directly determined experimentally. By moving along the contour line, one sees

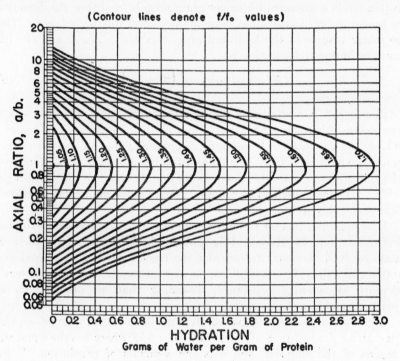

Fig. 13. Values of axial ratio and hydration in accord with frictional ratios (contour lines denote f/f_0 values). From Oncley.[3]

immediately the various values of asymmetry and hydration that are compatible with a given f/f_0 value. Further applications of this method, and of the important nomographic method of Wyman and Ingalls,[4] will be given later.

It will be seen that the interpretation of the f/f_0 values is somewhat ambiguous. Even if the degree of hydration is known, or assumed, such data alone give no basis for a decision as to whether the shape of the molecule is oblate or prolate. Moreover, there is no reason to assume that the actual shape of a protein molecule is particularly well approximated by an ellipsoid of revolution. This model has been assumed because it is mathematically the simplest available.   What we can hope to derive from such measurements is the size and shape of an "equivalent ellipsoid of revolution" which is chosen to fit as closely as possible the actual behavior of the protein molecule in solution.   In conjunction with other information, however, this can be extremely valuable in fixing the general dimensions of the protein, especially when the decision between prolate and oblate shape can be made on other grounds.

4. Change of Translational Diffusion Coefficient with Viscosity and Temperature

The frictional coefficient f is proportional to the viscosity of the medium η, and it is also a function of the dimensions of the particle. Also D, from Eq. (89), is equal to kT/f.   If the size, shape, and hydration of the particle are unaltered on changing the medium or the temperature or both, then the simple relation should hold:

$$D\eta/T = \text{constant} \qquad (94)$$

This equation has been much employed in order to express on a common basis the diffusion coefficients determined by different investigators on the same protein under different conditions.   It has become standard practice to express all diffusion coefficients as if they had been measured in pure water at 20°, for which $\eta = 0.01005$ poise.   The product $D\eta/T$ is calculated for the actual conditions under which D was determined; and this product is set equal to $D_{20}(0.01005)/293.16$.   The value here denoted by D_{20} is the reference value of D, and nearly all the values listed in Table VIII are expressed on this basis.   It must be noted that this procedure might lead to errors if the size, shape, or hydration of the protein were altered by changes of condition.   Such alterations generally appear to be very minor, however, if measurements are made in water or dilute salt solutions at temperatures between 0° and 25°.

XIV. Sedimentation and Diffusion: Molecular Weights and Frictional Ratios

1. The Sedimentation Constant and Its Relation to Molecular Weight

The final outcome of a process of unopposed translational diffusion is always an equal distribution of solute throughout any homogeneous phase.   However, if an applied force tends to drive the molecules in a particular direction, the state of the system at any time will depend on the intensity of this force, on the viscous resistance of the medium, and on the rapidity of the diffusion process which tends to diminish concentration gradients. The effect of the applied force is to set up a moving boundary within the liquid, between a region containing the protein molecules under study and a region from which they have moved away. The rate of motion of the boundary depends on the ratio of the applied force to the viscous resistance of the medium. At the beginning of the experiment, the boundary is generally quite sharp, but it becomes blurred by backward diffusion of the molecules as the experiment proceeds. If the solution contains several different proteins, several boundaries may be observed.

If the proteins carry a net charge, the force applied may be electrical. In that case, the process of electrophoresis is observed (Chap. 6). In electrophoresis it is still difficult to determine exactly the force acting on a charged particle in a particular solution; hence, important as this process is for the study of the electrical properties of proteins, and for their separation, it has been of relatively little use in the study of molecular size and shape.

The use of a gravitational field has proved valuable in the study of some very large colloidal particles, but such a field is far too weak to be useful in the study of proteins. The application of intense centrifugal fields, however, has yielded a vast number of results of the greatest importance. The development of the ultracentrifuge by Svedberg and others, and its construction, use, and applications have been well described in the monograph by Svedberg and Pedersen.[39] Here only a few significant points will be discussed, with particular stress on the results obtained with protein solutions.

Consider first the rate of motion of the sedimenting boundary, ignoring for the moment the process of back diffusion. The essential condition for motion of the solute molecules relative to the solvent is, of course, a density difference between the two. Let ρ_p be the density of the protein, which for the moment we identify as the reciprocal of the partial specific volume ($\rho_p = 1/\bar{v}$), and M its molecular weight; let ρ denote the density of the solvent. If the motion of the protein molecules is being observed at a distance x from the center of rotation, and the rotor is spinning with angular velocity ω, then the centrifugal acceleration is $\omega^2 x$. The centrifugal force on the molecule is then equal to $\omega^2 x$ times the effective mass of the molecule; that is, the difference between its actual mass $m = M/N$, and the mass of solvent which it displaces, which is equal to $m\bar{v}\rho$. The centrifugal force per molecule is thus

$$\phi = m\omega^2 x(1 - \bar{v}\rho) \qquad (95)$$

At the start of the experiment the velocity of the protein molecules, dx/dt, is zero. As dx/dt increases, the viscous resistance of the medium also increases, until it is just large enough to balance the centrifugal force. When this steady state is attained the net force on the molecule is zero, and it then moves through the medium with constant velocity.[171] The resisting force is equal to $f dx/dt$, where f is the frictional coefficient defined in Eq. (89). In the steady state, ϕ is equal to $f dx/dt$ and hence, using Eq. (89):

$$f(dx/dt) = (kT/D)dx/dt = m\omega^2 x(1 - \bar{v}\rho) \qquad (96)$$

If we multiply by Avogadro's number, thus converting k to R, and m to M, and rearrange, Eq. (96) becomes:

$$M = \frac{RT}{D(1 - \bar{v}\rho)} \frac{dx/dt}{\omega^2 x} \qquad (97)$$

The expression $(dx/dt)/\omega^2 x$ is the rate of motion of the boundary under unit centrifugal acceleration. It is the characteristic quantity determined by a sedimentation experiment in the ultracentrifuge, and is known as the sedimentation constant, s. Since ω has the dimensions of a reciprocal time (radians/second), s has the dimensions of time. The values of s observed for protein solutions are generally of the order of 10^{-13} to 10^{-12} sec., and a value of $s = 10^{-13}$ sec. is customarily referred to as one Svedberg unit (denoted by the symbol S). Inserting the quantity s, Eq. (97) may be written:

$$M = RTs/D(1 - \bar{v}\rho) \qquad (98)$$

This equation forms the basis for the determination of the molecular weights of macromolecules by the sedimentation-velocity method. It involves the determination, not only of the sedimentation and diffusion constants of the protein, at a known temperature and in a medium of known viscosity, but also that of the partial specific volume. The accurate determination of the latter is, indeed, the most important step of all; for the partial specific volumes of most proteins are between 0.70

(171) This statement ignores the fact that the centrifugal force increases with x; hence the actual speed of the molecule increases with time, as it moves away from the center of rotation. The statement is virtually true, however, over any given small region in which the change of the x-coordinate of the molecule with time is small compared with x. It is also assumed that the frictional resistance is proportional to the first power of dx/dt. This assumption is valid for all the sedimentation rates found for proteins, and even for large viruses, in the ultracentrifuge.

and 0.75, so that an error of 1 per cent in $\bar{v}$ produces an error of about 4 per cent in the factor $(1 - \bar{v}\rho)$.

2. Effects of Diffusion on Sedimentation Diagrams

The progressive blurring of the sedimenting boundary by diffusion gives a curve for concentration and concentration gradient that is in principle exactly like that observed in free diffusion. The point of maximum gradient, if the curve is symmetrical, fixes the position of the sedimenting boundary; hence it is possible to determine diffusion coefficients from optical measurements on the form of this boundary. The values so obtained, however, are generally not of high accuracy, although they may provide useful information.

Sometimes the sedimenting boundary remains much sharper than would be expected from the known diffusion coefficient of the protein. This has been observed, for instance, by Schachman[172] in studies on tobacco mosaic virus, for which the value of s decreases rapidly with increasing concentration, an effect discussed further below. Thus, at the sedimenting boundary, the molecules which at any moment are trailing behind are in a more dilute solution than those in front of them. Therefore they tend to catch up with those ahead of them, and the boundary remains sharp.

3. Relation to Frictional Coefficient

The frictional coefficient is immediately given in terms of M, s, and $\bar{v}$, from Eqs. (89) and (98):

$$f = M(1 - \bar{v}\rho)/Ns \tag{99}$$

Hence, if all the quantities on the right-hand side of the equation are determined, the frictional coefficient may be calculated without knowledge of the diffusion coefficient.

4. Correction to Standard Conditions

It is customary to correct the sedimentation constant, like the diffusion constant, to a standard state, which is taken as that of water at 20°. Such values are denoted by the symbol s_{20} (or $s_{20,w}$). The correction can be made if the viscosity η and density ρ are known for the medium in which the measurement is made, using the equation:

$$s_{20} = s \frac{\eta}{\eta_{20}} \frac{(1 - \bar{v}_{20}\rho_{20})}{(1 - \bar{v}\rho)} \tag{100}$$

(172) H. K. Schachman, *J. Am. Chem. Soc.* **73**, 4808 (1951).

In practice, $\bar{v}$ generally changes little with temperature, and it is often justifiable to set $\bar{v} = \bar{v}_{20}$, if the actual measurements are made within the range between 0 and 30°.

5. Effects of Solvation on Sedimentation Constants and on Molecular-Weight Determination

The values of M and of $\bar{v}$ appearing in Eq. (98) are those for the anhydrous protein. However, the molecule actually studied in sedimentation and diffusion experiments is the solvated molecule, carrying with it in its motion bound solvent, held either in the interior of the protein or on its surface or both. It appears at first sight paradoxical that anhydrous molecular weights can be derived from such measurements; and indeed the problem of the effects of solvation has raised numerous important questions, some of which are still unanswered. However, if the anhydrous partial specific volume—that is, the volume increment per gram of anhydrous protein added to the system—is employed in the calculations, then the measurement of s and D should lead to the anhydrous molecular weight, subject to one important assumption. This is that the bound solvent has the same density, ρ, when attached to the protein as when it is free in the surrounding medium. If 1 g. of protein binds w grams of solvent, then the molecular weight of the solvated protein is $M_h = M(1 + w)$. The partial specific volume of the solvated protein at infinite dilution, using the assumption just stated, is $\bar{v}_h = (\rho\bar{v} + w)/\rho(1 + w)$. It then follows directly that $M_h(1 - \bar{v}_h\rho)$ is equal to $M(1 - \bar{v}\rho)$, provided that s and D are determined at several concentrations and extrapolated to $c = 0$. Hence from s and D one obtains either the anhydrous or the solvated molecular weight, depending upon whether $\bar{v}$ or $\bar{v}_h$ is used in the calculation. This relation was first deduced by Lansing and Kraemer,[173,174] and as a first approximation it justifies the calculation of anhydrous molecular weights by sedimentation and diffusion. However, if for instance electrostriction of solvent occurs around the charged groups in the protein, the assumption that the bound solvent and the free solvent have the same density obviously breaks down. Such close-packed solvent molecules add to the molecular weight of the sedimenting or diffusing protein, without increasing its volume; the ratio s/D must therefore be increased by the electrostriction effect, as compared with that for the same protein in the (hypothetical) state in which it exerts no electrostrictive action on the solvent.

(173) W. D. Lansing and E. O. Kraemer, *J. Am. Chem. Soc.* **58**, 1471 (1936).

(174) E. O. Kraemer, *in* Svedberg and Pedersen[39] (p. 57). For the effect of hydration on sedimentation constants, see also H. K. Schachman and M. A. Lauffer, *J. Am. Chem. Soc.* **72**, 4266 (1950).

Moreover, as Lansing and Kraemer clearly pointed out, the simple treatment presupposes that the solvent consists of a single component; or if it consists of several components, all are bound by the protein in the same proportion in which they are present in the medium. Lately the problem has been further examined by Wales and Williams,[175] who have given a more general and more rigorous treatment than that of Lansing and Kraemer. However, the application of their equations requires more specific information concerning solvent–solute interactions in protein solutions than is usually available at present.

Attempts have been made to deduce the hydration of protein molecules from studies of the density and composition of their crystals in solvents of varying composition. (This subject is more fully discussed in Chap. 4.) Thus Perutz[176] concluded, from the study of horse methemoglobin crystals, that the water of the crystal was of two kinds: (a) "free" water, which was available to act as a solvent for salt ions entering from the surrounding medium, and (b) bound water, which was tightly held to the protein and did not act as a solvent for salt ions. The latter was estimated as very nearly 0.3 g. water/g. protein.

Recently Bragg and Perutz,[176a] using more refined methods of x-ray analysis, have inferred that the hydrated hemoglobin molecule is of dimensions approximately $65 \times 55 \times 55$ A., and therefore should resemble somewhat a prolate ellipsoid of axial ratio a little below 1.2. However an ellipsoid of these dimensions would have a volume of 103,-000 A.^{3}, whereas the volume of the hydrated molecule as estimated by Bragg and Perutz is 116,000 A.^{3}. The volume of the anhydrous molecule, from the molecular weight and partial specific volume, is 83,000 A.^{3}, giving $w = 0.3$. A hydrated molecule of this axial ratio should have a value of f/f_0 near 1.13, and such a value was actually obtained in a careful sedimentation measurement by H. Gutfreund (reported in Ref. 176). Some of the sedimentation constants reported in Table VIII, however, lead to significantly higher values of f/f_0.

The approach employed by Bragg and Perutz in deriving the value of $w = 0.3$ for hemoglobin appears to be essentially sound, although further evidence of its validity would be desirable. For some other proteins, however, the assumption that the layer of water immediately around the protein did not admit salt ions would certainly be incorrect. For instance, both human and bovine serum albumin bind many anions so strongly that they readily displace water and attach themselves to the

(175) M. Wales and J. W. Williams, *J. Polymer Sci.* **8**, 449 (1952); see also a general discussion by R. J. Goldberg, *J. Phys. Chem.* **57**, 194 (1953).
(176) J. Boyes-Watson, E. Davidson, and M. F. Perutz, *Proc. Roy. Soc.* (London) **A191**, 83 (1947); M. F. Perutz, *Trans. Faraday Soc.* **42B**, 187 (1946).
(176a) W. L. Bragg and M. F. Perutz, *Acta Cryst.* **5**, 277 (1952).

protein.[177,178]   Likewise, β-lactoglobulin combines strongly with various ions; the uptake of lithium salts by β-lactoglobulin crystals is so great that calculations of "bound water" by the method of Perutz[176] would give negative values.[178a]   If sedimentation studies are carried out on such proteins, the sedimenting unit is presumably the protein molecule with a considerable mass of water and also salt ions attached to it.

A slightly lower value, 0.2 g. water/g. protein has been taken as a working figure for hydration in calculating the shapes of a number of other proteins from sedimentation, diffusion, and viscosity data; for instance, this has been done by Oncley, Scatchard, and Brown[179] in their studies on a number of blood proteins.   However, in the case of one very unusual protein molecule, the β-lipoprotein of human plasma, they used a different procedure for calculating hydration.[179a]   Pedersen[180] had previously studied the sedimentation rate of this protein as a function of the density of the solvent medium, using salt solutions of varying concentration to vary the density.   The sedimentation rate fell to zero in a medium of density close to 1.04, corresponding to a partial specific volume of the protein of 0.97.   It was found by density and dry-weight determinations that the partial specific volume of the anhydrous protein was 0.95.   From this, Oncley, Scatchard, and Brown[86] calculated the hydration factor for the β-lipoprotein as 0.6 g. water/g. protein.   The experimental error in this factor is considerable, since a small change in the estimated specific volumes leads to a large change in hydration. However, this value was in good agreement with the value obtained from viscosity measurements on the assumption that the molecule was spherical and hydrated.

The use of sedimentation measurements in solvents of differing density has been extensively employed in studies on viruses to determine hydration values.   A number of earlier workers varied the density by adding

(177) G. Scatchard and E. S. Black, *J. Phys. & Colloid Chem.* **53**, 88 (1949); G. Scatchard, I. H. Scheinberg, and S. H. Armstrong, Jr., *J. Am. Chem. Soc.* **72**, 535, 540 (1950).

(178) J. Lewin, *J. Am. Chem. Soc.* **73**, 3906 (1951).

(178a) M. L. Groves, N. J. Hipp, and T. L. McMeekin, *Federation Proc.* **11**, 223 (1952).

(179) J. L. Oncley, G. Scatchard, and A. Brown, *J. Phys. & Colloid Chem.* **51**, 184 (1947).

(179a) This molecule actually consists, to the extent of approximately 75% by dry weight of lipide, principally cholesterol and phospholipides, only about 25% consisting of amino acid residues, although the lipoprotein is readily soluble up to a concentration of about 10% in dilute aqueous salt solutions. See also the discussion in sec. XXI.

(180) K. O. Pedersen, Ultracentrifugal Studies on Serum and Serum Fractions, Almqvist and Wiksells Boktryckeri A. B. Uppsala, 1945.

sodium chloride, sucrose, and other substances to the solvent medium; see, for example, the work of Smadel, Pickels, and Shedlovsky[181] in the study of vaccinia virus in sucrose solution. If the size, shape, and internal composition of the virus were unaltered by variation in the solvent medium, then the product of sedimentation constant s and viscosity of the medium (η) should be given by the relation

$$\eta s = \frac{M(\rho_p - \rho)}{6\pi N \left(\dfrac{3\bar{v}M}{4\pi N}\right)^{\frac{1}{3}} \left(\dfrac{f}{f_0}\right) \rho_p} \tag{101}$$

where ρ_p is the density of the particles and ρ that of the solvent. If this equation is applicable, ηs should be a linear function of ρ, and extrapolation of the linear plot to the value of ρ corresponding to zero sedimentation rate should give the density of the particles themselves. However, Smadel, Pickels, and Shedlovsky[181] found that the plot was definitely nonlinear for vaccinia virus in sucrose solution and concluded that sucrose was altering the density of the virus particles by removing water from them by osmotic action. This suggested that if the density could be altered by adding a substance of high molecular weight which would exert less osmotic effect the results would be different. Several years later Sharp et al.[182] studied several strains of influenza virus in serum albumin solutions of varying density. In this case the plot of sedimentation rate against density was actually found to be linear and the densities of the three strains of virus studied were estimated as being close to 1.10 in aqueous suspension. The same method was applied by Sharp, Taylor, and Beard[183] to estimate the density of rabbit papilloma virus which was thus determined as 1.133. All of these values indicated a large degree of hydration. Thus, for rabbit papilloma virus the partial specific volume based on dry weight was 0.671, corresponding to a hydration of 1.04 g. water/g. dry virus.

The later work of Schachman and Lauffer[184] on tobacco mosaic virus, employing the same method of approach, yielded some important results. They found a plot of ηs for this virus to be a linear function of the density of the solvent, both in sucrose and in serum albumin solutions. However, the density intercept for zero sedimentation rate was 1.13 for serum albumin and 1.27 for sucrose. If these data were directly interpreted

(181) J. E. Smadel, E. G. Pickels, and T. Shedlovsky, *J. Exptl. Med.* **68**, 607 (1938).

(182) D. G. Sharp, A. R. Taylor, I. W. McLean, D. Beard, and J. W. Beard, *J. Biol. Chem.* **159**, 29 (1945).

(183) D. G. Sharp, A. R. Taylor, and J. W. Beard, *J. Biol. Chem.* **163**, 289 (1946).

(184) H. K. Schachman and M. A. Lauffer, *J. Am. Chem. Soc.* **71**, 536 (1949).

according to the argument presented above, this would give a hydration of 1.9 ml. water/ml. dry virus from the serum albumin measurements and 0.37 from the sucrose measurements. This great discrepancy obviously raises a question as to the justifiability of this interpretation. Schachman and Lauffer[184] developed an alternative hypothesis suggested by Prof. W. Kauzmann of Princeton University. If the medium surrounding the virus contains large spherical molecules of radius a, then the center of one of these molecules cannot approach the surface of the virus particles to a distance less than a. Since a closer approach is impossible, it may be calculated that this corresponds to having a shell of water of thickness a surrounding the virus molecules, into which the larger molecules of the surrounding medium cannot penetrate. If we take serum albumin, following Oncley, Scatchard, and Brown,[179] as an ellipsoid of major axis $2a = 150$ A. and $2b = 38$ A., then the equivalent shell into which albumin molecules cannot penetrate may be taken as $(a + b)/2$ A. thick, following the arguments of Schulz.[82] Thus, the region of non-penetration around the virus particle should be 47 A. thick in serum albumin solution and only 6 or 7 A. thick in sucrose solutions. This concept offers a plausible explanation of the apparently much greater hydration of the tobacco mosaic virus in serum albumin than in sucrose. From the measurements in both media, Schachman and Lauffer[184] inferred that the true hydration, representing water actually bound to the virus, corresponded to a surface layer approximately 6 or 7 A. thick, which was equivalent to a hydration of 0.15 ml. water/ml. virus. This degree of hydration appears not unreasonable in the light of other available data. It should be noted that tobacco mosaic virus is chemically a nucleoprotein of highly regular internal structure, as indicated by the x-ray diffraction measurements of Bernal and Fankuchen,[185] while the vaccinia, influenza, and rabbit papilloma viruses are much more complex chemically, containing lipides and other components. It is highly probable that they lack the high degree of compactness and internal regularity of structure of the tobacco mosaic virus and may well be surrounded by some kind of a membrane across which water can pass. Therefore, the results of Schachman and Lauffer[184] are not directly applicable to the other viruses studied, but they may furnish a fairly reliable value for the hydration of tobacco mosaic virus. It is interesting to note that this figure is considerably lower than the estimated hydration of hemoglobin in solution, corresponding perhaps to the smaller ratio of surface to volume in the larger molecule.

The recent work of Beeman et al.[66] on two spherical viruses—southern bean mosaic and tobacco necrosis viruses—shows clearly the presence of a considerable amount of internal water of hydration in these molecules

(185) J. D. Bernal and I. Fankuchen, *J. Gen. Physiol.* **25**, 111, 147 (1941).

(see sec. III), as well as surface water of hydration. Molecules such as sucrose might well exchange with the water in such molecules, thereby altering the internal density, so that the method of study used on tobacco mosaic virus would probably be quite inapplicable.

6. Sedimentation Studies in Polydispersed Systems

Sedimentation measurements are probably superior to all others, except perhaps electrophoretic mobilities, for the resolution of a polydispersed system into several components. The resolving power of an ultracentrifuge is proportional to $\omega^2 xh$, where h is the length of the column of solution in the cell in which sedimentation occurs. With present instruments, it is possible to separate two proteins with molecular weights of the order of 20,000 and 40,000 if their partial specific volumes are near 0.75 and their frictional ratios not far from unity. Here, as always, resolving power refers to a particular property; two proteins may be very different in chemical structure, or in electrophoretic mobility, but will remain inseparable in the ultracentrifuge if they have the same sedimentation constant. For example, serum γ-globulin[179] and myosin[94] both sediment with a value of $s_{20} = 7S$, yet the former has a molecular weight near 160,000, and the latter near 850,000. For very elongated molecules, indeed, s is dependent almost entirely on molecular cross section and varies little with the length of the molecule. This is, for instance, the case in such a polydispersed system as gelatin.[12] However, many protein systems found in nature, or fractions separated from such systems, contain several components of different sedimentation constant; in the ultracentrifuge, they can be identified and their relative amounts determined. Details of procedure are given by Svedberg and Pedersen.[186] A detailed discussion of the different types of molecular-weight averages that can be derived from sedimentation and diffusion studies on polydispersed systems has been given by Jullander;[187] he was concerned with studies on cellulose, preparations of which consist of practically a continuous distribution of molecules of different molecular weights. Such systems are seldom encountered in protein chemistry, except in partly degraded systems like gelatin; generally the sedimentation diagrams can be analyzed in terms of a small number of discrete components, although

(186) See Ref. 39, Part IIIB, secs. 3 and 4 (the latter section is by E. O. Kraemer).
(187) I. Jullander, *Arkiv Kemi, Mineral. Geol.* **21A**, No. 8 (1945). For an important recent development in methods of analysis for such systems, see R. L. Baldwin and J. W. Williams, *J. Am. Chem. Soc.* **72**, 4325 (1950); J. W. Williams, R. L. Baldwin, W. M. Saunders, and P. G. Squire, *ibid.* **74**, 1542 (1952).

the gradient curves for two or more of them may show considerable overlapping.

7. EFFECTS OF PROTEIN CONCENTRATION ON SEDIMENTATION CONSTANT

Sedimentation constants of proteins, and indeed of macromolecules generally, are markedly sensitive to concentration. Except in the case that the protein dissociates on dilution (see sec. XXI for the discussion of insulin, arachin, and the hemocyanins) the sedimentation rate almost invariably increases with decreasing protein concentration. The effect is most marked with such highly asymmetrical molecules as calf thymus nucleohistone[188] or tobacco mosaic virus.[189] In both these cases, $1/s_{20}$ was found to be an approximately linear function of the protein concentration. For the nucleohistone, the extrapolated value at zero concentration, s_{20}^0, was $31S$, but the actual value of s_{20} at $c = 0.1$ g./100 cc. was 24.7, and at $c = 1.25$ it was only 3.1. For tobacco mosaic virus, Lauffer[189] gave the equation $10^3/s = 5.40(1 + 0.278c)$. He also pointed out that $s\eta/\eta_0$ was very nearly constant at all concentrations, where η/η_0 is the relative viscosity of the *solution* compared to that of the pure solvent. This relation was later confirmed, for tobacco mosaic virus, by Schachman and Kauzmann,[190] at least for certain solvents. However, they concluded, for reasons discussed further below, that such a relation could not be expected to hold for proteins in general.

For less asymmetrical proteins it is generally found, within the limits of error, that s_{20} can be described as a linear function of c:

$$s_{20} = s_{20}^0 - kc \ (c \text{ in g./100 cc.}) \tag{102}$$

Thus, for bovine fibrinogen, γ-globulin, and serum albumin, Koenig and Pedersen[191] found k values of 0.65, 0.25, and 0.25, respectively. The highly asymmetrical fibrinogen molecule, as would be expected, gives the largest value of k. For bovine serum albumin, Taylor[192] gives k as 0.235, and Miller and Golder[193] as 0.31, in satisfactory agreement with the above value. (Their values of s_{20}^0, however, as will be discussed later, are distinctly lower than that reported by Koenig and Pedersen.) A particularly careful study has been made by Kegeles and Gutter[194] on

(188) R. O. Carter, *J. Am. Chem. Soc.* **63**, 1960 (1941).
(189) M. A. Lauffer, *J. Am. Chem. Soc.* **66**, 1188, 1195 (1944).
(190) H. K. Schachman and W. J. Kauzmann, *J. Phys. & Colloid Chem.* **53**, 150 (1949).
(191) V. L. Koenig and K. O. Pedersen, *Arch. Biochem.* **25**, 97 (1950).
(192) J. F. Taylor, *Arch. Biochem. and Biophys.* **36**, 357 (1952).
(193) G. L. Miller and R. H. Golder, *Arch. Biochem. and Biophys.* **36**, 249 (1952).
(194) G. Kegeles and F. J. Gutter, *J. Am. Chem. Soc.* **73**, 3770 (1951).

bovine serum albumin, ovalbumin, human carbonylhemoglobin, and hog heart lactic dehydrogenase. For ovalbumin the k value was close to that for serum albumin; for hemoglobin the slope was very similar, but the curve appeared not quite linear at very low c; for the dehydrogenase, k was not far from unity.

The theory of the concentration dependence of sedimentation has been considered by several investigators.[195-197] At least two effects must be involved: a backward flow of solvent, moving in to take the place of the macromolecule as it advances; and a decrease in the effective concentration in the immediate neighborhood of a macromolecule, owing to the "excluded volume" effect (compare the discussion of hydration on p. 657). The problem is too complex for any adequate discussion here; some useful general remarks will be found in the paper of Schachman and Kauzmann,[190] and a comparison of the theories with some accurate experimental data is given by Kegeles and Gutter.[194]

One very important effect of the decrease of s with increasing protein concentration has been pointed out by Johnston and Ogston.[198] In a solution containing two proteins, one sedimenting faster than the other, the slow component will sediment more rapidly in the region behind the boundary of the fast component, since the total protein concentration is lower there. At this boundary, its sedimentation will be retarded; hence the slow component tends to accumulate behind the fast boundary and to be present at a lower concentration in front of this boundary than behind it. The situation is represented diagrammatically in Fig. 14. The result is that in such a mixture optical methods of measurement give too high a value for the apparent concentration of the slow component and too low a value for the fast component.

In describing the system, it is convenient to use the notation of Harrington and Schachman.[198a] Let $c_S{}^0$ be the true concentration of slow component in the mixed solution, s_S the sedimentation constant of slow component in the absence of fast component, $s_{S,\text{mixt}}$ its sedimentation constant in the mixture, and s_F the sedimentation constant of fast component in the mixture.

Then the measured concentration change across the slow boundary, as determined from the refractive index gradients in the solution, will be $c_S{}^{obs}$ at the beginning of the run.

(195) W. O. Kermack, A. G. McKendrick, and E. Ponder, *Proc. Roy. Soc. Edinburgh* **49**, 170 (1929).

(196) J. M. Burgers, *Proc. Acad. Sci. Amsterdam* **44**, 1045, 1177 (1941); **45**, 9, 126 (1942).

(197) R. E. Powell and H. Eyring, *Advances in Colloid Sci.* **1**, 183 (1942).

(198) J. P. Johnston and A. G. Ogston, *Trans. Faraday Soc.* **42**, 789 (1946).

$$c_S{}^{obs} = c_S{}^0 \left(\frac{s_F - s_{S,\text{mixt}}}{s_F - s_S} \right) \tag{102a}$$

This is the equation of Johnston and Ogston.[198] Since $s_{S,\text{mixt}}$ is always less than s_S, it follows that $c_S{}^{obs}$ is greater than $c_S{}^0$. Since the concentrations of the components change with time as they sediment outward in a sector-shaped cell, the s values in Eq. (102a) may be expected in general to be functions of the time in view of Eq. (102). Harrington and Schachman[198a] have given a more general equation which reduces to Eq. (102a) as the time elapsed after the beginning of the run approaches zero.

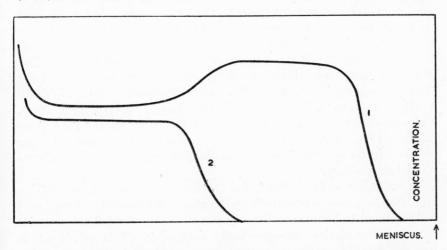

FIG. 14.   Sedimentation of two components. Direction of sedimentation is from right to left; hence component 2 is the fast and component 1 the slow component. From Johnston and Ogston.[198]

The value of $s_{S,\text{mixt}}$ should be given to a reasonably good approximation[198a] by an equation analogous to Eq. (102), but involving the concentrations of both components

$$s_{S,\text{mixt}} = s_{S,0}(1 - k_S c_{S,\text{mixt}} - k_F c_F) \tag{102b}$$

where $s_{S,0}$ is the extrapolated sedimentation constant of slow component at zero concentration of both components. The coefficient k_F may be taken as roughly the same as what would be found in a solution of fast component alone, for the effect of this component on its own sedimentation rate, according to Eq. (102).

Johnston and Ogston tested Eq. (102a) on mixtures containing β-lactoglobulin, serum albumin, or γ-globulin; they calculated $s_{S,\text{mixt}}$ from

(198a) W. F. Harrington and H. K. Schachman, *J. Am. Chem. Soc.* **75**, 3533 (1953).

a simplified form of Eq. (102b), assuming $k_S = k_F$, and the general results agreed well with the theory. A mixture of hemoglobin (slow component) and γ-globulin (fast component) afforded a crucial test, since the color of the hemoglobin permitted it to be distinguished from the γ-globulin. The "piling up" of hemoglobin behind the γ-globulin boundary was plainly visible, the concentration distribution being very like that shown in Fig. 14.

Recently a new type of ultracentrifuge cell has been developed, which permits the formation of boundaries in the central portion of the cell by a layering technique.[198b] Thus the lower layer may consist of a mixture of slow and fast components, the upper layer of fast component alone. In this cell it has been possible to measure directly the sedimentation rate of slow component in the presence of fast component, in any desired mixture.[198a] It was found, for instance, that the sedimentation of bushy stunt virus (BSV) in the presence of tobacco mosaic virus (TMV), was greatly retarded. Thus s_{20} for 0.3 per cent BSV was 133 S in the absence of TMV, and 83 S in the presence of 1 per cent TMV. The measured value of c_S^{obs}/c_S^0 was 5.6 in the latter solution; the value calculated from Eq. (102a) was 4.9. Considering the sources of error involved in measurement and calculation, the agreement may be considered satisfactory.

It follows from Eqs. (102a) and (102b) that if a mixture of proteins is studied at several concentrations, the area under the fastest boundaries will be found to increase as the concentration decreases, the area under the slow boundaries correspondingly decreasing. This effect, which may be denoted as the Johnston-Ogston effect, is to be sharply distinguished from effects due to reversible association and dissociation of protein components with change of total protein concentration. Such systems are exemplified by insulin, arachin, or the hemocyanins (sec. XXI). In accordance with the law of mass action, the dilution of such a system leads to increased dissociation, and therefore to increase in the relative amounts of the slower component or components. The effect of changing concentration on such a system, therefore, is exactly opposite to that arising from the Johnston-Ogston effect.

8. Experimental Methods and Results

In Table VIII are listed values of sedimentation and diffusion constants, partial specific volumes, molecular weights, and frictional ratios for a number of proteins. No attempt has been made to list all the

(198b) E. G. Pickels, W. F. Harrington, and H. K. Schachman, *Proc. Nat. Acad. Sci. U. S. A.* **38**, 943 (1952). See also G. Kegeles, *J. Am. Chem. Soc.* **74**, 5532 (1952).

hundreds of values that have now been published.   The values listed in the table are primarily those obtained for well-characterized crystalline proteins, but some other proteins of particular physiological or chemical interest are also included.   Zein, for example, has been an object of study by protein chemists for more than two generations, and data concerning it are therefore listed, although they should be taken with considerable reserve, since zein is actually a multicomponent system, and the values given are presumably those of the principal component.   Other data, not listed here, will be found in similar tables compiled by Svedberg and Pedersen,[39] by Cohn and Edsall,[2] by Alexander and Johnson,[5a] and especially in the very comprehensive table given by Lundgren and Ward.[40] Extensive data on the seed globulins of the Gramineae and Leguminosae have been given by Danielsson,[199] and a large number of comparative data have been listed by Pedersen.[200]

No attempt will be made here to discuss experimental procedures in detail, since excellent discussions are given elsewhere.[39,40,5a,201,202]   However, certain points should be borne in mind in interpreting the data.   In sedimentation velocity studies on small proteins, the rotor revolves at a speed of the order of magnitude of 1000 revolutions per second.   The meniscus, from which sedimentation proceeds, is commonly at a distance of 5.5–6.0 cm. from the axis of rotation.   The bottom of the cell containing the solution under study—that is, the outer boundary—may be 7.0–7.5 cm. from the axis.   The centrifugal acceleration, $\omega^2 x$, is thus of the order of 200,000–300,000 times gravity   The regions near the bottom of the cell are therefore under high pressure, which appreciably alters the density of the liquid and the partial specific volume of the solute. The alteration of the term $(1 - \bar{v}\rho)$ in Eq. (97), for liquid near the bottom of the cell, may be of the order of 6 per cent.[203]   For larger particles, such as viruses, lower centrifugal fields are used.

The form of the sedimenting boundary may be determined by any of the same methods already mentioned in the discussion on diffusion, or

(199) C. E. Danielsson, *Biochem. J.* **44**, 387 (1949).
(200) K. O. Pedersen, *Cold Spring Harbor Symposia Quant. Biol.* **14**, 140 (1950).
(201) J. B. Nichols and E. D. Bailey, *in* A. Weissberger, Physical Methods of Organic Chemistry, 2nd Ed., Interscience Publishers, New York, 1949, Vol. I, part I, p. 621.
(202) E. G. Pickels, *in* Uber, ed., Biophysical Research Methods, Interscience Publishers, New York, 1950.
(203) L. G. Longsworth, *Proc. Natl. Acad. Sci. U.S.* **36**, 502 (1950).   This, a report of a conference on the ultracentrifuge, held in 1949, summarizes the discussion of a number of important problems concerning experimental procedure and interpretation, and gives a valuable short bibliography.   For an earlier symposium on the ultracentrifuge, with all papers printed in full, see D. A. MacInnes, and others, *Ann. N. Y. Acad. Sci.* **43**, 176*ff.* (1942).

in Chap. 6 on electrophoresis. The most widely used methods give the refractive index gradient as a function of x, either by the scale method of Lamm,[148,149] or the schlieren method of Philpot[204] and Svensson.[205] Recently, Kegeles and Gutter[194] have reported a modification of the latter method, using a diagonal bar instead of a diagonal slit or knife edge. This gives a schlieren diagram outlined, not by a single broad line, but by several closely spaced parallel lines, which are Fresnel diffraction fringes. By making readings on the coordinates of these fringes, the position of the boundary can be determined with enhanced precision; values of s are reproducible within 1 per cent, on a given apparatus, if the concentration of protein is above 0.5 per cent.

The Svedberg ultracentrifuge[39] is driven by an oil turbine, and runs in an atmosphere of hydrogen at a pressure of a few millimeters of mercury. In the air-turbine-driven ultracentrifuge of J. W. Beams and E. G. Pickels (described by Bauer and Pickels in Ref. 39, pp. 191–212) the rotor runs in a high vacuum, turbine and rotor being connected by a flexible steel drive shaft, the vacuum around the rotor being maintained by sealing with an oil gland and with rubber tubing around the shaft. More recently, electrically driven vacuum ultracentrifuges have come into use, the Spinco ultracentrifuge, manufactured by the Specialized Instruments Corporation in Belmont, California, being much used in the United States.[206,206a] In Germany many laboratories have used an air-driven ultracentrifuge manufactured by the firm of Phywe in Göttingen. Bergold[207] has used this apparatus in studies on a number of proteins, and Schramm and Bergold[208] have used it in studies on tobacco mosaic virus. An important approach to a more nearly ideal type of instrument has been made in the recent work of Beams and his associates,[209] who have constructed a magnetically suspended and driven vacuum ultracentrifuge. The rotor runs suspended in a vacuum, and difficulties due to friction, and the resultant heating, are practically eliminated. Great constancy in the speed of rotation can also be achieved. This instrument, however, has not yet been produced in a form in which it is suitable for sedimentation studies on proteins.

(204) J. St. L. Philpot, *Nature* **141**, 283 (1938).
(205) H. Svensson, *Kolloid-Z.* **87**, 181 (1939).
(206) A description of the Spinco ultracentrifuge is given by E. L. Smith, D. M. Brown, J. B. Fishman, and A. E. Wilhelmi, *J. Biol. Chem.* **177**, 305 (1949).
(206a) E. G. Pickels, *Machine Design* **22**, 102 (1950).
(207) G. Bergold, *Z. Naturforsch.* **1**, 100 (1946).
(208) G. Schramm and G. Bergold, *Z. Naturforsch.* **2b**, 108 (1947).
(209) J. W. Beams, J. L. Young, and J. W. Moore, *J. Applied Phys.* **17**, 886 (1946); J. W. Beams, *J. Wash. Acad. Sci.* **37**, 221 (1947); J. W. Beams, J. D. Ross, and J. F. Dillon, *Rev. Sci. Instruments* **22**, 77 (1951).

Some emphasis must be laid on the problem of ultracentrifuge design, since recent studies have shown that there are significant discrepancies between sedimentation constants determined with different instruments. Thus Cecil and Ogston,[210] in a very careful and critical study of the factors involved, obtained s_{20}^0 for β-lactoglobulin as 2.83 S, whereas the earlier work of Pedersen[211] had given 3.12 S. Both laboratories used oil-turbine ultracentrifuges. More recently Koenig and Pedersen[191] studied bovine serum albumin, using the same type of instrument, and obtained $s_{20}^0 = 4.73$. On the other hand, four different laboratories,[192–194,212] all using Spinco ultracentrifuges, obtained values near 4.3 for the same protein. Similar discrepancies appear to exist between different laboratories with respect to ovalbumin.[193] Likewise, Portzehl[94] found $s_{20}^0 = 7.1$ for actin-free myosin, using a Phywe ultracentrifuge; Snellman and Erdös[213] obtained 7.2 with an oil-turbine instrument; while Mommaerts and Parrish[214] obtained the distinctly lower value of 6.7, using a Spinco ultracentrifuge. The exact source of the discrepancies is still not altogether clear, but it seems probable that control and calibration of temperature in the rotor offer the most serious problems. The critical discussions of Cecil and Ogston,[210] Taylor,[192] and Miller and Golder[193] deserve attention in this connection. Shulman,[212] who made careful comparative studies, using both an oil-turbine and a Spinco ultracentrifuge, obtained agreement in values of s_{20} within 3 per cent when the oil-turbine results were specially calibrated by direct temperature measurements on the rotor.[214a]

(210) R. Cecil and A. G. Ogston, *Biochem. J.* **43**, 592 (1948).

(211) K. O. Pedersen, *Biochem. J.* **30**, 961 (1936).

(212) The paper by Taylor[192] contains also a report of similar findings by S. Shulman in the chemistry laboratory of the University of Wisconsin. See also J. M. Creeth, *Biochem. J.* **51**, 10 (1952); P. A. Charlwood, *ibid.* **51**, 113 (1952); S. Shulman, *Arch. Biochem. and Biophys.* **44**, 230 (1953).

(213) O. Snellman and T. Erdös, *Biochim. et Biophys. Acta* **2**, 650 (1948).

(214) W. F. H. M. Mommaerts and R. G. Parrish, *J. Biol. Chem.* **188**, 545 (1951).

(214a) This small remaining discrepancy may perhaps have been resolved by the recent studies of D. F. Waugh and D. A. Yphantis, *Rev. Sci. Instr.* **23**, 609 (1952) who have determined the temperature of the spinning rotor in the Spinco ultracentrifuge by measuring the intensity of the infrared radiation emitted from it. The radiation is received by a copper disk placed beneath the base of the rotor and within a mass of metal used as a reference block, the temperature of which can be controlled. By this method it was found that the rotor becomes cooler by about 1°C., when the rotor is accelerated to 60,000 rpm, with a corresponding warming on deceleration. It can be shown thermodynamically that such an effect is to be expected from the applied stress on the metal of the rotor. The cooling effect observed on acceleration would not have been detected in Shulman's experiments; and the change in temperature and viscosity of the liquid produced by this temper-

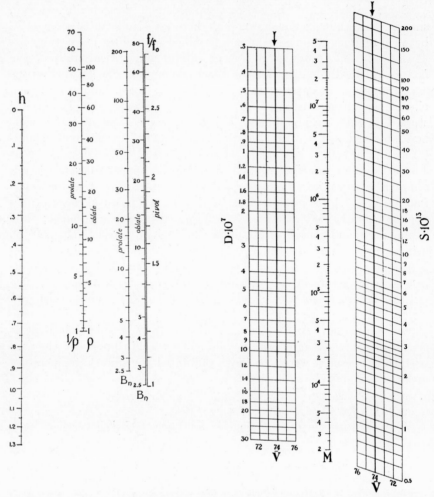

Fig. 15. Nomogram for sedimentation constant (s), diffusion constant (D), partial specific volume (v̄), molecular weight (M), frictional ratio (f/f₀), viscosity increment (Bη), axial ratio (p), and hydration (h). Values of those variables which depend on temperature are for 20°. From Wyman and Ingalls.[4]

These uncertainties must be borne in mind in evaluating the data of Table VIII, since they affect to some degree many of the estimates concerning molecular size and shape that can be deduced from these measurements. However, data obtained by these methods remain the richest

ature decrease are in the direction that would explain the small residual discrepancies between Shulman's findings on the Spinco and the oil turbine ultracentrifuges.

source of information available concerning protein size and the combined influence of molecular asymmetry and hydration. Analysis of the data in these terms is facilitated by Oncley's[3] contour diagram (Fig. 13) and by the nomogram of Wyman and Ingalls,[4] reproduced in Fig. 15. With the aid of this nomogram, it is possible to consider rapidly a number of possible models, involving varying degrees of asymmetry and hydration, that are compatible with a given set of experimental data, and to decide which gives the best fit. The figure also provides for the use of data derived from viscosity measurements, which are discussed in sec. XVIII.

9. Molecular Weights from Sedimentation Equilibrium

If an ultracentrifuge run is conducted for a sufficiently long time, and at a suitable speed, the backward flow of the molecules due to diffusion will eventually balance their motion due to the centrifugal force, and an equilibrium concentration distribution throughout the cell will be attained. The flow of solute across a surface of cross section A, perpendicular to the direction of flow, is $cA\,dx/dt$, while the backward flow due to diffusion is, from Fick's first law, $-DA\,dc/dx$. The velocity dx/dt is, as we have already seen [Eqs. (95) and (96)] equal to the driving force, ϕ, divided by the frictional coefficient, f. So we may write, for the net rate of flow of solute (dm/dt) across the area A:

$$\begin{aligned} dm/dt &= A(c\,dx/dt - D\,dc/dx) \\ &= A(\phi c/f - D\,dc/dx) \\ &= DA(\phi c/kT - dc/dx) \end{aligned} \qquad (103)$$

At equilibrium the net flow anywhere in the cell is zero, and using the value for ϕ given in Eq. (95).

$$\frac{dc}{dx} = \frac{\phi c}{kT} = \frac{\omega^2 x M(1 - \bar{v}\rho)c}{RT} \qquad (104)$$

Rearranging terms in c on the left-hand side, and in x on the right, and integrating, we obtain:

$$M = \frac{2RT \ln c_2/c_1}{\omega^2(1 - \bar{v}\rho)(x_2^2 - x_1^2)} \qquad (105)$$

Here c_2 and c_1 are the concentrations, and x_2 and x_1, the distances from the center of the rotor, at any pair of points within the cell. This is the fundamental equation of sedimentation equilibrium; it can also be derived from purely thermodynamic reasoning as Svedberg and Pedersen (Ref. 39, pp. 48–57) have shown in detail. In general, of course, it is necessary to use the activities, a_2 and a_1, of the solute component, rather than the concentrations c_2 and c_1, if the equation is to hold rigorously.

Sedimentation equilibrium experiments are generally carried out at much lower values of ω than are sedimentation velocity measurements. The attainment of equilibrium takes many days, and there is therefore the danger that an unstable protein may suffer alteration while the run is proceeding. This difficulty partly counterbalances the theoretical advantage of the method, which is that its derivation rests on rigorous thermodynamic foundations. Lansing and Kraemer[173] have shown that the molecular weights derived from such measurements are not appreciably affected by hydration of the solute, at least in a two component system. Numerous values of molecular weight for proteins have been derived by this method; they are listed in Table VIII, in the column headed M_e.

Archibald[215] has made interesting theoretical calculations to provide a basis for calculating molecular weights from the rate of approach to equilibrium in such systems, without waiting until equilibrium is actually attained. The suggested method does not yet appear to have been tested in practice; various experimental difficulties have been discussed.[203]

Sedimentation equilibrium studies provide a powerful tool for the study of polydispersed systems. Methods of deriving molecular-weight averages by equilibrium measurements on such systems have been discussed in detail by Wales, Williams, and their collaborators.[106,107,216]

XV. Rotary Diffusion Coefficients and Relaxation Times: Their Relation to Molecular Size and Shape

The random thermal motion of molecules involves rotation as well as translation; and the intensity of rotary Brownian movement can be defined by a rotary diffusion coefficient, very closely analogous to the translational diffusion coefficient. If the orientation of a molecule can be specified in terms of a particular axis within the molecule, we can define a distribution function, F, for a system of molecules. Let the axis of a molecule be defined by the direction OA in Fig. 16, while the Cartesian coordinates X, Y, and Z represent directions fixed with respect to the vessel containing the liquid. Then the orientation of the principal axis of the molecule can be specified in terms of the angles θ and ϕ, which are defined in Fig. 16. For a system of such molecules, the distribution function $F(\theta,\phi)$ specifies the relative number of molecules, dN, with axes pointing in a particular direction. Within a given element of solid angle, $d\Omega$, dN is given by the relation

$$dN = Fd\Omega = F \sin \theta d\theta d\phi \qquad (106)$$

(215) W. J. Archibald, *Ann. N. Y. Acad. Sci.*, **43**, 211 (1942); idem *J. Phys. & Colloid Chem.* **51**, 1204 (1947).

(216) M. Wales, *et al.*, *J. Phys. & Colloid Chem.* **55**, 145, 282 (1951). See also R. J. Goldberg.[175]

The function F is normalized by integrating over all angles and setting the integral $\int F d\Omega$ equal to unity.   If the molecular axes are distributed at random, this means that F is the same for all values of Ω (or of θ and ϕ), and is in this case equal to $\frac{1}{4}\pi$.   The function F in rotary diffusion is the analog of the concentration in translational diffusion.

If an orienting force acts on the system, a gradient of the distribution function F is set up.   Rotary diffusion (Brownian movement) tends to level out this gradient.   Suppose, to simplify the discussion, that we consider the molecular axes all to lie within the XY-plane (Fig. 16)—that is, the plane for which $\theta = 90°$.   Then the orientation of any molecule can be defined by the angle ϕ between its axis and the X-axis; and F is a

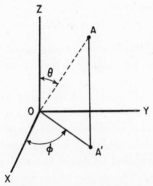

FIG. 16.   Diagram of coordinates to describe molecular orientation.   The origin O is taken at the center of the ellipsoidal molecule; the line OA denotes the orientation of the axis of revolution of the molecule.   The line OA' is the projection of OA on the XY plane.   The angles θ and ϕ specify the orientation.

function of ϕ only.   If a gradient of F has been produced by an orienting force, and this force then suddenly ceases to act, the subsequent course of disorientation is defined, for the value of F at any given value of ϕ, by the relation:

$$\partial F / \partial t = \Theta \partial^2 F / \partial \phi^2 \qquad (107)$$

This is the exact analog of Fick's second law of translational diffusion [Eq. (81)], and the rotary diffusion coefficient Θ corresponds to the translational diffusion coefficient D.   However, while D has the dimensions $l^2 t^{-1}$, Θ has the dimensions t^{-1}, and is commonly expressed in reciprocal seconds.

For rotary motion in three dimensions, Eq. (107) may be generalized to give, for any specified values of θ and ϕ:

$$\partial F / \partial t = \Theta \left(\frac{\partial^2 F}{\partial \theta^2} + \cot \theta \, \frac{\partial F}{\partial \theta} + \frac{1}{\sin^2 \theta} \frac{\partial^2 F}{\partial \phi^2} \right) = \Theta \nabla^2 F \qquad (108)$$

Here ∇^2 denotes the Laplacian operator (compare Eq. (82) for translational diffusion). For the derivation of Eqs. (107) and (108), see for example Williams and Cady.[145]

Rotary, like translational diffusion, may also be visualized in terms of average molecular displacements due to Brownian movement. Imagine all the molecules oriented by an external force so that their principal axes are parallel, and suppose this orienting force to be suddenly removed, so that the subsequent motion of the molecules is purely random. After the lapse of a short time, t, a given molecule will have shifted through an angle, ϕ, with respect to its original orientation.[217] Then Θ, as defined by Einstein, is directly proportional to the mean square value of ϕ for all molecules in the system.

$$\Theta = \bar{\phi}^2/2t \tag{109}$$

The derivation of Eq. (109) is exactly analogous to the derivation of the corresponding equation for translational diffusion (see, for instance, Williams and Cady).[145]

Θ, like D, is directly proportional to the thermal energy of the molecule; similarly, it is inversely proportional to a rotary frictional coefficient, ζ, which is a function of the size and shape of the molecule and the viscosity of the medium in which it is immersed; ζ is a measure of the torque which must be applied to cause the molecule to rotate with unit angular velocity:[218]

$$\Theta = kT/\zeta \tag{110}$$

Here k is Boltzmann's constant, and T the absolute temperature. In the general case of an ellipsoid with three semiaxes, a, b, and c, of different lengths, three different rotary frictional coefficients are required to characterize the resistance of the medium to rotation of the molecule about each of these axes. There are three corresponding rotary diffusion constants:

$$\Theta_a = kT/\zeta_a; \; \Theta_b = kT/\zeta_b; \; \Theta_c = kT/\zeta_c \tag{111}$$

We shall confine our subsequent discussion to ellipsoids of revolution, for which

$$\zeta_b = \zeta_c$$

(217) Here the angle ϕ is not the total angular displacement of the molecule, but the projection of this angle on the plane onto which the observer is looking. For instance, if one could observe the molecule through a microscope and measure the angle with the aid of a micrometer and cross hairs, the measured angle would be the angle of rotation as observed in projection on a plane perpendicular to the axis of the microscope tube.

(218) F. Perrin, *J. phys. radium* [7], **5**, 497 (1934).

For many purposes, it is more convenient to characterize the rotary Brownian movement by another quantity, the relaxation time τ. We may imagine the molecules oriented by an external force so that the a-axes are all parallel to the x-axis (which is fixed in space). If this force is suddenly removed, the Brownian movement leads to their disorientation. The position of any molecule after an interval of time may be characterized by the cosine of the angle θ between its a-axis and the x-axis. (The molecule is now considered to be free to turn in any direction in space—its motion is not confined to a single plane, but instead may have components about both the b- and c-axes.) When the mean value of cosine θ for the entire system of molecules has fallen to $1/e$ ($e = 2.718 \cdots$, the base of natural logarithms), the elapsed time is defined as the relaxation time τ_a, for motion of the a-axis.[219] The relaxation time is greater, the greater the resistance of the medium to rotation of the molecule about this axis, and it is found that a simple reciprocal relation exists between the three relaxation times τ_a, τ_b, and τ_c, for rotation of each of the axes, and the corresponding rotary diffusion coefficients defined in Eq. (111)

$$\tau_a = \frac{1}{\Theta_b + \Theta_c}; \tau_b = \frac{1}{\Theta_a + \Theta_c}; \tau_c = \frac{1}{\Theta_a + \Theta_b} \tag{112}$$

For an ellipsoid of revolution, these equations become:

$$\tau_a = \frac{1}{2\Theta_b}; \tau_b = \tau_c = \frac{1}{\Theta_a + \Theta_b} \tag{112a}$$

If the solute molecule is spherical, and is very large in comparison to the solvent molecules, the inner frictional constant ζ is given by a formula due to Stokes:

$$\zeta_{\text{sphere}} = 8\pi\eta r^3 \tag{113}$$

where r is the radius of the sphere and η is the viscosity of the solvent. The molecule is characterized by a single rotary diffusion coefficient Θ, and a single relaxation time:

$$\Theta_{\text{sphere}} = (2\tau_{\text{sphere}})^{-1} = kT/8\pi\eta r^3 \tag{114}$$

This formula, due to Einstein, was experimentally verified by Jean Perrin[221] by direct microscopic observation of spherical colloidal mastic particles (with radius 6.5×10^{-4} cm.), which contained small enclosures of impurities on the surface, thus permitting their rotary motion to be directly followed.

(219) Concerning relaxation times, see Debye[220] and Perrin.[218]
(220) P. Debye, Polar Molecules, Chemical Catalog Co., New York, 1929.
(221) J. Perrin, Compt. rend. 149, 549 (1909).

Generalizing the hydrodynamical equations derived by Stokes for spheres, Edwardes[222] calculated the coefficients, ζ_a, ζ_b, and ζ_c for ellipsoids as a function of their axial ratios. The general equations are complicated; but for ellipsoids of revolution, which may be characterized by only two values of ζ, they assume a simpler form, and have been employed by Gans[223] and F. Perrin[218] to evaluate the rotary diffusion coefficients of molecules which may be treated as ellipsoids of revolution. The formulas of Gans and Perrin are not identical, but the numerical values of Θ calculated from them are nearly so, so that the formulas of either author may be used in practice. In the following discussion we shall employ Perrin's equations.

The volume of the ellipsoid (of axial ratio a/b) is

$$V = 4\pi ab^2/3 \tag{115}$$

The rotary diffusion coefficient Θ_0 and relaxation time ζ_0 of a sphere of the same volume would be given by the relations

$$\Theta_0 = (2\tau_0)^{-1} = kT/8\pi ab^2\eta \tag{116}$$

Consider first the case of an elongated ellipsoid of revolution ($a > b$). Rotary Brownian movement of the a-axis about the b-axis is characterized by the relaxation time τ_a and the corresponding rotary diffusion coefficient $\Theta_b = (2\tau_a)^{-1}$ [see Eq. (112a)]. These constants are conveniently expressed by their values relative to those for a sphere of the same volume. Denoting by q the ratio b/a, Perrin's equation reads

$$\tau_a/\tau_0 = \Theta_0/\Theta_b = \frac{2(1 - q^4)}{\dfrac{3q^2(2 - q^2)}{\sqrt{1 - q^2}} \ln\left(\dfrac{1 + \sqrt{1 - q^2}}{q}\right) - 3q^2} \tag{117}$$

τ_a/τ_0 is always greater than unity, and increases very rapidly as a/b increases. If $a \gg b$, Eq. (117) reduces approximately to the simpler formula:

$$\Theta_b/\Theta_0 = \tau_0/\tau_a = \frac{3b^2}{2a^2}\left[2 \ln \frac{2a}{b} - 1\right] \tag{117a}$$

If $a > 5b$, the values of Θ_b and τ_a, calculated from formula (117a) agree within 1 per cent with those calculated from the exact formula (117). Hence Θ_b, from Eqs. (116) and (117a), equals approximately:

$$\Theta_b = \frac{3kT}{16\pi\eta a^3}\left[2 \ln \frac{2a}{b} - 1\right] \tag{118}$$

(222) D. Edwardes, *Quart. J. Pure and Applied Math.* **26**, 70 (1893).
(223) R. Gans, *Ann. Physik* **86**, 628 (1928).

Thus, for a given value of a/b, the rotary diffusion coefficient of an elongated ellipsoid is inversely proportional to the cube of its length.

For the relaxation time τ_b of an elongated ellipsoid of revolution involving rotation of the b-axis, which may involve turning about both the a- and the c ($=b$)-axis, Perrin finds

$$\tau_b/\tau_0 = 2\Theta_0/(\Theta_a + \Theta_b) = \frac{4(1 - q^4)}{\dfrac{3q^2(1 - 2q^2)}{\sqrt{1 - q^2}} \ln\left(\dfrac{1 + \sqrt{1 - q^2}}{q}\right) + 3} \tag{119}$$

If $a \gg b$, then ($q \to 0$), and Eq. (119) reduces approximately to

$$\tau_b/\tau_0 = 2\Theta_0/(\Theta_a + \Theta_b) = \frac{4}{3\left(1 - \dfrac{b^2}{a^2} \ln \dfrac{2a}{b}\right)} \tag{119a}$$

Thus τ_b for an elongated ellipsoid is always greater than τ_0 but never becomes greater than $4\tau_0/3$, even when a/b becomes infinite.

For a flattened ellipsoid ($a < b$, and $q > 1$), a different set of equations holds. For rotation about the equatorial (b) axis

$$\tau_a/\tau_0 = \Theta_0/\Theta_b = \frac{2(1 - q^4)}{\dfrac{3q^2(2 - q^2)}{\sqrt{q^2 - 1}} \tan^{-1}(\sqrt{q^2 - 1}) - 3q^2} \tag{120}$$

and for rotation about the a-axis (axis of revolution)

$$\tau_b/\tau_0 = 2\Theta_0/(\Theta_a + \Theta_b) = \frac{4(1 - q^4)}{\dfrac{3q^2(1 - 2q^2)}{\sqrt{q^2 - 1}} \tan^{-1}(\sqrt{q^2 - 1}) + 3} \tag{121}$$

If $b \gg a$, both Eqs. (120) and (121) reduce approximately to

$$\tau_a/\tau_0 \cong \tau_b/\tau_0 \cong \frac{2b}{a[3 \tan^{-1}(b/a)]} \cong \frac{4b}{3\pi a} \tag{121a}$$

and substituting the value of τ_0 from Eq. (116)

$$\tau_a \cong \tau_b \cong \frac{16\eta b^3}{3kT} \cong (2\Theta_b)^{-1} \cong (2\Theta_a)^{-1} \tag{121b}$$

Thus for a flattened ellipsoid, as b/a becomes infinite, both relaxation times become infinite, and the corresponding rotary diffusion coefficients approach zero. When b/a is very large, the relaxation times are proportional to the cube of the b-semiaxis, and do not depend at all on the length of the a-semiaxis.

For a flattened (oblate) ellipsoid, τ_a is always less than τ_b, but never differs from it by more than about 10 per cent, the ratio of the two relaxa-

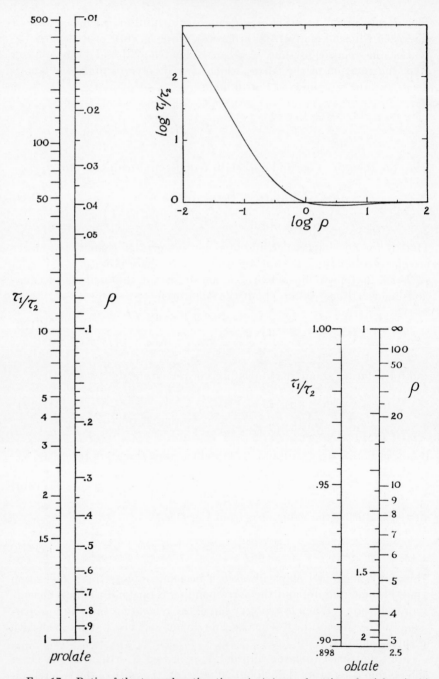

FIG. 17.   Ratio of the two relaxation times (τ_1/τ_2) as a function of axial ratio (ρ) for oblate and prolate ellipsoids calculated from the equations given by Perrin. ρ in this figure denotes the ratio b/a.   It is, therefore, greater than 1 for oblate and less than 1 for prolate ellipsoids.   From Wyman and Ingalls.[4]

tion times approaching unity as a/b approaches the value 1 (spheres) or zero (flat disks).   Thus, if it can be established that a given molecule has two distinct relaxation times differing by considerably more than 10 per cent, the molecule cannot be represented by an oblate ellipsoid of revolution, and a prolate model must be assumed.   The use of this criterion of

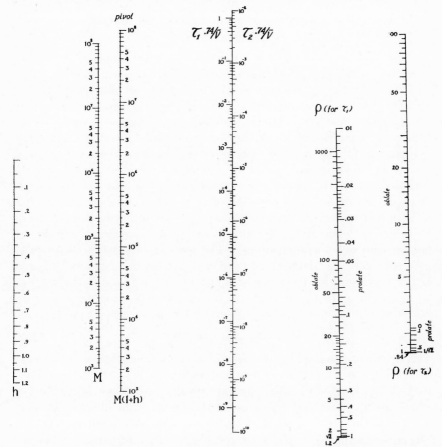

FIG. 18.   Nomogram for relaxation times (τ_1 and τ_2), axial ratio (ρ), molecular weight (M), and hydration (h).   Note that hydration is here expressed as volume fraction rather than in weight units as in most of the discussion in the text of the present review.   Values of τ_1 and τ_2 are for 20°.   From Wyman and Ingalls.[4]

shape will be considered further in connection with dielectric dispersion. The relaxations between the shape of the ellipsoid and the ratio of the two relaxation times are shown in Fig. 17 taken from the work of Wyman and Ingalls (4).

Figure 18, also taken from their work, gives a nomographic representation of the relation between the molecular weight, the two relaxation times, and the axial ratio of oblate and prolate ellipsoids. In this figure M denotes the molecular weight, h denotes the hydration, *expressed as volume fraction*, and τ_1 and τ_2 denote the relaxation times which we have denoted here as τ_a and τ_b, respectively.

XVI. Rotary Diffusion Coefficients from Direct Measurements of Disorientation Rates

The most direct method of determining rotary diffusion coefficients would be to orient a system of molecules by an applied force, and then to follow the rate of disorientation after the force had ceased to act. Recently this has been achieved in a straightforward manner by Benoit,[224] who produced the orientation by suddenly applying an electric field, the field being again suddenly switched off after a brief interval. The interval required for the field strength to rise from zero to its maximum value was of the order of 10^{-6} sec., with a similar interval at the end for the field to fall from its maximum value to zero. The field was maintained at maximum intensity for a period of the order of 10^{-2} sec., an interval which proved adequate to permit a steady state of partial orientation to be achieved, while still sufficiently short to avoid disturbances due to heating and other complications. The relative orientation attained at different times was determined by measuring the induced birefringence. If the maximum birefringence attained in the steady state be denoted by Δn_0, then, as Benoit showed, the birefringence Δn at a time t after the field strength had fallen to zero should be given by the simple formula:

$$\Delta n / \Delta n_0 = e^{-6\Theta t} \tag{122}$$

This simple exponential relation should hold if all the solute molecules can be characterized by the same rotary diffusion coefficient. If several different kinds of molecules with different Θ values are present, the observed effects are given by the summation of the effects of the different kinds of molecules; the resultant summation curve is in general not exponential. The equation for the increase of birefringence, from zero to Δn_0, when the field is applied, is in general more complex than the "die-away" curve; the orientation depends both on the electric moment induced in the molecule by the field and on the permanent dipole moment.

Benoit applied this method to tobacco mosaic virus, working in very dilute solutions—0.035 to 0.0035 per cent—to minimize the effects of interaction between the particles. The observed curves indicated the presence of several components, and this was in accord with electron

(224) H. Benoit, Thesis (University of Strasbourg, 1950); *Ann. phys.* **6**, 561 (1951).

microscope observations, which showed that particles of several lengths were present.   The prevailing length was in the neighborhood of 2800 A.; and Benoit's analysis of his measurements, at temperatures of 15–18°, indicated that the rotary diffusion coefficient of the main component was very nearly 550 sec.$^{-1}$, a value in close accord with that to be expected for a rod 2800 by 150 A.

The study of the curves for the development of birefringence led to the rather surprising result that no evidence could be found for a permanent dipole moment of the virus particle.   The data could be described on the assumption that the development of birefringence was due entirely to the moment induced by the field.

Benoit has also applied this beautiful method to the sodium salt of thymonucleic acid and to vanadium pentoxide particles, but it has not yet been applied to other proteins.   It should be mentioned also that Lauffer[225] in 1939 studied the birefringence of tobacco mosaic virus in an electric field (Kerr effect), but his measurements were not adapted for the determination of rotary diffusion coefficients.

XVII. Double Refraction of Flow: Its Relation to Rotary Diffusion and to Molecular Size and Shape

Instead of orienting the molecules by an electric field, one may apply a mechanical shearing force to orient them, if they are asymmetrical in shape.   This is most readily achieved by applying a velocity gradient. The most widely used experimental technique is to place the liquid containing the molecules between two concentric cylinders, one of which is rotated while the other is held fixed.   If the field between the cylinders is observed between crossed polarizers, with light traveling parallel to the cylinder axes, the flowing liquid appears optically like a uniaxial spherocrystal (Fig. 19).   The field is bright, except for four dark regions spaced like the arms of a cross (the "cross of isocline").   In these regions the optic axis of the solution is parallel to the plane of vibration of the light transmitted by either the polarizer or the analyzer.   It is found experimentally that at very low velocity gradients the arms of the cross bisect these planes at 45°.   As the gradient is increased, the position of the cross shifts, and at very high gradients approaches coincidence with the planes of vibration.   The smaller of the two angles between these planes and an adjoining arm of the dark cross is known as the extinction angle, χ, which thus tends from a value of 45° at very low gradients to 0° at very high gradients.   At values near 45°, χ is a nearly linear function of the velocity gradient G, and the increment $-d\chi/dG$ increases very rapidly with increase in the major axis of the asymmetric particle being

(225) M. A. Lauffer, *J. Am. Chem. Soc.* **61**, 2412 (1939).

studied. At higher gradients, the χ–G curve of course becomes flatter, but the gradient required to achieve a given χ value is always much smaller for a long particle than for a short one.

It follows from the above definition, that χ is the angle between the streamlines and the optic axis in the flowing liquid—this axis being so defined as to be always between 45 and 0°, relative to the streamlines. The refractive index for light vibrating with the electrical vector parallel to this axis is denoted by n_e; for light vibrating perpendicular to it, by n_0. The sign and magnitude of the double refraction is given by the value of $n_e - n_0$. In general, $n_e - n_0$ is a nearly linear function of G when χ is near 45°, and approaches a limiting saturation value as χ approaches 0°.

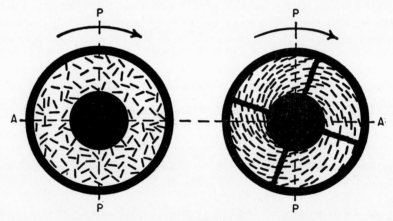

FIG. 19. Orientation of particles in a doubly refractive fluid placed between concentric cylinders. From von Muralt and Edsall.[241]

Qualitatively these phenomena can be explained as follows. The velocity gradient tends to rotate the molecules in the streaming liquid. If the major axis of one of the molecules lies across the streamlines, the torque produced by the flowing liquid tends to turn the molecule toward the direction in which its long axis lies parallel with the streamlines. The rotation of the molecule due to streaming, however, is very slow if the long axis already lies parallel to the streamlines. The effect of streaming alone, therefore, is to bring the molecules into a favored orientation in which their long axes point chiefly in this direction. This effect, however, is opposed by the rotary Brownian movement, the intensity of which, for a prolate ellipsoid, is characterized by the rotary diffusion coefficient Θ_b, defined in Eq. (118). As a good approximation, one may say that χ represents the angle, relative to the streamlines, at which the maximum value of the resulting distribution function F occurs for a given gradient G. This maximum is very small, and lies at 45° to the streamlines at very low gradients; it tends to a limiting value, parallel to the streamlines ($\chi = 0°$) at very high gradients.   The value of $n_e - n_0$, on the other hand, is correlated with the steepness of the maximum in the distribution function F; it is therefore very small at very low gradients, and levels off to a limiting saturation value at very high gradients.

The fundamental treatment of the problem, for thin rod-shaped particles, was first given by Boeder.[226]   A more general theory, applicable to rigid ellipsoids of any axial ratio, was developed by Peterlin and Stuart[227,228] and independently by Snellman and Björnståhl.[229]   A general review of the field of induced double refraction has been given by Peterlin and Stuart;[230] two reviews of the fundamentals of double refraction of flow (streaming birefringence) were published[231,232] in 1942 and 1943.   Recently a comprehensive review of more recent developments in the field has been given by Cerf and Scheraga.[233]   The latter authors have considered in detail both the theory for rigid ellipsoidal particles, which is now well developed, and the more difficult problem of the behavior of flexible molecules in a velocity gradient.   In the present discussion only rigid molecules will be considered, since most of the native proteins appear to be fairly rigid structures.

The discussion will be restricted to molecules which can be described as ellipsoids of revolution.   We shall denote the semiaxis of revolution by a, the equatorial semiaxis by b.   The orientation of a molecule may thus be completely described by the orientation of the a-semiaxis; the frame of reference is shown in Fig. 20.   The center of the coordinate system is located in the center of gravity of the ellipsoid.   The velocity gradient in the liquid, indicated in Fig. 20, tends to rotate the molecule clockwise.   The orientation of the a-semiaxis of the molecule is specified by the angles θ and ϕ as defined in the figure and the accompanying legend.   The velocity gradient G (see Fig. 20) is equal to dV_x/dY; in a concentric cylinder apparatus, with an inner cylinder of radius R_1 and a very narrow gap of width d between the cylinders, G is given to a close approximation by the equation

$$G \cong R_1 \Omega / d \tag{123}$$

(226) P. Boeder, Z. Physik **75**, 258 (1932).

(227) A. Peterlin, Z. Physik **111**, 232 (1938).

(228) A. Peterlin and H. A. Stuart, Z. Physik **112**, 1, 129 (1939).

(229) O. Snellman and Y. Bjornstahl, Kolloid-Beih. **52**, 403 (1941).

(230) A. Peterlin and H. A. Stuart, Hand- und Jahrbuch der chem. Physik **8**, 1 (1943).

(231) J. T. Edsall, Advances in Colloid Sci. **1**, 269 (1942).

(232) J. T. Edsall, see Cohn and Edsall,[2] Chap. 21.

(233) R. Cerf and H. A. Scheraga, Chem. Revs. **51**, 185 (1952).   See also W. Kuhn, H. Kuhn, and P. Buchner, Ergeb. exakt. Naturw. **25**, 1 (1951).

where Ω is the angular velocity of the rotating cylinder.[234] More elaborate formulas are needed if d is not very small compared to R_1 (see for instance Edsall[231] for details).

Consider for simplicity only the molecules for which the a-axes lie in the XY-plane in Figs. 16 or 20. For a very thin rodlike molecule, the

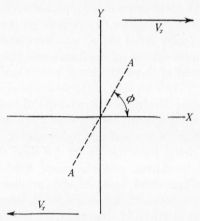

FIG. 20. Orientation of an ellipsoidal molecule in a flowing liquid of constant velocity gradient. The positive Z-axis points perpendicularly upward from the plane of the paper. The projection of the axis of revolution of the ellipsoid on the XY-plane is denoted by AA. The movement of the liquid is parallel to the X-axis, and is described by the equation $V_x = GY$, where V_x is the velocity and G is the velocity gradient. The significance of the angle ϕ is shown in the figure ($\phi = 90°$ when the axis of the ellipsoid lies in the YZ-plane). ϑ is the smaller of the two angles between the a-axis of the ellipsoid and the positive Z-axis. The origin is taken at the center of the ellipsoid. From Cohn and Edsall[2] (Chap. 21, p. 506).

effect of the streaming is to cause the molecule to rotate with an angular velocity ω:

$$\omega = d\phi/dt = -G \sin^2 \phi \qquad (124)$$

At any particular value of ϕ, denoted by ϕ_0, the rate at which molecules are streaming into the orientation ϕ_0 is given by the distribution function F [see Eq. (106)] for this orientation multiplied by the angular velocity ω. That is, this number is $(F\omega)_{\phi_0}$. The number of molecules streaming out of this orientation, at a neighboring angle $\phi_0 + d\phi$, is $(F\omega)_{\phi_0+d\phi}$. The difference of these two expressions gives the time rate of change of F, in the narrow range between ϕ_0 and $\phi_0 + d\phi$, due to the streaming:

$$(\partial F/\partial t)_{\text{streaming}} = -\partial(F\omega)/\partial\phi \qquad (125)$$

(234) Thus, for an apparatus developed in this laboratory (J. T. Edsall, C. G. Gordon, J. W. Mehl, H. Scheinberg, and D. W. Mann, *Rev. Sci. Instruments* **15**, 243 (1944), R is 2.5 cm. and d is 0.025 cm. For a speed of 1000 r.p.m., G is approximately 10,500/sec.

The total rate of change of F with t includes also the diffusion effect due to the Brownian movement, which is given by Eq. (107). Thus, making use of Eq. (124),

$$\partial F/\partial t = \Theta \frac{\partial^2 F}{\partial \phi^2} - \frac{\partial(F\omega)}{\partial \phi} = \Theta \frac{\partial^2 F}{\partial \phi^2} - G \frac{\partial(F \sin^2 \phi)}{\partial \phi} \qquad (126)$$

When the system has attained a steady state, we may set $\partial F/\partial t$ equal to zero. Also, we introduce the parameter $\alpha = G/\Theta$, which gives a measure of the relative strength of the orienting forces due to G and the disorienting forces due to the Brownian movement. Then Eq. (126) becomes:

$$\frac{\partial^2 F}{\partial \phi^2} + \alpha \frac{\partial(F \sin^2 \phi)}{\partial \phi} = 0 \qquad [(127)$$

An exact solution of this two-dimensional equation was obtained by Boeder.[226] In three dimensions the equation corresponding to Eq. (126) becomes [compare Eq. (108)]:

$$\frac{\partial F}{\partial t} = \Theta \nabla^2 F - \nabla \cdot (F\omega) = 0 \qquad (128)$$

where the operator $\nabla \cdot$ denotes the divergence of the function $F\omega$. In general the angular velocity ω due to the streaming depends on both the angles θ and ϕ; it also depends on the semiaxes a and b of the ellipsoid; the detailed form of the equations was derived by Jeffery.[235] The general solution for the distribution function F was given by Peterlin[227] for rigid ellipsoids, as a function of the parameter α and of the axial ratio a/b. From this function, Peterlin and Stuart[228] obtained a limiting formula for the extinction angle χ at low values of α. If χ be expressed in radians, then:

$$\chi = \frac{\pi}{4} - \frac{\alpha}{12}\left[1 - \frac{\alpha^2}{108}\left(1 + \frac{24p^2}{35}\right) + \cdots \right] \qquad (129)$$

Here $p = [a^2 - b^2]/[a^2 + b^2]$; hence $p = 1$ for an infinitely thin rod, zero for a sphere, and -1 for a flat disk. Equation (129) is valid for values of α up to about 1.5; it shows, in agreement with experiment, that χ tends to the limiting value of 45° ($\pi/4$ radians) as G (or α) approaches zero, and decreases as the gradient increases.

The double refraction, $n_e - n_0$, increases linearly with G (or α) at relatively low α values; it then gradually levels off and approaches a limiting value at very high α. The observed $n_e - n_0$ is the product of an optical factor, which depends on the refractive indices of the molecules and the medium, and an orientation factor f; the latter would become

(235) G. B. Jeffery, *Proc. Roy. Soc.* (London) **A102**, 161 (1922-3).

equal to unity if all the molecules were lined up with their major axes parallel. The optical factor has been discussed in detail by Peterlin and Stuart,[228] and does not concern us further here. The orientation factor, for low α values, is given by them as:

$$f = \frac{\alpha p}{15}\left(1 - \frac{\alpha^2}{72}\left[1 + \frac{6p^2}{35}\right] + \cdots\right) \tag{130}$$

Here p has the same meaning as in Eq. (129); note that even the limiting slope of the curve for f as a function of α depends on the axial ratio, through p; while the limiting slope for χ as a function of α is independent of axial ratio.

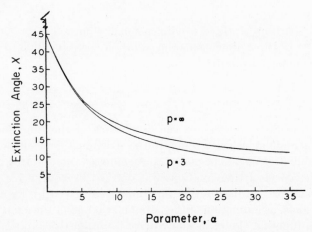

FIG. 21.   Extinction angle, χ, vs. parameter α together with its dependence on axial ratio, p.   From Scheraga et al.[236]

Recently, with the Mark I computer of the Harvard Computation Laboratory, it has been possible[236] to determine χ and f over a wide range of values of α, and for any axial ratio of the ellipsoid, by numerical evaluation of Peterlin and Stuart's solution of the fundamental equations. Figure 21 shows graphs of the curves obtained for χ, for axial ratios of 3 and infinity,[237] while Fig. 22 shows similar curves for f as a function of α. A very large number of data for other axial ratios were also tabulated.[236]

The procedure for determining rotary diffusion constants and molecular lengths from the experimental data is then quite simple. A rough

(236) H. A. Scheraga, J. T. Edsall, and J. O. Gadd, Jr., *J. Chem. Phys.* **19**, 1101 (1951).

(237) The curve for a prolate ellipsoid of axial ratio x is identical with that for an oblate ellipsoid of axial ratio $1/x$, if the appropriate value of Θ is used in each case for computing α.

estimate of the order of magnitude of the axial ratio a/b may be obtained from the frictional ratio f/f_0 (sec. XIII-3) or from viscosity measurements (sec. XVIII). Then, if the solution is monodispersed, a single measurement of χ fixes a corresponding value of α, from data such as those shown in Fig. 21. The parameter α is G/Θ; and G is known from the dimensions of the apparatus and the speed of the rotating cylinder. Hence the rotary diffusion coefficient Θ is directly given; knowing the temperature and the viscosity of the medium, and the axial ratio a/b, Eq. (118) can then be solved to obtain the semimajor axis $a.$; the length, l, of the molecule, is of course equal to $2a$, assuming the model of an ellipsoid of

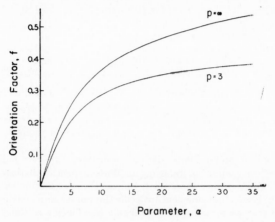

Fig. 22. Orientation factor, f, vs. parameter α together with its dependence on axial ratio, p. From Scheraga *et al.*[236]

revolution. The calculated value of the length is very insensitive to the assumed value of a/b. Further details of the procedure involved are given in several papers.[238] The dimensions so obtained for a number of proteins are listed in Table IX.

Clearly it is important in practice to measure χ at a considerable number of different values of G, and to compute α and Θ for each of these values. If the system is polydispersed with respect to length, it will generally be found that the calculated length decreases with increasing G; for at low gradients only the longest particles will be moderately well oriented, and the observed χ value will be determined primarily by them.

(238) J. F. Foster and J. T. Edsall, *J. Am. Chem. Soc.* **67,** 617 (1945); J. T. Edsall, J. F. Foster, and H. Scheinberg, *ibid.* **69,** 2731 (1947); J. T. Edsall and J. F. Foster, *ibid.* **70,** 1860 (1948). A useful nomogram for correlating χ with molecular length, for prolate and oblate ellipsoids, at various values of $G\eta$, has been published by H. A. Scheraga, *Arch. Biochem. and Biophys.* **33,** 277 (1951).

TABLE IX
DIMENSIONS OF CERTAIN PROTEIN MOLECULES FROM SEDIMENTATION AND DIFFUSION, VISCOSITY AND DOUBLE REFRACTION OF FLOW

Protein	Molecular weight(a)	a/b(b)	Length from f/f$_0$, A.	Length from double refraction of flow, A.(c)
Helix hemocyanin	8.9×10^6	8	1130	820
	4.3×10^6	7.5	820	890
	1×10^6	15	820	960
Horse antibody globulin	9×10^5	20	960	1280
Human fibrinogen	5×10^5	18	700	700
Bovine fibrinogen	4.4×10^5	18	(700)	670
Human serum γ-globulin	1.6×10^5	5	235	230
Human serum albumin	7×10^4	4	150	190
Zein	5×10^4	16	320	350

(a) Hemocyanin from Brohult(1); horse antibody globulin from Kabat(2); human blood proteins from Cohn *et al.* (3) and from Oncley, Scatchard, and Brown(4); bovine fibrinogen from Nanninga(5) and Koenig and Pedersen(6); zein, see Svedberg and Pedersen(7) or Cohn and Edsall(8); present revised value from Foster and Edsall(9).

(b) Values of a/b, and of length derived from them, are from sedimentation and diffusion, or viscosity, data as indicated in these papers. All these molecules are assumed to be prolate rather than oblate ellipsoids in calculating the lengths. The weight of the evidence is not sufficient to decide this point completely in all these cases, but does make the assumption highly probable (see Oncley in Cohn and Edsall(8), pp. 560–8).

(c) First four values from Snellman and Bjornstahl(10); human fibrinogen from Edsall, Foster, and Scheinberg(11); bovine fibrinogen from Hocking, Laskowski, and Scheraga(12); serum albumin and globulin from Edsall and Foster(13); zein from Foster and Edsall(9). The zein preparations studied were all polydisperse, containing some molecules of length greater than 400 A., and others probably shorter than 300 A. The value given, therefore, indicates only a number lying between these upper and lower limits.

(1) S. Brohult, *Nova Acta Regiae Soc. Sci. Upsaliensis* **12**, No. 4 (1940).

(2) E. A. Kabat, *J. Exptl. Med.* **69**, 103 (1939).

(3) E. J. Cohn, J. L. Oncley, L. E. Strong, W. L. Hughes, Jr., and S. H. Armstrong, Jr., *J. Clin. Invest.* **23**, 417 (1944).

(4) J. L. Oncley, G. Scatchard, and A. Brown, *J. Phys. & Colloid Chem.* **51**, 184 (1947).

(5) L. B. Nanninga, Thesis, University of Amsterdam, 1947; *Arch. néerl. physiol.* **28**, 241 (1946).

(6) V. L. Koenig and K. O. Pedersen, *Arch. Biochem.* **25**, 97 (1950).

(7) T. Svedberg and K. O. Pedersen, The Ultracentrifuge. Oxford Univ. Press, New York, 1940.

(8) E. J. Cohn and J. T. Edsall, Proteins, Amino Acids and Peptides. Reinhold Publishing Corporation, New York, 1943.

(9) J. F. Foster and J. T. Edsall, *J. Am. Chem. Soc.* **67**, 617 (1945).

(10) O. Snellman and Y. Björnstahl, *Kolloid-Beih.* **52**, 403 (1941).

As the gradient increases, the shorter particles also become oriented to a significant degree, and contribute increasingly to the total observed effect. Quantitative equations for double refraction of flow in poly-dispersed systems were given by Sadron.[239] These equations assume that the different components of the system orient independently and do not interact; their use also requires that values of χ and of $n_e - n_0$ be known, or assumed, as a function of G for the various components, in order to compute the behavior of the system as a whole.

Figure 23, taken from the recent work of Hocking, Laskowski, and Scheraga,[240] shows a comparison of the experimental data for bovine

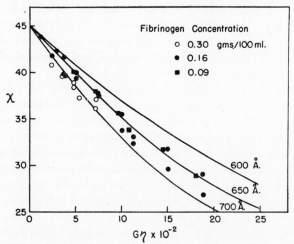

Fig. 23. Extinction angle, χ, as a function of $G\eta$ for several concentrations of bovine fibrinogen. The curves are theoretical ones for the lengths indicated. From Hocking *et al.*[240]

fibrinogen with the calculated curves for molecules of length 600, 650, and 700 A. The preparation appeared to consist of molecules fairly uniform with respect to length; the effect of concentration, however, showed that the orientation of the molecules was modified by interaction effects at the higher concentrations, as was already well known from studies on other proteins.[238]

(239) C. Sadron, *J. phys. radium* [7], **9**, 381, 384 (1938).

(240) C. S. Hocking, M. Laskowski, Jr., and H. A. Scheraga, *J. Am. Chem. Soc.* **74**, 775 (1952).

[References to Table IX (continued)]

(11) J. T. Edsall, J. F. Foster, and H. Scheinberg, *J. Am. Chem. Soc.* **69**, 2731 (1947).

(12) C. S. Hocking, M. Laskowski, and H. A. Scheraga, *J. Am. Chem. Soc.* **74**, 775 (1952).

(13) J. T. Edsall and J. F. Foster, *J. Am. Chem. Soc.* **70**, 1860 (1948).

For a given axial ratio, the rotary diffusion coefficient of a prolate ellipsoid varies inversely as the cube of the length [Eq. (118)]. Hence the method of double refraction of flow becomes inapplicable to molecules that are shorter than about 200 A.; the study of shorter molecules would generally require velocity gradients so large that the flow of the liquid might become turbulent, and in any case the heat generated in the liquid to maintain the viscous flow becomes a serious disturbing factor. The value for serum albumin, recorded in Table IX, represents something approaching a lower limit for the range of dimensions that can be studied by this method. In this case the studies were made in glycerol–water mixtures of very high viscosity in order to achieve appreciable orientation of such very short molecules, and the result is certainly not very accurate. For such molecules, and for those still smaller, the method of dielectric dispersion (sec. XIX), when it can be applied, is the method of choice for obtaining rotary diffusion coefficients.

For highly elongated molecules, however, double refraction of flow is a powerful method of study. It was the first method to reveal the high asymmetry of what is now known as actomyosin of muscle,[241] and to demonstrate the breakdown of the actomyosin threads by various reagents,[242] and the effects of adenosine triphosphate upon actomyosin in solution.[243] The method has also been used more recently to study the effects of molecular unfolding and aggregation in the denaturation of ovalbumin[244,245] and of bovine serum albumin.[246] It has been used as an important tool in studies on the length distribution of tobacco mosaic virus particles,[247] and in the study of the elongated intermediates which are formed during the conversion of fibrinogen to fibrin.[248]

XVIII. Viscosity in Relation to Molecular Shape

1. STUDIES WHEN THE MOLECULAR AXES ARE DISTRIBUTED AT RANDOM

It has long been known that the viscosity of a liquid made up only of small molecules is increased by the addition of larger molecules. At a

(241) A. L. von Muralt and J. T. Edsall, *J. Biol. Chem.* **89**, 315, 351 (1930).
(242) J. T. Edsall and J. W. Mehl, *J. Biol. Chem.* **133**, 409 (1940).
(243) A. S. C. Lawrence, J. Needham, *et al.*, *J. Gen. Physiol.* **27**, 201, 233, 355 (1944).
(244) E. Fredericq, *Bull. soc. chim. Belges* **56**, 223 (1947).
(245) J. F. Foster and E. G. Samsa, *J. Am. Chem. Soc.* **73**, 3187, 3190, 5388 (1951).
(246) M. Joly and E. Barbu, *Bull. soc. chim. biol.* **31**, 1642 (1949).
(247) M. Joly, *Biochim. et Biophys. Acta* **8**, 134, 245 (1952).
(248) J. F. Foster, E. G. Samsa, S. Shulman, and J. D. Ferry, *Arch. Biochem. and Biophys.* **34**, 417 (1951); H. A. Scheraga and J. K. Backus, *J. Am. Chem. Soc.* **74**, 1979 (1952).

given volume concentration, the effect on the viscosity is greater for very asymmetrical large molecules than it is for those which are spherical, or nearly so. The effect for spherical molecules was first theoretically treated by Einstein[249] in 1906.

To picture the general significance of the results obtained by Einstein and later investigators, it is helpful to consider the viscosity of a liquid in terms of the work required to maintain the viscous flow. If the viscosity of the liquid be η, and the velocity gradient being maintained within the liquid be G, then in a volume V of liquid the rate of expenditure of work (dW/dt) required to maintain the flow is:[250]

$$(dW/dt)/V = G^2\eta \tag{131}$$

The introduction of large particles, of any shape, into a flowing liquid distorts the streamlines in such a way that additional work is required to maintain the gradient. The effect is most readily calculated for spheres; in making the calculation, Einstein assumed that the spherical molecules were large compared with the molecules of the solvent, so that the latter could be treated in effect as a continuous medium. The spheres were also considered to be rigid and incompressible. At concentrations of only a few per cent by volume, the increase of viscosity was found to depend only on the volume fraction of the system occupied by the spheres. Denoting this volume fraction as Φ, Einstein's equation is:

$$\lim_{\Phi \to 0} [(\eta/\eta_0) - 1] = 2.5\Phi \tag{132}$$

Here η_0 is the viscosity of the pure solvent, and η that of the solution. This limiting equation is valid for values of Φ below 0.03 approximately. It is important to note that the absolute size of the spheres does not enter into the equation, as long as they are large compared with the molecules of the solvent; only the total volume fraction which they occupy is of importance.

For solutions of asymmetrical molecules, the situation is more complicated. The distortion of the lines of flow produced by an ellipsoidal molecule, for instance, varies with the orientation of the ellipsoid axes relative to the streamlines. This orientation, of course, is continually changing owing to the rotation of the molecule produced by the velocity gradient. At the same time, because of the rotary Brownian movement of the molecules, the gradient of the distribution function F produced by the streaming leads to a flow of the directions of the molecular axes back

(249) A. Einstein, *Ann. Physik* **19**, 289 (1906); *ibid.* **34**, 591, (1911).
(250) For a simple derivation of Eq. (131), see Robinson, J. R., *Proc. Roy. Soc.* (London) **A170**, 519 (1939).

toward a more random average distribution. Both these effects—we may call them the velocity gradient effect and the distribution gradient effect, respectively—involve added work which is needed to maintain the streaming of the liquid relative to the ellipsoidal molecules. Both effects, therefore, contribute to the viscosity. Earlier calculations of the effect of molecular shape on the viscosity, such as those of Burgers[251] and Peterlin[227] treated only the velocity gradient effect, and therefore yielded too low a viscosity increment for particles of a given shape. The importance of the distribution gradient effect appears to have been first explicitly pointed out by Kuhn and Kuhn,[252] although Simha[253] actually employed the complete equation in the calculation of viscosities at very low velocity gradients.

In any case, the effect of the dissolved molecules on the viscosity depends on the distribution of orientations of the molecular axes, as given by the distribution function F. The situation has already been treated in the discussion of double refraction of flow (sec. XVII) and the state of the system is characterized by the dimensionless constant $\alpha = G/\Theta$, that is, the ratio of the velocity gradient to the rotary diffusion coefficient. For small proteins, such as hemoglobin or serum albumin, the value of the latter coefficient, in water near 20°, is of the order of 10^6/sec., whereas the velocity gradients employed in ordinary capillary viscometers vary from a few hundred to a few thousand per second. Hence the value of α in such systems is very much less than unity, and the distribution of molecular axes may be regarded as almost completely random. Under such circumstances, the theory of Simha[253] is valid for ellipsoidal particles. In dilute solutions, Simha's equation is similar to that of Einstein in form, but with a variable coefficient ν replacing the factor 2.5 for spheres:

$$\lim_{\Phi \to 0} [(\eta/\eta_0) - 1] = \nu\Phi \qquad (133)$$

Equations for ν, as a function of axial ratio, were given by Simha; it is generally more convenient, however, to use numerical values derived from the equations, and these are listed in Table X, for both prolate and oblate ellipsoids. Equation (133), like (132), is valid only at rather low solute concentrations; the more asymmetrical the ellipsoid, the lower, in general, the concentration at which the effects of interactions between the solute molecules become significant. The limiting value of ν, however, depends only on the axial ratio of the ellipsoids, not on their molecu-

(251) J. M. Burgers, Second Report on Viscosity and Plasticity, *Proc. Amsterdam Acad. Sci.* (1st Sec.) [4], **16**, 113 (1938).

(252) W. Kuhn and H. Kuhn, *Helv. Chim. Acta* **28**, 97 (1945).

(253) R. Simha, *J. Phys. Chem.* **44**, 25 (1940).

lar size. A given value of ν corresponds to one particular value of the axial ratio if the ellipsoid is assumed to be prolate, and to another if it is assumed oblate. A choice between the prolate and the oblate shape cannot be made on the ground of viscosity measurements alone.

TABLE X

RELATION OF THE VISCOSITY INCREMENT ν TO AXIAL RATIO FOR ELLIPSOIDAL MOLECULES(a)

Axial ratio	Prolate	Oblate	Axial ratio	Prolate	Oblate
1 0	2.50	2.50	20	38.6	14.8
1.5	2.63	2.62	25	55.2	18.2
2.0	2.91	2.85	30	74.5	21.6
3.0	3.68	3.43	40	120.8	28.3
4.0	4.66	4.06	50	176.5	35.0
5.0	5.81	4.71	60	242.0	41.7
6.0	7.10	5.36	80	400.0	55.1
8.0	10.10	6.70	100	593.0	68.6
10.0	13.63	8.04	150	1222.0	102.3
12 0	17.76	9.39	200	2051.0	136.2
15 0	24.8	11.42	300	4278.0	204.1

(a) From J. W. Mehl, J. L. Oncley, and R. Simha, *Science* **92**, 132 (1940); this table is also given by Cohn and Edsall(2) p. 519.

The volume fraction, Φ, of solute, in Eqs. (132) and (133), refers to the *solvated* solute molecules, since these are the molecules which actually interact with the solvent in viscous flow. However, the exact degree of hydration is in general unknown, whereas the weight concentration of anhydrous protein in unit volume of solution can be determined by straightforward analytical procedures.[254] Hence it has become customary to define a quantity commonly termed the intrinsic viscosity, $[\eta]$, by the equation:[255]

$$[\eta] = [(\eta/\eta_0) - 1]/100c \qquad (134)$$

where c, as before, is the concentration in grams anhydrous protein/ml. For comparison with calculated values of ν and of ν',—see below—it is convenient to consider the quantity 100 $[\eta]$, rather than $[\eta]$ itself. What is of interest, of course, is the limiting value of $[\eta]$ as c approaches zero.

Likewise we can define the "volume fraction of anhydrous protein"

(254) There are, in fact, some difficulties in determining the dry weight of protein samples, because of their strong affinity for water. The uncertainty in dry-weight determinations, however, is very small compared to that involved in estimates of solvation for proteins in solution.

(255) E. O. Kraemer and W. D. Lansing, *J. Phys. Chem.* **39**, 153 (1935).

in the system, which is simply equal to $\bar{v}c$, and a corresponding viscosity coefficient, which we may denote as ν', defined by the equation:

$$\lim_{c \to 0} [(\eta/\eta_0) - 1]/\bar{v}c = \nu' \tag{135}$$

The coefficient ν', like $[\eta]$, is directly accessible to determination by experiment; it depends both on the solvation (hydration) and on the axial ratio of the particle. If 1 g. of protein combines with w grams of solvent, the density of the latter being ρ, then we may write for the ratio of the volume fraction of hydrated protein to that of the anhydrous protein:

$$\Phi/\bar{v}c = 1 + \frac{w}{\bar{v}\rho} = \nu'/\nu \tag{136}$$

the second equality in Eq. (136) follows directly from Eqs. (134) and (135). The relations shown in Eq. (136) depend upon the assumption that bound and free solvent have the same density. This cannot be exactly true, but is probably a reasonable approximation.

In making such viscosity studies, it is important to eliminate the electroviscous effects which arise if the protein carries a considerable net charge in a solution of low ionic strength. Such effects can generally be abolished by studying the protein in salt solution, at a concentration of 0.1–$0.2\ M$; under such conditions the viscosity increment, ν', is generally found to be independent of pH over the range in which the protein is stable.

The calculation of axial ratios from ν' is possible only if a hydration value for the protein is known or assumed. Oncley[3] has given a very useful contour chart, reproduced in Fig. 24, from which the range of possible values of axial ratio and hydration that are compatible with a given value of ν' may be immediately seen. Wyman and Ingalls[4] have given another type of nomogram from which the same information may be obtained; this has already been given in Fig. 15. The value of the nomograms of Wyman and Ingalls (see also Figs. 17 and 18) is largely in the simplication which they permit for a given protein in the simultaneous comparison of many different categories of experimental data relating to molecular size and shape.

Values of ν' and of $100\ [\eta]$ are listed for a number of proteins in Table XI. In view of our present knowledge concerning the water binding of proteins—see, for example, the data of Bull represented in Fig. 1—it can be taken as quite certain that all of these proteins are hydrated to the extent of at least 10 per cent ($w = 0.1$). Studies such as those of Perutz[176] on hemoglobin crystals suggest a higher figure, near 30 per cent ($w = 0.3$), and in some cases considerably greater values than this may be plausible. In Table XI, therefore, calculated axial ratios are given, for both prolate and oblate ellipsoids, for assumed values of w equal to 0.1 and 0.3. In some cases a definite choice between the prolate and oblate models can be made on other grounds. Thus the electron microscope studies on fibrinogen and tobacco mosaic virus recorded in Table III indicate clearly that these molecules are rod-shaped, and therefore that the prolate model is the appropriate one to use. For

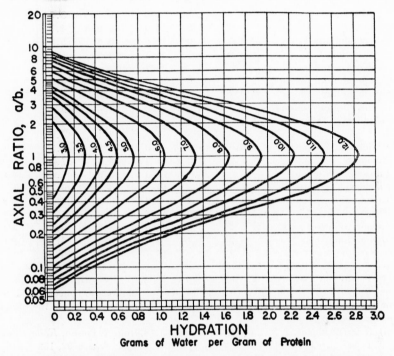

FIG. 24. Values of axial ratio and hydration in accord with various viscosity coefficients (contour lines denote $(\eta/\eta_0 - 1)1000/vc$ values). From Oncley.[3]

hemoglobin, the latest studies of Bragg and Perutz[176a] indicate a molecular shape which is not far from spherical, the dimensions of the molecule being approximately $65 \times 55 \times 55$ A. Hence the axial ratio is slightly less than 1.2. The viscosity data indeed suggest a rather higher axial ratio for hemoglobin than is compatible with the x-ray studies; but in view of the discrepancy between the two values of v' for hemoglobin recorded in the table, the subject would appear to call for reinvestigation. Perhaps, also, even the value of $w = 0.3$ represents too low a figure for hydration; if a higher value were assumed, it would of course reduce the calculated axial ratio. Oncley, Scatchard, and Brown[179] obtained an

TABLE XI
Intrinsic Viscosities, Viscosity Increments, and Calculated Axial
Ratios for Certain Proteins
Proteins in this table are arranged in order of increasing molecular weight

Protein	100 [η]	ν′	a/b prolate		a/b oblate	
			w = 0.1	w = 0.3	w = 0.1	w = 0.3
1. Myoglobin	3.1	4.2	3.0	2.1	3.5	2.3
2. Pepsin	3.9	5.2	4.0	3.0	4.9	3.5
3. β-Lactoglobulin	4.5	6.0	4.6	3.6	5.6	4.3
4. Ovalbumin	4.3	5.7	4.4	3.3	5.5	4.0
5. Tropomyosin(a)	52.	74.	28.	24.	94.	76.
6. Serum albumin (horse?)	4.9	6.5	4.9	4.0	6.2	4.9
7. Serum albumin (horse)	6.2	8.2	6.0	5.0	8.8	6.3
8. Serum albumin (human)	4.2	5.6	4.2	3.3	5.4	4.0
9. Hemoglobin (horse)	3.6	4.7	3.5	2.5	4.2	2.8
10. Hemoglobin (horse)	4.0	5.3	4.1	3.1	5.0	3.5
11. γ-Globulin (human)	6.0	8.1	6.0	5.0	8.3	6.8
12. Amandin	5.25	7.0	5.4	4.3	7.3	5.4
13. Fibrinogen (human)	25.	35.	17.5	15.0	44.	26.
14. Fibrinogen (bovine)	27.	37.	19.	16.	46.	36.
15. Hemocyanin (homarus)	4.7	6.4	4.8	3.9	6.1	4.8
16. Thyroglobulin	7.1	9.9	7.1	5.9	11.1	8.4
17. Hemocyanin (octopus)	6.7	9.0	6.6	5.5	9.8	7.4
18. Hemocyanin (helix)	5.2	6.4	4.8	3.9	6.1	4.8
19. Tobacco mosaic virus	28.	39.	18.	16.	56.	40.

(a) The intrinsic viscosity of tropomyosin varies markedly with the conditions of the experiment. The value given here is for neutral solutions in concentrated urea or for acid solutions at pH 2.1. For details of data in other solvents the original paper must be consulted.

(b) References Nos. 2, 3, 4, 6, 10, 12, 15, 16, 17, 18, from A. Polson, *Kolloid-Z.* **88**, 51 (1939); see also J. W. Mehl, J. L. Oncley, and R. Simha, *Science* **92**, 132 (1940).

No. 1 from J. Wyman and E. N. Ingalls, *J. Biol. Chem.* **147**, 297 (1943).

No. 5 from T.-C. Tsao, K. Bailey, and G. S. Adair, *Biochem. J.* **49**, 27 (1951).

No. 7 from K. R. Fahey and A. A. Green, *J. Am. Chem. Soc.* **60**, 3039 (1938).

Nos. 8, 11, and 13, from J. L. Oncley, G. Scatchard, and A. Brown, *J. Phys. & Colloid Chem.* **51**, 184 (1947).

No. 9 from E. J. Cohn and A. M. Prentiss, *J. Gen. Physiol.* **8**, 619 (1927).

No. 14 from L. Nanninga, *Arch. néerl. physiol.* **28**, 241 (1947).

No. 19 from M. A. Lauffer, *J. Am. Chem. Soc.* **66**, 1188 (1944).

intrinsic viscosity of 0.041 for the β-lipoprotein of human blood plasma, which corresponds to ν′ = 4.3, since this molecule has a partial specific volume of 0.95. They concluded that this and the other data on this protein were best explained by taking the molecule to be approximately spherical, with hydration, w, equal to 0.6 or slightly greater. However it seems unlikely that any of the proteins listed in Table XI is as nearly spherical as the β-lipoprotein appears to be.   It should be noted, however, that the axial ratios calculated from viscosity measurements are the axial ratios of the hydrated proteins; for these are the molecules which are actually being studied in such dynamic measurements.   The shape of the anhydrous protein cannot be obtained directly from measurements which involve the translational or rotary motion of the molecules in solution; the information derived from such studies tells us only about the solvated protein.

2. EFFECTS OF MOLECULAR ORIENTATION ON VISCOSITY; NON-NEWTONIAN FLOW

All the molecules listed in Table XI were studied in capillary viscometers, at velocity gradients sufficiently low to permit the assumption that orientation due to flow was negligible.   This assumption was not strictly true in the case of tobacco mosaic virus, but Lauffer[189] advanced good reasons for believing that the amount of orientation was very small even in this case.   However, for very elongated structures, such as actomyosin, considerable orientation occurs even at low gradients.   In such cases, when the parameter α becomes of the order of unity or higher, the measured viscosity depends significantly on the gradient.   The viscosity in such systems is always found to decrease as the gradient increases, but appears to level off toward a constant limiting value as the gradient—that is, the value of α—becomes very large.   Such systems are said to be non-Newtonian, since they do not conform to Newton's original definition of viscosity, which clearly implies that the viscosity coefficient is independent of the gradient.   The viscosity increment ν' should then be a function of α and of the axial ratio, and the variation of ν' with α should show a general correlation with the variation of the extinction angle as observed in studies of double refraction of flow.

Viscosity which varies with the velocity gradient is sometimes referred to as structural viscosity; this is an appropriate term to denote what is observed in fairly concentrated solutions, where the molecules interact strongly and may become entangled with one another, the entanglements then being broken more and more as the gradient increases.   However, the phenomenon with which we are here concerned persists even down to infinite dilution, since it depends on the orientation of the individual molecule in the field of flow.   It seems more appropriate, therefore, to denote it as non-Newtonian viscosity.

For adequate study of such phenomena, capillary viscometers are unsatisfactory; the velocity gradient in a capillary varies over a wide range, from zero at the center to a maximum value at the walls. The concentric cylinder type of viscometer, of the general type which commonly bears the name of Couette, is far better suited for such studies.[256] Studies in a capillary viscometer at varying rates of flow can indeed reveal evidence that flow is non-Newtonian, as in the measurements of Edsall and Mehl[242] on actomyosin. The Couette type of viscometer, however, not only can be used to give a well-defined velocity gradient, but also can operate at extremely low gradients, considerably below 1/sec. if necessary, which is very important for studies on highly elongated molecules. Such studies have been carried out on a highly aggregated preparation of tobacco mosaic virus by Robinson[250] and on actomyosin systems by Needham, Lawrence, and their associates.[243] However, studies by this method on solutions of monodispersed, well-defined, highly asymmetrical proteins do not yet appear to have been carried out. Thus for purified myosin, free of actin, Weber and Portzehl[257] find an intrinsic viscosity near 0.22 at gradients near 1000/sec., and do not note much increase in viscosity at lower gradients. This value would suggest an axial ratio in the neighborhood of 15 to 1, slightly less than that of fibrinogen; yet studies of sedimentation, diffusion, osmotic pressure, and light scattering indicate a far higher axial ratio for myosin, near 100 to 1 (secs. VII and VIII). Perhaps the myosin molecule is too flexible to permit application of the theory for a rigid ellipsoid; but it is probably unwise to speculate on this point until viscosity studies at extremely low velocity gradients have been carried out.

A quantitative theory of viscosity as a function of velocity gradient for ellipsoidal particles is now being developed. It rests on the use of the distribution function derived by Peterlin,[227] with the formulation of the viscosity problem in terms of this distribution along the lines first explicitly stated by Kuhn and Kuhn,[252] and later developed with more precision by Kirkwood and his associates[258] and by Saito.[259] It appears, indeed, that this problem has now been fundamentally solved, although there are still computational problems to be overcome before precise numerical values of ν can be given as a function of velocity gradient and axial ratio.

(256) Concerning methods of measuring viscosity, see for instance E. Hatschek, The Viscosity of Liquids, van Nostrand, New York, 1928; and Alexander and Johnson,[5a] Chap. XIII. The latter reference also gives considerable discussion of viscosity in solutions of large molecules.
(257) H. H. Weber and H. Portzehl, Advances in Protein Chem. 7, 161 (1952); see especially p. 207 and Fig. 25 on p. 215.
(258) J. G. Kirkwood and J. Riseman, J. Chem. Phys. 16, 565 (1948); 17, 442 (1949); 18, 512 (1950); and especially J. G. Kirkwood and P. L. Auer, ibid. 19, 281 (1951).
(259) N. Saito, J. Phys. Soc. Japan 6, 302 (1951).

When this is achieved, it should provide a powerful new tool for the study of highly asymmetrical molecules.

3. The Use of "Equivalent Ellipsoids" in Interpreting the Hydrodynamic Properties of Protein Molecules

Recently a new approach to the analysis of the hydrodynamic properties of proteins has been proposed by Scheraga and Mandelkern.[259a] They reject the assumption, contained, for instance, in Eq. (91) of this chapter, that the molecular volume of the solvated protein can be expressed as the sum of two terms $(M\bar{v} + Mw/\rho)/N$, and the further implied view that the volume so formulated is equal to the hydrodynamically effective volume, V_e, of the protein when in motion relative to the liquid. As they point out, this assumption "neglects possible flow of solvent through the domain (of the protein molecule), deviations of the shape of the domain from that of an ellipsoid of revolution, deformation of the domain by the hydrodynamic forces, selective adsorption from mixed solvent, electrostriction, and similar effects." They hold that Eq. (91) involves an incorrect interpretation of $\bar{v}$ as the specific volume of anhydrous protein, and of w as the amount of water bound to the protein. It is, of course, clear, from the discussion in sec. III, that the partial specific volume is the rate of increase of the volume of the solution per unit mass of anhydrous protein added; to set this quantity equal to the reciprocal of the density of the anhydrous protein involves additional special assumptions, which are quite independent of the experimental measurement of $\bar{v}$.

Scheraga and Mandelkern propose to interpret observed physical properties of the protein, such as frictional ratio, sedimentation or diffusion coefficient, and intrinsic viscosity in terms of a rigid "equivalent ellipsoid of revolution," characterized by its effective volume, V_e, and its axial ratio a/b. The size and shape of this equivalent ellipsoid are not necessarily closely related to the size and shape of the actual molecule; if the actual molecule deviates greatly in shape from an ellipsoid of revolution, or if any of the factors cited above are of appreciable significance, the geometry of the molecule may be quite different from that of the equivalent ellipsoid. The values of V_e and a/b for the latter are determined by the condition that they must give the observed values of the physical constants of the actual protein. Thus the frictional ratio, f/f_0, of the equivalent ellipsoid (where f_0 is the frictional coefficient of a sphere of the same effective volume, V_e, as that of the equivalent ellipsoid) is given by Eq. (92) or (93), and is a function only of the axial ratio of this

(259a) H. A. Scheraga and L. Mandelkern, *J. Am. Chem. Soc.* **75**, 179 (1953). Closely similar ideas were advanced much earlier by C. Sadron; for an important recent review see ref. 5b, especially pp. 254–260, inclusive.

ellipsoid. The viscosity increment, ν (see Eq. 133), of the ellipsoid is given as a function of a/b by the relations derived by Simha and listed numerically in Table X. Calculation of the properties of the equivalent ellipsoid from the experimental data could be carried out graphically, by methods similar to those illustrated in Figs. 13, 15, 17, 18, and 24. In the formulation of Scheraga and Mandelkern, however, it is simpler to determine the relation by an analytical method. They evaluated a function denoted as β, from the sedimentation constant, s, the molecular weight, M, the intrinsic viscosity, $[\eta]$, the partial specific volume, $\bar{v}$, and the viscosity of the solvent, η. The diffusion coefficient, D, may, of course, be used to evaluate β, instead of s and $\bar{v}$ (see Eqs. 89 and 99).

$$\beta \equiv Ns[\eta]^{\frac{1}{3}}\eta/M^{\frac{2}{3}}(1 - \bar{v}\rho) = D[\eta]^{\frac{1}{3}}M^{\frac{1}{3}}\eta/kT = \gamma F\nu^{\frac{1}{3}}$$

Here $\gamma = N^{\frac{1}{3}}/(16200\pi^2)^{\frac{1}{3}}$, F is the reciprocal frictional ratio f_0/f, and the other terms have meanings already given. Since F and ν are functions only of the axial ratio a/b, and γ is a constant, β is a function only of axial ratio, which has been tabulated by Scheraga and Mandelkern. Once the axial ratio is determined, the effective hydrodynamic volume, V_e, is obtainable from the equation

$$V_e = (fF)^3/162\pi^2\eta^3 = 100M[\eta]/N\nu$$

The value of β for a sphere is 2.12×10^6. For oblate ellipsoids of any axial ratio up to 300, β varies only from 2.12 to 2.15×10^6. For prolate ellipsoids, however, β increases rapidly with axial ratio, from 2.12×10^6 when $a/b = 1$, to 3.22×10^6 when $a/b = 100$. This provides a basis for distinguishing prolate from oblate equivalent ellipsoids.

It must be noted that the value of the axial ratio obtainable from β is extremely sensitive to errors in the experimental data; only when the data are known with high precision is it profitable to calculate the size and shape of an equivalent ellipsoid. Scheraga and Mandelkern have also defined another quantity, denoted as δ, which is a function of the molecular weight, the rotary diffusion coefficient, the intrinsic viscosity, the viscosity of the medium, and the temperature. This function, like β, depends only on the axial ratio of the equivalent ellipsoid; however, the axial ratio calculated from δ is also extremely sensitive to small errors in the experimental data..

Since this analytical approach is still new, the full significance of its applications is yet to be determined. Other hydrodynamic methods of study provide independent information concerning size and shape of an equivalent ellipsoid. For instance, two distinct relaxation times τ_1 and τ_2 may be found for a molecule by the method of dielectric dispersion (sec. XIX). These are, of course, equivalent to two rotary diffusion coefficients, as may be seen by examining Eqs. (112) to (121b) inclusive.[259b] If the two relaxation times differ markedly, this is strong evidence that the shape of the equivalent ellipsoid in solution is prolate rather than oblate (pp. 673–75).   The ratio τ_1/τ_2 gives a measure of the axial ratio of the equivalent ellipsoid, and the absolute values of τ_1 and τ_2 give its volume (V_e).   The equivalent ellipsoid so calculated may be compared with the equivalent ellipsoid as calculated from the functions β or δ.   If there is good agreement between the two, this provides confidence in the description of the molecule in terms of an equivalent ellipsoid.   If there are marked discrepancies, this suggests—assuming the reliability of the experimental data and the purity of the protein preparation—that the concept of an equivalent ellipsoid is not the best representation of the hydrodynamic properties of the protein under study.   If it *were* possible to determine the actual molecular configuration, a comparison of the latter with the equivalent ellipsoid would give some indication of the possible importance of permeation by the solvent or other factors which may exert a modifying influence on the size and shape of the molecule in solution.

Independent evidence may be employed to limit the range of possible configurations that might be found compatible with the analysis of Scheraga and Mandelkern.   If, for instance, the calculated value of V_e were several times as great as the "anhydrous molecular volume," $M\bar{v}/N$, this would require that the molecule must be much swollen by imbibition of solvent.   Such a configuration might occur, for instance, in a solution of a denatured protein in concentrated urea, since the urea molecules probably tend to form strong hydrogen bonds with the peptide linkages, and thereby to separate the coiled peptide chains of the native protein from one another, giving a rather loose and open configuration, in which large volumes of solvent may be enmeshed.   This problem is discussed in more detail in Chap. 9.

The structure of native proteins, although it may involve some internal as well as external hydration, is certainly more compact than this.   Estimates of the magnitude of the domain occupied by the protein molecule may be obtained from the radii of gyration and approximate axial ratios derived from low angle x-ray scattering (sec. X) making due allowance for the fact that this method probably does not detect *external* hydration.   The packing of the molecules in the unit cells of wet protein crystals (Chap. 4) provides what is probably the most decisive evidence

(259b) This discussion assumes the validity of interpreting the relaxation times in terms of the orientation of the molecule as a rigid unit, in the electric field. The theory of Kirkwood and Shumaker,[275b] discussed in sec. XIX, if it becomes established, may involve some revisions of these concepts.

concerning size and shape, for the few protein crystals which have been studied intensively, and this evidence appears to be incompatible with anything but a rather compact structure for such molecules as hemoglobin, serum albumin, or β-lactoglobulin.

In short, the total weight of the evidence concerning size and shape, by all available methods, must be considered. If different methods give seemingly incompatible results, this may be due to inaccuracy of the experimental data, to impurities in the protein preparations studied, or to the introduction of illegitimate assumptions into the analysis of the data, from which conclusions are drawn that are not inherent in the experimental evidence.

XIX. Dielectric Constants of Proteins, Amino Acids and Peptides: Their Relation to Dipole Moments, Rotary Diffusion Coefficients and Relaxation Times

1. INTRODUCTORY CONSIDERATIONS

Proteins, amino acids, and peptides carry positively and negatively charged ionic groups, which give to the whole molecule an extremely polar character, even when the pH is so adjusted that the net charge is zero, and the molecule is therefore isoelectric. This polar character is most directly manifested in studies of the dielectric constants of such solutions. Qualitatively, a high dielectric constant reflects the presence of highly polar molecules in the system; some of the quantitative relations involved are discussed below. The measurement of the dielectric constant of any medium is generally carried out by measuring the capacitance of a condenser containing the medium in question between the plates. The electric field applied across the plates leads to orientation of polar molecules, and hence to an increase in the capacitance of the condenser. If the orientation takes place in a static or very slowly alternating field, the time taken by the molecules to orient themselves after the field is applied has no effect on the measured dielectric constant. If, however, the field is alternating very rapidly, the molecules turn so slowly compared with the period of alternation that they follow the field only with an appreciable lag. At still higher frequencies, the molecules fail to follow the field at all; this is true for all molecules at the very high frequencies of visible light, only the very mobile electrons being capable of moving back and forth at such frequencies. Thus, if the dielectric constant of a system of polar molecules is studied over a range of frequencies, it will be found to be relatively high at low frequencies; over a certain critical range characteristic of the molecule the dielectric constant decreases as the frequency increases. The larger and more asymmetrical the molecule, the lower the frequency range in which this transition occurs. This critical frequency is directly proportional to the rotary diffusion coefficient of the molecule and inversely proportional to its relaxation time. This phenomenon of dielectric dispersion—that is, the variation of dielectric constant with frequency—has provided more information than any other method concerning rotary diffusion coefficients. It has been the convention among workers in this field to express their results in terms of relaxation times, and we shall follow this practice here. The transformation from relaxation times (τ) to rotary diffusion coefficients (Θ) is readily carried out, using the simple reciprocal relations given in Eqs. (112–121) inclusive.

Dielectric dispersion studies have been used to cover a very wide range of relaxation times. Studies on proteins, expressed as τ values in water at 25°, have covered the range from about 10^{-8} sec. for insulin to about 250×10^{-8} sec. for horse serum γ-pseudoglobulin. A number of peptides and amino acids have also been studied, with relaxation times in the range between 10^{-9} and 10^{-11} sec. The method of double refraction of flow, on the other hand, is best suited for the study of rather long relaxation times, from 1 sec. or even more down to about 10^{-4} sec. Molecules with somewhat shorter relaxation times in water can, however, be studied by double refraction of flow if they are dissolved in highly viscous solvents, such as glycerol–water mixtures.

Dielectric dispersion methods have the advantage that they can determine two different relaxation times if the molecule is asymmetric, one related to the turning of the long, the other of the short axis. If both relaxation times are indeed to be detected, it is a necessary condition that the molecule should possess components of dipole moment along both axes. Experimentally the method is limited by the fact that dielectric-constant measurements can be carried out only in solutions of fairly low conductivity, the disturbances due to conductivity being especially great at low frequencies. Thus euglobulins, if they are soluble only in salt solutions at the isoelectric point, cannot be studied by this method. However, β-lactoglobulin, for instance, is soluble in solutions of dipolar ions such as glycine, a fact which has made this important protein amenable to study by the dielectric method.

Studies of dielectric constant have been of the greatest importance in our understanding of the dipolar-ion structure of amino acids and peptides; an excellent review of many of the major developments in this field has been given by Wyman.[260] The application to proteins of the

(260) J. Wyman, Jr., *Chem. Revs.* **19**, 213 (1936).

method of dielectric dispersion has been primarily due to Oncley, who has discussed the major results in three valuable reviews.[261-263]

The possibility of making use of dielectric measurements for the study of relaxation times is largely dependent on the highly polar nature of amino acids, peptides, and proteins. We must therefore discuss briefly the relation between dielectric constant and dipole moment in polar liquids, the discussion being for the moment restricted to static fields, or fields of frequency small compared to the rotary diffusion constants of the molecules.

2. DIPOLE MOMENTS AND DIELECTRIC INCREMENTS OF AMINO ACIDS, PEPTIDES AND PROTEINS

Dielectric constants of solutions of amino acids, peptides, and proteins always are higher than those of the pure solvent, ϵ_s, even when the solvent is a liquid as polar as water, provided the measurements are made at sufficiently low frequencies. In dilute solution the dielectric constant ϵ is a linear function of the solute concentration, C, and this equation is

$$\epsilon = \epsilon_s + \delta C \qquad (137)$$

frequently valid up to C values of several moles per liter. The dielectric increment δ is a function of the polarity of the solute; for amino acids and peptides it is nearly a linear function of the number of atoms in the chain separating the charged —NH_3^+ and COO— groups. Some typical dielectric increment values are given for amino acids and peptides in Table XII, and for proteins in Table XIII.

Qualitatively, it is clear that the δ values are correlated with the dipole moments of the solute molecules. For α-amino acids, electric moments may be approximately estimated on the assumption that a charge $+e$ ($e = 4.8 \times 10^{-10}$ e.s.u.) is concentrated at the nitrogen atom of the —NH_3^+ group, and a charge $-e$ is located midway between the two oxygens of the COO$^-$ group. Consideration of a space model of an α-amino acid (see Cohn and Edsall,[2] Chaps. 6 and 14) indicates that the distance between the two charges is very nearly 3 A., giving a moment of $3 \times 4.8 \times 10^{-18} = 14.4 \times 10^{-18}$ e.s.u. = 14.4 Debye units.

Dipole moments may also be derived from the dielectric-constant data themselves. Since amino acids and proteins are soluble only in polar solvents, the treatment which is applicable to dilute solutions of polar molecules in a nonpolar medium cannot be applied here. How-

(261) J. L. Oncley, J. Phys. Chem. **44**, 1103 (1940).
(262) J. L. Oncley, Chem. Revs. **30**, 433 (1942).
(263) J. L. Oncley, in Cohn and Edsall,[2] Chap. 22.

ever, the general theory of polar liquids developed by Onsager[264] and Kirkwood[265] (see also Kirkwood in Cohn and Edsall,[2] Chap. 12), can be applied. According to Kirkwood the dipole moment (μ) of an individual molecule in the liquid is in general different from its moment in the gaseous state (μ_0) since the attractions of neighboring polar molecules alter its configuration. Conversely, the neighbors of any given molecule

TABLE XII

DIPOLE MOMENTS AND RELAXATION TIMES OF AMINO ACIDS AND PEPTIDES

Values of δ from the more extensive tables given by Wyman(1) and Edsall(2). See also Conner, Clarke, and Smyth(3). Values of moment calculated from δ values by equation in Ref. (4). Relaxation times from Bateman and Potapenko(5), Conner and Smyth(6), and Marcy and Wyman(7). See also Oncley(8).

Substance	Dielectric increment, δ	Dipole moment, in Debye units	Relaxation time, $\tau_{H_2O} \times 10^{11}$	Calculated for rigid sphere, $\tau_0 \times 10^{11}$
Glycine	23	15.5	4.9	6.2
α-Alanine	23	15.5	6.4	7.9
β-Alanine	35	19.5	6.7	7.9
ϵ-Aminocaproic acid	77	28.9	12.9	13.2
Glycylglycine	70	27.6	11.4	10.1
Triglycine	113	35.1	18.1	14.0
Tetraglycine	159	41.6	24.7	17.0
Pentaglycine	213	48.4	36.3	21.9
Hexaglycine	234	50.0	—	—
Lysylglutamic acid	345	61.3	48	22.8

(1) J. Wyman, Jr., *Chem. Revs.* **19**, 213 (1936).
(2) E. J. Cohn and J. T. Edsall, Proteins, Amino Acids and Peptides, Reinhold Publishing Corporation, New York, 1943, Chap. 6.
(3) W. P. Conner, R. P. Clarke, and C. P. Smyth, *J. Am. Chem. Soc.* **64**, 1379 (1942).
(4) H. Gutfreund, *Biochem. J.* **42**, 544 (1948).
(5) J. B. Bateman and G. Potapenko, *Phys. Rev.* **57**, 1185 (1940).
(6) W. P. Conner and C. P. Smyth, *J. Am. Chem. Soc.* **64**, 1870 (1942).
(7) H. O. Marcy and J. Wyman, Jr., *J. Am. Chem. Soc.* **63**, 3388 (1941).
(8) J. L. Oncley, Chap. 22 of Ref. 2, p. 543.

are affected by it; their orientation with respect to its electric moment is generally not random, because electrostatic forces and steric factors prevent them from rotating freely. This tendency for the molecules to interact is expressed by Kirkwood in terms of a total electric moment, μ, which represents not only the moment of a given individual molecule, but is the vector sum of this moment plus the moments of all the neighbor-

(264) L. Onsager, *J. Am. Chem. Soc.* **58**, 1486 (1936).
(265) J. G. Kirkwood, *J. Chem. Phys.* **7**, 911 (1939).

ing molecules in the liquid. Only the first two or three shells of neighboring molecules need to be considered in evaluating this sum; more distant molecules may be regarded as distributed at random with respect to the molecule under consideration. If the immediate neighbors are also distributed at random, $\bar{\mu}$ becomes equal to μ. In general, however, the two quantities may be different, both in magnitude and in direction.

TABLE XIII
DIELECTRIC INCREMENTS, DIPOLE MOMENTS, RELAXATION TIMES AND CALCULATED AXIAL RATIOS OF CERTAIN PROTEINS AT 25°

$\Delta\epsilon_t/g$ = dielectric increment/g. protein/l.; μ = dipole moment in Debye units; τ_{H_2O} is the relaxation time in water at 25° (correcting for the relative viscosity of water and the solvent actually employed); τ_0 = relaxation time of a sphere, of volume equal to that of the protein, in water at 25°; a/b is the ratio of the major to minor axis calculated from τ_0 and observed relaxation times, by the equations of Perrin(1) (see also Cohn and Edsall(2)), neglecting hydration.

Insulin was studied in 80 per cent propylene glycol; lactoglobulin in 0.5 M and 0.25 M glycine in water; edestin in 2 M glycine in water; gliadin in 56 per cent aqueous ethanol; secalin in 54 per cent ethanol; zein in 72 per cent ethanol; other proteins in water. This table is adapted from Oncley(3).

Protein	$\Delta\epsilon_t/g$	Assumed mol. wt. $\times 10^{-3}$	μ	$\tau_{H_2O} \times 10^8$	$\tau_0 \times 10^8$	a/b
Egg albumin	0.17	45	250	18; 4.7	3.7	5
Horse serum albumin (carbohydrate free)	0.24	70	380	36; 7.5	6.0	6
Horse carboxyhemoglobin	0.42	67	480	8.4	(6.6)	(1.6)
Pig carboxyhemoglobin	0.3	(67)	(410)	13		
Horse serum pseudoglobin	1.14	142	1100	250; 28	22	9
Insulin	0.38	40	360	1.6		
β-Lactoglobulin	1.58	40	730	15; 5.1	4.3	4
Gliadin	0.10	42	190	27; 3.8	3.1	8
Secalin	1.0	24	440	29; 2.7	2.1	10
Zein	0.45	40	380	24; 4.2	3.3	7
Myoglobin	0.15	17	170	2.9	1.45	(2.6)

(1) F. Perrin, *J. phys. radium* [7], **5**, 497 (1934).

(2) E. J. Cohn and J. T. Edsall, Proteins, Amino Acids and Peptides, Reinhold Publishing Corporation, New York, 1943.

(3) J. L. Oncley, *Chem. Revs.* **30**, 433 (1942); see also Oncley in Ref. 2, Chapter 22.

Kirkwood's analysis for highly polar liquids leads to the following relation between the dielectric constant, ϵ, and the molar polarization, P, of the liquid.

$$\epsilon - 1 = 9P/2V = \frac{6\pi N}{V}\left(\alpha_0 + \frac{\mu\bar{\mu}\cos\theta}{3kT}\right) \tag{138}$$

Here V is the molar volume of the liquid, N is Avogadro's number, k the Boltzmann constant, T the absolute temperature, and θ the angle between the vectors μ and $\bar{\mu}$. α_0 is the polarizability of the molecules in the liquid; it can be derived from refractive-index measurements. For highly polar substances α_0 is small compared to the second term in the parentheses. The high dielectric constant of water is well accounted for by Eq. (138) on the basis of the known dipole moment of water and the orientation of the water molecules relative to one another. The molar polarization of the liquid is defined in terms of the polarizability and the dipole moment of the molecules by Eq. (138). In a solution containing several components, Eq. (138) becomes

$$\epsilon - 1 = \tfrac{9}{2}(C_1P_1 + C_2P_2 + \cdots) \tag{139}$$

where C_1, C_2 . . . are the concentrations of components 1, 2, . . . expressed in moles per cubic centimeter.

Equation (139) is directly applicable to solutions of amino acids or proteins in which there are two components, protein (or amino acid) and water. When the solute is dissolved in water, the polarization of the mixture is somewhat decreased by the displacement of some water molecules, but the effect of this displacement is far more than counterbalanced by the extremely high polarization due to the solute molecules themselves. Neglecting the decrease in polarization due to the displacement by the water, a simple relation may be obtained between the dielectric increment δ of the amino acid and the quantity $\mu\bar{\mu} \cos \theta$.

$$\mu\bar{\mu} \cos \theta = 10.9\delta \tag{140}$$

Details of the derivatives of Eq. (140) from Eq. (139) are given by Kirkwood in Cohn and Edsall,[2] pp. 294–6. Thus for glycine δ equals 22.6, and $\mu\bar{\mu} \cos \theta$ is therefore 246, μ and $\bar{\mu}$ being expressed in Debye units. If we define a mean moment μ_m by the relation $\mu_m{}^2 = \mu\bar{\mu} \cos \theta$, then $\mu_m = 15.7$ for glycine. This value is only slightly different from the value of 14.4 estimated from the consideration of a space model.

The dipole moments of amino acids and peptides with a larger separation between the charged amino and carboxyl groups increase approximately in proportion to the square root of the number of atoms separating the groups carrying the electric charge. This can be interpreted on the basis of a statistical argument, for the mean square distance between the ends of the chain should be approximately proportional to the number of atoms in the chain, if there is more or less free rotation around the valence bonds (Kuhn,[266] Kuhn and Kuhn,[267] and compare also Treloar[268]); and the dipole moment is proportional to the square root of this mean square

(266) W. Kuhn, *Kolloid-Z.* **68**, 2 (1934).
(267) W. Kuhn and H. Kuhn, *Helv. Chim. Acta* **26**, 1394 (1943).
(268) L. R. G. Treloar, The Physics of Rubber Elasticity. Oxford, 1949.

distance. The very high value for lysylglutamic acid (Table XII) is due to the fact that this molecule contains two positive charges near one end and two negative charges near the other end, with a wide distance of separation between them.

The dipole moments calculated for the protein molecules in Table XIII are much larger than those of ordinary polar molecules. However, they are very small in comparison with the maximum conceivable dipole moments which these proteins might exhibit if all the positive charges were concentrated near one end of the molecule and all the negative charges near the other. On the whole, the calculated moments suggest that the distribution of positive and negative charges on the surface of the molecule is a fairly even one.

3. DIELECTRIC DISPERSION AND RELAXATION TIMES

In an alternating field of low frequency, the dielectric constant of a liquid is the same as in a static field, provided the rate of alternation is so slow that the molecules have time to orient themselves so as to follow the changing field. If the rate of alternation becomes very high, however, this is no longer possible because of the inertia of the molecules. Hence, if the frequency of the applied field is gradually increased, a region will be found over which the dielectric constant declines from its static value ϵ_0 to a lower value ϵ_∞. The latter value represents the dielectric constant measured at a frequency so high that the permanent dipoles of the solute cannot follow the field at all[269] (Fig. 25). If the solute molecule can be described as if it were an ellipsoid of revolution, then the dielectric constant ϵ, as a function of the frequency ν, can be described by the equation

$$\epsilon = \epsilon_0 - \frac{\Delta\epsilon_1 \nu^2}{\nu^2 + \nu_1{}^2} - \frac{\Delta\epsilon_2 \nu^2}{\nu^2 + \nu_2{}^2} \tag{141}$$

The two characteristic frequencies, ν_1 and ν_2, are the critical frequencies of the ellipsoidal molecule, and they are related to the corresponding relaxation times τ_a and τ_b by the equations.

$$\nu_1 = (2\pi\tau_a)^{-1}; \; \nu_2 = (2\pi\tau_b)^{-1} \tag{142}$$

The total increase in dielectric constant produced by the solute is given by

$$\Delta\epsilon_\tau = \epsilon_0 - \epsilon_\infty = \Delta\epsilon_1 + \Delta\epsilon_2 \tag{143}$$

(269) It is assumed, however, that ϵ_∞ is measured at a frequency which is sufficiently low that the solvent has the same dielectric constant as in a static field. ϵ_∞ is, in general, lower than the dielectric constant of the pure solvent because some of the space in the liquid is occupied by the solute molecules which do not orient in the field.

The form of these dielectric dispersion curves is shown in Fig. 26 for a series of elongated ellipsoids of revolution of varying axial ratios. The magnitude of the contribution to the dielectric constant made by the two different portions of the curve, corresponding to the two different relaxation times, depends upon the components of the total dipole moment which are parallel to the a- and b-axis, respectively. It has been assumed in drawing Fig. 26 that the components along both axes are equal; that

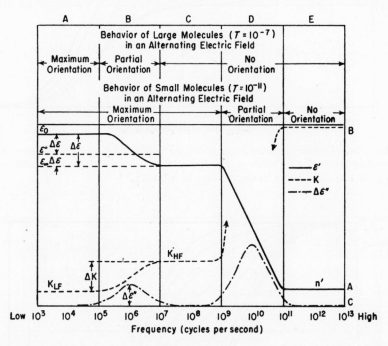

FIG. 25. Schematic diagram of anomalous dispersion of the dielectric constant (ϵ'), the specific conductivity (η), and the dielectric absorption $[\Delta\epsilon'' = 1.80(\eta - \eta_0)/\nu]$ for two widely separated critical frequencies. From J. Shack.[282] See also Oncley et al.[283]

is, that the dipole moment is at 45° to the axes. In Fig. 27 a series of dielectric dispersion curves are given, for molecules of constant size and shape, but with varying angle between the axes and the total moment. It is apparent from Figs. 26 and 27 that a spherical molecule, or a molecule in which the dipole moment is parallel to either the major or the minor axis, shows only a single relaxation time by dielectric dispersion measurements. For practical purposes the same is true for an oblate ellipsoid of virtually any axial ratio (see the discussion on page 673). Thus, it should be possible to distinguish two relaxation times, if the

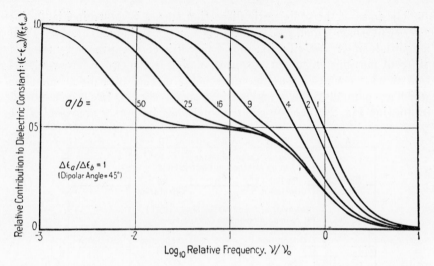

FIG. 26. Dielectric dispersion curves for elongated ellipsoids of revolution (according to Perrin). Constant dipole angle ($\vartheta = 45°$) and varying axial ratio (a/b from 1 to 50). From Oncley.[261] See also Oncley.[262]

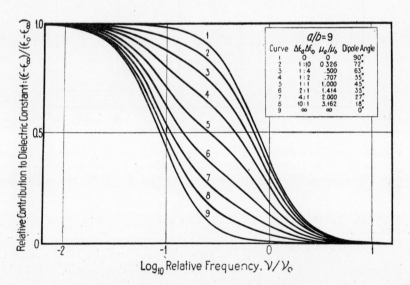

FIG. 27. Dielectric dispersion curves for elongated ellipsoids of revolution (according to Perrin). Constant axial ratio ($a/b = 9$) and varying dipole angle (ϑ from 0° to 90°). From Oncley.[261] See also Oncley.[262]

molecule is for a prolate ellipsoid of considerable asymmetry, provided the dipole angle is sufficiently far from either 0 or 90°.

In Fig. 28 is shown a series of dielectric dispersion curves for various proteins. It is to be noted in this figure, that the values of $\epsilon_0 - \epsilon_\infty$ for all the proteins are reduced to the same scale, although the actual dielectric increments for these proteins may differ quite widely among themselves, as may be seen from Table XIII. It is apparent that the curves for edestin and horse γ-pseudoglobulin cannot be fitted by a single relaxation time; presumably horse γ-pseudoglobulin is to be regarded therefore as shaped more or less like a prolate ellipsoid. Edestin, however, has been

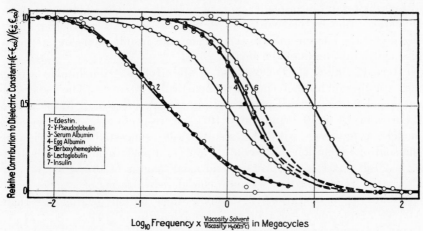

FIG. 28.   Dielectric dispersion curves of proteins.   From Oncley.[261,262]

reported from studies in the electron microscope (Table III), and by low-angle x-ray scattering,[134] to be practically spherical. It now seems not improbable, in the light of present information, that the two relaxation times found by dielectric dispersion were due to the presence of two different species of molecule in the preparation studied by dielectric measurements (personal communication from J. L. Oncley).

Horse carboxyhemoglobin, on the other hand, is well described by a single relaxation time. This is to be expected, since according to the x-ray studies of Bragg and Perutz,[176a] the best available approximation to the shape of this molecule somewhat resembles a prolate ellipsoid of a relatively low degree of asymmetry. Dielectric dispersion data on myoglobin which were obtained by Marcy and Wyman[270] have been critically discussed in relation to other physical measurements on this protein by Wyman and Ingalls,[4] and by Wyman.[10] Wyman's final con-

(270) H. O. Marcy and J. Wyman, Jr., J. Am. Chem. Soc. 64, 638 (1942).

clusion is that all the data for myoglobin are best fitted by an oblate ellipsoidal molecule with an axial ratio of approximately 1 to 3.6. A prolate ellipsoidal model of axial ratio 2.5 to 1 also fitted the data fairly well, but the oblate model seems inherently more probable, particularly in the light of x-ray diffraction studies on this protein by Kendrew.[271]

The curve for insulin is interesting in that the observed relaxation time is shorter than would be calculated for an anhydrous sphere of molecular weight 36,000. When these observations were made in 1939, no explanation of this phenomenon was available. However, it is now known—see the discussion on pages 717–19—that insulin under certain conditions dissociates into smaller units of molecular weight 12,000; and there is evidence that in the solution of 80 per cent propylene glycol in which the dielectric measurements were made, the insulin molecule actually dissociates into units of the smaller size.

Recent studies of Oncley, Dintzis and Hollies[271a] on human serum mercaptalbumin have given results of particular interest. The dispersion curve indicated two distinct relaxation times; referred to water at 0°, these were 4.4×10^{-7} and 1.6×10^{-7} sec. respectively. Two possible models, compatible with the results, were suggested. One was an ellipsoid of revolution with axial ratio 4:1, dipole angle 30°, hydration 0.15–.20 g. water per g. protein, and axial lengths of 147 × 37 A. An alternative representation was also considered in terms of a generalized ellipsoid with axial ratio 6:2:1, dipole angle 30°, hydration less than 0.05 g. water per g. protein, and axial lengths of 144 × 48 × 24 A. Extensive studies of mercaptalbumin mercury dimer were also carried out but the conclusions drawn cannot be briefly summarized.

Interesting findings were also obtained on the dielectric increments of the mercaptalbumin solutions. Preparations which had been carefully treated with ion exchange resins, so that nearly all of the rather tightly bound fatty acids commonly present in serum albumin had been removed, gave total dielectric increments of 0.93 per g. protein per l., far higher than any values previously recorded for serum albumin. When various anions were added to such albumin preparations, the dielectric increments decreased; addition of four moles of oleate per mole of albumin reduced the total dielectric increment to less than half its value in the absence of oleate. The binding of certain neutral molecules, such as decanol, which are strongly bound by albumin, also decreased the dielectric increment but the effect was much less than for the bound

(271) J. C. Kendrew, *Proc. Roy. Soc.* (London) **A201,** 62 (1950).
(271a) J. L. Oncley, H. M. Dintzis, and N. R. S. Hollies, Abstract of Papers, 122nd Meeting, *Am. Chem. Soc.* 1952, p. 12P; H. M. Dintzis, Thesis, Harvard University (1952).

anions.   The calculated dipole moment for albumin free of bound fatty acid was 700 Debye units for mercaptalbumin monomer and 1080 Debye units for the mercaptalbumin dimer.

The dielectric properties of proteins reveal again a striking difference between their behavior and that of synthetic long-chain polymers.   Polar molecules of the latter type, according to the calculations of Fuoss and Kirkwood,[272] should show a broad statistical distribution of relaxation times, even for a monodisperse system, because the different polar groups in the polymer molecule are distributed in a nearly random fashion relative to one another, owing to rotation around valence bonds.   Orientation in an electric field is primarily the orientation of molecular segments.   According to the statistical distribution of polar groups, the oriented segment may be of any size, from a single polar group to the whole molecule, the most probable size being, of course, somewhere between these two extremes.   Experimental measurements of Fuoss[273] on concentrated solutions of polyvinyl chloride and other polymers reveal just such a broad distribution of relaxation times.   The measurements of Bridgman and Williams[274] and of Wyman,[275] on poly-ω-hydroxy-decanoic acids in dilute solution, are in harmony with this statistical picture, at least so far as the electric moments are concerned.   The polarization per gram of solute in unit volume was found to be independent of polymer size, from the monomer unit up to molecules composed of more than 150 such units.   The dielectric constants of these solutions are independent of frequency up to frequencies of 5×10^7 cycles/sec., or greater.   Hence the relaxation times must be less than 10^{-8} sec., perhaps much less.

Proteins, on the other hand, are characterized by one or two well-defined relaxation times, which are of the magnitude to be expected if the protein molecule rotates as a fairly compact and rigid unit in the electric field.   If the protein molecule is denatured and caused to unfold in a solvent such as concentrated aqueous urea, it is possible that it would behave more like the synthetic polymers in an electric field; but such studies still remain to be carried out.

Recent dielectric measurements at very high frequencies[275a] have provided important information regarding protein hydration.   The wave-

(272) R. M. Fuoss and J. G. Kirkwood, *J. Am. Chem. Soc.* **63**, 385 (1941); J. G. Kirkwood and R. M. Fuoss, *J. Chem. Phys.* **9**, 329 (1941).

(273) R. M. Fuoss, "The Electrical Properties of High Polymers" *in* The Chemistry of Large Molecules, Interscience Publishers, New York, 1943, p. 191.

(274) W. B. Bridgman and J. W. Williams, *J. Am. Chem. Soc.* **59**, 1579 (1937).

(275) J. Wyman, Jr., *J. Am. Chem. Soc.* **60**, 328 (1938).

(275a) T. J. Buchanan, G. H. Haggis, J. B. Hasted and B. G. Robinson, *Proc. Roy. Soc.* (London) **A213**, 379 (1952).

lengths employed were between 1 and 10 cm.; measurements of dielectric constant and dielectric loss in this range are determined only by the orientation of the water molecules, since the frequencies are far too high to permit any orientation of the protein. Thus the measured dielectric constant values depend upon freedom of the water molecules to orient at these high frequencies; partial or complete inhibition of rotational freedom leads to lowering of the dielectric constant. Buchanan, *et al.*, distinguish between "bound" water molecules which are considered to be attached to polar or ionic groups in the protein by strong attractions, but are still free to rotate around their axes, and "irrotationally bound" water which is held so firmly that the molecules are not free to rotate at all in a high frequency field. Egg albumin, hemoglobin, lysozyme, β-lactoglobulin and bovine serum albumin were studied. The estimated total hydration for these proteins was in some cases as high as 0.4 g. water/g. protein, about one-third of this bound water being estimated as irrotationally bound.

Recently Kirkwood and Shumaker[275b] have proposed a new interpretation for the dielectric properties of protein molecules. The high dielectric increments of such molecules containing many acid and basic groups could be explained in terms of fluctuations of proton charge among these groups. Certainly many microscopically different distributions of charge must exist in a solution of protein molecules at any moment, even if all the molecules are chemically identical. These configurations are not fixed; any given molecule must constantly be changing from one configuration to another as it gives up or takes on protons. (See for instance the discussion in Ref. 2, pages 460–468.) It is still too early to say how adequately this fluctuation theory can account for the dielectric properties of proteins. Indeed the interpretation of the relaxation times of protein molecules in terms of these concepts is still almost entirely undeveloped. It is not yet clear whether the interpretation which has been presented here, which explains the relaxation times of protein molecules in terms of the orientation of rigid ellipsoids, will require any significant modification in terms of proton fluctuation theory. Kirkwood and Shumaker have further pointed out the important influence of these charge fluctuations on the intermolecular forces between protein molecules in solution.

4. Methods of Dielectric-Constant Measurement

No attempt at detailed descriptions of the methods used will be given here.

(275b) J. G. Kirkwood and J. B. Shumaker, *Proc. Natl. Acad. Sci. U.S.A.* **38**, 855, 863 (1952).

(1) The most widely used method for the study of protein solutions over a broad range of frequencies is the bridge method, involving the comparison of the resistance and capacitance of a cell containing the solution under investigation with some arrangement of standard resistances and capacitances. The most highly developed apparatus of this type is that of Oncley[276,261] (see also Ferry and Oncley[277]); further developments in Dr. Oncley's laboratory are now proceeding.

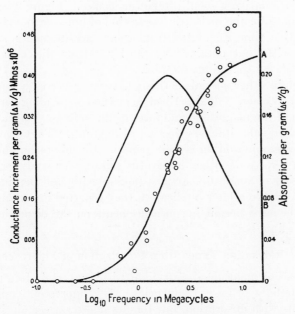

FIG. 29. Dielectric absorption of carboxyhemoglobin solutions: 0, experimental measurements of $(k - k_0)/g$; curve A: $(k - k_0)/g$, and curve B: $\Delta\epsilon''/g$, calculated from Eq. (1) of Oncley, Ferry, and Shack, using the constants, recorded in Table I of their paper, for the calorimetric method (J. Shack[282]). From Oncley et al.[283] See also Oncley.[262]

(2) For a higher frequency range the resonance method has been widely used, especially for measurements on amino acids and peptides. Discussion and references are given in the review by Wyman.[260]

(3) The force method, which involves the measurement of the deflecting force exerted by an electric field on a conducting ellipsoid suspended in the solution being studied, was developed by Fürth,[278,279] and was later

(276) J. L. Oncley, J. Am. Chem. Soc. 60, 1115 (1938).

(277) J. D. Ferry and J. L. Oncley, J. Am. Chem. Soc. 63, 272 (1941).

(278) R. Fürth, Z. Physik 22, 98 (1924).

(279) R. Fürth, Handbuch Biol. Arbeitsmethoden IIIB, 835 (1929).

used by Shutt and his co-workers (see for instance Dunning and Shutt[280] and Carr and Shutt[281]). It is most satisfactory at low frequencies.

(4) The calorimetric method involves the measurements of the expansion of the solution which results from the heat produced in it by an applied field of high frequency. The details, as applied to protein solutions, have been described by Shack[282] (see also Oncley, Ferry, and Shack[283]). It is particularly well adapted for use at high frequencies and, therefore, for relatively small protein molecules. Figure 29 shows some of Shack's data for the dielectric absorption of horse carboxyhemoglobin. The relaxation time calculated from these measurements was in good agreement with that obtained by Oncley[276] from dielectric dispersion measurements by the bridge method.

(5) Certain other special methods have been used by some authors. Marcy and Wyman[284,270] described a method depending on the direct comparison of the magnitude and force of the voltage across an unknown and a standard capacitance, using an oscillograph. They made observations on myoglobin and on certain peptides by this technique. Conner and Smyth[285] have described apparatus suitable for studying the dielectric dispersion of small dipolar ions (amino acids and peptides) at high frequencies, and in a later publication they reported its extension to still higher frequencies, permitting measurements on the dispersion of water and organic liquids.[286]

XX. Relaxation Times from Polarization of Fluorescence

A fluorescent molecule absorbs light within a certain frequency range and re-emits light of lower frequencies. This fluorescent emission is not simultaneous with absorption, but follows it after a certain interval, t^*, which represents the duration of the excited state. Commonly t^* is of the order of 10^{-8} sec., for many fluorescent dyes. A small molecule, of molecular weight less than 1000, in a medium such as water, will have turned extensively at random, due to its rotary Brownian movement, in the interval t^*. Hence its orientation at the end of this interval will be quite independent of its orientation at the beginning. On the other hand, a macromolecule with a long relaxation time will have changed its orientation relatively little during the same interval. If the molecules were immersed in a medium of infinite viscosity, so that they could

(280) W. J. Dunning and W. J. Shutt, *Trans. Faraday Soc.* **34**, 479 (1938).
(281) W. Carr and W. J. Shutt, *Trans. Faraday Soc.* **35**, 579 (1939).
(282) J. Shack, Thesis, Harvard University, 1939.
(283) J. L. Oncley, J. D. Ferry, and J. Shack, *Ann. N. Y. Acad. Sci.* **40**, 371 (1940).
(284) H. O. Marcy and J. Wyman, Jr., *J. Am. Chem. Soc.* **63**, 3388, (1941).
(285) W. P. Conner and C. P. Smyth, *J. Am. Chem. Soc.* **64**, 1870 (1942).
(286) W. P. Conner and C. P. Smyth, *J. Am. Chem. Soc.* **65**, 382 (1943).

not rotate at all during the time t^*, the emitted fluorescent light would be at least partially polarized. On the other hand, if the molecules rotate so rapidly that their distributions become random during this time, the fluorescence will be completely depolarized. Intermediate rates of rotary diffusion correspond to intermediate values of the polarization. These phenomena have served as a basis for a method which has been used in the study of relaxation times. The fundamental theory is due to Perrin,[287] and has recently been extended by Weber.[288] A valuable general discussion of fluorescence in organic molecules has recently been given by Förster.[289]

The polarization, p, of the fluorescence, is defined as follows. Take the direction of the plane-polarized incident light beam as the X-axis, the direction of the electrical vector in this light being parallel to the vertical Z-axis. The origin, O, is taken at the element of the fluorescent solution which is being observed. The observer measures the intensity of the fluorescent light emitted in the Oy direction, the intensities I_x and I_z of the horizontal and vertical components, respectively, being measured. Then p is defined by the equation

$$p = \frac{I_z - I_x}{I_z + I_x} \tag{144}$$

The same kind of measurement may be made using unpolarized incident light, the direction of observation and the definition of p remaining the same. For a spherical molecule of volume V, Perrin's[287] theory leads to the equation:

$$\left(\frac{1}{p} \mp \frac{1}{3}\right) \Big/ \left(\frac{1}{p_0} \mp \frac{1}{3}\right) = 1 + \frac{kTt^*}{V\eta} = 1 + \frac{3t^*}{\tau} \tag{145}$$

Here p_0 is a limiting value of p, approached as p tends toward zero, and actually in many cases practically attained in media of very high viscosity. The value of τ, the relaxation time of a spherical molecule, is given by Eq. (113).

Perrin's treatment has been extended by Weber[288] to the case of an ellipsoidal macromolecule with two relaxation times, τ_a and τ_b (see Eqs. (117–121) inclusive) to which are attached small fluorescent units arranged in random orientation. The equation analogous to (145) then becomes:

(287) F. Perrin, *J. phys. radium* [6], **7**, 390 (1926); [7], **7**, 1 (1936).

(288) G. Weber, *Biochem. J.* **51**, 145 (1952).

(289) T. Förster, Fluoreszenz organischer Verbindungen, Vandenhook and Ruprecht, Göttingen, 1951.

$$\left(\frac{1}{p} \mp \frac{1}{3}\right) \Big/ \left(\frac{1}{p_0} \mp \frac{1}{3}\right) \cong 1 + \frac{3t^*}{\rho_h} \tag{146}$$

Here ρ_h is the harmonic mean of τ_a and τ_b, defined by

$$\frac{1}{\rho_h} = \frac{1}{2}\left(\frac{1}{\tau_a} + \frac{1}{\tau_b}\right) \tag{147}$$

On the left-hand sides of Eqs. (145) and (146), the minus signs are used if the incident light is plane polarized and the plus signs if it is unpolarized, as in the studies discussed below.

The application of these equations to proteins—or rather to chemically modified forms of natural proteins—has been made by Weber.[290] Since natural proteins are not fluorescent, Weber conjugated them with 1-dimethylaminonaphthalene-5-sulfonyl chloride, under mild conditions, the resulting conjugated protein molecules being strongly fluorescent. He determined the value of p in solutions of these substances over a temperature range between 2 and 50° in water, giving a variation in the values of T/η from 1.6×10^4 to 6×10^4. Lower values of T/η were obtained by working in concentrated sucrose solutions, up to 600 g. sucrose/l. solution.

In the analysis of the results, it should be noted that $1/\tau_a$ and $1/\tau_b$ in Eq. (147) are both proportional to kT/η. Hence, in applying Eq. (146) to studies on proteins, it is convenient to plot $(1/p + \frac{1}{3})$ against T/η. Weber's measurements on conjugates of ovalbumin and bovine serum albumin, plotted in this manner, are shown in Fig. 30. The curves are linear within the limits of experimental error, as Eq. (146) would predict, except that there is a distinct curvature in the extreme upper portion of the serum albumin curve, corresponding to temperatures between 50 and 60°. However, on cooling again, after an hour at 59°, the values at low temperatures were found to be unaltered.

The intercept on the ordinate axis gives the value of $1/p_0 + \frac{1}{3}$ for each protein, and the slope depends on the ratio t^*/ρ_h. Using Oncley's[262] values for the relaxation times of ovalbumin to obtain ρ_h for this protein, Weber[290] calculated t^* for the ovalbumin conjugate as 1.4×10^{-8} sec., and used the same value for the serum albumin conjugate also. On this basis he obtained $\rho_h = 1.27 \times 10^{-7}$ sec., in water at 25°, for bovine

(290) G. Weber, *Biochem. J.* **51**, 155 (1952). The attention of the reader should be called to the notation used by various authors. Weber, also Perrin[287] and Förster,[289] use the symbol τ, or τ_0, to denote the duration of the excited state, which we have denoted here by t^*. Weber uses ρ_1 and ρ_2 to denote the two relaxation times which we have here denoted by τ_a and τ_b (following the notation used earlier in this chapter, and in Ref. 2, Chaps. 21 and 22).

serum albumin; whereas, the value calculated from Oncley's data on dielectric dispersion[262] of horse serum albumin was 1.24×10^{-7} sec.

Weber[288] showed that, for prolate ellipsoids, it was possible to make an approximate estimate of axial ratio by plotting $(1/p + \frac{1}{3})/(1/p_0 + \frac{1}{3})$

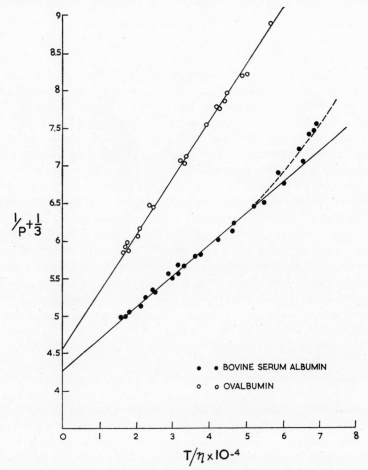

FIG. 30. Fluorescence polarization: measurements on ovalbumin and serum albumin. From the data of Weber.[288]

against the ratio t^*/τ_0, where τ_0 is the relaxation time of a sphere of the same volume as the actual solvated molecule [see Eq. (116)]. Considering a series of ellipsoids of constant volume but increasing axial ratio, it is found that the initial slope of such curves decreases with increasing axial ratio. These slopes (S) are related to the slope of the line for the hypothetical equivalent sphere (S_0) by the equation:

$$S/S_0 = \frac{\tau_0}{2}\left(\frac{1}{\tau_a} + \frac{1}{\tau_b}\right) \tag{148}$$

For nearly spherical molecules, or for oblate ellipsoids of any axial ratio, the curves are linear within experimental error, even at large values of t^*/τ_0—or of T/η, which is proportional to this. However, for prolate ellipsoids of high axial ratio, for which the two relaxation times differ markedly, the curves are concave to the abscissa axis. This concavity does not appear in Eq. (146), which would give a linear relation, but is predicted by equations developed by Weber[288] [see his Eqs. (28) and (29)] for randomly oriented fluorescent oscillators attached to a large ellipsoidal molecule. Weber[290] applied this method to evaluate the shape of the bovine serum albumin molecule, estimating the hydration, w, as 0.15 g. water/g. protein, from the high-frequency dielectric studies of Haggis, Buchanan, and Hasted.[291] He concluded that the data were best fitted by assuming a prolate ellipsoid with an axial ratio of 4.

A residual uncertainty in these studies remains, since t^* has not been directly and independently determined; it is not at all impossible that t^* varies, for a given protein derivative, with changes in the solvent or in the state of ionization of the protein. Direct methods for the determination of t^* have been discussed by Förster,[289] and the direct determination of this quantity, in addition to p, would enhance the power of the method and make conclusions drawn from it more certain. However, available evidence indicates that variations of t^* in these systems are small; hence the assumption that t^* is a constant for a given protein derivative is a reasonable first approximation.

The fluorescence depolarization method was also used by Weber[290] in the study of denaturation changes in both ovalbumin and serum albumin. Indications were obtained that the latter molecule dissociates into smaller subunits below pH 2.5–3, and above pH 11–12. The method has also been used by Laurence[292] to study the binding of fluorescent dyes by serum albumin.[293] The fluorescence from the free dye in water is completely depolarized, while that from the dye bound to albumin is fairly highly polarized; and this permits the equilibria between the free and bound dye to be determined.

XXI. Size and Shape of Certain Important Proteins

To conclude this chapter, we may consider the present state of our knowledge of a few important proteins which have received considerable study.

(291) G. H. Haggis, T. J. Buchanan, and J. B. Hasted, *Nature* **167**, 607 (1951); see also ref. 275a.

(292) D. J. R. Laurence, *Biochem. J.* **51**, 168 (1952).

(293) See the general discussion of dye binding by proteins in Chap. 10 of this volume.

1. INSULIN

Insulin has now been characterized in more detail than any other protein. The molecular weight in neutral solution, from sedimentation and diffusion studies, has been reported by some workers as near 36,000, by others as 46,000–48,000 (see Table VIII). The sources of these discrepancies will, in part at least, be apparent from the discussion which follows. A deeper insight into the problem of structure was obtained in the x-ray studies of Crowfoot,[294] on insulin crystallized from neutral solution. The crystals were rhombohedral, with one molecule, of anhydrous molecular weight 36,000, in the unit cell. However, the three-fold symmetry of the structure indicated plainly that this molecule was composed of three identical subunits, each of molecular weight 12,000.

More recent evidence from amino acid analysis—see for instance Sanger[295]—indicated a minimum molecular weight of either 6000 or 12,000 for beef insulin. If the latter figure be taken, the molecule contains four polypeptide chains, two containing glycine α-amino groups as terminal residues, and the other two containing free phenylalanine α-amino groups. Each of the former—designated as A-chains by Sanger because they contain more acidic than basic side-chain groups—contains 21 residues, four of which are half-cystine groups. Each of the latter— designated as B-chains by Sanger, since they contain more basic than acidic side chains—contains 30 amino acid residues, two of which are half-cystine. The detailed sequence of amino acid residues in both types of chain has now been worked out by Sanger and his collaborators[16,296] (see Chap. 3 for further details). It is clear that the chains are cross-linked by disulfide bridges of cystine residues; if the molecular weight is 12,000 there are two A- and two B-chains, and six disulfide bridges could be formed to tie the four together. If the molecular weight is 6000—a figure apparently quite compatible with the analytical data, since only one kind of A-chain and one kind of B-chain has been isolated—there would be two interchain disulfide bridges; two of the four sulfur atoms on the A-chain would presumably have to form an intrachain —S—S— cross link, since there are no free cysteine sulfhydryl groups in native insulin.

Abundant evidence has now been obtained from physical measurements that insulin, in acid solution, exists largely in units of molecular weight 12,000 (or possibly 6000) in a mobile equilibrium with association

(294) D. Crowfoot, *Proc. Roy. Soc.* (London) **A164,** 580 (1938); *idem, Chem. Revs.* **28,** 215 (1941).

(295) F. Sanger, *Biochem. J.* **45,** 563 (1949); *idem, Cold Spring Harbor Symposia Quant. Biol.* **14,** 153 (1949).

(296) F. Sanger and E. O. Thompson, *Biochem. J.* **53,** iii (1952); **53,** 353, 366 (1953).

products of weight 24,000 (dimer), 36,000 (trimer), 48,000 (tetramer), and possibly some still larger units. Qualitatively, the general situation seems quite clear, but there are numerous discrepancies in detail between the reports of different investigators. In any case the equilibrium is very sensitive to pH and ionic strength; at pH near 2, and at low ionic strength, the smaller molecules are most common, their relative numbers of course increasing as the protein concentration is diminished. Moody[297] in 1944 carried out sedimentation and diffusion studies on insulin at pH 3 and inferred a molecular weight of 12,000. He also found that on addition of salt, the sedimentation constant at this pH increased from approximately 1.6 to 3.3 $\times$ 10^{-13}. Oncley and Ellenbogen[298] concluded, from studies of sedimentation and boundary spreading in the ultracentrifuge, that the equilibrium was principally between the monomer (12,000) and the trimer (36,000) in such solutions. Doty, Gellert, and Rabinovitch[299] concluded from light-scattering measurements that, at pH below 2.2, the equilibrium was between monomer and dimer, and that a single equilibrium constant could describe their measurements over a 50-fold concentration range. At higher pH values there were indications that tetramer and probably trimer were present also, the tetramer being the predominant form at pH above 3.2 and protein concentrations above 0.3 per cent. These studies were considered by the authors as only preliminary to more precise studies in conjunction with J. L. Oncley.

Fredericq and Neurath[139a] concluded, from sedimentation and diffusion studies in acid solution, that the insulin molecule actually dissociates into units of molecular weight 6000. Their analysis of their data, however, involved difficult and rather uncertain extrapolations, not yet confirmed by other investigators. Tietze and Neurath[300] undertook light-scattering studies on the same insulin preparation and found a molecular weight of 12,000 when the measurements were extrapolated to zero protein concentration. Gutfreund[98] obtained the same value from osmotic-pressure measurements; the correspondence with the light-scattering value indicated that the weight-average and number-average molecular weights were the same and hence that the molecules were of uniform size at infinite dilution.

Another investigation of the insulin system in acid solution by Pedersen,[200] using sedimentation and diffusion measurements, led him to

(297) L. S. Moody, Thesis, University of Wisconsin, 1944; cited by J. W. Williams, *Ann. Rev. Phys. Chem.* **2**, 412 (1951).

(298) See J. L. Oncley, E. Ellenbogen, D. Gitlin, and F. R. N. Gurd, *J. Phys. Chem.* **56**, 85 (1952); also E. Ellenbogen, Thesis, Harvard University, 1949.

(299) P. Doty, M. Gellert, and B. Rabinovitch, *J. Am. Chem. Soc.* **74**, 2065 (1952).

(300) F. Tietze and H. Neurath, *J. Biol. Chem.* **194**, 1 (1952). H. Neurath, *Discussions Faraday Soc.* **No. 13**, 93 (1953) reports a revised $S^0{}_{20}$ of 1.75 S, which accords with a molecular weight of 12,000.

the conclusion that an equilibrium existed between a unit of 21,000 molecular weight and a dimer of this unit. These values differ widely from those of all other investigators, and it is also difficult to reconcile them with the amino acid composition.

The countercurrent distribution studies of Harfenist and Craig[60a] on dinitrophenyl derivatives of insulin have already been discussed on p. 571. Unlike all the other studies here reported, they give unequivocally a molecular weight of the order of 6000. It should be noted that they involve the distribution of several insulin derivatives between an aqueous solution and an organic solvent.

The weight of the evidence appears to be strongly in favor of the 12,000 molecular weight unit as the fundamental unit in acid aqueous solution. It is possible, however, that this unit is composed of two identical subunits linked by bonds which are not covalent, so that it can be split into these subunits by treatment with organic solvents, as in Craig's experiments, though remaining stable in water. The evidence also suggests that different insulin preparations may differ considerably in behavior. The increased tendency for the larger units to dissociate at low pH was interpreted by Oncley and Ellenbogen[297] as an effect of electrostatic repulsion, due to the large positive net charge on the molecules under these conditions. The nature of the forces leading to the strong association tendency at higher pH values is more obscure.

Recently Low[301] has reported x-ray studies of orthorhombic crystals of insulin sulfate from acid solution. From these she has drawn conclusions concerning the orientation of the polypeptide chains and their dimensions, which are further discussed in Chap. 4.

2. Myoglobin

The most thoroughly studied of the myoglobins is that from horse heart. Its molecular weight is near 17,000 (Table VIII), and it contains one heme group per molecule. There is one free terminal α-amino group, belonging to a glycine residue, so that the molecule appears to contain only a single polypeptide chain. An extensive, though preliminary, x-ray investigation has been reported by Kendrew,[271] who has also given a comprehensive summary of earlier work on this protein. The polypeptide chain appears to be folded into several nearly parallel rodlike elements; these may all lie in a single layer, though a two-layer structure is not excluded. The optical dichroism of the crystal, in the wavelength region of the heme absorption bands, indicates that the plane of the heme group is nearly perpendicular to the direction of the polypeptide rodlike elements. Assuming a single layer of such elements, the molecule should

(301) B. W. Low, *Nature* **169**, 955 (1952).

be rather like a flattened ellipsoid with an axial ratio of 3.5 to 1, or 4 to 1; this is a shape quite compatible with the estimate made by Wyman and Ingalls on the physical properties of the molecule in solution.   Further discussion of myoglobin is given in Chap. 4.

3. Hemoglobin

Studies on the size and shape of the hemoglobin molecule—especially horse and human hemoglobin—have been more numerous and more searching than those on any other protein.   From the iron content, and from the data recorded in Tables V and VIII, it is clear that the molecular weight is near 66,800, and that the molecule contains four heme groups. From studies of oxygen affinity and other related reactions, it is evident that the heme groups are in some manner interlinked so that they interact strongly.   Evidence from x-ray studies—discussed in more detail in Chap. 4—indicates that the interior of the molecule contains chains, presumably polypeptide chains, arranged in parallel.[302]   The optical dichroism of the crystal, in the region of the heme absorption bands, shows that the heme groups are all parallel to a plane which is nearly perpendicular to the direction of the chains.   Earlier studies[176] had suggested a structure consisting of four layers of folded polypeptide chains, but a later and more searching examination of the problem[303] indicates that a structure of five superposed layers accords better with the facts. The number of polypeptide chains, as judged by the number of free α-amino groups, is six for horse and four or five for human hemoglobin; these terminal amino groups are all valine residues in both these species.[11]

The data from viscosity (Table XI) and dielectric dispersion (Table XIII) indicate that hemoglobin must be a nearly symmetrical molecule, with an axial ratio not far from unity.   The very recent x-ray studies of Bragg and Perutz[176a,303] indicate over-all dimensions of approximately 65 × 55 × 55 A., but the authors emphasize that no detailed estimate of the form of the molecule is implied by these figures.   They also give the volume of the anhydrous molecule as 83,000 A.^{3}, and that of the hydrated molecule as 116,000 A.^{3}.

4. Tropomyosin

This asymmetric molecule, obtained from rabbit muscle, appears to have a molecular weight close to 53,000.   However it shows a very strong tendency to aggregate in most solvents.[304]   The high viscosity increment

(302) M. F. Perutz, *Proc. Roy. Soc.* (London) **A195**, 474 (1949).

(303) W. L. Bragg and M. F. Perutz, *Acta Cryst.* **5**, 277 (1952); *idem Proc. Roy. Soc.* (London) **A213**, 425 (1952).

(304) T.-C. Tsao, K. Bailey, and G. S. Adair, *Biochem. J.* **49**, 27 (1951).

(Table XI) indicates an axial ratio, assuming a prolate shape, of approximately 22 to 1, taking the hydration as 0.25 g. water/g. protein, a value determined by the method of Adair and Robinson.[305]   There is no free terminal α-amino group,[306] and the molecule is therefore assumed to be a cyclopeptide.   It is suggested[304] that it consists of a closed looped polypeptide chain, of length 385 A. and mean width 14.5 A.   The latter figure does not include the water of hydration, which presumably forms a layer along the chains.

5. SERUM ALBUMIN

Intensive studies of both human and bovine serum albumin have been made; many of the results are to be found in Tables V–IX, XI, and XIII. Although they show some differences in amino acid composition,[57] human and bovine albumin appear to be remarkably alike in size and shape.   The molecular weight has generally been taken in recent years as 69,000,[78] but the recent x-ray and analytical studies of Low[307] lead to a value of 65,600; and an almost identical value has been obtained for bovine albumin by Creeth[308] from sedimentation and diffusion studies.

Human serum albumin has been resolved by Hughes[18] into mercaptalbumin, which contains one sulfhydryl group per molecule, and another fraction which is free of sulfhydryl groups.   By interaction with mercuric chloride, or with certain organic mercurials containing two or more mercury atoms, two molecules of mercaptalbumin may be linked together through their sulfhydryl groups to form a dimer.   Since such a dimer can be formed with a single mercury atom serving as the link, the fitting together of the two albumin molecules over the surface of contact must be extremely close.   The kinetics and equilibria of the processes involved have been studied in detail by light scattering.[309]

As yet, no particular difference has been found in size or shape between mercaptalbumin and other serum albumin molecules.   The evidence from dielectric dispersion (Table XIII) indicates two relaxation times which differ sufficiently to suggest that the molecule is of prolate shape, with an axial ratio near 4 to 1.   This value is compatible with the viscosity measurements also (Table XI).   Oncley, Scatchard, and Brown[179]

(305) G. S. Adair and M. E. Robinson, *J. Physiol.* **72**, 2P (1931).
(306) K. Bailey, *Biochem. J.* **49**, 23 (1951).
(307) B. W. Low, *J. Am. Chem. Soc.* **74**, 4830 (1952).
(308) J. M. Creeth, *Biochem. J.* **51**, 10 (1952).
(309) R. Lontie, P. R. Morrison, H. Edelhoch, and J. T. Edsall, Abstract of Papers 114th Meeting, *Am. Chem. Soc.*, 1948, p. 25c.; W. L. Hughes, Jr., R. Straessle, H. Edelhoch, and J. T. Edsall, Abstracts of Papers, 117th Meeting, *Am. Chem. Soc.*, 1950, p. 51c.; R. Straessle, *J. Am. Chem. Soc.* **73**, 504 (1951).

suggested a prolate ellipsoid, 150 A. long and 38 A. in diameter, as a suitable model, taking the hydration as 0.2. More recently a modified model, first suggested by Oncley, has been elaborated by Low[307] to describe the conclusions drawn from her x-ray studies on human albumin crystals. It is a prism, approximately 145 A. long, nearly 50 A. in diameter at the center, and 22 A. thick. Like all other models of the sort today, this must be regarded as only a very rough first approximation. Moreover, it is to be noted that low-angle x-ray scattering in solutions[310] of bovine albumin and human mercaptalbumin, although indicating a distinct asymmetry of the molecule, gives results which appear to be in best accord with an oblate ellipsoidal shape, with an axial ratio approximately 3.5 to 1. On the other hand, Riley and Oster[137] have claimed from their x-ray studies in highly concentrated solution that the molecule has an axial ratio very near unity. The weight of the evidence appears to be against this conclusion, and in favor of an axial ratio near 4 to 1; but there are certain puzzling discrepancies in the findings at present available, which need to be cleared up.

Finally, it may be noted that human, bovine, and horse serum albumins all contain only a single N-terminal α-amino group per molecule; in all cases this is an aspartic acid (or asparagine) residue.[311] Serum albumin thus appears to consist of a single polypeptide chain.

6. ARACHIN

Arachin, the principal globulin of the ground nut (peanut), has been found by Johnson and Shooter[312] to exist as a reversible association-dissociation system, described by the formula $A_2 \rightleftharpoons 2A$. The parent molecule (A_2) was found, by sedimentation and diffusion, to have a molecular weight of 330,000; the dissociation product, a molecular weight of 180,000. The value of the frictional ratio, f/f_0, was 1.216 for the former and 1.352 for the latter. The dissymmetry is therefore greater for the smaller molecule, the calculated axial ratio for the latter being nearly twice as great as for the former, whether the shape be assumed to be prolate or oblate. Johnson and Shooter studied the equilibrium between the two forms as a function of pH, salt concentration, and the nature of the salt present. The lowering of pH tended to increase association and also increased reaction rates; the lowering of salt concentration increased dissociation. The presence of sulfate ion strongly favored association.

(310) J. W. Anderegg, Thesis, University of Wisconsin (1952).
(311) H. van Vunakis and E. Brand, Abstracts, 119th Meeting, *Am. Chem. Soc.*, 1951, p. 28c.
(312) P. Johnson and E. M. Shooter, *Biochim. et Biophys. Acta* **5**, 361 (1950).

7. Fibrinogen

The high viscosity (Table XI) and marked double refraction of flow (Table IX) in fibrinogen solutions indicate that the molecule is decidedly asymmetrical, with a length of the order of 700 A., and an axial ratio near 18 to 1, assuming a prolate shape. The electron microscope studies of Hall (Table III) indicate an elongated rodlike form, but suggest also that the molecule is made up of several smaller subunits, linked together like a string of beads. The reported values of molecular weight have for the most part been in the range 400,000–500,000, but recently, in what appears to be very careful work,[313] a value near 340,000 has been reported from light-scattering measurements. In this study also, the length determined from angular dissymmetry of scattering was calculated as 520 A. if a rodlike model was assumed, and 650 A. on the basis of a prolate ellipsoid. This calculation shows how sensitive the inferred absolute dimensions are to the choice of a particular type of model to describe the data.

The characteristic property of fibrinogen is its interaction with thrombin to form fibrin. This transformation is associated with the appearance of new α-amino groups of glycine residues,[314] approximately four or five per molecule, if the molecular weight be taken as 500,000. Moreover, a peptide, known as fibrinopeptide, is split off from the fibrinogen in the process, the amount of material in the peptide being about 3 or 4 per cent of the weight of the fibrinogen.[315] Further discussion of the size, shape, and chemistry of fibrinogen has been given elsewhere.[316]

8. β-Lipoprotein of Human Plasma

This molecule has been studied particularly by Oncley, Melin, and Gurd.[317] It is remarkable in containing nearly 75 per cent of lipide material, mostly cholesterol, cholesterol esters and phospholipide. The amino acid residues present make up only 25 per cent of the dry weight. Nevertheless in its physical properties the lipoprotein is a typical globulin, soluble near its isoelectric point in dilute salt solutions, and precipitated by such reagents as alcohol and acetone. As yet, this type of protein has been found only in human plasma.

(313) S. Katz, K. Gutfreund, S. Shulman, and J. D. Ferry, *J. Am. Chem. Soc.* **74**, 5706 (1952).

(314) K. Bailey, F. R. Bettelheim, L. Lorand, and W. R. Middlebrook, *Nature* **167**, 233 (1951).

(315) L. Lorand, *Nature* **167**, 992 (1951).

(316) J. T. Edsall, *in* J. L. Tullis, ed., Blood Cells and Plasma Proteins, Academic Press, New York, 1953.

(317) J. L. Oncley, F. R. N. Gurd, and M. Melin, *J. Am. Chem. Soc.* **72**, 458 (1950).

The evidence that the β-lipoprotein is highly hydrated—$w = 0.6$, approximately—has already been briefly discussed on page 655. To explain the high solubility in aqueous media, it has been suggested[317] that the surface is covered with a layer of amino acid residues and phosphatide groups, with their polar or ionic portions oriented outward toward the aqueous phase. The water of hydration is involved in binding together the lipide and the polypeptide components. The anhydrous molecular weight has been estimated[179] as near 1,300,000. Consideration of the degree of hydration in conjunction with the viscosity increment (Table XI) led to the conclusion that the hydrated molecule was almost spherical, with a diameter of approximately 185 A. One such molecule would contain[317] more than 1000 molecules of cholesterol and about 500 molecules of phospholipide. It is therefore most unlikely that this lipoprotein is a definite stoichiometric compound; rather the preparations consist of a whole class of related molecules, differing somewhat among themselves in the precise amount and arrangement of the lipide transported by each.

The important ultracentrifugal studies of Gofman and his associates[317a] have revealed the presence of other lipoprotein components of rabbit and human plasma, but as yet these have not been isolated and characterized as chemical individuals.

9. MYOSIN

The preparation of actin-free myosin is primarily due to Szent-Györgyi and his school,[318] who have also investigated its interaction with actin. Extremely important investigations have also been carried out by H. H. Weber and his associates in Tübingen.[257] The molecular weight is near 840,000, and the molecule is extremely asymmetric, with a length of the order of 2000 A. and an axial ratio of the order of 100 to 1 (see page 595). The best preparations are remarkably uniform in size and shape, as indicated by the form of the concentration gradient curves in sedimentation and diffusion,[94] and there is probably no other molecule of such high asymmetry which has been obtained in such a degree of purity.

10. THE HEMOCYANINS: THEIR ASSOCIATION AND DISSOCIATION REACTIONS

The hemocyanins, the copper-containing respiratory proteins of lobsters, squids, horseshoe crabs, many snails, and other invertebrates, form a remarkable group of proteins. Their molecular weights are

(317a) J. W. Gofman, et al., Science 111, 166 (1950).
(318) A. Szent-Györgyi, Chemistry of Muscular Contraction, 2nd Ed., Academic Press, New York, 1951.

generally large, ranging from a few hundred thousand to several million in different species (see Table VIII). Moreover, the hemocyanin of a given species consists often of several different molecular sizes, the proportions of the different components changing with pH and salt concentration. These systems have been particularly investigated by Eriksson-Quensel and Svedberg,[319] and an extensive review of the subject has been given by Svedberg and Pedersen.[320] Thus the hemocyanin of the horseshoe crab, *Limulus polyphemus*, contains four components with sedimentation constants (s_{20}) of 56.6, 34.6, 16.1, and 5.9. These are stable over the pH range 5.2–10.5, but the first three disappear above this pH and are replaced by the fourth. Below pH 5.2 more complicated dissociation reactions occur. These changes are quite reversible between pH 4 and 10.8. The hemocyanin of the snail, *Helix pomatia*, also shows four main components, but not all are present at any one pH. The heaviest component, with $s_{20} = 98.9$, is present alone in neutral solution, but dissociates into smaller components acid to pH 4.6 or alkaline to 7.4. The reactions are reversible on the alkaline side up to about pH 9. In all these and other cases studied, only a few well-defined components of sharply discrete sedimentation constants are involved. The electron microscope studies of Polson and Wyckoff[62] (Table III) on certain hemocyanins give important evidence as to the nature of the molecular alterations occurring in these processes.

11. Tobacco Mosaic Virus

This virus has been one of the most intensively studied of all protein molecules, and information concerning it will be found in practically all the tables of data in this chapter, with the exception of those for osmotic pressure. Few, if any, preparations are entirely uniform with respect to molecular size and shape. Bernal and Fankuchen,[185] from x-ray studies, found that the elongated particles packed side by side in the dried *para* crystals, the interparticle spacing lateral to the long axis being 152 A. They also deduced an intraparticle unit cell, rhombohedral in shape, with edge lengths of 87 A. and a length along the axis of 68 A. Groups of three of these would fit into the structure of the virus particle if it were shaped like a hexagonal prism, with edges 87 A. long. Recently Williams[321] has brought forward evidence from electron microscopy that the cross section of the virus is indeed hexagonal. The most probable length of the intact virus particle has been estimated by Williams and Steere (see footnote to

(319) I.-B. Eriksson-Quensel and T. Svedberg, *Biol. Bull.* **71**, 498 (1936).

(320) See Ref. 39, pp. 363–72; a briefer review of the field is given by Cohn and Edsall,[2] pp. 437–41.

(321) R. C. Williams, *Biochim. et Biophys. Acta* **8**, 227 (1952).

Table III) as 2980 ± 10 A. The hydration has been estimated by
Schachman and Lauffer[184] as $w = 0.15$. This estimate is open to some
question, for reasons already indicated (page 657), but it seems highly
probable that the hydration is much less than for most viruses, and very
likely less than for most smaller proteins. The most probable value for
the molecular weight is in the neighborhood of 40,000,000.

12. Some Concluding Remarks

The proteins discussed here represent only a very small sample from
an infinite variety, but they do serve to give some indication of the
diversity of size, shape, chemical properties, and biological functions that
may be found among the proteins. The sizes of many proteins are now
known with considerable accuracy, although even here there are sources
of error which are often insufficiently appreciated. The determination
of shapes and of hydration factors is beset with pitfalls at every turn in
the investigator's way, and some conclusions which now appear established may still be shaken. Nevertheless, with the variety of powerful
tools now available for the study of these problems, progress should be
rapid. In the past, studies of the general size and shape of large molecules have proceeded for the most part independently of studies of chemical composition and the details of chemical structure. Now there are
signs that these two general lines of investigation are converging, and
that a far more detailed picture of the size, shape, and structural pattern
of protein molecules will be available within a few years. As this objective is achieved, a far deeper understanding of the biological functions of
proteins will also surely be attained.

ACKNOWLEDGMENTS

Most of this chapter was written while the author was a Fulbright Visiting Lec-
turer at the University of Cambridge in 1952.   He is indebted to numerous colleagues
in Cambridge for fruitful discussions during that period.   Valuable advice and suggestions have also come from several colleagues at Harvard, notably J. L. Oncley and
Barbara W. Low.   The work of Walter B. Dandliker, who assumed the very considerable task of preparing Table VIII, is gratefully acknowledged.   The author is
also indebted to Springer-Verlag (Berlin, Göttingen and Heidelberg) for permission
to make use of certain passages from an article in the *Fortschritte der Chemischen
Forschung* (reference 5).

CHAPTER 8

Protein Interactions

By IRVING M. KLOTZ

727

I. Introduction

The concept of protein complex has been extended to an increasing number of biological responses in efforts to provide a molecular basis for the interpretation of these phenomena. Protein interactions have been recognized particularly in investigations of drug activity and of the mechanism of action of specific ions on various tissues, as well as in studies of the role of enzymes in metabolic transformations.

Before examining the nature of some of these interactions we might profitably group the large number of examples of protein complexes into a limited number of interrelated categories so that relationships may be visualized readily (Table I). For this purpose it is convenient to distinguish first between stable complexes, which can be studied by conventional equilibrium techniques, and dynamic or transition complexes, short-lived intermediates which must be studied by instruments with very fast response or by kinetic methods. In each of these major divisions we recognize examples of high specificity in regard to the chemical nature of the interacting components as well as cases where wide ranges of structural configuration are possible. Thus among protein-large molecule complexes of the stable type, we find relatively high specificity in serological reactions, and practically no specificity, beyond certain restrictions as to type of electrostatic charge, in protein–nucleate interactions. Similarly, in complexes involving small molecules we observe globin–heme complexes and metal enzymes, near one extreme, contrasted by albumin binding of a great variety of small molecules and ions. The visual pigment rhodopsin, a specific opsin–retinene complex, may be contrasted with the nonspecific complexes of wool with a host of dye molecules.

TABLE I
PROTEIN COMPLEXES

Stable			Dynamic	
Specific	Nonspecific		Specific	Nonspecific
Antigen–antibody	Protein–nucleic acids	Protein–		Chymotrypsin
Actin–myosin	Plasma proteins	large		Trypsin
Insulin–insulin		molecule		
Globin–heme	Serum albumin–anions	Protein–	Succinic	
Metal enzymes	Insulin–anions	small	dehydrogenase	
Opsin–retinene	Wool–dyes	molecule	Carboxypeptidase	

Enzymatic complexes can be divided similarly, except that examples of extreme nonspecificity seem to be lacking. On the other hand, the looseness of the term specific is illustrated by the proteolytic enzymes, such as trypsin and chymotrypsin, which can split ester as well as amide bonds (at least in synthetic substrates). For this reason these enzymes have been placed in a straddling position in Table I. Carboxypeptidase is also allowed to overlap two columns to emphasize its relative catholicity in taste with respect to acyl amino acids or tripeptides as small-molecule substrates. Succinic dehydrogenase represents, in contrast, an example of extreme specificity, for minor variations in the structure of the succinate ion lead to molecules which almost invariably are no longer dehydrogenated enzymatically.

Descriptions of a variety of protein interactions form a major portion of the contents of this treatise. It is the purpose of this chapter to discuss some problems which are common to all of these interactions, and to point out features in which protein complexes are largely alike and others in which they show marked differences. The particular examples to be described will be chosen mostly from more recent studies with relatively homogeneous proteins and from investigations which have been quantitative and have been analyzed from an adequate theoretical background.

The vast literature on studies with insoluble proteins, such as wool, or with only poorly characterized proteins will be referred to only in passing.

II. Methods of Investigation

Numerous methods have been devised for examination of the interactions of proteins with other molecules. All of these fall into one of two categories in that they depend on changes (1) in the properties of the interacting molecule or (2) in the behavior of the protein. (In some circumstances changes in properties of both species may be evident.) It will be convenient, therefore, in describing the principles and procedures of these various approaches to treat them as members of one of these categories.

1. METHODS DEPENDENT ON CHANGES IN INTERACTING SUBSTANCE

a. Solubility

This method is suitable only with a substance of relatively limited solubility. When a solute in solution is in equilibrium with its pure phase, crystalline or liquid, its thermodynamic activity is fixed. In a specified solvent at a fixed temperature its concentration is also fixed. If protein is added to the solution, however, and if some of the solute (or one of its ions if it is an electrolyte) is bound by the protein, the total quantity of dissolved solute will increase to compensate for the bound quantity. For a nonelectrolyte, the amount of bound molecule may be equated to the increase in solubility. For electrolytes, the concentration (or strictly speaking the thermodynamic activity) of the unbound ion as well as the solubility product must be known.

Among some nonelectrolytes whose interactions with serum proteins have been studied in this way are chloroform,[1] naphthoquinones,[2] and steroids.[3] The investigations of Weir and Hastings[4] with calcium carbonate afford an excellent example of quantitative studies with an electrolyte. In this case the free calcium must obey the solubility product relationship

$$[Ca^{++}][CO_3^{--}] = K_{s.p.}', \tag{1}$$

where $K_{s.p.}'$ is the solubility product constant for the particular temperature and ionic strength used. The carbonate-ion concentration was calculated from the known CO_2 tension and pH. The bound calcium was then equated to the difference between total calcium and the $[Ca^{++}]$

(1) B. Moore and H. E. Roaf, *Proc. Royal Soc.* (London) **B77**, 86 (1905).

(2) H. Heymann and L. F. Fieser, *J. Pharmacol. Exptl. Therap.* **94**, 97 (1948).

(3) F. Bischoff and H. R. Pilhorn, *J. Biol. Chem.* **174**, 663 (1948).

(4) E. C. Weir and A. B. Hastings, *J. Biol. Chem.* **114**, 397 (1936).

calculated from Eq. (1).   Extensive data on calcium–protein complexes have been accumulated by this method.

b. Reduction in Thermodynamic Activity

A group of methods, similar in principle, measures the decrease in thermodynamic activity of the bound species.   Since activity coefficients are generally neglected, the concentration of the free, i.e., unbound, form of the species is actually determined.   Together with a knowledge of the total concentration of the interacting molecule, this information enables one to calculate the quantity of bound substance.

(1) *Equilibrium Dialysis.*   In this procedure a vessel is divided into two compartments by an especially prepared membrane which is impermeable to the protein molecules but fully permeable to the smaller molecules.   If the protein is confined to one compartment and if it binds some of the small molecules, then at equilibrium the total number of small molecules in the protein compartment will exceed that in the protein-free chamber.   The difference between these two concentrations is a measure of the concentration of bound molecule.

In practice, two possible sources of error must be recognized.   Some asymmetry in distribution of the small molecule may be obtained, if it is ionic, because of the Donnan effect.   Suitable corrections can be made for this Donnan effect, or an innocuous electrolyte may be added to reduce it to negligible proportions.   Secondly, some absorption of the small molecule may occur on the membrane itself.   In this case suitable corrections can be made[5] by setting up control dialyses in which the protein is absent and measuring the depletion of the small molecule from the solution.

The usefulness of the dialysis method for demonstrating protein interaction with salts was appreciated at least a half-century ago.[5a] Its wide potentialities were emphasized especially by Northrop and Kunitz[6] in studies of metal–protein complexes.   Numerous recent investigations of other protein interactions have also adopted this technique.

(2) *Ultrafiltration.*   This technique differs from the dialysis method primarily in that the protein-free phase is separated from the protein-containing solution by being forced through a semipermeable membrane. The concentration of small molecule in the ultrafiltrate is then determined and is assumed to be equal to the unbound concentration in the presence of protein.   Again, given the total concentration of small

(5) I. M. Klotz, F. M. Walker, and R. B. Pivan, *J. Am. Chem. Soc.* **68**, 1486 (1946).

(5a) W. A. Osborne, *J. Physiol.* **34**, 84 (1906).

(6) J. H. Northrop and M. Kunitz, *J. Gen. Physiol.* **7**, 25 (1924–5); *ibid.* **9**, 351 (1925–6); *ibid.* **11**, 481 (1927–8).

molecule, the quantity bound may be computed readily. Thermo-dynamically, ultrafiltration is equivalent to dialysis insofar as the composition of the ultrafiltrate and dialyzate are concerned.[7]

The sources of error which are important in the equilibrium dialysis method appear also in the ultrafiltration technique, and similar corrections must be made. Further difficulties may also arise from the accumulation of protein on the membrane and, possibly, from the continuous increase in protein concentration during the ultrafiltration.[8]

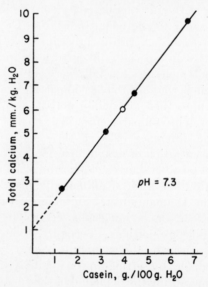

FIG. 1.   Distribution of total calcium ion concentration versus casein concentration in ultracentrifugation experiment.   Taken from A. Chanutin et al.[13]

This method has also been used widely,[9-11] including recently in studies of fatty acid interactions with albumin.[12]

(3) Ultracentrifugation.   A third method of separating the protein in the solution is to subject it to centrifugal fields of the magnitude (200,000 × g) used in sedimentation velocity measurements.   Gradients both of protein and of small molecule concentration are thereby established in the container tube.   After several hours of centrifugation, the

(7) L. B. Flexner, J. Biol. Chem. 121, 615 (1937).

(8) A. Grollman, J. Gen. Physiol. 9, 813 (1926).

(9) S. M. Rosenthal, J. Pharmacol. Exptl. Therap. 25, 449 (1925).

(10) D. M. Greenberg and L. Gunther, J. Biol. Chem. 85, 491 (1930).

(11) T. B. Coolidge, J. Biol. Chem. 135, 541 (1940).

(12) P. D. Boyer, G. A. Ballou, and J. M. Luck, J. Biol. Chem. 167, 407 (1947).

(13) A. Chanutin, S. Ludewig, and A. V. Masket, J. Biol. Chem. 143, 737 (1942).

tube is removed with a minimum of disturbance and the solution separated into fractions according to increasing distance from the axis of the ultracentrifuge. Each fraction is analyzed for content of protein and of interacting molecule. A graph is then made of concentration of the latter against that of the former (Fig. 1). An extrapolation to zero protein concentration gives the concentration of unbound small molecule. Knowing the total quantity of small molecule, one can calculate the portion bound. Such a procedure has been used by Chanutin, Ludewig, and Masket[13] in their examination of the calcium complexes of casein and serum proteins. A similar, though only qualitative, investigation has also been made of dye complexes with serum albumin by Rawson.[14] In the latter case it was even possible to see the dye move along with the protein, and the supernatant solution become colorless.

(4) *Distribution Between Phases.* If an aqueous phase containing a solute is equilibrated with an immiscible organic solvent, the solute will distribute itself between the two solvents. The ratio of equilibrium concentrations of solute, the partition coefficient, is a fixed number under given conditions of temperature, pH, and ionic strength. If now protein is added to the aqueous phase, and if it forms complexes with the other solute, the concentration of unbound solute in the aqueous phase is reduced, and hence some solute moves in from the organic phase. If the partition coefficient can be assumed to be unaffected by the presence of protein, then a determination of the new equilibrium concentration of solute in the organic phase allows one to compute directly the corresponding concentration of unbound small molecule in the aqueous protein solution, and thus ultimately the quantity bound.

This method, called partition analysis by Karush,[14a] has been used to study protein interactions with mercurials[15] as well as with organic anions.[16] It possesses certain distinct advantages over some of the preceding methods in that no corrections need be made for Donnan effects or adsorption of solute by a membrane. On the other hand, the organic solvent is generally slightly soluble in the aqueous phase where it may exert a competitive effect in the protein interactions with the primary solute. Also a liquid-liquid interface encourages any tendency toward surface denaturation of the protein.

Of course the phase immiscible with water need not be another liquid. In studies of metal–protein complexes the free-metal concentration could be determined by equilibrating the aqueous solution with an ion

(14) R. A. Rawson, *Am. J. Physiol.* **138**, 708 (1943).
(14a) F. Karush, *J. Am. Chem. Soc.* **72**, 2705 (1950).
(15) W. L. Hughes, Jr., *Cold Spring Harbor Symposia Quant. Biol.* **14**, 79 (1950).
(16) F. Karush, *J. Am. Chem. Soc.* **73**, 1246 (1951).

exchanger, for example. Such a procedure has been used widely in the study of complex ions,[17-19] and its possible application to protein complexes has been pointed out.[20] In a qualitative form similar methods with charcoal as the solid phase were utilized to compare the adsorption capacity of plasma in various clinical manifestations.[21] Staining of cellophane has likewise been used to compare the affinities of proteins for dyes.[14,22]

(5) Electromotive Force. In studies of the interactions of a protein with an ion it may be possible to find an electrode which undergoes a reversible reaction with the ion. In such a case, the electromotive force of a suitable cell can be measured,[23,24] which will permit the calculation of the concentration of unbound ion in the presence of the protein.

This method is, of course, the one which has been used most widely in quantitative studies of acid–base properties of proteins. Since such interactions have been discussed widely elsewhere (see Chap. 6), we might consider instead, as an example, the recent work of Scatchard, Scheinberg, and Armstrong[25] on the binding of chloride ions by albumin. Two solutions were prepared containing substantially identical concentrations of NaCl but only one containing albumin. An Ag-AgCl electrode, which is reversible to chloride ion, was placed in each solution, and the solutions were then joined electrically through a saturated potassium chloride bridge. The resultant cell may be represented as

Ag, AgCl, Protein solution + NaCl, satd. KCl, NaCl solution, AgCl, Ag.   (2)

The electromotive force (e.m.f.) of such a cell can be shown[25] to be given by

$$\varepsilon = \frac{RT}{F} \ln \frac{[Cl^-]'}{[Cl^-]},\tag{3}$$

where $[Cl^-]'$ is the activity of the chloride ion in the absence of protein, $[Cl^-]$ in the presence of albumin, and R, T, and F have the usual significance in electrochemical measurements. If we make the reasonable assumption that the activity coefficients of Cl^- are approximately equal in both solutions, then the equation for the e.m.f. gives one directly the

(17) K. H. Gustavson, *Svensk Kem. Tid.* **56**, 14 (1944); *ibid.* **58**, 274 (1946).

(18) K. H. Gustavson, *J. Soc. Leather Trades' Chemists* **34**, 259 (1950).

(19) J. Schubert, *J. Phys. & Colloid Chem.* **52**, 340 (1948).

(20) J. Schubert, *J. Phys. Chem.* **56**, 113 (1952).

(21) M. C. Ehrström, *Acta Med. Scand.* **91**, 191 (1937).

(22) T. H. Allen and P. D. Orahovats, *Am. J. Physiol.* **161**, 473 (1950).

(23) D. I. Hitchcock, *J. Gen. Physiol.* **16**, 357 (1932–33).

(24) N. R. Joseph, *J. Biol. Chem.* **130**, 203 (1939).

(25) G. Scatchard, I. H. Scheinberg, and S. H. Armstrong, Jr., *J. Am. Chem. Soc.* **72**, 535, 540 (1950).

ratio of concentrations of free chloride ion, or in other words the decrease in free concentration due to the presence of protein. The calculation of the bound chloride follows directly from a knowledge of the total ion present.

Several difficulties limit the applicability of the e.m.f. method. It is necessary first to find an electrode reversible to the ion being studied. Even when such an electrode is available, the presence of protein may cause it to perform erratically.[25] Also, reliable e.m.f. measurements are generally difficult to obtain at very low concentrations of electrolyte. Where technical difficulties can be overcome, this method is likely to be of most value in studies of protein interactions with metallic ions.

c. Migration in Electric Field

It is apparent that an ion bound to a protein will exhibit a pronounced change in electrical mobility. The conductivities of alkaline earth salts of casein or serum globulin are markedly lower than those of alkali metal salts.[26-28] Zinc complexes of serum albumin have also been investigated by conductivity methods.[29] Conductometric titrations have been used, furthermore, in studies of gelatin–dye combinations.[30] Also, transport numbers have been measured[28] to study interactions between proteins and ions.

These methods are very sensitive to the presence of small quantities of ionic impurities which often accompany proteins. Nevertheless, it is evident from the literature that they have not yet been fully exploited even within their limitations.

d. Polarographic Reduction

With the dropping mercury electrode it is possible to reduce certain substances at a characteristic potential, and slightly above this potential to obtain a limiting current, the diffusion current, which is dependent on the concentration of the reducible substance. If this substance is bound to a protein, its diffusion coefficient will be essentially that of the protein and hence much smaller than that of the free reducible substance. Consequently, the diffusion current should drop with increasing protein concentration. One thus has at hand a method of measuring the quantity of protein-bound reducible substance.

Polarographic reduction has been used recently to study metal com-

(26) T. B. Robertson, *J. Phys. Chem.* **14**, 601 (1910); *ibid.* **15**, 166 (1911).
(27) M. Adolf, *Kolloid-Beihefte* **17**, 1 (1923).
(28) D. M. Greenberg and C. L. A. Schmidt, *J. Gen. Physiol.* **8**, 271 (1926).
(29) W. Pauli and M. Schön, *Biochem. Z.* **153**, 253 (1924).
(30) A. E. Stearn, *J. Biol. Chem.* **91**, 325 (1931).

plexes of proteins[31-34] as well as the binding of methyl orange[35] by albumin.   With azo-coupled antigens it is also possible to detect interactions with antibodies.[36]

It is difficult to know beforehand whether polarographic reduction can be used with a particular substance in the presence of protein.   Protein adsorption on the mercury may affect the surface of the drop, and viscosity changes may also affect the diffusion current.[37]   With most instruments, furthermore, the diffusion current cannot be measured with a precision which compares with some of the other methods of measuring uptake of molecules by proteins.   An analysis of the potentialities of the polarographic approach has been given by Saroff and Mark.[32]

e. Diffusion

The free diffusion of a molecule may be greatly affected by its combination with a protein.   A particularly striking demonstration of such an effect has been used very extensively by Bennhold.[38]   A 5 per cent gelatin gel is formed in a test tube, and an aqueous dye solution, e.g., naphthol yellow, is placed on top.   A corresponding tube is also prepared with an aqueous protein solution containing the dye, on top of the gel. The diffusion of the color, and thus of the dye into the gel, can be followed readily.   With albumin as protein, for example, the naphthol yellow diffuses more slowly into the gel, in fact with the same speed as the albumin—a clear demonstration of the combination of the dye with albumin.

In some cases, e.g., Brilliant Congo R, the dye itself will not diffuse into the gel, presumably because it actually exists as a micellar aggregate of large size in aqueous solution.   In the presence of albumin, diffusion into the gel can be brought about, evidently because this protein produces some disaggregation of the dye, binds the monomer, and carries it along into the gel.

Some very attractive colored diagrams of both types of effect on diffusion have been published by Bennhold.[38]   Unfortunately this method does not lend itself conveniently to quantitative formulation.

(31) E. Pfankuch and K. Hagenguth, *Biochem. Z.* **313**, 1 (1942).
(32) H. A. Saroff and H. J. Mark, Naval Medical Research Institute Reports, Project NM 000 006, Report No. 1, 1949.
(33) T. Suzutani, *Japan. J. Physiol.* **1**, 213 (1951); *C. A.* **45**, 6895 (1951).
(34) C. Tanford, *J. Am. Chem. Soc.* **73**, 2066 (1951).
(35) W. Stricks and I. M. Kolthoff, *J. Am. Chem. Soc.* **71**, 1519 (1949).
(36) B. Breyer and F. J. Radcliff, *Nature* **167**, 79 (1951).
(37) I. M. Kolthoff and J. J. Lingane, Polarography, Interscience Publishers, Inc., New York, 1941.
(38) H. Bennhold, E. Kylin, and St. Rusznyak, Die Eiweisskörper des Blutplasmas, T. Steinkopff, Dresden, 1938, pp. 220–303.

f. Changes in Spectra

Since bound molecules are in a different environment from that of the aqueous solution, it is not surprising to find that spectra of molecules that can be bound are modified in the presence of suitable proteins.[39-41] The changes (Fig. 2) may be used to calculate the extent of binding.[42]

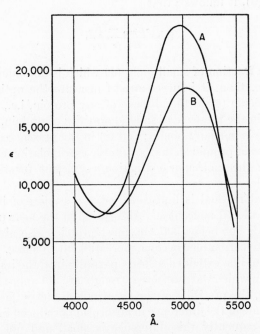

Fig. 2. Absorption spectra of azosulfathiazole (A), in buffer at pH 6.9; (B), in buffer containing 0.2 % bovine albumin at pH 6.9.[42]

In solutions of low protein concentration which contain both bound and unbound small molecules, the absorption of light may be expressed as the sum of the contributions of both forms:

$$\log (I_0/I) = E_1 C_1 d + E_2 C_2 d. \tag{4}$$

In this equation E_1 represents the molecular extinction coefficient of the unbound molecule, C_1 its concentration, E_2 and C_2 are the corresponding values for the bound molecule, d is the depth of the optical path, and I_0

(39) T. B. Robertson, The Physical Chemistry of Proteins, Longmans, Green and Co., New York, 1918.

(40) R. Hill and H. F. Holden, Biochem. J. 20, 1326 (1926).

(41) S. E. Sheppard and A. L. Geddes, J. Chem. Phys. 13, 63 (1945).

(42) I. M. Klotz, J. Am. Chem. Soc. 68, 2299 (1946).

and I are the intensities of the light emerging from pure solvent and solution, respectively. If we define the apparent value of E, E_{app}, by the relation

$$\log (I_0/I) = E_{app}(C_1 + C_2)d, \tag{5}$$

then since a particular optical density, $\log (I_0/I)$, is applicable in both Eqs. (4) and (5), it follows[42] that

$$\alpha = \frac{E_{app} - E_2}{E_1 - E_2}, \tag{6}$$

where α is the fraction of small molecule which is unbound.

In practice, then, it is necessary to measure the optical density of the small molecule (a) in the absence of any protein, i.e., when entirely unbound; (b) in the presence of small quantities of protein, i.e., when the small molecule is partially bound; and (c) in the presence of increasingly large quantities of protein so that a suitable extrapolation can be made to determine E_2, the molecular extinction coefficient for the completely bound molecule.

This optical method is limited largely to studies of interactions of proteins with colored molecules. Absorption in the near ultraviolet can also be utilized, but below 300 mμ, most proteins also absorb strongly, and appropriate corrections become more difficult to make. In principle, the method could be extended at least partially into the infrared, so long as the regions in which water absorbs strongly are not approached.

In practice, the precision of the spectrophotometric method depends on the magnitude of the difference in absorption produced by the presence of protein. Frequently this difference is small and not adaptable to quantitative measurements.

g. Biological Activity

A variety of biological responses are sensitive to the concentration of specific molecules, particularly ions. McLean and Hastings,[43] for example, utilized the contractile response of the isolated frog heart to estimate free calcium. In essence the free Ca^{++} was determined by matching the unknown solution with standard solutions in their effects on the amplitude of ventricular contraction. By this procedure, binding constants for Ca^{++} with a variety of proteins were calculated.

Other biological indicators, such as hemolysis of erythrocytes[12] or growth of microorganisms[44] have also been used, but primarily for qualita-

(43) F. C. McLean and A. B. Hastings, *J. Biol. Chem.* **107**, 337 (1934); *ibid.* **108**, 285 (1935).

(44) B. D. Davis and R. J. Dubos, *J. Exptl. Med.* **86**, 215 (1947).

tive studies of protein interactions. Semiquantitative results for biotin–avidin combinations have been obtained by microbiological assay.[45] In general, the precision of a biological indicator is poor and the response is sensitive to only a limited range of concentrations. Furthermore, there is always the possibility that the tissue itself binds an appreciable fraction of the ion or molecule being studied so that it competes with the protein and thus changes the equilibrium.

2. METHODS DEPENDENT ON CHANGES IN PROTEIN

a. Changes in pH

If ions are bound by a protein, their electrostatic fields alone will affect the acid–base character of the titratable side chains of the protein. This effect can be measured conveniently either by (1) determination of changes in titration curves or (2) measurement of shifts in isoionic pH.

(1) *Titration Curves.* The effect of anion binding on acid-titration curves has been demonstrated most strikingly by Steinhardt, Fugitt, and Harris[46,47] for the case of wool (Fig. 3). Comparison of titrations with over forty different strong acids (only five of which are illustrated in Fig. 3) showed an increasing displacement toward higher pH's the larger the acid anion. The magnitude of the displacement is a measure of the degree of binding of the anion by the protein. With certain simplifying assumptions it is also possible to calculate affinity constants for these anion associations.[48]

Similar results, though somewhat smaller in magnitude, were obtained with a soluble protein, egg albumin.

Base titration curves of wool are sensitive to the type of cation present, and shifts along the pH axis have been observed[49] which are comparable in magnitude to those described with acids. These curves may be used, therefore, to estimate qualitatively cation affinities for the protein. Technical difficulties, such as the instability of proteins, especially those containing sulfur, in the presence of even dilute alkali, as well as the presence of several types of titratable groups in the basic region, make it difficult to use these curves for quantitative calculations of affinity constants.

(2) *Shifts in Isoionic pH.* If an electrodialyzed protein is dissolved

(45) L. D. Wright and H. R. Skeggs, *Arch. Biochem.* **12**, 27 (1947).
(46) J. Steinhardt, C. H. Fugitt, and M. Harris, *J. Research Natl. Bur. Standards* **26**, 293 (1941).
(47) J. Steinhardt, *Ann. N. Y. Acad. Sci.* **41**, 287 (1941).
(48) J. Steinhardt, *J. Research Natl. Bur. Standards* **28**, 191 (1942).
(49) J. Steinhardt and E. M. Zaiser, *J. Biol. Chem.* **183**, 789 (1950).

in water, the pH of the solution may be defined as the isoionic point.[49a] To this aqueous solution we could add another solute which when dissolved by itself in water produces no hydrogen or hydroxyl ions. Let this additional solute be a salt, for example. The pH of the protein solution containing the salt will differ, in general, from that of the salt-free solution. We shall continue to call this new pH the isoionic point, so long as the salt itself produces no hydrogen or hydroxyl ions in water,

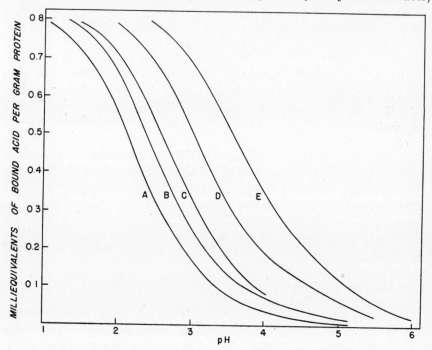

FIG. 3. Combination of wool protein with strong acids: A, hydrochloric acid; B, nitric acid; C, o-nitrobenzenesulfonic acid; D, β-naphthalenesulfonic acid; E, picric acid. Data taken from J. Steinhardt et al.[46]

and recognize that the isoionic point may change as the character of the aqueous solution is altered.

Salts may change the isoionic pH of a protein solution purely because of ion-cloud effects, and the magnitude of this change has been calculated quantitatively[50] with the aid of the Debye-Hückel theory. If, in addition, one of the salt ions, for example the anion, is bound to the protein, there will be an additional effect on the pH of the solution because the

(49a) S. P. L. Sørensen, K. Linderstrøm-Lang, and E. Lund, J. Gen. Physiol. **8**, 543 (1927).

(50) G. Scatchard and E. S. Black, J. Phys. & Colloid Chem. **53**, 88 (1949).

bound anion will decrease the ionization of protons from the protein or, in other words, increase the uptake of protons from the solution by the protein. Thus, binding of anions by a protein produces a shift of the isoionic point toward a higher pH. By similar reasoning one can show that binding of cations by a protein shifts the isoionic point to lower pH's.

Examples of such shifts for serum albumin and a variety of anions are illustrated in Fig. 4. It is apparent that rather marked changes can be obtained, especially with large organic anions.

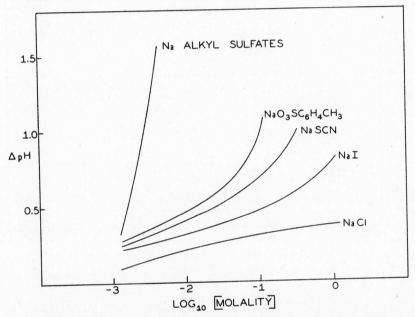

FIG. 4. Displacement of pH of isoionic albumin by salts. Data for mixture of C_8–C_{18} alkyl sulfates with horse serum albumin, taken from F. W. Putnam and H. Neurath.[96a] All other curves refer to human serum albumin and are taken from data of G. Scatchard and E. S. Black.[50]

Shifts in isoionic pH may also be used to make quantitative estimates of the binding of ions by a protein. For this purpose we may use the equation derived by Scatchard and Black[50]

$$r = W(\Delta pH), \tag{7}$$

where r is the number of moles of bound univalent ion per mole of protein,[51] ΔpH is the observed shift in isoionic point, and W is a factor which

(51) For these calculations it is assumed that either the cation or anion of the added salt is bound by the protein. If both are bound, r represents the difference in number of bound ions.

depends on the ionic strength of the solution. To facilitate calculations from pH measurements, Fig. 5 has been prepared from data given by Scatchard and Black.[50] Values of W may be read off easily and substituted into Eq. (7) so that r may be computed readily.

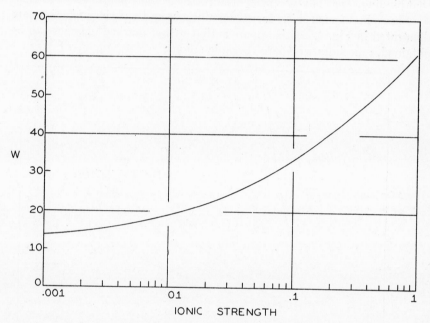

FIG. 5.   Factor for calculation of extent of binding from displacement of isoionic pH.

b. Optical Properties

Interactions of proteins with radiation may also be modified if the protein forms complexes with other molecules. These changes may become visible by any one of four optical techniques: (1) spectrophotometry, (2) refractometry, (3) light scattering, or (4) polarimetry.

(1) Spectrophotometry. Changes in absorption spectra are particularly useful in studying unstable transition complexes between substrates and enzymes. This method has been exploited especially with the heme proteins. With catalase, for example, the initial observations of Stern[52] of spectroscopic alterations when a complex was formed with ethyl hydroperoxide have been extended and clarified by Chance[53] by some very elegant optical methods. Similar methods have been used to

(52) K. G. Stern, J. Biol. Chem. 114, 473 (1936).
(53) B. Chance, J. Biol. Chem. 179, 1331 (1949).

study anion complexes of catalase.[53-55] The kinetics of these enzymatic reactions may be followed quantitatively by these methods.

One need only be reminded that numerous investigations of hemoglobin equilibria with oxygen and with carbon monoxide have also utilized photometric methods.[56-60]

(2) *Refractometry.* Small changes in refractive index of solutions have been observed in mixtures of sulfanilamide and serum[61] which have been attributed to combination between the two substances. Refractive indices of gelatin–detergent complexes have also been measured.[62] This technique is not very sensitive to complex formation.

(3) *Light Scattering.* The application of light scattering to the analysis of the behavior of macromolecules has been especially useful in establishing molecular weights and shapes. Thus where interactions lead to protein aggregations, light scattering is a convenient tool in studying the complex.[15,63] Binding of small ions by proteins may also be detected[64] by the effect on the second virial coefficient in the turbidity equation. With highly charged molecules, however, large changes in turbidity may be produced by electrostatic effects.

Light scattering has been used to study the kinetics and equilibria of dimerization of serum albumin in the presence of mercuric ion.[15,63]

Some information on the binding by albumin of calcium ions[64] and of dodecyl sulfate[65] has also been gleaned by this technique. The method has only limited abilities in the study of interactions of proteins with small molecules, but it is exceptionally suitable in interactions involving changes in size and shape, particularly because of the short time required to complete observations. Thus it is being used with special effectiveness in investigations of antigen–antibody reactions.[66,67]

(4) *Optical Rotation.* Changes in optical rotation have been shown

(54) B. Chance, *J. Biol. Chem.* **179**, 1341 (1949).
(55) K. Agner and H. Theorell, *Arch. Biochem.* **10**, 321 (1946).
(56) J. Haldane, *J. Physiol.* **18**, 430 (1895).
(57) C. G. Douglas and J. S. Haldane, *Skand. Arch. Physiol.* **25**, 169 (1911).
(58) M. L. Anson, J. Barcroft, A. E. Mirsky, and S. Oinuma, *Proc. Roy. Soc.* (London) **B97**, 61 (1925).
(59) R. Hill, *Proc. Roy. Soc.* (London) **B120**, 472 (1936).
(60) J. Wyman, Jr., *Advances in Protein Chem.* **4**, 407 (1948).
(61) M. Paget and C. Vittu, *Compt. rend. soc. biol.* **140**, 227 (1946).
(62) K. G. A. Pankhurst and R. C. M. Smith, *Trans. Faraday Soc.* **43**, 511 (1947).
(63) P. Doty and J. T. Edsall, *Advances in Protein Chem.* **6**, 37 (1951).
(64) J. T. Edsall, H. Edelhoch, R. Lontie, and P. R. Morrison, *J. Am. Chem. Soc.* **72**, 4641 (1950).
(65) J. A. Friend, B. S. Harrap, and J. H. Schulman, *Nature* **168**, 910 (1951).
(66) D. Gitlin and H. Edelhoch, *J. Immunol.* **66**, 67 (1951).
(67) R. J. Goldberg and D. H. Campbell, *J. Immunol.* **66**, 79 (1951).

744   IRVING M. KLOTZ

to occur in interactions of egg albumin with detergents.[67a,68] The interpretation would be very much complicated by accompanying denaturation effects[69] which seem evident from the prolonged time over which these optical effects extend.

c. Osmotic Pressure

When a molecule combines with a protein, the osmotic pressure of the solution is definitely altered. Scatchard, Batchelder, and Brown[70] were able to detect by this means the binding of chloride ions by albumin. In general, however, this method can give only indications of complex formation, and any results would have to be verified by other methods.

d. Sedimentation

In some cases the interaction of protein molecules with small molecules or ions leads to the formation of protein dimers or aggregates. In such a situation sedimentation properties may be altered in a clearly interpretable fashion. Thus, Hughes[15,71] was able to study the equilibria of mercaptalbumin in the presence of mercuric ion,

$$
\text{Alb—SH} + \text{HgCl}_2 \rightleftharpoons \text{Alb—S—HgCl} + \text{H}^+ + \text{Cl}^-
$$
$$
+
$$
$$
\text{Alb—S—H}
$$
$$
\text{Alb—S—Hg—S—Alb} + \text{H}^+ + \text{Cl}^- \tag{8}
$$

by means of the ultracentrifuge, for the dimer appeared with a sedimentation constant, S_{20}, of 6.5 in contrast to that of 4.6 for normal albumin. Similar studies of insulin–thiocyanate combinations have been carried out by Fredericq and Neurath[72] and of albumin–benzene interactions by Bresler,[73] though light-scattering measurements are likely to be more convenient for quantitative studies of such dimerization equilibria as well as of the kinetics of association.

(67a) H. P. Lundgren and R. A. O'Connell, *Ind. Eng. Chem.* **36**, 370 (1944).
(68) S. N. Timasheff and F. F. Nord, *Arch. Biochem. and Biophys.* **31**, 309 (1951).
(69) W. Kauzmann, R. B. Simpson, M. T. Watson, B. Levedahl, J. Schellman, and H. K. Frensdorff, Abstracts of the 120th Meeting of the American Chemical Society, New York, Sept. 3–7, 1951, p. 11P.
(70) G. Scatchard, A. C. Batchelder, and A. Brown, *J. Am. Chem. Soc.* **68**, 2320 (1946).
(71) W. L. Hughes, Jr., *J. Am. Chem. Soc.* **69**, 1836 (1947).
(72) E. Fredericq and H. Neurath, *J. Am. Chem. Soc.* **72**, 2684 (1950).
(73) S. E. Bresler, *Biokhimiya* **14**, 180 (1949).

e. Electrophoresis

Changes in electrophoretic mobility of proteins have been used widely to investigate interactions with large molecules, such as nucleic acids,[74-76] polysaccharides,[77,78] or other proteins,[79,80] as well as with a variety of small ions.[38,81-88a] In some cases[75,83,85] the complex appears as a clearly distinguishable new peak, but such behavior need not be observed generally.

The electrophoretic technique as a method of obtaining thermodynamic data for protein complexes has been carefully analyzed by Smith and Briggs[86] and, in somewhat greater detail, by Alberty and Marvin[87,88] (see also Chap. 6). If a protein, P, exists in equilibrium with a complexing constituent, A, so that a number of forms $PA, PA_2, \ldots PA_i$ occur, then, as was shown by Tiselius,[81] a constituent mobility $\bar{u}_P$ may be defined for the protein which in essence gives the sum of the contributions of each complex to the resultant mobility of the protein. Similarly, a constituent mobility $\bar{u}_A$ may be defined for the other interacting substance. These constituent mobilities, $\bar{u}_P$ and $\bar{u}_A$, may be evaluated from the slower-ascending boundary and the faster-descending boundary, respectively, of the electrophoretic pattern. If the mobilities of free P and free A are also known, then the extent of complex formation can be computed in certain special cases. Such computations have been made for complexes of serum albumin with methyl orange[86] and with chloride,[88] and the results obtained have been in good agreement with other methods.

The moving-boundary technique possesses the distinct advantage of being applicable to a wide variety of protein complexes with large and

(74) E. Stenhagen and T. Teorell, *Trans. Faraday Soc.* **35**, 743 (1939).
(75) L. G. Longsworth and D. A. MacInnes, *J. Gen. Physiol.* **25**, 514 (1942).
(76) E. Goldwasser and F. W. Putnam, *J. Phys. & Colloid Chem.* **54**, 79 (1950).
(77) E. Chargaff, M. Ziff, and D. H. Moore, *J. Biol. Chem.* **139**, 383 (1941).
(78) F. B. Seibert and D. W. Watson, *J. Biol. Chem.* **140**, 55 (1941).
(79) L. G. Longsworth, R. K. Cannan, and D. A. MacInnes, *J. Am. Chem. Soc.* **62**, 2580 (1940).
(80) G. W. Schwert, F. W. Putnam, and D. R. Briggs, *Arch. Biochem.* **4**, 371 (1944).
(81) A. Tiselius, *Nova Acta Regiae Soc. Sci. Upsaliensis* [4], **7**, No. 4 (1930).
(82) E. Stenhagen and E. K. Rideal, *Biochem. J.* **33**, 1591 (1939).
(83) H. P. Lundgren, D. W. Elam, and R. A. O'Connell, *J. Biol. Chem.* **149**, 183 (1943).
(84) G. A. Ballou, P. D. Boyer, and J. M. Luck, *J. Biol. Chem.* **159**, 111 (1945).
(85) F. W. Putnam and H. Neurath, *J. Biol. Chem.* **159**, 195 (1945).
(86) R. F. Smith and D. R. Briggs, *J. Phys. & Colloid Chem.* **54**, 33 (1950).
(87) R. A. Alberty and H. H. Marvin, Jr., *J. Phys. & Colloid Chem.* **54**, 47 (1950).
(88) R. A. Alberty and H. H. Marvin, Jr., *J. Am. Chem. Soc.* **73**, 3220 (1951).
(88a) E. Volkin, *J. Biol. Chem.* **175**, 675 (1948).

small molecules. In some cases, however, it is not capable of obtaining data with the same precision as other methods.

f. Precipitation

, The formation of insoluble complexes has been the classical method of analysis of antigen–antibody combinations, to be discussed in Vol. II. Other protein-protein interactions have also been studied in this way.[89,90] Information on the stoichiometry of a variety of complexes of proteins with small molecules has also been obtained by precipitation techniques.[89-95] Conversely, with suitable precautions, these interactions may be used to estimate the number of charged side chains in proteins.[93,96] Likewise, estimates of the isoelectric point of proteins may be made from the pH limit of precipitation with anionic detergents[96a] though not with cationic detergents.

It is also frequently possible to isolate complexes in which not all sites on the protein are saturated. Thus a crystalline derivative of β-lacto-globulin containing two moles of dodecyl sulfate has been obtained.[97] A very large number of crystalline serum albumin complexes have been isolated with only a few small ions associated with the protein.[98]

g. Viscosity

Changes in viscosity have been used in a qualitative way to detect complex formation between proteins and nucleic acids,[99] as well as between proteins and smaller molecules such as detergents[100] or fatty acids.[100a] Occasionally discontinuities may be detected in curves of viscosity increment as a function of concentration and these have been

(89) F. Haurowitz, Kolloid-Z. 74, 208 (1936).
(90) A. Kleczkowski, Biochem. J. 40, 677 (1946).
(91) L. M. Chapman, D. M. Greenberg, and C. L. A. Schmidt, J. Biol. Chem. 72, 707 (1927).
(92) F. W. Putnam and H. Neurath, J. Biol. Chem. 150, 263 (1943).
(93) H. Fraenkel-Conrat and M. Cooper, J. Biol. Chem. 154, 239 (1944).
(94) G. A. Kausche and F. Hahn, Z. Naturforsch. 36, 437 (1948).
(95) E. Fredericq and H. Neurath, J. Am. Chem. Soc. 72, 2684 (1950).
(96) G. E. Perlmann, J. Biol. Chem. 137, 707 (1941).
(96a) F. W. Putnam and H. Neurath, J. Am. Chem. Soc. 66, 692 (1944).
(97) T. L. McMeekin, B. D. Polis, E. S. Della Monica, and J. H. Custer, J. Am. Chem. Soc. 71, 3606 (1949).
(98) J. Lewin, J. Am. Chem. Soc. 73, 3906 (1951).
(99) J. P. Greenstein and W. V. Jenrette, Cold Spring Harbor Symposia Quant. Biol. 9, 236 (1941).
(100) H. Neurath and F. W. Putnam, J. Biol. Chem. 160, 397 (1945).
(100a) P. D. Boyer, G. A. Ballou, and J. M. Luck, J. Biol. Chem. 162, 199 (1946).

interpreted in terms of the stoichiometry of the complexes. In general, though, such investigations serve only for qualitative examination.

h. Surface Tension

Again in these measurements monolayers of proteins may show discontinuities in their surface pressure–area curves in the presence of molecules such as detergents[101,101a] or fatty acids.[102] Some qualitative ideas about the strength of the interaction and the stoichiometry may be obtainable from an examination of such curves.

i. Magnetic Properties

Most proteins, containing only covalent, paired-electron bonds, exhibit only diamagnetic properties. In metalloproteins, however, atomic paramagnetism, attributable roughly to unpaired electrons in the metal ion, may be appreciable. Furthermore, the magnitude of the magnetic susceptibility in such a system depends strongly on the nature of the bond between the metal and complexing groups. Thus ferrohemoglobin has a large magnetic moment whereas oxyhemoglobin and carbonylhemoglobin have zero moments.[103] Consequently it is readily possible to make a quantitative study of the uptake of oxygen by ferrohemoglobin.[104] Similarly, the conversion of hemin to hematin produces a change in bond type of the Fe^{+++} ion, accompanied by a drop in magnetic susceptibility, and hence again equilibrium constants can be evaluated from a magnetic titration.[105,106]

The primary drawback of the magnetic method is its practical limitation to proteins containing metals, and furthermore, relatively high percentages ($\gtrsim 1\%$) of metal. Also, it is generally necessary to use larger quantities of protein than are required for optical methods. In the actual evaluation of equilibrium constants, therefore, other methods prove more convenient; for an investigation of the nature of the bonds involved, however, the magnetic method is very powerful.

j. Biological Activity

With proteins having enzymatic properties, the extent of binding of the prosthetic group, coenzyme, or substrate may be determined by biological activity. With tyrosinase, for example, rates of oxygen uptake

(101) H. B. Bull, *J. Am. Chem. Soc.* **67**, 10 (1945).
(101a) H. B. Bull, *J. Am. Chem. Soc.* **68**, 747 (1946).
(102) R. Goiffon and N. Larthe, *Ann. biol. clin.* (Paris) **6**, 245 (1948).
(103) L. Pauling and C. D. Coryell, *Proc. Natl. Acad. Sci. U. S.* **22**, 210 (1936).
(104) C. D. Coryell, L. Pauling, and R. W. Dodson, *J. Phys. Chem.* **43**, 825 (1939).
(105) C. D. Coryell, F. Stitt, and L. Pauling, *J. Am. Chem. Soc.* **59**, 633 (1937).
(106) C. D. Coryell and F. Stitt, *J. Am. Chem. Soc.* **62**, 2942 (1940).

show a definite sigmoid dependence[107] on the cupric ion concentration and could be used for quantitative binding studies. In a complementary direction, decrease in activity may be used to study inhibitor interactions. The protection of serum proteins against heat coagulation in the presence of suramin,[108] and the stabilization of albumin to denaturation in the presence of fatty acids,[109,100a] have been extensively employed in investigations of protein complexes. Similarly, from the effect of iodide and thiocyanate on the clotting process Edsall and Lever[110] have shown that these ions combine with fibrin or fibrinogen.

Most often, reactions involving enzymes are too rapid to be studied by equilibrium techniques. Under suitable conditions, nevertheless, kinetic measurements interpreted by the Michaelis-Menten equation[111] may be employed to extract some thermodynamic information on the enzyme–substrate complexes. A critical discussion of the applicability of this approach has been given recently by Neurath and Schwert.[112]

III. Theory of Multiple Equilibria

Practically all protein combinations produce complexes with the components present in molecular quantities other than in a simple ratio of one to one. This feature of these interactions must be kept in mind in the interpretation of derived data, as well as in the design of experimental procedures. A full appreciation of the characteristics of multiple equilibria is, therefore, desirable as a prelude to a discussion of the significance of the experimental findings.

1. SINGLE ASSOCIATION

Let us consider first the simplest situation in which the protein, P, combines with only one molecule of the type A to form the single complex, PA:

$$P + A = PA. \tag{9}$$

The association constant, k, is defined by the equation

$$\frac{(PA)}{(P)(A)} = k, \tag{10}$$

(107) A. B. Lerner, T. B. Fitzpatrick, E. Calkins, and W. H. Summerson, J. Biol. Chem. **187**, 793 (1950).
(108) W. A. Collier, Z. ges. exptl. Med. **54**, 606 (1927).
(109) P. D. Boyer, F. G. Lum, G. A. Ballou, J. M. Luck, and R. G. Rice, J. Biol. Chem. **162**, 181 (1946).
(110) J. T. Edsall and W. F. Lever, J. Biol. Chem. **191**, 735 (1951).
(111) L. Michaelis and M. L. Menten, Biochem. Z. **49**, 333 (1913).
(112) H. Neurath and G. W. Schwert, Chem. Revs. **46**, 69 (1950).

in which the quantities in parentheses represent the concentrations of the respective species. It follows readily from Eq. (10) that

$$(PA) = k(P)(A). \tag{11}$$

In addition, we shall find it useful to make a substitution for (P) in Eq. (11) by means of the relation

$$(P_t) = (PA) + (P), \tag{12}$$

where (P_t) represents the total protein concentration. We thus obtain

$$(PA) = k(A)[(P_t) - (PA)], \tag{13}$$

and by rearrangement

$$(PA) + k(A)(PA) = k(A)(P_t), \tag{14}$$

or

$$\frac{(PA)}{(P_t)} = \frac{k(A)}{1 + k(A)}. \tag{15}$$

The ratio $(PA)/(P_t)$ is evidently the number of moles of bound A per mole of total protein and we shall designate it by the symbol r, in anticipation of future use. Thus

$$r = \frac{k(A)}{1 + k(A)}. \tag{16}$$

Equation (16) will strike many as familiar. It is essentially the same as that derived by Langmuir[113] to describe certain adsorption isotherms. It seems appropriate to emphasize, therefore, that the adherence of a set of binding data to Eq. (16) does not justify the assertion that the process is one of adsorption. Equation (16) is also an expression of the law of mass action.[114-116] In a homogeneous solution there is probably little to be gained by describing interactions between solutes in terms of adsorption. A much clearer insight becomes available by application of the concepts of stoichiometric equilibria.

Several alternative forms of Eq. (16) are also useful, particularly in connection with the fitting of the equation to data. For such purposes, a linear equivalent is especially desirable. If we transpose the factor (A) in the numerator on the right-hand side to the left and invert the resultant, we obtain

$$\frac{(A)}{r} = \frac{1}{k} + (A). \tag{17}$$

(113) I. Langmuir, J. Am. Chem. Soc. **40**, 1361 (1918).
(114) K. Linderstrøm-Lang, Compt. rend. trav. lab. Carlsberg. Sér. chim. **15**, No. 7 (1924).
(115) L. Michaelis, Z. physiol. Chem. **152**, 183 (1925).
(116) D. I. Hitchcock, J. Am. Chem. Soc. **48**, 2870 (1926).

An equivalent form is

$$\frac{1}{r} = \frac{1}{k}\frac{1}{(A)} + 1.$$ (18)

A third form[117,117a,117b,118] is obtained if we use Eq. (16) to derive first a relation for $1 - r$:

$$1 - r = 1 - \frac{k(A)}{1 + k(A)} = \frac{1}{1 + k(A)}.$$ (19)

With the aid of Eq. (19) we find that

$$\frac{r}{1 - r} = k(A).$$ (20)

A simple linear relation is obtained by transposition to the form

$$\frac{r}{(A)} = k - kr.$$ (21)

2. Two Sites for Association

We may turn now to the situation where P combines with one or two molecules of A to form the complexes PA or PA_2:

$$P + A = PA; PA + A = PA_2.$$ (22)

The experimentally measured equilibrium constants, k_1 and k_2, are defined by the equations

$$\frac{(PA)}{(P)(A)} = k_1,$$ (23)

$$\frac{(PA_2)}{(PA)(A)} = k_2.$$ (24)

From these it follows readily, furthermore, that

$$(PA) = k_1(P)(A),$$ (25)
$$(PA_2) = k_2(PA)(A) = k_1k_2(P)(A)^2.$$ (26)

a. No Interaction Between Sites

In certain situations, k_1 and k_2 may be simply related. If the two sites on P available for attachment of A are identical in their intrinsic affinity for A and yet distinguishable from each other, we may designate them, for purposes of the following discussion, by placing one on the left side of P and the other on the right:

$$-P-.$$

(117) G. S. Eadie, *J. Biol. Chem.* **146**, 85 (1942).
(117a) A. Katchalsky and P. Spitnik, *J. Polymer Science* **2**, 432 (1947).
(117b) A. Katchalsky and J. Gillis, Proceedings of the International Colloquium on Macromolecules, Amsterdam, 1949, page 277; *Rec. chim. trav.* **68**, 879 (1949).
(118) G. Scatchard, *Ann. N. Y. Acad. Sci.* **51**, 660 (1949).

Thus the first complex PA is actually composed of the sum of the two distinguishable complexes

$$A—P— \text{ and } —P—A.$$

Each one of these may be considered to maintain its equilibrium with the component species, $—P—$ and A. Thus

$$—P— + A = A—P—; k = \frac{(A—P—)}{(—P—)(A)} \tag{27}$$

$$—P— + A = —P—A; k = \frac{(—P—A)}{(—P—)(A)}. \tag{28}$$

Since the two sites are identical in their intrinsic affinity for A, the intrinsic equilibrium constants, k, are the same in Eqs. (27) and (28). The intrinsic constant k may be then related to the experimental constant k_1 by keeping in mind that by our rules of designation

$$(A—P—) + (—P—A) = (PA). \tag{29}$$

It follows from Eq. (23) that

$$k_1 = \frac{(PA)}{(P)(A)} = \frac{[(A—P—) + (—P—A)]}{(P)(A)} = \frac{(A—P—)}{(P)(A)} + \frac{(—P—A)}{(P)(A)} = k + k = 2k. \tag{30}$$

A similar approach may be used to relate k_2 with k. For this purpose, let us visualize the formation of PA_2 as occurring in each of two possible ways:

$$A—P— + A = A—P—A; k = \frac{(PA_2)}{(A—P—)(A)} \tag{31}$$

$$—P—A + A = A—P—A; k = \frac{(PA_2)}{(—P—A)(A)}. \tag{32}$$

Again we may conclude that the k in Eq. (31) is identical with that in Eq. (32) since the two sites involved are identical in their affinity for A. For similar reasons we may conclude that

$$(—P—A) = (A—P—), \tag{33}$$

that is, that the concentrations of these distinguishable species are actually equal. [One way to be assured of this equality is to note that $(PA)_2$, (A), and k are identical in Eqs. (31) and (32).] Turning to Eq. (24), we find, then,

$$k_2 = \frac{(PA_2)}{(PA)(A)} = \frac{(PA_2)}{[(A—P—) + (—P—A)](A)} = \frac{(PA_2)}{2(A—P—)(A)} = \frac{k}{2}. \tag{34}$$

From Eqs. (30) and (34) it follows, therefore, that if the two sites on P are identical in their intrinsic affinity for A, then the experimentally determined constants are related simply by the expression

$$\frac{k_1}{k_2} = \frac{2k}{k/2} = 4. \tag{35}$$

Organic dibasic acids, HOOC—R—COOH, are analogous to the class of molecule PA_2, if the H^+ ion is identified with A. If R is a short chain, then carboxylate groups are sufficiently close to exert marked electrostatic effects on each other and hence their intrinsic affinities for H^+ are not the same. As R is lengthened, however, the electrostatic effect becomes less important and the carboxylate groups act more nearly independently. As the data in Table II illustrate, the ratio of the association constants for the aliphatic dibasic acids does approach 4 as the length of the chain is increased.

TABLE II

ASSOCIATION CONSTANTS OF DIBASIC ALIPHATIC ACIDS[a]

	$k_1 = \dfrac{(HR^-)}{(R^{--})(H^+)}$	$k_2 = \dfrac{H_2R}{(HR^-)(H^+)}$	k_1/k_2
HOOC—COOH	0.156×10^5	0.170×10^2	920
HOOC—CH$_2$—COOH	0.455×10^6	0.70×10^3	650
HOOC—(CH$_2$)$_2$—COOH	0.394×10^6	0.157×10^5	25
HOOC—(CH$_2$)$_3$—COOH	0.265×10^6	0.224×10^5	12
HOOC—(CH$_2$)$_4$—COOH	0.189×10^6	0.256×10^5	7.4
HOOC—(CH$_2$)$_5$—COOH	0.205×10^6	0.300×10^5	6.8
HOOC—(CH$_2$)$_6$—COOH	0.212×10^6	0.326×10^5	6.5
HOOC—(CH$_2$)$_7$—COOH	0.216×10^6	0.355×10^5	6.1

[a] These association constants were computed from the dissociation constants assembled from various sources by H. T. S. Britton in Hydrogen Ions, 3rd Ed., Van Nostrand and Company, New York, 1943, p. 248. See also, H. M. Peek and T. L. Hill, J. Am. Chem. Soc. 73, 5305 (1951).

The relation $(k_1/k_2) = 4$ was first pointed out by E. Q. Adams[119] in 1916, although the corresponding problem of the relation between the ionization constants of a dibasic organic acid and its half ester was treated earlier by Wegscheider.[120] Equation (35) can be derived also from appropriate statistical considerations. The probability of an A molecule combining with P should be twice as great as its chance to combine with PA, since P has two sites open whereas PA has only one. This factor alone would make k_1 twice as large as k_2. In addition, we can see that the probability of PA_2 *dissociating* should be twice as great as that of PA. This factor should in addition make k_2 one-half as large

(119) E. Q. Adams, J. Am. Chem. Soc. 16, 1503 (1916).
(120) R. Wegscheider, Monatsh. 16, 153 (1895).

as k_1. The combination of both factors[121] would make k_1 four times as large as k_2. The factor "4" is often called the "statistical factor" in discussions of relations between ionization or association constants in a combination of the type PA_2.

b. Electrostatic Interaction Between Sites

If the sites of attachment on P are electrostatically charged, and if the interacting species A is also charged, then the uptake of A by the first site produces a definite effect on the attraction of the second site for A. Considering the aliphatic dibasic acids as an example, we can see that the ^-OOC—$(CH_2)_n$—COO^- species should have[122] a greater affinity for H^+ ion than does the $HOOC$—$(CH_2)_n$—COO^- species because of the added electrostatic attraction of the second $-COO^-$ group in the former. This electrostatic factor tends to make k_1, the first *association* constant, greater than k_2 by a factor even larger than the 4 predicted by Eq. (35). The electrostatic contribution to the ratio k_1/k_2 was first estimated by Bjerrum,[123] and the calculations were refined by Gane and Ingold[124] and by Kirkwood and Westheimer.[125] The principle of the correction may be readily understood by the following considerations.

Even in the absence of electrostatic interactions

$$k_1 = 4k_2. \qquad (36)$$

Hence electrostatic interactions can be invoked only to account for deviations in which

$$\frac{k_1}{4k_2} > 1. \qquad (37)$$

Turning to Eqs. (22), if we subtract the second from the first, we obtain

$$P + PA_2 = 2PA, \qquad (38)$$

for which reaction

$$K = \frac{(PA)^2}{(P)(PA_2)} = \frac{(PA)}{(P)(A)} \frac{(A)(PA)}{(PA_2)} = \frac{k_1}{k_2}. \qquad (39)$$

The standard free-energy change $\Delta F°$ for reaction (38) is given by the expression

$$\Delta F° = -RT \ln K = -RT \ln \frac{k_1}{k_2}. \qquad (40)$$

(121) E. Valko, *Kolloid-Z.* **51**, 130 (1930).
(122) W. Ostwald, *Z. physik. Chem.* **9**, 551 (1892).
(123) N. Bjerrum, *Z. physik. Chem.* **106**, 219 (1923).
(124) R. Gane and C. K. Ingold, *J. Chem. Soc.* **1931**, 2153.
(125) J. G. Kirkwood and F. H. Westheimer, *J. Chem. Phys.* **6**, 506, 513 (1938).

In the absence of electrostatic interactions it follows from Eq. (36) that

$$\Delta F^\circ = -RT \ln 4. \tag{41}$$

When electrostatic factors do arise, we might visualize them as being due to the differences in free energy of charging of the various species in Eq. (38); that is,

$$\Delta F^\circ_{\text{elec.}} = (2\bar{F}^\circ_{PA} - \bar{F}^\circ_{PA_2} - \bar{F}^\circ_P)_{\text{elec.}}, \tag{42}$$

where each $\bar{F}^\circ$ represents the electrical standard free energy for the indicated species. Consequently Eq. (40) may be replaced by

$$\Delta F^\circ = -RT \ln \frac{k_1}{k_2} = -RT \ln 4 + \Delta F^\circ_{\text{elec.}}$$
$$= -RT \ln 4 + (2\bar{F}^\circ_{PA} - \bar{F}^\circ_{PA_2} - \bar{F}^\circ_P)_{\text{elec.}}. \tag{43}$$

The electrical standard free energies, $\bar{F}^\circ$, may be calculated from the equation proposed by Born:[126]

$$\bar{F}^\circ_{\text{elec.}} = \frac{NZ^2e^2}{2Db}, \tag{44}$$

where N is Avogadro's number, Z is the number of charges on the ion, e the electronic charge, D the dielectric constant of the medium, and b the radius of the ion. For the aliphatic dibasic acids, Eqs. (44) and (42) lead to

$$\Delta F^\circ_{\text{elec.}} = -\frac{Ne^2}{Db}, \tag{45}$$

if we assume that the radius of any anion is not significantly different with or without a proton. Thus

$$\Delta F^\circ = -RT \ln \frac{k_1}{k_2} = -RT \ln 4 - \frac{Ne^2}{Db}. \tag{46}$$

Since e, D, and b are positive numbers, it is apparent that k_1/k_2 exceeds 4 when the electrostatic effect is significant. Comparisons of quantitative predictions with experimental values of the dissociation constants of numerous dibasic acids have been made by several investigators.[124,127,128]

(126) M. Born, Z. Physik 1, 45 (1920).

(127) F. H. Westheimer and M. W. Shookhoff, J. Am. Chem. Soc. 61, 555 (1939).

(128) A slightly different form of the electrostatic free energy change, based on a model with localized charges, has been used in these calculations[124,127] with dibasic acids. The equations derived here are of the same type as those used with protein polyelectrolytes.

3. Three Sites for Association

In anticipation of the method of treatment of the general case of n sites of attachment, let us consider the problem of three sites on the central molecule, P.

By analogy to the preceding situations we may write

$$P + A = PA,$$
$$PA + A = PA_2, \tag{47}$$
$$PA_2 + A = PA_3.$$

The experimentally determined equilibrium constants, k_1, k_2, and k_3 are defined by the equations

$$\frac{(PA)}{(P)(A)} = k_1, \tag{48}$$

$$\frac{(PA_2)}{(PA)(A)} = k_2, \tag{49}$$

$$\frac{(PA_3)}{(PA_2)(A)} = k_3. \tag{50}$$

From these it follows, furthermore, that

$$(PA) = k_1(P)(A), \tag{51}$$
$$(PA_2) = k_2(PA)(A) = k_1k_2(P)(A)^2, \tag{52}$$
$$(PA_3) = k_3(PA_2)(A) = k_1k_2k_3(P)(A)^3. \tag{53}$$

Once again we shall assume that each site is uninfluenced by its neighbor and has the same intrinsic affinity for A. We may distinguish the three individual sites by the following designation for P:

The first complex, PA, is actually composed, then, of the sum of three distinguishable complexes,

Each of these may be considered to maintain its equilibrium with the component species, P and A. Thus we may write

$$\tag{54}$$

$$\diagdown\!\!\underset{|}{P}\!\!\diagup + A = \underset{|}{P}\!\!\diagup^{A} \quad ; \quad k = \dfrac{\left(\diagdown\underset{|}{P}\diagup^{A}\right)}{(P)(A)}, \tag{55}$$

$$\diagdown\!\!\underset{|}{P}\!\!\diagup + A = \underset{\underset{A}{|}}{P}\!\!\diagup \quad ; \quad k = \dfrac{\left(\diagdown\underset{\underset{A}{|}}{P}\diagup\right)}{(P)(A)}. \tag{56}$$

Since the three sites are identical in their intrinsic affinity for A, the intrinsic equilibrium constants, k, are the same in Eqs. (54), (55), and (56). We might also note in passing that

$$\left(^{A}\diagdown\!\!\underset{|}{P}\!\diagup\right) = \left(\diagdown\!\!\underset{|}{P}\!\diagup^{A}\right) = \left(\diagdown\underset{\underset{A}{|}}{P}\diagup\right). \tag{57}$$

The equality of concentrations of each of these species must be true, for in Eqs. (54–56) the factors k, (P), and (A) are identical.

We may proceed now to relate k with the experimentally determined constant k_1. It follows from our rules of designation that

$$\left(^{A}\diagdown\!\!\underset{|}{P}\!\diagup\right) + \left(\diagdown\!\!\underset{|}{P}\!\diagup^{A}\right) + \left(\diagdown\underset{\underset{A}{|}}{P}\diagup\right) = 3\left(^{A}\diagdown\!\!\underset{|}{P}\!\diagup\right) = (PA). \tag{58}$$

Consequently

$$k_1 = \frac{(PA)}{(P)(A)} = \frac{3\left(^{A}\diagdown\!\!\underset{|}{P}\!\diagup\right)}{(P)(A)} = 3k. \tag{59}$$

By analogous methods, it can be shown that

$$(PA_2) = \left(^{A}\diagdown\!\!\underset{|}{P}\!\diagup^{A}\right) + \left(\diagdown\!\!\underset{\underset{A}{|}}{P}\!\diagup^{A}\right) + \left(^{A}\diagdown\!\!\underset{\underset{A}{|}}{P}\!\diagup\right) \tag{60}$$

$$= 3\left(^{A}\diagdown\!\!\underset{|}{P}\!\diagup^{A}\right).$$

Therefore

$$k_2 = \frac{(PA_2)}{(PA)(A)} = \frac{3\left(^{A}\diagdown\!\!\underset{|}{P}\!\diagup^{A}\right)}{3\left(^{A}\diagdown\!\!\underset{|}{P}\!\diagup\right)(A)} = k. \tag{61}$$

Furthermore, for the third measured association constant, k_3, we find

$$k_3 = \frac{(PA_3)}{(PA_2)(A)} = \frac{(PA_3)}{3\left(\begin{array}{c}A\;\diagdown\;\;\diagup\;A\\P\\|\end{array}\right)(A)} = \frac{k}{3},\qquad(62)$$

keeping in mind that there is only one possible form of PA_3.

It follows from these considerations that the ratios of the measured constants should be

$$k_1:k_2:k_3 = 9:3:1 \qquad (63)$$

when the sites of binding are independent of each other. Data of Maxwell and Partington[128a] on some tribasic aromatic acids have been converted into association constants, which are assembled in Table III. The

TABLE III
ASSOCIATION CONSTANTS OF TRIBASIC ORGANIC ACIDS[a]

	k_1	k_2	k_3	$k_1:k_2:k_3$
COOH HOOC——COOH (benzene ring)	0.74×10^6	0.159×10^5	0.63×10^3	$1200:25:1$
HOOC——COOH —COOH (benzene ring)	0.159×10^6	0.69×10^4	0.33×10^3	$480:21:1$
HOOC——COOH COOH (benzene ring)	0.5×10^5	0.77×10^4	0.133×10^4	$38:6:1$

[a] These association constants were computed from the dissociation constants obtained by W. R. Maxwell and J. R. Partington, *Trans. Faraday Soc.* **33**, 670 (1937).

ratios are much higher than would be expected from statistical considerations alone. Evidently electrostatic factors must enter once again. It is of interest to note in this connection that the nearest approach to the statistical ratio of $9:3:1$ is obtained with symmetrically substituted

(128a) W. R. Maxwell and J. R. Partington, *Trans. Faraday Soc.* **33**, 670 (1937).

benzene-1,3,5-tricarboxylic acid, in which the charged groups are spaced most widely apart.

4. n Sites for Association

We are now in a position to generalize our discussion[5,129] to the case of any fixed number, n, of sites of attachment to the central molecule, P.

a. Definition of Equilibria

It is obvious from the treatment of the preceding situations that we may write for the equilibria involved

$$
\begin{aligned}
P + A &= PA, \\
PA + A &= PA_2, \\
&\cdots\cdots\cdots\cdots\cdots \\
PA_{i-1} + A &= PA_i, \\
&\cdots\cdots\cdots\cdots\cdots \\
PA_{n-1} + A &= PA_n.
\end{aligned}
\tag{64}
$$

These equilibria may be represented also in equations defining their equilibrium constants:

$$
\frac{(PA)}{(P)(A)} = k_1,
\tag{65}
$$

$$
\frac{(PA_2)}{(PA)(A)} = k_2,
\tag{66}
$$

$$
\cdots\cdots\cdots\cdots\cdots
$$

$$
\frac{(PA_i)}{(PA_{i-1})(A)} = k_i,
\tag{67}
$$

$$
\cdots\cdots\cdots\cdots\cdots
$$

$$
\frac{(PA_n)}{(PA_{n-1})(A)} = k_n.
\tag{68}
$$

From these equations we can obtain the following relations, which we shall shortly find useful:

$$
(PA) = k_1(P)(A),
\tag{69}
$$

$$
(PA_2) = k_2(PA)(A) = k_1k_2(P)(A)^2,
\tag{70}
$$

$$
\cdots\cdots\cdots\cdots\cdots\cdots\cdots\cdots\cdots
$$

$$
(PA_i) = k_i(PA_{i-1})(A) = (k_1k_2 \cdots k_i)(P)(A)^i,
\tag{71}
$$

$$
\cdots\cdots\cdots\cdots\cdots\cdots\cdots\cdots\cdots\cdots
$$

$$
(PA_n) = k_n(PA_{n-1})(A) = (k_1k_2 \cdots k_i \cdots k_n)(P)(A)^n.
\tag{72}
$$

b. Relationships Among Equilibrium Constants in Absence of Interactions

If each site is uninfluenced by its neighbor and if each has the same intrinsic affinity for A, then the equilibrium constants $k_1 \ldots k_n$ are not independent but bear certain definite relationships to each other. These relationships can be worked out readily by application of the rules of combinations and permutations.

(129) I. M. Klotz, *Arch. Biochem.* **9**, 109 (1946).

Let us consider first the complex PA. It is apparent (Fig. 6) that there are n possible forms of PA, depending upon the particular site on P to which A is attached. We may distinguish these complexes by the notation $_1PA$, $_2PA$ . . . $_nPA$, the subscript at the left indicating the particular site on P to which A is bound. If the intrinsic affinity of

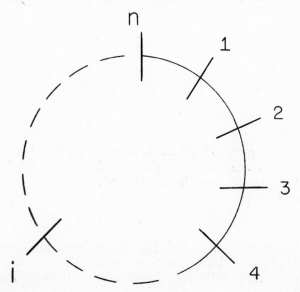

FIG. 6. Schematic diagram of a molecule P with n sites for attachment of A molecules.

each site for A is identical, then the equilibrium constant, k, for the association

$$P + A = {_1PA} \tag{73}$$

is the same as for the reaction

$$P + A = {_2PA}. \tag{74}$$

Thus we may write

$$k = \frac{(_1PA)}{(P)(A)} = \frac{(_2PA)}{(P)(A)} = \cdots = \frac{(_nPA)}{(P)(A)}. \tag{75}$$

Keeping in mind that

$$(PA) = (_1PA) + (_2PA) + \cdots + (_nPA), \tag{76}$$

we find that Eq. (65) leads to

$$k_1 = \frac{(PA)}{(P)(A)} = \frac{(_1PA) + (_2PA) + \cdots + (_nPA)}{(P)(A)}$$
$$= k + k + \cdots + k = nk. \tag{77}$$

Thus we have a relation between k_1 and the intrinsic constant k. A similar relation may be obtained between k_2 and k. If we examine the

PA_2 complex (Fig. 6), we find that there are $\dfrac{n(n-1)}{2}$ possible forms depending on the particular combination of two sites on P to which the two A's are attached. The quantity $\dfrac{n(n-1)}{2}$ is derived from the general algebraic relationship for the number of possible combinations of n sites taken m at a time,

$$_nC_m = \frac{n!}{m!(n-m)!}. \tag{78}$$

For $m = 2$,

$$_nC_2 = \frac{n!}{2!(n-2)!} = \frac{n(n-1)(n-2)(n-3)\;\cdots}{2(n-2)(n-3)\;\cdots}$$

$$= \frac{n(n-1)}{2}. \tag{79}$$

The different complexes of type PA_2 may be denoted by the symbols $_{1,2}PA_2$, $_{1,3}PA_2$, $\cdots$ $_{j,l}PA_2$, where the subscripts at the left indicate the sites on P at which the two A's are attached.

It follows from Eq. (75) that

$$(_1PA) = (_2PA) = \cdots = (_nPA), \tag{80}$$

since the values of k, (P), and (A), respectively, are identical. An analogous set of equilibrium expressions can be written for the complexes involving $_{j,l}PA_2$, from which it is a simple matter to prove that

$$(_{1,2}PA_2) = (_{1,3}PA_2) = \cdots = (_{j,l}PA_2) \tag{81}$$

if we assume as before that the intrinsic affinity constant, k, is the same for any single site taking up one A. It follows, therefore, that

$$k_2 = \frac{(PA_2)}{(PA)(A)} = \frac{[(_{1,2}PA_2) + \cdots + (_{j,l}PA_2) + \cdots]}{[(_1PA) + \cdots (_iPA) + \cdots](A)}$$

$$= \frac{\dfrac{n(n-1)}{2}\,(_{1,2}PA_2)}{n(_1PA)(A)}$$

$$= \frac{n-1}{2}\,k. \tag{82}$$

This type of treatment may be generalized by extension to the constant k_i. We may start by repeating equation (67)

$$k_i = \frac{(PA_i)}{(PA_{i-1})(A)}. \tag{67}$$

To obtain a relation between k_i and the intrinsic constant k, we must determine first the number of possible forms of the complex PA_i. Again our problem is essentially how many combinations of n binding sites are possible if we take i of them at a time. Application of Eq. (78) leads to the answer

$$_nC_i = \frac{n!}{i!(n-i)!},\tag{83}$$

that is, there are $\dfrac{n!}{i!(n-i)!}$ different forms of the complex PA_i. Each one of these forms $_\lambda PA_i$ is present in a concentration equal to any other form of PA_i. Similar operations lead us to the conclusion that there are $\dfrac{n!}{(i-1)![n-(i-1)]!}$ different forms of the complex PA_{i-1}. Each one of these forms $_\delta PA_{i-1}$ is present in a concentration equal to any other form of PA_{i-1}. Therefore

$$k_i = \frac{\dfrac{n!}{i!(n-i)!}}{\dfrac{n!}{(i-1)!(n-i+1)!}} \frac{(_\lambda PA_i)}{(_\delta PA_{i-1})(A)}$$

$$= \frac{(i-1)!(n-i+1)!}{i!(n-i)!}k$$

$$= \frac{[(i-1)(i-2)\cdots][(n-i+1)(n-i)(n-i-1)\cdots]}{[i(i-1)(i-2)\cdots][(n-i)(n-i-1)\cdots]}k \tag{84}$$

or

$$k_i = \frac{n-i+1}{i}k. \tag{85}$$

Thus we have a general relationship between the experimental constant k_i for the formation of the ith complex, PA_i, and the intrinsic affinity constant, k. Exemplary values have been assembled in Table IV for the case where 10 sites are available on P for the binding of A.

TABLE IV

STATISTICAL FACTORS IN EQUILIBRIUM CONSTANTS FOR COMPLEX WITH TEN SITES

$$
\begin{array}{ll}
k_1 = 10k & k_6 = \tfrac{5}{6}k \\
k_2 = \tfrac{9}{2}k & k_7 = \tfrac{4}{7}k \\
k_3 = \tfrac{8}{3}k & k_8 = \tfrac{3}{8}k \\
k_4 = \tfrac{7}{4}k & k_9 = \tfrac{2}{9}k \\
k_5 = \tfrac{6}{5}k & k_{10} = \tfrac{1}{10}k
\end{array}
$$

The factor $(n-i+1)/i$ of Eq. (85) can also be derived from statistical considerations, and hence is frequently referred to as the statistical factor. If we recall the reaction to which k_i refers

$$PA_{i-1} + A = PA_i, \tag{64}$$

we can see that the complex PA_i has i times the chance of dissociating an A group than has a species containing only one site with the same intrinsic affinity for A. Thus the association constant for PA_i should be decreased by the factor $1/i$. On the other hand, the complex PA_{i-1} has a large number of unoccupied spaces at which A may be attached. If the total number of available sites is n and $(i - 1)$ are occupied, then $n - (i - 1)$ must still be open in PA_{i-1}. Therefore, the chance of an A combining with PA_{i-1} is $n - (i - 1)$ times greater than that of a species which has only one available site with the same intrinsic affinity constant. Consequently, the association constant for the formation of PA_i should be increased by the factor $(n - i + 1)/1$ as well as decreased by the factor $1/i$. The net result of both factors is $(n - i + 1)/i$, the so-called statistical factor.

These statistical relationships apply to a large variety of chemical equilibria. Reference should be made to the original literature for their applications to specific problems, such as inorganic complex ions or enzyme reactions.[114,130-135]

c. General Equations for Extent of Binding

A convenient measure of the extent of combination of A with the protein is the quantity

$$\frac{\text{Moles bound } A}{\text{Moles total protein}} = r. \tag{86}$$

Since the number of moles of bound A equals the number of moles of PA plus twice the number of moles of PA_2, etc., we may write

$$r = \frac{(PA) + 2(PA_2) + \cdots + i(PA_i) + \cdots + n(PA_n)}{(P) + (PA) + (PA_2) + \cdots + (PA_i) + \cdots + (PA_n)}. \tag{87}$$

In view of Eqs. (69–72), it is necessary, furthermore, that

$$r = \frac{k_1(P)(A) + 2k_1k_2(P)(A)^2 + \cdots + i(k_1k_2 \cdots k_i)(P)(A)^i + \cdots}{(P) + k_1(P)(A) + \cdots + (k_1k_2 \cdots k_i)(P)(A)^i + \cdots},$$

or

$$r = \frac{k_1(A) + 2k_1k_2(A)^2 + \cdots + i(k_1k_2 \cdots k_i)(A)^i + \cdots + n(k_1k_2 \cdots k_n)(A)^n}{1 + k_1(A) + k_1k_2(A)^2 + \cdots + (k_1k_2 \cdots k_i)(A)^i + \cdots + (k_1k_2 \cdots k_n)(A)^n} \tag{88}$$

(130) H. S. Simms, *J. Am. Chem. Soc.* **48**, 1231 (1926).

(131) W. Pauli and E. Valko, Elektrochemie der Kolloide, J. Springer, Vienna, 1929, pp. 107–19.

(132) A. von Muralt, *J. Am. Chem. Soc.* **52**, 3518 (1930).

(133) J. Bjerrum, Metal Ammine Formation in Aqueous Solution, P. Haase and Son, Copenhagen, 1941.

(134) S. Filitti-Wurmser, Y. Jacquot-Armand, and R. Wurmser, *Compt. rend.* **226**, 844 (1948).

(135) L. Michaelis, *Advances in Enzymol.* **9**, 1 (1949).

d. Reduced Equations for Single Set of Binding Sites with No Interactions

If each site has the same intrinsic affinity for A and if each is uninfluenced by its neighbors, then the individual constants, $k_1, k_2, \cdots k_n$, of Eq. (88) may be replaced by the appropriate special case of Eq. (85) to give

$$r = \frac{nk(A) + \dfrac{2n(n-1)}{2!} k^2(A)^2 + \cdots + i\,\dfrac{n(n-1)\,\cdots\,(n-i+1)}{i!}\,k^i(A)^i + \cdots + n\,\dfrac{n!}{n!}\,k^n(A)^n}{1 + nk(A) + \dfrac{n(n-1)}{2!} k^2(A)^2 + \cdots + \dfrac{n(n-1)\,\cdots\,(n-i+1)}{i!}\,k^i(A^i) + \cdots + \dfrac{n!}{n!}\,k^n(A)^n}. \tag{89}$$

Reference to the binomial theorem will show that the denominator of Eq. (89) is simply the expansion of

$$[1 + k(A)]^n. \tag{90}$$

Furthermore if (A) is factored out in the numerator of Eq. (89), we obtain the derivative of the denominator with respect to (A), as can be shown readily in a term-by-term differentiation. Hence

$$\text{numerator} = (A)\,\frac{\partial}{\partial(A)}\,(\text{denominator}) = (A)\,\frac{\partial}{\partial(A)}\,[1 + k(A)]^n$$
$$= (A)nk[1 + k(A)]^{n-1}. \tag{91}$$

Taking cognizance of the relations in Eqs. (90) and (91), we obtain

$$r = \frac{(A)nk[1 + k(A)]^{n-1}}{[1 + k(A)]^n} \tag{92}$$

or

$$r = \frac{nk(A)}{1 + k(A)}. \tag{93}$$

Thus if we have n independent binding sites, the equation for the extent of binding is merely n times that for a single site [Eq. (16)] with the same intrinsic constant, k. Hence we obtain equations analogous to equations (18) and (21):

$$\frac{1}{r} = \frac{1}{nk}\frac{1}{(A)} + \frac{1}{n} \tag{94}$$

and

$$\frac{r}{(A)} = kn - kr. \tag{95}$$

Either of these latter two equations provides a linear relationship which may be useful in the evaluation of the constants n and k.

e. Equations for Single Set of Sites with Electrostatic Interactions Between Them

If charged ions are bound by a protein, the first bound ion tends to reduce the affinity of the protein for the second oncoming ion because of electrostatic repulsion between these species of like charge. Under these circumstances, Eq. (85) for the relationship between binding constants is no longer valid, even if the intrinsic affinity of each site on the protein is the same for the small ion, A.

Two methods have been devised for taking account of the electrostatic factor in protein interactions with small ions. The first[5] of these raises the question of how two successive binding constants, k_{i-1} and k_i, should be related when electrostatic factors are taken into account. The answer can be obtained by considering the stoichiometric equations to which the two constants refer:

$$PA_{i-2} + A = PA_{i-1}; \quad k_{i-1} \tag{96}$$
$$PA_{i-1} + A = PA_i; \quad k_i. \tag{97}$$

By analogy to the treatment of electrostatic interactions in dibasic acids, we may write an equation corresponding to the ratio of these two constants:

$$PA_{i-2} + PA_i = 2PA_{i-1}; \quad \frac{k_{i-1}}{k_i}. \tag{98}$$

The free-energy change for reaction (98) in the absence of electrostatic effects may be expressed as

$$\Delta F^\circ = -RT \ln \frac{k_{i-1}}{k_i} = -RT \ln \left[\frac{n - (i - 2)}{n - (i - 1)} \frac{i}{i - 1} \right], \tag{99}$$

the latter part of Eq. (99) following from Eq. (85). An additional term for the electrostatic free-energy change, $\Delta F^\circ_{elec.}$, may be derived by considering the difference between the charging energy of two PA_{i-1} ions and the sum of the charging energies of the PA_i and PA_{i-2} ions. For the charging energy of an ion in an electrolyte solution we may use the relation developed from the Born and Debye-Hückel theories,[136,137]

(136) D. A. MacInnes, Principles of Electrochemistry, Reinhold Publishing Company, New York, N. Y., 1939, p. 146.
(137) E. J. Cohn and J. T. Edsall, Proteins, Amino Acids and Peptides, Reinhold Publishing Company, New York, N. Y., 1943, pp. 445, 473–5.

$$\bar{F}^{\circ}_{\text{elec.}} = \frac{Nz^2e^2}{2D}\left[\frac{1}{b} - \frac{\kappa}{1 + \kappa a}\right], \tag{100}$$

where b is the radius of the protein molecule, a the distance of closest approach of the small molecule to the protein, κ is the familiar function of the ionic strength in the Debye-Hückel theory, and the other factors are as defined in connection with Eq. (44). If z, the charge on the protein complex, is represented as

$$z = q + iz', \tag{101}$$

where q is the charge on the protein itself and z' is the charge on each bound small ion, then it can be shown that $\Delta F^{\circ}_{\text{elec.}}$ for reaction (98) is given by the expression

$$\Delta F^{\circ}_{\text{elec.}} = -\frac{N(z')^2e^2}{D}\left[\frac{1}{b} - \frac{\kappa}{1 + \kappa a}\right]. \tag{102}$$

Thus q does not appear in this equation. The total free-energy change for reaction (98) may be obtained then by addition of Eq. (102) to Eq. (99):

$$\Delta F^{\circ} = -RT \ln \frac{k_{i-1}}{k_i} = -RT \ln \left[\frac{n - (i - 2)}{n - (i - 1)}\frac{i}{i - 1}\right]$$
$$-\frac{N(z')^2e^2}{D}\left[\frac{1}{b} - \frac{\kappa}{1 + \kappa a}\right]. \tag{103}$$

In practice, to calculate any constant k_i, k_1 should be obtained first from a suitable extrapolation of the experimental data (see sec. IV). Then k_2 may be calculated from Eq. (103) by insertion of 2 for i, after parameters such as the radius of the protein, b, have been estimated. By an analogous procedure, k_3 may be computed from k_2, etc. Once the successive binding constants are known, values of r may be calculated from Eq. (88).

A much simpler approximate method[117a,117b,118] can also be used to take account of electrostatic interactions. If we consider merely the reaction

$$PA_{i-1} + A = PA_i, \tag{104}$$

we may write in the absence of electrostatic interactions, in view of Eq. (85),

$$\frac{(PA_i)}{(PA_{i-1})(A)} = k_i = \frac{n - i + 1}{i}k. \tag{105}$$

For reaction (104), $\Delta F^{\circ}_{\text{elec.}}$ is essentially the electrostatic free energy of increasing the charge on PA_{i-1} by that on A, or the difference in charging energy of PA_i and PA_{i-1}. In view of Eq. (100), this difference becomes, for an isoionic protein,

$$\Delta F^{\circ}_{elec.} = (2i - 1) \frac{N(z')^2 e^2}{2D} \left[\frac{1}{b} - \frac{\kappa}{1 + \kappa a} \right]. \tag{106}$$

Hence, for reaction (104), if we take account of the electrostatic factor

$$\Delta F^{\circ} = -RT \ln k_i = -RT \ln \left(\frac{n - i + 1}{i} k \right) + \Delta F^{\circ}_{elec.} \tag{107}$$

and consequently

$$k_i = \frac{n - i + 1}{i} k e^{-\frac{\Delta F^{\circ}_{elec.}}{RT}}. \tag{108}$$

Following Scatchard,[118] we may define w by the equation

$$w = \frac{N(z')^2 e^2}{2RTD} \left[\frac{1}{b} - \frac{\kappa}{1 + \kappa a} \right], \tag{109}$$

so that in place of Eq. (106) we may write

$$\Delta F^{\circ}_{elec.} = (2i - 1)RTw. \tag{110}$$

Thus we may substitute into Eq. (108) and obtain

$$k_i = \frac{(PA_i)}{(PA_{i-1})(A)} = \frac{n - i + 1}{i} k e^{-(2i-1)w}. \tag{111}$$

By an approximation method, quite accurate for values of n above 4, Katchalsky et al.[117a,117b] and Scatchard[118] were able to deduce a very simple relation from Eq. (111) for uptake of ions by a macromolecule. For binding by an isoionic protein this takes the form:

$$r = \frac{nke^{-2wr}(A)}{1 + ke^{-2wr}(A)}. \tag{112}[138]$$

For correspondence to Eq. (95) we obtain

$$\frac{r}{(A)} e^{2wr} = kn - kr. \tag{113}$$

Thus a graph of $\frac{r}{(A)} e^{2wr}$ vs. r should give a straight line from the intercepts of which both k and n can be evaluated.

f. n Sites with Independent Intrinsic Affinities

Binding sites may be sufficiently different in their configuration so that their intrinsic affinities for a specified ion may differ widely. A

(138) If the initial protein, P, is not isoionic, the exponential in this equation includes an additional factor dependent on the protein charge. See Ref. (25) for further details.

special case of interest treated by Karush and Sonenberg[139] is that in which the independent binding constants can be correlated in terms of a Gaussian error function for the free energies of binding. If k_0 is the average binding constant and σ a measure of the range of values of k, then the normalized Gaussian function is[139,140]

$$\frac{1}{\sqrt{\pi}\,\sigma}\exp -\left(\frac{1}{\sigma}\ln\frac{k}{k_0}\right)^2. \tag{114}$$

If we consider an infinitesimally small region, then the fraction of total sites, n, on the molecule with a specified binding constant, k, may be expressed as

$$\frac{dn}{n} = \frac{1}{\sqrt{\pi}\,\sigma}\exp -\left(\frac{1}{\sigma}\ln\frac{k}{k_0}\right)^2 d\left(\ln\frac{k}{k_0}\right). \tag{115}$$

For the sites with binding constant k we may write

$$\frac{(PA)}{(P)(A)} = k, \tag{116}$$

where (P) now represents the concentration of open sites *with this specific binding constant.* Thus

$$\Sigma(P) = P_f \tag{117}$$

where P_f represents the *total* concentration of free sites. Since

$$(P) + (PA) = \text{total concentration of sites of constant } k \tag{118}$$

and, if P_t is the total concentration of protein,

$$nP_t = \text{total concentration of sites of all constants,} \tag{119}$$

then

$$\frac{dn}{n} = \frac{(P) + (PA)}{nP_t}. \tag{120}$$

From Eq. (116) it follows that

$$(PA) = k(P)(A) \tag{121}$$

and hence that

$$(P) + (PA) = (P)[1 + k(A)]. \tag{122}$$

Consequently eliminating dn/n from Eqs. (115) and (120) we obtain

$$\frac{(P) + (PA)}{nP_t} = \frac{(P)[1 + k(A)]}{nP_t} = \frac{1}{\sqrt{\pi}\,\sigma}\exp\left[-\left(\frac{1}{\sigma}\ln\frac{k}{k_0}\right)^2\right]d\left(\ln\frac{k}{k_0}\right) \tag{123}$$

(139) F. Karush and M. Sonenberg, *J. Am. Chem. Soc.* **71**, 1369 (1949).
(140) L. Pauling, D. Pressman, and A. L. Grossberg, *J. Am. Chem. Soc.* **66**, 784 (1944).

or

$$(P) = \frac{nP_t}{\sqrt{\pi}\,\sigma} \frac{\exp\left[-\left(\frac{1}{\sigma}\ln\frac{k}{k_0}\right)^2\right]}{1 + k(A)} d\left(\ln\frac{k}{k_0}\right). \tag{124}$$

From Eq. (117), it follows furthermore that

$$P_f \simeq \frac{nP_t}{\sqrt{\pi}\,\sigma} \int_{-\infty}^{+\infty} \frac{\exp\left[-\left(\frac{1}{\sigma}\ln\frac{k}{k_0}\right)^2\right]}{1 + k(A)} d\ln\frac{k}{k_0}. \tag{125}$$

The fraction of free sites of all types may also be expressed as

$$\frac{P_f}{nP_t} = \phi_f. \tag{126}$$

Similarly the fraction of occupied sites is

$$\frac{rP_t}{nP_t} = \frac{r}{n} = \phi_B. \tag{127}$$

Since

$$\phi_f + \phi_B = 1, \tag{128}$$

we find that

$$\frac{r}{n} = 1 - \frac{1}{\sqrt{\pi}\,\sigma} \int_{-\infty}^{+\infty} \frac{\exp\left[-\left(\frac{1}{\sigma}\ln\frac{k}{k_0}\right)^2\right]}{1 + k(A)} d\ln\frac{k}{k_0}. \tag{129}$$

Equation (129) may be rearranged into a more concise form if we define

$$\alpha = \frac{1}{\sigma}\ln\frac{k}{k_0}, \tag{130}$$

from which it follows that

$$k = k_0 e^{\alpha\sigma} \tag{131}$$

and, since σ is a constant for a given protein–ion interaction,

$$d\alpha = \frac{1}{\sigma} d\ln\frac{k}{k_0}. \tag{132}$$

Thus we obtain in place of Eq. (129):

$$\frac{r}{n} = 1 - \frac{1}{\sqrt{\pi}} \int_{-\infty}^{+\infty} \frac{e^{-\alpha^2}}{1 + k_0(A)e^{\alpha\sigma}} d\alpha$$
$$= 1 - f[(A)]. \tag{133}$$

For computational purposes it is convenient to rearrange Eq. (133) into the expression

$$\frac{n}{r} = \frac{1}{1 - f[(A)]}. \tag{134}$$

Although the integral in Eq. (133) cannot be evaluated analytically, the expression can be applied by graphical means. Theoretical curves of $\frac{n}{r}$ vs. $\frac{1}{k_0(A)}$ have been calculated by Karush and Sonenberg[139] by numerical integration for a variety of σ's. Procedures for evaluating k_0 and σ have been described by Karush.[14a]

As has been mentioned, Eq. (133) for a Gaussian distribution of binding energies cannot be evaluated analytically. It has been shown recently by Sips,[141,142] however, that a distribution function very close to the Gaussian does lead to an explicit equation, which in terms of our notation may be written as

$$\frac{r}{n} = \frac{k(A)^a}{1 + k(A)^a}, \quad 0 \leq a \leq 1 \tag{135}$$

where a is a constant for interaction between a given pair of species. When $a = 1$, all of the sites possess the same intrinsic free energy of binding, and Eq. (135) reduces to Eq. (93).[143]

g. Single Set of Sites with Cooperative Interactions Between Them

There are some examples of protein complexes, notably those of hemoglobin with oxygen, where the uptake of the first molecule makes it easier for the second to come onto the protein. In such cooperative interactions, the second binding constant will never be reduced, compared to the first, as much as would be expected from statistical considerations; in fact, the second association constant may be even larger than the first.

The ratio between successive association constants, corrected for statistical factors, may be defined as an interaction constant. In hemoglobin–oxygen equilibria, Pauling[144] has described the application of mass law analysis based on the assumption of a single interaction constant with a stabilizing effect. More recently, Wyman[145] has demonstrated the necessity of assuming two interaction constants for a more precise

(141) R. Sips, J. Chem. Phys. **16**, 490 (1948).
(142) R. Sips, J. Chem. Phys. **18**, 1024 (1950).
(143) An exponential distribution of binding energies can be shown to lead to an equation of the form $r/n = k(A)^a$ [cf. G. Halsey and H. S. Taylor, J. Chem. Phys. **15**, 640 (1947)]. This expression, however, is not useful for correlating protein bindings since it does not reach a saturation limit as (A) increases to very large values.
(144) L. Pauling, Proc. Natl. Acad. Sci. U. S. **21**, 186 (1935).
(145) J. Wyman, Jr., Advances in Protein Chem. **4**, 407 (1948).

description of this system. The details of these analyses will not be described here. Nevertheless, it should be pointed out that where stabilizing interactions occur, the exponent a in Eq. (135) is always greater than unity.

$$\frac{r}{n} = \frac{k(A)^a}{1 + k(A)^a}, \quad a > 1 \tag{136}$$

and can be related to the interaction constant by methods such as those described by Coryell.[146]

h. Interactions with Solid Proteins

Insoluble proteins, such as wool, undergo reactions with acids and bases as well as with a variety of organic ions, particularly dyes. In these interactions the fiber or solid phase remains practically neutral electrically, for if there were any excess of positive or negative bound ions, an enormous electric potential would be established. Furthermore, with insoluble proteins the number of available sites per protein molecule, n, becomes so large that it cannot be distinguished experimentally and hence is replaced by a parameter which gives the saturation limit for the fiber as a whole.

The most convenient theoretical approach[147,148] to interactions of this type involves essentially a thermodynamic analysis of the distribution of a substance, e.g., a dye, between two phases, the solid and the aqueous. With a suitable selection of a standard state for the bound dye, free energies and heats of combination may be calculated. Inasmuch as the vast literature on dyeing, which forms the best example of this type of interaction, will not be discussed in this review, the details of the thermodynamic treatment[48,149-151] will also be omitted.

In serological reactions, interactions are usually followed by the formation of antigen–antibody precipitates. Mass-law treatments of these interactions have also been described for certain simplified cases,[152-154a] but these will not be discussed in this chapter.

(146) C. D. Coryell, *J. Phys. Chem.* **43**, 841 (1939).
(147) G. A. Gilbert and E. K. Rideal, *Proc. Roy. Soc.* (London) **A182**, 335 (1944).
(148) G. A. Gilbert, *Proc. Roy. Soc.* (London) **A183**, 167 (1944).
(149) E. I. Valko, *in* J. Alexander, ed., Colloid Chemistry, vol. VI, Reinhold Publishing Corp., New York, N. Y., 1946, pp. 594–619.
(150) T. Vickerstaff, The Physical Chemistry of Dyeing, Oliver and Boyd, London, 1950, pp. 83–118.
(151) F. T. Wall and T. J. Swoboda, *J. Phys. Chem.* **56**, 50 (1952).
(152) M. Heidelberger and F. E. Kendall, *J. Exptl. Med.* **61**, 559 (1935).
(153) A. D. Hershey, *J. Immunol.* **42**, 455 (1941).
(154) L. Pauling, D. Pressman, D. H. Campbell, C. Skela, and M. Ikawa, *J. Am. Chem. Soc.* **64**, 2994 (1942).
(154a) T. Teorell, *J. Hyg.* **44**, 15 (1946).

IV. Methods of Representation of Binding Data

1. Complex Formation as a Function of Concentration

A convenient method of representation of information on equilibrium complexes is the use of a semilogarithmic graph in which the extent of binding is plotted as a function of the logarithm of the concentration of the unbound small molecule. Such a curve is shown for copper–albumin

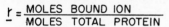

$$\bar{r} = \frac{\text{MOLES BOUND ION}}{\text{MOLES TOTAL PROTEIN}}$$

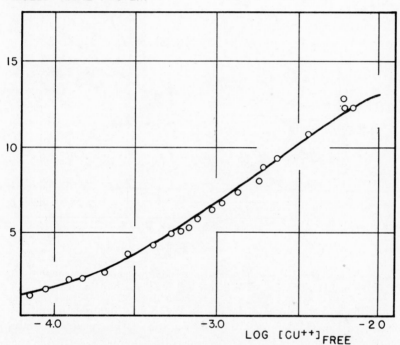

Fig. 7. Binding of cupric ions by bovine serum albumin,[155] at 25° and pH 4.83.

interactions[155] in Fig. 7. It resembles a titration curve and allows one to present data over a wide range of concentration. Furthermore, relative binding abilities can be seen qualitatively at a glance and under some conditions can be estimated directly from the midpoints of the binding curves.

2. Extrapolation Procedures for Evaluating Parameters

In a few cases, protein combinations with a small molecule may occur in a 1:1 stoichiometric ratio. In general, however, multiple complexes

(155) I. M. Klotz and H. G. Curme, *J. Am. Chem. Soc.* **70**, 939 (1948).

are formed and the maximum number of available sites must be obtained by extrapolation.

As has been indicated in the theoretical section, either of two functional relationships may form the basis of the graphical representation. Figure 8 shows a typical example of a graph of $1/r$ vs. $1/A$ prepared[156] from the experimental data of Chanutin, Ludewig, and Masket[13] for calcium–casein complexes. As Eq. (94) requires, the intercept on the ordinate is $1/n$; its reciprocal, n, is 16 in this case. Since the graph is linear, electrostatic interactions between successively bound ions are

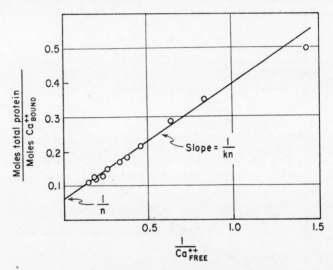

Fig. 8. One type of extrapolation to determine the maximum number of small molecules (or ions) which may be bound by a protein molecule.

negligible and the slope of the line in Fig. 8 may be used to calculate kn, or k_1 [see Eq. (85)]. An alternative graph of the very same data, but plotted according to Eq. (95), is illustrated in Fig. 9. In this case the intercept on the abscissa (at which point $r/(A)$ is zero) gives n directly, and the intercept on the ordinate gives kn.

The latter type of graph (Fig. 9) has some virtue over the former (Fig. 8) in that the length of the extrapolation to obtain n is emphasized, and one is not likely to be deceived about the relative reliability of the calculated value. In Fig. 8 there seems to be less uncertainty in the intercept from which n is calculated, but since the numerical value of this intercept is generally near zero, a very small error in the extrapolation to $1/n$ may be reflected into a large uncertainty in n.

When interactions between sites are significant, neither of the pre-

(156) I. M. Klotz, *Cold Spring Harbor Symposia Quant. Biol.* **14,** 97 (1950).

ceding graphs will be linear. A suitable factor for such interactions, shown in Eq. (113), may then be placed in the ordinate values. The interaction factor, w, may be calculated from electrostatic theory [Eq. (109)] or may be treated purely as an empirical parameter.

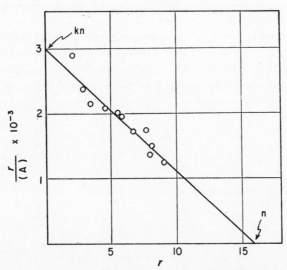

FIG. 9.   Another type of extrapolation to determine the maximum number of small molecules (or ions) which may be bound by a protein molecule.

V. Interactions of Proteins with Small Anions

Complexes of proteins with small ions have been studied extensively because a vast number of small molecules of biological import normally occur as charged species in aqueous media. In addition, studies of these interactions offer a method of examining protein configurations with small probes of known structure. In the following paragraphs some of the major problems of interactions with anions will be outlined, and the significant conclusions in molecular and thermodynamic terms will be described.

1. Effect of Anion Concentration

It is of interest to consider first one of the basic distinctions between a specific and a nonspecific ion–protein interaction as exhibited in a binding–concentration curve. Figure 10 illustrates typical data for a variety of anion complexes with albumin. In each case a substantial number of ions is bound by a single albumin molecule. Despite the wide range in anion concentration which has been covered, there is no indication of an approach to saturation. Only under special conditions is a plateau reached and then a stoichiometric relation is observed between the number of bound anions and the large number of cationic groups in the protein.[93,96,157,158]   Generally, stoichiometry in these nonspecific reactions is observed only if an insoluble complex is formed.   In the investigations of soluble complexes summarized in Fig. 10, the maximum number of available sites has been estimated in each case by the extrapolation procedures outlined in sec. IV.   In no case, however, has it been possible to reach this limit experimentally.   Thus even with decyl sulfate the highest measured r is less than 11, yet the number of available sites is at least 14.   In contrast, in studies[159] of the specific binding of the hapten

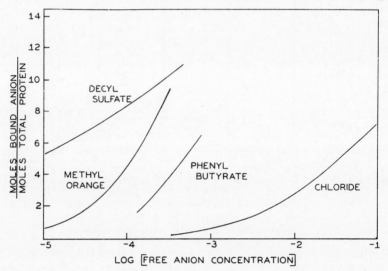

FIG. 10.   Extent of complex formation between serum albumin and decyl sulfate,[139] methyl orange,[5] phenylbutyrate[160] and chloride ions,[25] respectively.

anion $HO—C_6H_4—N=N—C_6H_4—AsO_3H^-$ by a specific antibody γ-globulin, saturation of the two available sites has been attained at a concentration of only 10^{-4} molar free anion.

It is necessary to recognize that in a solution of intermediate concentration of small ion, a variety of complexes exist, both in specific and nonspecific interactions.   Thus in copper–albumin interactions (Fig. 7) at a free Cu^{++} concentration of 10^{-2} molar, for example, the average number of bound ions is 13 per protein molecule.   However, complexes exist in this solution which have fewer than 13 cupric ions on each protein

(157) J. B. Speakman and M. C. Hirst, *Trans. Faraday Soc.* **29**, 148 (1933).
(158) A. Porai-Koschitz, *J. prakt. Chem.* **137**, 179 (1933).
(159) H. N. Eisen and F. Karush, *J. Am. Chem. Soc.* **71**, 363 (1949).
(160) J. D. Teresi and J. M. Luck, *J. Biol. Chem.* **174**, 653 (1948).

molecule, and there are also some present that have more than 13. With such multiple interactions it is not feasible to measure the concentration of each species by direct experiment. Nevertheless, these concentrations can be calculated from the fundamental equations of sec. III if adequate data are available for the variation of the average number of bound ions with changes in concentration of free ion.

As an example of the results of such a calculation a hypothetical situation has been presented in Fig. 11 in which it has been assumed that ten sites are available on the protein molecule, P. The fraction of the protein in the form of any specific complex has then been computed at each of several concentrations of free A. In Fig. 11, this fraction is given by the

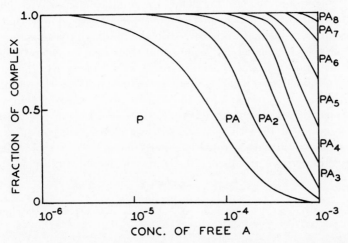

FIG. 11.   Different types of complex formed in a hypothetical case in which ten sites are available on a protein and the intrinsic binding constant is 1000.

ratio of the vertical distance between two adjacent curves to the height of the entire ordinate. Thus at a concentration of 10^{-5} molar free ion, approximately 0.9 of the protein is non-complexed and 0.1 is in the form PA_1. As the free ion concentration is increased, higher complexes are formed. At a concentration of 10^{-4} molar free A, the fraction of free P has dropped to 0.38 whereas that of PA_1 has risen to 0.39, and approximately 0.17 of PA_2 has been formed. In this solution, the average number of bound ions, calculated by the equations of sec. III, is 0.9 mole per mole of total protein. It is thus apparent that even though the average number of bound ions is less than one per protein molecule, a substantial quantity (about 17 per cent) of the protein is in the form of PA_2. The results cited in this simple hypothetical example are typical of soluble protein complexes in general.

In principle, if the anion concentration is increased progressively, a point should ultimately be reached in which all sites on the protein are saturated, even in nonspecific interactions, such as those illustrated in Fig. 10. Such a procedure would offer the most convincing method of obtaining values of n, the maximum number of sites available. In practice, sufficiently high concentrations cannot be attained, usually because of the limited solubility of free A. Recourse is then had to extrapolation methods.

In soluble albumin–anion complexes, which have been studied most extensively in this respect, several surprising features have become apparent. First, it has been universally observed that extrapolated n values for bound anions are far below the number of positively charged sites on albumin,[5,25,139,160] even though there is little doubt that such cationic sites are intimately involved in the binding process. Secondly, there have been increasing indications that there may be several groups of sites with significantly differentiated intrinsic binding constants and that n values obtained by extrapolation procedures refer to the number of sites within such a group. In studies of chloride and of thiocyanate interactions with albumin, for example, there is a hint of two classes of sites, one group of 10 with a single intrinsic association constant and a second group of 30 with a much smaller constant.[25] A more clear-cut demonstration of two groups of sites is present in the studies of albumin

complexes with [structure] $-N{=}N-$ [structure] $-CO_2^-$ ions,[14a] where one class containing near 5 and another near 17 sites seem to be available on albumin.

2. Electrostatic Interactions of Successively Bound Anions

As has been pointed out in sec. III, if charged ions are bound by a protein, the first bound ion should tend to reduce the affinity of the protein for the second oncoming ion because of electrostatic repulsion between these species of like charge. With univalent anions and albumin this electrostatic effect has not actually been detected. In studies with methyl orange,[5,161] for example, linear relations are obtained in graphs following Eq. (94) or (95). Similarly with p-(2-hydroxy-5-methyl-phenylazo)benzoate ion, in which two groups of sites seem accessible,[14a] the binding data fit well without corrections for electrostatic factors. Such corrections have been inserted in the treatment of chloride and

(161) G. E. Cogin and B. D. Davis, *J. Am. Chem. Soc.* **73**, 3135 (1951).

thiocyanate binding by albumin,[25] but inspection of the data indicates that agreement within experimental error could be obtained with equations omitting electrostatic factors.

With bivalent and trivalent anions, electrostatic repulsions between successively bound ions become manifest.[162] In the first place, the increase in r with increasing free anion concentration (Fig. 12) is much more gradual with the bivalent anion than with the univalent, with the trivalent than with the bivalent. Quantitative calculations of the electrostatic factor from Eq. (100) fit the experimentally observed behavior. Furthermore, the mutual repulsion in these multivalent

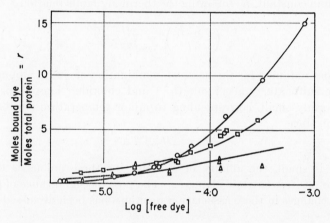

FIG. 12.   Binding of sulfonate compounds[162] by bovine serum albumin at pH 5.7: O, methyl orange (univalent); □, azosulfathiazole (bivalent); Δ, amaranth (trivalent).

anions is so great that even though at low concentrations they are bound more than the univalent anion (because of a greater intrinsic constant) the latter forges ahead as concentration increases (Fig. 12).

3. EFFECT OF TEMPERATURE

Quantitative investigations of temperature effects on equilibrium complexes have been limited largely to combinations with serum albumin. In addition, numerous studies have been made of the effect of temperature on the kinetics of reactions involving transition complexes, but these lead to information on the thermodynamic properties of these complexes only in certain favorable situations.[163]

Many investigations have demonstrated that temperature changes do not greatly affect the extent of binding of ions by serum albumin.   In

(162) I. M. Klotz and F. M. Walker, *J. Am. Chem. Soc.* **69**, 1609 (1947).
(163) H. Neurath and G. W. Schwert, *Chem. Revs.* **46**, 69 (1950).

his exploratory work on sulfonamide–plasma protein complexes, Davis[164] observed no marked change in the degree of binding with rise in temperature. Similarly, Putnam and Neurath[85] in their electrophoretic studies of complexes between albumin and dodecyl sulfate obtained no indication of a temperature dependence. Boyer, Ballou, and Luck[12] also reported a zero temperature coefficient in the binding of caprylate by serum albumin.

Recent quantitative investigations have confirmed the general conclusions reached in earlier qualitative work. Enthalpies of binding, $\Delta H°$, may be computed conveniently from temperature coefficients of the equilibrium constant, K, following the thermodynamic relation

$$\left(\frac{\partial \ln K}{\partial T}\right)_P = \frac{\Delta H°}{RT^2}. \tag{137}$$

The values obtained for the heats of combination of serum albumin with aromatic sulfonate,[165] alkyl sulfate,[129] and chloride[25] ions, respectively, are uniformly small, corresponding to minor temperature effects. Furthermore, since

$$\Delta F = \Delta H - T\Delta S \tag{138}$$

and ΔH is small, the affinity of albumin for these anions is due primarily to positive entropy changes. The possible significance of positive entropy changes in these association reactions has been discussed in some detail.[14a,165]

4. EFFECT OF pH AND NATURE OF BUFFER

Buffers, generally being constituted of at least one anion, may also be bound to proteins. Unless the extent of buffer interaction can be estimated, competition with other anions may obscure the effect of pH on binding ability. We may consider first, therefore, investigations carried out in the absence of buffer ions.

In studies of caprylate binding by bovine albumin, Boyer, Ballou, and Luck[12] found slight decreases as the pH was increased from 6.8 to 10.8 and somewhat greater decreases thereafter to pH 11.8. No corrections for Donnan effects were made and these would be substantial in 5 per cent protein solutions at the pH's examined. Nevertheless, from several sources[162,164,166] it is clear that albumin interactions with anions disappear at pH's near and above 12. This is also the region where lysine groups lose their charge, and hence the drop in binding ability

(164) B. D. Davis, *J. Clin. Invest.* **22**, 753 (1943).
(165) I. M. Klotz and J. M. Urquhart, *J. Am. Chem. Soc.* **71**, 847 (1949).
(166) H. W. Robinson and C. G. Hogden, *J. Biol. Chem.* **137**, 239 (1941).

suggests that these amino acid side chains are intimately involved in the binding process.

A most careful study of the effect of pH has been carried out by Karush[16] with methyl orange and bovine albumin. These measurements, having been made by the partition method, require no correction for Donnan effects despite the low ionic strength of the aqueous phase. From pH 7.6 up there is again a definite drop in binding ability, although not as much as might be expected from the increased negative charge on the protein. Even more surprising, however, is the observed slight increase in binding ability of albumin as the pH is increased from 6.4 to 7.6. The concomitant change in charge is from −8 to −16, a modification which would be expected to reduce affinity for anions substantially.

Essentially similar trends have been observed in measurements with buffered solutions.[167] Thus in phosphate buffer at pH 6.8, a limiting value of 0.72×10^5 has been observed for $r/(A)$ and hence for k_1 in methyl orange binding by albumin. If a correction is made for the competitive effect of phosphate, on the basis of Karush's results, the limit rises to 1.0×10^5. In glycinate buffer at pH 9.1, where albumin has more than twenty additional negative charges, the limit of $r/(A)$ not only does not drop substantially but is slightly higher, 1.1×10^5. If any correction need be made for the competitive effect of glycine, $r/(A)$ in this buffer would be even higher.

Thus there is no doubt that binding of anions by albumin does not decrease over the pH region of 6 to 9 to the extent one would expect from the increased negative charge on the protein. The large discrepancies in the quantitative calculations may lie in an inadequacy of the Debye-Hückel theory when applied to a complex protein molecule. On the other hand, it is apparent from other observations that configurational changes occur in albumin molecules in this pH range. Spectrophotometric observations demonstrate the appearance of new groups as pH values near 7 are approached.[168,169] Furthermore, studies with optically isomeric anions[170] show that binding ability increases with one stereoisomer as the number of bound ions increases, a trend which indicates that the protein molecule unfolds or expands as anions are bound. Such configurational rearrangements could change both n and k in a direction which could more than compensate for the repulsive electrostatic effects of increased pH.

Experiments in solutions acid to the isoelectric point are much more

(167) I. M. Klotz and J. M. Urquhart, *J. Phys. & Colloid Chem.* **53**, 100 (1949).
(168) I. M. Klotz and F. M. Walker, *J. Phys. & Colloid Chem.* **51**, 666 (1947).
(169) I. M. Klotz, R. K. Burkhard, and J. M. Urquhart, *J. Phys. Chem.* **56**, 77 (1952).
(170) F. Karush, *J. Phys. Chem.* **56**, 70 (1952).

sparse. In a single experiment with human albumin and chloride ion, binding has been observed to increase substantially as the pH is lowered to 3.2, and quantitative calculations indicate good agreement with electrostatic theory.[25] Similar results have been observed in a comparison of methyl orange binding by bovine albumin at pH 3.7 with data at higher pH's.[171]

In the discussion of pH effects so far, it has been assumed tacitly that the anion which is bound remains completely in the ionized form throughout the region of investigation. If the anion is a relatively weak electrolyte, account must be taken of its dissociation in any analysis of the effect of pH on binding. Thus the increased binding of sulfonamides[164] or of nitrophenols[160] with an increase in pH can be readily understood in terms of increased concentration of the anionic form.

As has already been indicated, anion binding by albumin is definitely affected by specific buffers because of competition with the buffer anion. The intensity of the buffer effect depends on the structure of the buffer anion in the same manner that structure determines the extent of binding by the protein.

Specific buffer effects have been particularly evident from electrophoretic measurements (see also Chap. 6). Thus Davis and Cohn[172] found ion–protein associations in studies with carboxyhemoglobin in phosphate and citrate buffers. Detailed comparisons for various buffers have been made by mobility measurements by Smith,[173] by Alberty,[174] and by Longsworth and Jacobsen.[175]

Quantitative comparisons of buffer effects can be made more conveniently by equilibrium dialysis measurements.[167] Most of the common buffers have been examined for their competitive effect in albumin binding. Glycinate, borate, and phosphate buffers have been observed to cause minimum interference in binding. Veronal and phthalate, on the other hand, cause major lowerings. While not buffers, chloride and nitrate are frequently used to attain desired ionic strengths in solution; the former produces distinctly less competition in binding experiments.

5. Effect of Molecular Structure of Anion

In correlating the structure of an anion with its ability to be bound by a protein, we may consider examples of high specificity and nonspecificity within several categories of structural differences.

(171) I. M. Klotz and J. M. Urquhart, *J. Am. Chem. Soc.* **71,** 1597 (1949).

(172) B. D. Davis and E. J. Cohn, *J. Am. Chem. Soc.* **61,** 2092 (1939).

(173) F. R. B. Smith, *J. Biol. Chem.* **108,** 187 (1935).

(174) R. A. Alberty, *J. Phys. & Colloid Chem.* **53,** 114 (1949).

(175) L. G. Longsworth and C. F. Jacobsen, *J. Phys. & Colloid Chem.* **53,** 126 (1949).

a. Similarly Charged Groups

The classic studies of Landsteiner[176] with proteins containing azo-coupled chemical groups provide excellent examples of high selectivity in antigen–antibody interactions. Thus an antibody to an antigen containing the $-N{=}N-\langle\bigcirc\rangle-CO_2^-$ hapten group does not react with an $-N{=}N-\langle\bigcirc\rangle-SO_3^-$ or an $-N{=}N-\langle\bigcirc\rangle-AsO_3H^-$ hapten. Quantitative studies by Eisen and Karush[159] have further emphasized these distinctions. The purified antibody homologous to the azophenyl-arsonate group shows strong affinity for the anion

$$HO-\langle\bigcirc\rangle-N{=}N-\langle\bigcirc\rangle-AsO_3H^- \quad (\Delta F^\circ = -7700 \text{ cal./mole}),$$

yet does not bind significant quantities of

$$(CH_3)_2N-\langle\bigcirc\rangle-N{=}N-\langle\bigcirc\rangle-SO_3^-.$$

In contrast, serum albumin shows roughly equal affinities toward each of the following anions:[169,177]

$$(CH_3)_2N-\langle\bigcirc\rangle-N{=}N-\langle\bigcirc\rangle\begin{matrix}-CO_2^-\\-SO_3^-\\-PO_3H^-\\-AsO_3H^-.\end{matrix}$$

Binding energies as well as the spectra of the complexes are very similar.

In structural terms, the specificity of serological reactions has been attributed[178–181] to a rigid complementariness in configuration of the haptenic group and the active site of the homologous antibody. With albumin, in contrast, it is apparent that each anionic substituent has ready access to a binding site.

b. Positional Isomers

Here again antigen–antibody reactions offer an instructive contrast to albumin interactions. Thus immune serum homologous to the

(176) K. Landsteiner, The Specificity of Serological Reactions, Harvard University Press, Cambridge, Mass., 1945.
(177) I. M. Klotz, R. K. Burkhard, and J. M. Urquhart, J. Am. Chem. Soc. 74, 202 (1952).
(178) F. Breinl and F. Haurowitz, Z. physiol. Chem. 192, 45 (1930).
(179) J. Alexander, Protoplasma 14, 296 (1931).
(180) S. Mudd, J. Immunol. 23, 423 (1932).
(181) L. Pauling, J. Am. Chem. Soc. 62, 2643 (1940).

—N=N—⟨C₆H₄⟩ (with CO₂ substituent) group does not react with antigens containing

—N=N—⟨C₆H₄⟩—CO_2^- haptenic groups.[176] On the other hand, serum albumin does form complexes of roughly comparable stability with azo dyes in which the —CO_2^- group is switched from the *ortho* to the *meta* to the *para* position, respectively.[169,177]

Even with serum albumin, nevertheless, differences are observed in the nature and extent of interaction of the protein with positional isomers. Particularly interesting examples are those in which a hydrogen donor substituent is shifted from the *ortho* to the *para* position in a benzene ring. Thus *o*-aminobenzoate ion (**I**) is bound more strongly by serum

(I) (II) (III) (IV)

albumin[42] than is *p*-aminobenzoate (**II**). Similarly, *o*-hydroxyphenyl-acetate (**III**) shows a greater affinity for albumin[182] than does the corresponding *para* compound (**IV**). If the second substituent is not a hydrogen donor, the difference between *ortho* and *para* isomers disappears. Thus *o*-chlorobenzoate and *p*-chlorobenzoate form complexes with albumin of roughly equal stability.[42]

The greater affinity of the *o*-substituted hydroxybenzoate or aminobenzoate ion probably is due to less competition between the protein and the solvent water. An intramolecular hydrogen bond is formed in these compounds so that the —OH or —NH₂ group does not interact strongly with solvent water molecules. On the other hand, in the corresponding *para* derivatives, the position of the —OH or —NH₂ group precludes formation of an internal hydrogen bond. Since hydrogen linkages may then form readily with water molecules, these ions would be subject to a greater attraction by the solvent than would their corresponding *ortho* compounds.

(182) J. M. Luck and A. S. Schmit, *Stanford Med. Bull.* **6**, 133 (1948).

c. Stereoisomers

The importance of spatial configuration in serological reactions is emphasized in a comparison of antigens prepared with D- and L-α-(N-p-aminobenzoyl)aminophenylacetic acid (**V**). In a classic paper Land-

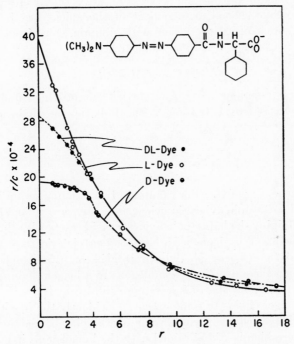

(**V**)

steiner and van der Scheer[183] described the production of antibodies which could distinguish between the two isomeric antigens. Thus a

FIG. 13. Binding of optically isomeric dyes by bovine serum albumin. Taken from F. Karush.[170]

change in the arrangement in space of the same four groups around the asymmetric carbon atom suffices to alter serological specificity.

Studies of the uptake of optically active substances by wool began almost 50 years ago with Willstätter,[184] who reported no selective adsorp-

(183) K. Landsteiner and J. van der Scheer, *J. Exptl. Med.* **48**, 315 (1928).

(184) R. Willstätter, *Ber.* **37**, 3758 (1904).

tion of optical antipodes. Occasional reports of some selectivity, especially in the *rate* of uptake, have appeared subsequently and have been summarized by Bradley and Easty.[185] Most of this work is of questionable significance, however, for the criterion of selectivity was the appearance of optical rotatory power in the solution containing the racemic mixture. It has been shown[185] that wool can produce optical activity in aqueous solutions of optically inactive compounds. Nevertheless, careful work by Bradley and Easty in which the adsorbed molecule was actually recovered has demonstrated some selectivity for (+)mandelic acid, for example, by wool and by casein. A definitive study has been made recently by Karush[170] with pure samples of optical isomers in which he has detected small but unequivocal differences in the affinity of albumin for the *dextro* and *levo* forms, respectively (Fig. 13). Thus while spatial arrangement of the anion does influence the nature and extent of its interaction with albumin, stereoisomerism is not the critical factor that it is in serological reactions.

d. Size of Molecule

Serological reactions have been carried out in which molecular size has been increased by extension of an aliphatic side chain attached to

$$-N{=}N-\langle\!\!\!\bigcirc\!\!\!\rangle-(CH_2)_n-COO^-$$

(VI)

the azobenzene ring (**VI**). For example, if an immune serum is prepared homologous to the phenylacetic acid group (i.e., $n = 1$ in **VI**), then an antigen containing the hapten phenylacetic acid reacts with the antibody. On the other hand, antigens with haptens benzoic acid ($n = 0$), phenylbutyric acid ($n = 3$), or phenylcaproic acid ($n = 5$), respectively, do not.[176] When the antibody is homologous to a longer chain than acetic, e.g., caproic acid, its specificity is more diffuse and it will react with shorter or longer chains to some extent. Evidently the freedom of rotation of the longer chains permits some overlapping in reactions, but the greatest interaction is still obtained with the homologous hapten. Likewise, in the inhibition of enzymatic reactions, such as the hydrolysis of acetyl-L-tyrosinamide, inhibitors of the structure $R-(CH_2)_n-COO^-$, where R is a cyclic substituent, show maximum activity when $n = 2$,[185a] that is, when the number of carbon atoms between ring and carboxyl groups corresponds to that in tyrosine.

In interactions with albumin, in contrast, a smooth increase in binding

(185) W. Bradley and G. C. Easty, *J. Chem. Soc.* **1951**, 499.
(185a) H. Neurath and J. A. Gladner, *J. Biol. Chem.* **188**, 407 (1951).

ability generally occurs as chain length is increased. Thus Boyer, Ballou, and Luck[12] observed increased affinity in the order: butyrate, caproate, caprylate, and caprate. Similarly with octyl, decyl, and dodecyl sulfates, $-\Delta F$ increases with chain length.[139]

In nonspecific protein interactions, furthermore, a general increase can be predicted in extent of binding as the size of the anion is increased. Realization of this principle is implicit in Sørensen's observation that the protein error in colorimetric pH measurements is generally smaller with indicators of simpler constitution.[186] Similar conclusions were reached by Steinhardt[47] in studies with wool, by McMeekin[187] in studies of precipitation by detergents, and by several investigators in work with albumin.[12,42,139] This trend of increased binding is generally attributed to stronger van der Waals' forces which accompany increased molecular size.

Within a small range of molecular weight, particular structures may be favored even in relatively nonspecific interactions such as with albumin. Thus, in the barbiturate series[188] thio compounds are more firmly bound than oxy analogs, and allyl substituents increase affinity more than corresponding saturated chains. A huge variety of substituents in sulfadiazine have also been compared,[189] but here interpretation is complicated by the absence of full information on the effect of these substituents on ionization of the sulfonamides. Nitro groups tend to increase binding energies substantially,[160] although added polar groups such as SO_3^- reduce affinity generally because of their interaction with water.[42,190] The literature on binding of drugs has been surveyed in great detail by Goldstein,[191] and from his analysis many interesting correlations of pharmacological significance may be drawn.

Quantitative studies of free energies of binding have been limited largely to serum albumin. Typical data are summarized in Table V in terms of ΔF_1^0, the free energy of formation of the first complex being chosen to avoid any decision as to n, the maximum number of available sites.

6. COMPARISON OF PROTEINS

It may be instructive to make again a clear distinction between specific and nonspecific interactions. Specificity is characteristic of the vast

(186) S. P. L. Sørensen, *Biochem. Z.* **21**, 131 (1909).
(187) T. L. McMeekin, *Federation Proc.* **1**, 125 (1942).
(188) L. R. Goldbaum and P. K. Smith, *Federation Proc.* **7**, 222 (1948).
(189) H. B. van Dyke, N. A. Tupikova, B. F. Chow, and H. A. Walker, *J. Pharmacol. Exptl. Therap.* **83**, 203 (1945).
(190) E. K. Rideal, *Trans. Faraday Soc.* **39**, 368 (1943).
(191) A. Goldstein, *J. Pharmacol. Exptl. Therap.* **95**, 102 (1949).

TABLE V
Free Energies of Binding of Some Anions by Proteins

Ion	Protein	$-\Delta F_1^\circ$	Reference
Acetate	Aldolase	2,620	192
Thiocyanate	Insulin	3,000	72
Chloride	Human serum albumin	3,660	25
Phenylacetate	Bovine serum albumin	4,015	160
Phenylbutyrate	Bovine serum albumin	5,165	160
Thiocyanate	Human serum albumin	5,460	25
Methyl orange	Bovine serum albumin	6,410	165
Decyl sulfate	Bovine serum albumin	7,660	139
Dodecyl sulfate	Bovine serum albumin	8,750	139
Diphosphopyridine nucleotide	Glyceraldehyde phosphate dehydrogenase	10,000	193

majority of enzymatic and physiological reactions, but one example, serological specificity, will suffice to illustrate the general principle. Referring to quantitative work, we may cite again the binding of

$$HO-\langle\bigcirc\rangle-N=N-\langle\bigcirc\rangle-AsO_3H^-$$

by the antibody γ-globulin homologous to the azophenylarsonic acid group, which occurs with a free-energy change of -7.7 kcal.[159] Closely related γ-globulins, however, will not bind organic anions of this size to any detectable extent.[171]

Fairly detailed molecular pictures have been developed to account for this specificity.[181,194] In general, the lock-and-key concepts of E. Fischer and P. Ehrlich have been elaborated in detail to include modern information on atomic sizes and interatomic distances. Thus the specific interaction of antibody with the azophenylarsonate hapten is attributed to the presence on the protein surface of an invaginated region into which the hapten can fit well, but toward which other anions can approach only with difficulty owing to steric repulsions or to insufficient interaction energy because of looseness of fit. It is perhaps unnecessary to carry the lock-and-key analogy to the extent of picturing an actual invagination, but the postulate of a very specific configuration on the antibody surface which is complementary to the hapten structure is certainly the best molecular interpretation available at present.

At the other extreme are anion–protein interactions, such as with

(192) S. F. Velick, *J. Phys. & Colloid Chem.* **53**, 135 (1949).
(193) S. F. Velick, *Federation Proc.* **10**, 264 (1951).
(194) L. Pauling, *Endeavour* **7**, 43 (1948).

albumin, in which specificity is essentially nonexistent, although gradations in affinity among proteins are marked. Serum albumin seems superior to all other proteins in its ability to bind anions of practically all types. Since molecular size of the anion as well as pH of the solution may affect the extent of combination with protein, a comparison of proteins is best made with a single reference ion in a solution of fixed pH. Such a comparison with methyl orange and a pH near 7 indicates that among approximately a dozen proteins examined, only serum albumin and β-lactoglobulin show appreciable complex formation.[171] In the same pH region, Velick[192] has found that the enzyme aldolase combines with acetate ions, as well as with phosphate. The intrinsic binding constant with acetate, however, seems to be smaller with aldolase than with albumin,[167] especially when account is taken of the positive charge on the former protein and the negative one on the latter at the pH's of the measurements.

Under more favorable conditions other proteins may also combine with anions. Thus although egg albumin does not bind significantly at pH 7, from shifts in indicator equilibria[195,196] as well as from titration curves[46] it is apparent that this protein does form complexes with methyl orange and other small anions in solutions acid to the isoelectric point. Comparable results have been reported with insulin.[72,88a] No binding of thiocyanate ion could be detected at pH 7, but substantial combination occurs near pH 3, where the protein is positively charged.

If an anion is used which is bound even more strongly, for example a long-chain alkyl sulfate or sulfonate, then almost all proteins seem to form complexes (see Chap. 9 and reviews by Putnam[197] and by Glassman[198]). Thus Lundgren, Elam, and O'Connell[83] demonstrated the existence alkaline to the isoelectric point of ovalbumin combinations with alkylbenzene sulfonates by means of electrophoretic measurements, and Bull[101] studied ovalbumin complexes with dodecyl sulfate by surface-film methods. Extensive investigations have also been carried out by Pankhurst and Smith[62,199] of gelatin–dodecyl sulfate interactions alkaline to the isoelectric point, and by Elkes and Finian[200] of hemoglobin–hexadecyl sulfate combinations.

The question naturally arises as to whether it is possible to account for the binding characteristics of different proteins toward anions in

(195) A. Thiel and G. Schulz, *Z. anorg. u. allgem. Chem.* **220**, 225 (1934).
(196) J. F. Danielli, *Biochem. J.* **35**, 470 (1941).
(197) F. W. Putnam, *Advances in Protein Chem.* **4**, 80 (1948).
(198) H. N. Glassman, *Bact. Revs.* **12**, 105 (1948).
(199) K. G. A. Pankhurst and R. C. M. Smith, *Trans. Faraday Soc.* **41**, 630 (1945).
(200) J. Elkes and J. B. Finean, *in* Surface Chemistry, Interscience Publishers, New York, N. Y., 1949, p. 281.

terms of molecular structure. It should be pointed out at the outset that abundant evidence indicates that cationic side chains of proteins participate in interactions with anions. Thus combinations with anionic detergents take place stoichiometrically[201,202] according to the number of cationic groups. Comparison of affinities toward pairs of small molecules of nearly equal size and structure, but with the negative charge absent in one, shows a marked reduction in affinity with loss of charge.[42,109] Furthermore, if lysine or arginine side chains are blocked by chemical reactions which remove their charge, anion affinity of the protein drops sharply.[171,203]

On the other hand, mere possession of cationic side chains does not seem to be adequate; thus several proteins with little affinity toward anions, for example γ-globulin, contain very substantial quantities of arginine, lysine, and histidine residues. It has been suggested frequently[204,205] that one or more other residues, particularly with organic side chains such as those of leucine or phenylalanine, must be in proper juxtaposition to the cationic nitrogen to supply the additional attraction to insure binding. It seems unlikely, however, that a particular secondary residue need be at a specific distance from the cationic locus, since anions of all sizes and shapes, organic and inorganic, form associations with serum albumin. Furthermore, if these nonpolar residues are required, they should be expected to assist in the binding of organic cations at anionic sites of the protein about as much as they are assumed to assist in the binding of organic anions at cationic sites. Recent studies[206] indicate, however, that cations of moderately large size are not bound by albumin under circumstances in which anion binding is great.

An alternative explanation[171] of the special affinity of albumin lays much stress on the relatively low content of hydroxy amino acids in this protein as compared to a nonbinding protein such as γ-globulin (Table VI). It seems reasonable to visualize these —OH chains as forming hydrogen bonds with other side chains containing —COO$^-$ or $\equiv$NH$^+$ groups. When the content of hydroxy amino acids is very high, crosslinks may be formed with practically all —COO$^-$ and $\equiv$NH$^+$ groups. A relatively rigid structure would thus be obtained in which $\equiv$NH$^+$ groups would be "bound" internally, hence they would be unavailable to small anions. On the other hand, in a protein such as albumin, fewer —OH

(201) H. P. Lundgren, *Textile Research J.* **15**, 335 (1945).

(202) F. W. Putnam and H. Neurath, *J. Biol. Chem.* **159**, 195 (1945).

(203) J. D. Teresi, *J. Am. Chem. Soc.* **72**, 3972 (1950).

(204) B. D. Davis, *Am. Scientist* **34**, 611 (1946).

(205) J. M. Luck, *Discussions Faraday Soc.* No. 6, 44 (1949).

(206) I. M. Klotz, E. W. Gelewitz, and J. M. Urquhart, *J. Am. Chem. Soc.* **74**, 209 (1952).

TABLE VI
Polar Amino Acid Composition of Some Proteins[a]

Protein	Sum of hydroxy side chains	Sum of carboxyl side chains	Sum of cationic nitrogens
Bovine albumin	128	133	145
β-Lactoglobulin	118	141	105
Egg albumin	134	98	90
Insulin	150	63	72
Ribonuclease	233	48	128
Bovine γ-globulin	216	67	99
Pepsin	248	109	18

[a] Based on weight of 100,000 g. for each protein. For sources of data see I. M. Klotz and J. M. Urquhart, *J. Am. Chem. Soc.* **71**, 1597 (1949). Newer data would modify some of these values slightly.

groups are present and must be shared among a larger number of —COO⁻ and $\equiv$NH⁺ side chains. From figures of the energies of hydrogen bonds[207] as well as from x-ray investigations of the structure of threonine,[208] it seems likely that an —OH $\cdots$ OOC— would be formed preferentially. The presence of fewer —OH groups would tend to make albumin a less rigid structure and in particular would permit many more $\equiv$NH⁺ groups to remain in a relatively open position available for anion binding.

VI. Interactions of Proteins with Small Cations

1. Interactions with Hydrogen Ion

The most extensively studied interactions of proteins are those with hydrogen ions (see Chap. 6). Acid–base titrations based on electromotive force measurements were initiated by Bugarszky and Liebermann[209] over 50 years ago. An adequate theoretical analysis, however, was introduced only some time later by Linderstrøm-Lang[114] and has been extended by Cannan, Kibrick, and Palmer[210] and much simplified by Scatchard.[118] Tanford's[211] analysis of titration curves of human serum albumins presents a detailed theoretical treatment of some very precise measurements.

(207) L. Pauling, The Nature of the Chemical Bond, 2nd Ed., Cornell University Press, Ithaca, N. Y., 1945, pp. 333–4.

(208) D. P. Shoemaker, J. Donohue, V. Schomaker, and R. B. Corey, *J. Am. Chem. Soc.* **72**, 2328 (1950).

(209) S. Bugarszky and L. Liebermann, *Pflüger's Arch. ges. Physiol.* **72**, 51 (1898).

(210) R. K. Cannan, A. C. Kibrick, and A. H. Palmer, *Ann. N. Y. Acad. Sci.* **41**, 243 (1941).

(211) C. Tanford, *J. Am. Chem. Soc.* **72**, 441 (1950).

The general approach in treating these titration curves may be illustrated by consideration of the electrostatic changes as H^+ ions are added to the isoionic protein, P. If we assume that we are dealing with a single type of basic group, e.g. COO^-, then the average number of bound H^+ ions per mole of total protein, r, is given, according to Eq. (112), by the expression

$$r = \frac{nke^{-2wr}(H^+)}{1 + ke^{-2wr}(H^+)}, \tag{139}$$

where k represents the association constant for hydrogen ions. The average number of unoccupied sites is

$$n - r = \frac{n}{1 + ke^{-2wr}(H^+)}, \tag{140}$$

since n represents the total number of sites with the intrinsic constant k. Thus

$$\ln \frac{r}{n - r} = \ln k + \ln (H^+) - 2wr, \tag{141}$$

or

$$\log \frac{n - r}{r} = pk + pH + \frac{2wr}{2.303}. \tag{142}$$

Since acid–base equilibria are usually represented as dissociation processes rather than association, we may replace k by

$$K = \frac{1}{k}, \tag{143}$$

where K represents the dissociation constant. Thus we obtain

$$\log \frac{n - r}{r} = pH - pK + \frac{2wr}{2.303}. \tag{144}$$

Analyses of titration data according to Eq. (144) allow the evaluation of pK for each type of basic group in a protein. The results obtained by this approach as well as by earlier methods are listed in Table VII.

In the derivation of Eq. (144) no account has been taken of possible anion binding accompanying the acid uptake. Such binding can be included as a correction in the electrostatic term and has been done so by Tanford[211] in titrations with HCl acid to the isoionic point. The number of bound chloride ions which must be postulated in order to fit the equation is about twice as high as that actually measured. In practice this means that the electrostatic interaction term, which would depend on the difference between the number of bound H^+ and bound Cl^- ions, is smaller than would be expected on the basis of the measured Cl^- binding.

In fact, it is frequently possible to neglect the third term on the right-hand side of Eq. (144) and obtain a single, constant pK.

The pK's listed in Table VII are reasonably close to those of the corresponding groups in small molecules. On the whole, then, interactions

TABLE VII

IONIZATION PROPERTIES OF GROUPS IN PROTEINS

Group	pK			Heat of ionization,[137] kcal./mole
	Egg albumin[210]	β-Lactoglobulin[212]	Human serum albumin[211]	
Carboxyl	4.29	4.60	4.00	±1.5
Imidazole	6.7	6.80	6.10	6.9–7.5
α-Amino			8.00	10–13
ε-Amino	10.07		9.40	10–12
Phenolic OH			9.60	6.0

of hydrogen ions with proteins depend primarily on the side chains available, with the over-all electrostatic properties of the protein also expressing themselves to some extent.

2. INTERACTIONS WITH ORGANIC CATIONS

Investigations of these interactions have been relatively few as compared to the extensive studies with anions. Recent work indicates that interactions with cations show some similarities to those with anions as well as some major differences. Many of the results of pharmacological interest have been tabulated by Goldstein.[191]

In studies with long-chain detergents, Glassman[213] found that serum albumin forms a stoichiometric complex with benzylcetyldimethylammonium chloride, in which the number of detergent molecules corresponds approximately to the number of carboxyl groups of the protein. Analogous results have been reported by Polonovski and Macheboeuf.[214,215] Similarly, stoichiometric combination was observed in interactions of egg albumin with dodecylamine hydrochloride,[68] of lysozyme with benzylcetyldimethylammonium[216] ion, and of acriflavine

(212) R. K. Cannan, A. H. Palmer, and A. C. Kibrick, *J. Biol. Chem.* **142**, 803 (1942).
(213) H. N. Glassman, *Ann. N. Y. Acad. Sci.* **53**, 91 (1950).
(214) J. Polonovski and M. Macheboeuf, *Ann. inst. Pasteur* **74**, 196 (1948).
(215) J. Polonovski, Thesis, University of Paris, 1950.
(216) H. N. Glassman and D. M. Molnar, *Arch. Biochem. and Biophys.* **32**, 170 (1951).

with tobacco mosaic virus.[217] The stoichiometry of these reactions has allowed their use in determining protein concentrations in some fluids.[218,219] These combinations are thus analogous to the stoichiometric ones between anionic detergents, such as dodecyl sulfate, and serum albumin.[96a] In both cases the importance of electrostatic attraction by specific sites on the protein molecule is emphasized.

Similarities between cation and anion interactions with proteins have also been pointed out by Steinhardt and Zaiser[49] in their studies of titration curves of wool. For both types of ion, affinity for the protein increases with chain length and in about the same way for various modifications in structure. Increases in binding with chain length have been reported also in interactions of egg albumin with acridines.[220]

Important differences are also evident in comparisons of organic anion and cation combinations with proteins. Whereas with anions precipitation with albumin occurs slightly below the isoelectric pH (i.e., as soon as the protein has a small net positive charge), with cations a protein such as albumin must be taken more than 3 pH units above its isoelectric point (i.e., given a substantial negative charge) before precipitation is brought about.[213] Here we have an indication that with ions of equal size anions combine more strongly with albumin. Similar indications are evident from the inability of aliphatic amines to protect albumin against heat denaturation[205] and from the absence of pH displacements of isoionic albumin in the presence of quarternary ions such as tetrapropylammonium or trimethylphenylammonium.[50]

Quantitative comparisons of binding ability by the equilibrium dialysis method show unequivocally that among ions of equal size organic cations are bound much less[206] than anions by serum albumin. Similarly such cations are not bound appreciably by proteins such as serum γ-globulin or trypsin. This behavior indicates that —COO⁻ chains in proteins are blocked, perhaps by interaction with —OH groups from hydroxy amino acid residues. Such blocking has already been suggested above in connection with the interpretation of the unique anion affinity of serum albumin. Because of this internal bonding, an organic cation must have a much stronger interaction energy to be bound at a —COO⁻ site than an organic anion requires to be bound at an ≡NH⁺ site. If the —COO⁻ side chain is fixed in position, there is little chance of its moving sufficiently close to a lipophilic side chain on the protein and thereby providing an additional van der Waals' attraction to supplement the electrostatic attraction for the small organic cation.

(217) G. Oster and H. Grimsson, *Arch. Biochem.* **24**, 119 (1949).
(218) F. P. Chinard, *J. Biol. Chem.* **176**, 1439 (1948).
(219) J. Polonovski and M. Macheboeuf, *Ann. inst. Pasteur* **74**, 203 (1948).
(220) D. L. Hammick and S. F. Mason, *J. Chem. Soc.* **1950**, 348.

It is of interest in this connection to note that organic cations do form soluble complexes with nucleic acids and that these interactions can be treated theoretically by the same equations used to describe protein interactions.[221,222]

3. Complexes with Metallic Ions

a. Comparison of Metallic Ions

Complexes of proteins with almost all types of metal ion have been examined. For purposes of this discussion it may be convenient to divide metals into three classes: (a) those which may be bound very strongly and by several possible functional groups, (b) those bound more weakly and primarily at charged sites, and (c) those which do not ordinarily form stable complexes with proteins.

In the first group we may include transition metals, typified by mercury, silver, copper, or zinc. These metals may be bound to any one of several side chains in a protein. At very low concentrations interactions with —SH groups seem to be most significant. Thus Hughes[15] found that mercuric ion or its monoalkyl derivatives couple with the single sulfhydryl group on serum albumin molecules. Other mercurials evidently react in a similar manner.[223] If Hg^{++} is used, an albumin dimer may be formed when one mole of Hg^{++} is present for every two moles of albumin. Higher ratios of Hg^{++} to albumin favor the protein monomer, as indicated by Eq. (8). With methylmercury salts, CH_3HgX, this reaction may actually be used to determine quantitatively the number of sulfhydryl groups in a protein. The ability of Ag^+ ions to react with —SH groups has also been used for quantitative estimations.[224] With CH_3HgI the equilibrium constant for the reaction

$$CH_3HgI + Alb—SH \rightleftharpoons Alb—S—HgCH_3 + H^+ + I^- \qquad (145)$$

has been measured[15] and corresponds to a pK of 4.45. The mercury-sulfur bond is evidently much stronger than that between mercury and other common functional groups in proteins.

Quantitative studies with copper have been carried to much higher metal:protein ratios (Fig. 7), so that it is evident that groups other than sulfhydryl are involved. At high pH's the nature of the spectra[225] of common copper–protein complexes (Fig. 14) leaves no doubt that $Cu:N$ bonds are involved. In strongly basic solutions quantitative measure-

(221) L. F. Cavalieri and A. Angelos, *J. Am. Chem. Soc.* **72**, 4686 (1950).

(222) L. F. Cavalieri, A. Angelos, and M. E. Balis, *J. Am. Chem. Soc.* **73**, 4902 (1951).

(223) J. P. Milnor, *Proc. Soc. Exptl. Biol. Med.* **75**, 63 (1950).

(224) R. Benesch and R. E. Benesch, *Arch. Biochem.* **19**, 35 (1948).

(225) I. M. Klotz and H. A. Fiess, *J. Phys. & Colloid Chem.* **55**, 101 (1951).

ments[226] indicate that each copper is bonded to four peptide nitrogen atoms.[227]

In investigations of zinc–albumin interactions Gurd and Goodman[228] have found that the number of available sites (in the pH region of 6–7.5) corresponds to the number of histidine residues in the protein. Further, the intrinsic affinity constant agrees well with that for simple zinc–imidazole complexes. Thus strong evidence has been presented for the

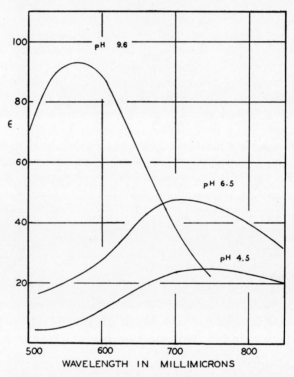

Fig. 14. Spectra of cupric ion complexes with bovine serum albumin.[225]

involvement of imidazole side chains in albumin binding of zinc, at least in the pH range 6–7.5.

With some metals, complex–ion equilibria in aqueous solution greatly complicate the interpretation of interactions with proteins. Extensive studies of chromium fixation by collagen, such as those of Gustavson,[18] have demonstrated the critical influence of the state of the chromium complex. In general, factors such as concentration, which favor non-

(226) J. W. Mehl, E. Pacovska, and R. J. Winzler, *J. Biol. Chem.* **177**, 13 (1949)
(227) M. M. Rising and P. S. Yang, *J. Biol. Chem.* **99**, 755 (1932–3).
(228) F. R. N. Gurd and D. S. Goodman, *J. Am. Chem. Soc.* **74**, 670 (1952).

cationic chromium complexes decrease the extent of chrome fixation by collagen markedly.[229] Such behavior, as well as the nature of the dependence of fixation on pH, indicates that carboxyl groups of the protein are primarily involved.[18]

The alkaline-earth group of elements, and in particular calcium, has been studied very extensively. Stoichiometric data were compared first by Northrop and Kunitz[6] in equilibrium dialysis experiments with gelatin. Equilibrium constants have been estimated by a variety of methods,[230] and intrinsic constants near 10^2–10^3 have been calculated for serum proteins as well as for casein. The extent of binding of alkaline-earth ions by proteins is generally less than that of the transition metals under comparable conditions. This affinity parallels that of small ligands for these ions (Table VIII).

TABLE VIII
AFFINITY CONSTANTS FOR METAL COMPLEXES[a]

Metal ion	Complexing ligand			
	CH_3COO^-	$CH_2(OH)COO^-$	NH_3	$CH_2(NH_2)COO^-$
Cu^{++}	146	830	1.4×10^4	2.5×10^{15}
Ca^{++}	3.4	13	0.6	—
Mg^{++}	3.2	8.3	1.7	$ca.\ 10^4$

[a] The numbers given are the equilibrium constants, $K = \dfrac{[MeA]}{[Me][A]}$, except in the glycine complexes where K refers to the formation of MeA_2. The values listed have been obtained from Refs. (231–236).

Numerous studies have also been made with the alkali-metal ions Na^+ and K^+, which give no evidence of protein combinations. Early investigators were unable to detect any binding of sodium by blood serum.[237–239] Similar results have also been reported for solutions as

(229) K. H. Gustavson, *Svensk Kem. Tid.* **58**, 2 (1946).
(230) D. M. Greenberg, *Advances in Protein Chem.* **1**, 121 (1944).
(231) R. K. Cannan and A. C. Kibrick, *J. Am. Chem. Soc.* **60**, 2314 (1938).
(232) J. Bjerrum, Metal Ammine Formation in Aqueous Solution, P. Haase and Son, Copenhagen, 1941, p. 149.
(233) K. J. Pedersen, *Kgl. Danske Videnskab. Selskab Mat.-fys. Medd.* **22**, No. 12 (1945).
(234) N. R. Joseph, *J. Biol. Chem.* **164**, 529 (1946).
(235) A. Albert, *Biochem. J.* **46**, xxxix (1950).
(236) M. Lloyd, V. Wycherley, and C. B. Monk, *J. Chem. Soc.* **1951**, 1786.
(237) B. S. Neuhausen and E. K. Marshall, Jr., *J. Biol. Chem.* **53**, 365 (1922).
(238) W. E. Ringer, *Z. physiol. Chem.* **130**, 270 (1923).
(239) L. Michaelis and S. Kawai, *Biochem. Z.* **163**, 1 (1925).

high as 10 per cent in concentration of gelatin[6] as well as for concentrated solutions of albumin,[25] casein,[240] crystalline hemoglobin, or hemerythrin.[241] Recent electrometric measurements with permselective membranes[242] indicate some lowering of the activity of Na^+ in solutions of casein at high pH. No corrections for Donnan effects were made, however, and these would be appreciable for such a highly phosphorylated protein, especially at high pH values. Below pH 7, Carr and Topol[242] and Kirk and Schmidt[243] could detect no change of activity of Na^+ in the presence of casein.

Thus there seems to be no unequivocal evidence for binding of alkalimetal ions by commonly available proteins. It is of interest to note that these ions also form no complexes with common organic or inorganic small molecules or ions. Only a few unusual organic linkages show some affinity for Na^+ or K^+.

On the other hand, sodium and potassium ions are immobilized by many anionic polymeric electrolytes, natural or synthetic. The colligative properties of the sodium salts of nucleic acids[244] and of heparin[245] are abnormally low if compared with calculations on the basis of complete ionization of the salt. Likewise, electrophoresis[246] and conductance[247] measurements with arabic acid indicate complex formation with potassium ions. Parallel observations have been reported in investigations of the physicochemical properties of the sodium and of the potassium salts of synthetic polyelectrolytes, such as polyacrylate molecules.[248-251] It seems possible, therefore, that under conditions where they acquire a large negative charge, proteins too may be capable of binding alkalimetal ions.

b. Comparison of Proteins

Practically all common proteins are able to combine with metals to some extent. There are some proteins (besides special enzymatic or respiratory ones[252]) which have in addition a few sites of unusually high

(240) S. Miyamoto and C. L. A. Schmidt, *J. Biol. Chem.* **99**, 335 (1933).
(241) E. H. Battley and I. M. Klotz, *Biol. Bull.* **101**, 215 (1951).
(242) C. W. Carr and L. Topol, *J. Phys. & Colloid Chem.* **54**, 176 (1950).
(243) P. L. Kirk and C. L. A. Schmidt, *J. Biol. Chem.* **76**, 115 (1928).
(244) E. Hammarsten, *Biochem. Z.* **144**, 383 (1924).
(245) O. Wilander, *Skand. Arch. Physiol.* **81**, No. 15 (1938).
(246) H. Svensson, *Arkiv Kemi, Mineral. Geol.* **22**, No. 10 (1946).
(247) A. Veis, Ph.D. Dissertation, Northwestern University, 1951.
(248) W. Kern, *Makromol. Chem.* **2**, 279 (1948).
(249) D. Edelson and R. M. Fuoss, *J. Am. Chem. Soc.* **72**, 306 (1950).
(250) J. R. Van Wazer and D. A. Campanella, *J. Am. Chem. Soc.* **72**, 655 (1950).
(251) J. P. Huizenga, P. F. Grieger, and F. T. Wall, *J. Am. Chem. Soc.* **72**, 2636 (1950).
(252) A. L. Lehninger, *Physiol. Revs.* **30**, 393 (1950).

affinity for certain metals. Thus siderophilin, the metal-binding component of plasma, shows a marked affinity for both iron and copper.[253,254] In each case two metal ions combine with the protein with great avidity, though more can be bound if the concentration of cation is high. Conalbumin behaves in a similar fashion,[255-258] again two metal ions combining with one mole of protein. With each of these proteins, the evidence seems strong that carbon dioxide is required for the formation of the metal complex, although some doubts have been expressed by Fraenkel-Conrat.[259] The nature of these specific sites with high avidity for iron or copper is still not clearly established,[259,260] although the displacement of H^+ ions by the combining metal[254] suggests $\equiv NH^+$ side chains. The similarity in absorption spectra of these iron–protein complexes with those of iron complexes with aspergillic acid, hydroxylamine–bicarbonate mixtures, and other simple molecules containing the cyclic hydroxamic group, has led Fiala and Burk[260] to suggest a common molecular grouping, which may be represented as

Since almost all proteins have side chains with carboxyl groups and basic nitrogen atoms, it is perhaps not surprising that they are capable of forming complexes of moderate stability with many metals, such as calcium or copper, except when electrostatic factors are especially unfavorable. Thus calcium forms complexes of approximately equal strength with serum globulins, with serum albumin, and with casein.[230,261] A more precise comparison with copper[262] leads to the detailed order of affinities listed in Table IX.

In the case of copper a rather striking parallelism between binding constant and isoelectric point of the protein is apparent. This correlation suggests that electrostatic influences are involved. The binding measurements were carried out in a buffer at pH 6.5. On the whole, we can expect that the lower the isoelectric pH as compared to pH 6.5, the greater should be the negative charge on the protein. If each protein

(253) A. L. Schade and L. Caroline, *Science* **104**, 340 (1946).
(254) A. L. Schade, R. W. Reinhart, and H. Levy, *Arch. Biochem.* **20**, 170 (1949).
(255) A. L. Schade and L. Caroline, *Science* **100**, 14 (1944).
(256) G. Alderton, W. H. Ward, and H. L. Fevold, *Arch. Biochem.* **11**, 9 (1946).
(257) H. Fraenkel-Conrat and R. E. Feeney, *Arch. Biochem.* **29**, 101 (1950).
(258) R. C. Warner and I. Weber, *J. Biol. Chem.* **191**, 173 (1951).
(259) H. Fraenkel-Conrat, *Arch. Biochem.* **28**, 452 (1950).
(260) S. Fiala and D. Burk, *Arch. Biochem.* **20**, 172 (1949).
(261) N. Drinker and H. H. Zinsser, *J. Biol. Chem.* **148**, 187 (1943).
(262) H. A. Fiess and I. M. Klotz, *J. Am. Chem. Soc.* **74**, 887 (1952).

has approximately the same number of binding sites, then the greater the over-all negative charge on the protein, the greater should be the attraction for Cu^{++}.   The observed affinities fit this electrostatic trend.

TABLE IX

RELATIVE AFFINITIES OF PROTEINS FOR CUPRIC ION[a]

Protein	ΔF_1°, kcal./mole	Isoelectric pH
α-Casein	−7.30	4.0[263]
β-Casein	−7.16	4.5[263]
Serum albumin	−6.49	4.7[175]
β-Lactoglobulin	−5.81	5.2[175]
Lysozyme	−4.39	11.0[264]

[a] For purposes of comparison a unit weight of 100,000 has been taken for each protein.   Measurements made at 0°C., pH 6.5, 0.2 M acetate solution.

VII. Interactions of Protein with Small Neutral Molecules

Perhaps the most important interactions of this category are those of proteins with water.   Basic thermodynamic data[265-268a] have been derived from extensive studies of solid–water vapor equilibria.   Gas-phase interactions between other polar gases and proteins have also been investigated.[269,270]   From the molecular viewpoint, most detailed studies have been carried out by Mellon, Korn, and Hoover,[271,272] who have demonstrated by chemical blocking techniques that polar amino side chains contribute very strongly to water absorption, at least by casein, despite their small contribution to the total weight of protein.   Peptide groups also appear to be responsible for a major fraction of water uptake.   It is of interest to note that severe treatments of proteins such as ovalbumin or wool, which markedly alter their internal structure, produce little

(263) R. C. Warner, J. Am. Chem. Soc. **66**, 1725 (1944).
(264) W. H. Ward and H. L. Fevold, J. Biol. Chem. **157**, 43 (1945).
(265) H. B. Bull, J. Am. Chem. Soc. **66**, 1499 (1944).
(266) M. Dole and A. D. McLaren, J. Am. Chem. Soc. **69**, 651 (1947).
(267) S. Davis and A. D. McLaren, J. Polymer Sci. **3**, 16 (1948).
(268) R. A. Robinson, J. Chem. Soc. **1948**, 1083.
(268a) L. Pauling, J. Am. Chem. Soc. **67**, 555 (1945).
(269) W. D. Bancroft and C. E. Barnett, J. Phys. Chem. **34**, 449 (1930).
(270) S. W. Benson and J. M. Seehof, J. Am. Chem. Soc. **73**, 5053 (1951).
(271) E. F. Mellon, A. H. Korn, and S. R. Hoover, J. Am. Chem. Soc. **69**, 827 (1947); ibid. **70**, 3040 (1948); ibid. **71**, 2761 (1949).
(272) E. F. Mellon, A. H. Korn, E. L. Kokes, and S. R. Hoover, J. Am. Chem. Soc. **73**, 1870 (1951).

effect on their water absorption. Evidently, sites for water absorption are always accessible in proteins.

The hydration of proteins in aqueous solution has also been the subject of extensive investigation.[273,274] At best, though, it is possible to obtain only an approximate estimate of the quantity of bound water. It is impossible as yet to establish any correlations with protein structure.

Interactions with small nonelectrolytes other than water have been studied, largely in a qualitative way. From sedimentation measurements Bresler[73] estimated that 360 molecules of urea can combine with one of serum albumin. Combinations of urea, guanidine, and urethan with serum globulin, as well as with serum albumin, have been described by Pasynskii and Chernyak,[275] and the possibility of urea binding by hemoglobin has been pointed out by Ralls.[276]

Alcohols are also bound by several proteins. Serum albumin crystallized with the aid of decanol contains from two to ten moles of this molecule per mole of protein.[277] Similarly, hexanol binding to albumin has been detected by its competition with anions.[16] Other polyhydroxy compounds, particularly glycosides, have been studied widely especially in connection with pharmacological problems.[191] Only in investigations of glucose interactions in the "browning" reaction of proteins has some progress been made toward establishing the primary sites involved in the protein.[278]

It has also been known for some time that cholesterol, some of its esters, and related steroids form complexes with serum albumin and globulins.[3,279,280] Compounds related to the steroids, such as digitoxin, one of the cardioactive glycosides, also form complexes with serum proteins, particularly albumin. Detailed comparisons have been made of the effects of sera of different origin, as well as of the relative combining powers of serum versus pure albumin, on a large number of these glycosides.[281,282] These studies have shown[282] that the carbohydrate por-

(273) E. J. Cohn and J. T. Edsall, Proteins, Amino Acids and Peptides, Reinhold Publishing Co., New York, N. Y., 1943, pp. 379–81, 424–5, 516–22.
(274) F. Haurowitz, Chemistry and Biology of the Proteins, Academic Press, Inc., New York, N. Y., 1950, pp. 86–103.
(275) A. G. Pasynskii and R. S. Chernyak, Doklady Akad. Nauk S. S. S. R. 73, 771 (1950); C. A. 45, 685 (1951).
(276) J. O. Ralls, J. Biol. Chem. 151, 529 (1943).
(277) E. J. Cohn, Blood 3, 471 (1948).
(278) A. Mohammad, H. Fraenkel-Conrat, and H. S. Olcott, Arch. Biochem. 24, 157 (1949).
(279) J. A. Gardner and H. Gainsborough, Biochem. J. 21, 141 (1927).
(280) E. G. Boettiger, J. Cellular Comp. Physiol. 28, 139 (1946).
(281) R. A. Hoekstra, Arch. exptl. Path. Pharmakol. 162, 649 (1931).
(282) A. Farah, J. Pharmacol. Exptl. Therap. 83, 143 (1945).

tion of these glycosides is not required for combination with serum proteins, for experiments with the aglucones give comparable effects.

The combination of hemoglobin with oxygen is an example of an interaction with a neutral molecule which has been studied in great detail quantitatively. The original mass-law analysis of Adair[283] in terms of four consecutive complex species, containing one, two, three, or four oxygen molecules per hemoglobin, was shown by Ferry and Green[284] to fit a wide range of data if the four equilibrium constants were treated as completely independent but corresponding to different intrinsic affinities. A great simplification was suggested by Pauling[144] in the assumption that a cooperative interaction occurs between pairs of hemes, i.e., that the second O_2 molecule is bound more tightly than the first because an adjacent heme containing O_2 assists in uptake of the second O_2. In this way, the four equilibrium constants could be related in terms of a single interaction factor and the usual a priori statistical relations between equivalent sites. More recently, Wyman[145] has shown that precise measurements cannot be interpreted in terms of a single interaction constant, but that one strong and one weak cooperative interaction must be assumed. Structural studies of the hemoglobin molecule tend to fit this picture.[284a,284b]

VIII. Interactions of Proteins with Other Proteins

Protein reactions with other large molecules have been recognized for many years in studies with nucleic acids,[74–76,284c] with polysaccharides,[77,78] with other proteins,[79,80] and with numerous polymeric materials.[285] One can distinguish in these combinations two general categories of complex: (a) those in which electrostatic factors are of prime importance, and (b) those in which specific structural factors are of major significance.

Interactions of proteins with nucleic acids form excellent examples of cases where opposite electrostatic charge is the primary condition for reaction. Likewise the precipitation of many anionic proteins by cationic proteins or by protamines or histones has been recognized for over fifty years[286,287] as being saltlike in nature.

It has also been realized that similar interactions between species of

(283) G. S. Adair, *J. Biol. Chem.* **63,** 529 (1925).

(284) R. M. Ferry and A. A. Green, *J. Biol. Chem.* **81,** 175 (1929).

(284a) R. C. C. St. George and L. Pauling, *Science* **114,** 629 (1951).

(284b) J. Wyman, Jr., and D. W. Allen, *J. Polymer Sci.* **7,** 499 (1951).

(284c) K. B. Bjornesjo and T. Teorell, *Arkiv Kemi, Mineral. Geol.* **19A,** No. 34 (1945).

(285) H. Morawetz and W. L. Hughes, Jr., *J. Phys. Chem.* **56,** 64 (1952).

(286) A. Kossel, *Deut. med. Wochschr.* **1894,** 147.

(287) F. Haurowitz, P. Schwerin, and S. Tunc, *Arch. Biochem.* **11,** 515 (1946).

opposite net charge may occur in natural systems, such as among milk[288] or serum proteins[289] (see Chaps. 16 and 21). For example, in recent investigations of the interactions of serum β-lipoprotein with γ-globulin[290] marked decreases in the solubility of the former in the presence of the latter have been observed in the pH range between the isoelectric points of the two proteins. As would be expected for an interaction of this type, the decreases in solubility due to added globulin disappear at pH's at which each protein carries the same type of net charge. On the other hand, the proportion of γ-globulin in the complex increases, in the inter-isoelectric pH region, as the pH approaches the isoelectric point of γ-globulin. Evidently as the positive charge on the globulin becomes smaller, and the negative charge on the lipoprotein becomes larger, neutral complexes are obtained only with a larger proportion of the former protein.

In recent studies with mucopolysaccharides it has been shown that chondroitin sulfate, for example, is fixed by gelatin at pH's at which the protein is cationic.[291] Furthermore, anionic dyes can compete with the polysaccharide anion. Likewise, chondroitin sulfate, as well as other polymeric anions such as agar, alginate, and cellulose sulfate, inhibit catalase activity on the acidic side of its isoelectric point.[292] Opposite electric charge also seems to play a major role in the attachment of virus particles to host cells[293] and in nucleic acid–albumin interactions.[294]

In saltlike protein-protein complexes, solubility is very sensitive to ionic strength,[290] particularly because of the tendency of the ion cloud to promote dissociation between oppositely charged species. Similarly, in interactions with nucleic acids, sodium chloride tends to dissociate protein complexes.[40,295]

Even in these many examples cited where electrostatic charge seems to play the dominant role in complex formation, closer examination reveals many indications of specific effects also. With the nucleic acids, for example, no precipitation seems to occur when the protein is also negatively charged, but electrophoretic examination[74,76] gives definite evidence of complex formation. Electrophoretic investigation also

(288) H. Nitschmann and H. Zürcher, *Helv. Chim. Acta* **33**, 1698 (1950).

(289) A. A. Green, *J. Am. Chem. Soc.* **60**, 1108 (1938).

(290) J. L. Oncley, E. Ellenbogen, D. Gitlin, and F. R. N. Gurd, *J. Phys. Chem.* **56**, 85 (1952).

(291) J. Einbinder and M. Schubert, *J. Biol. Chem.* **188**, 335 (1951).

(292) H. Terayama, *J. Chem. Soc. Japan*, Pure Chem. Sect. **70**, 320 (1949); *C. A.* **45**, 2989 (1951).

(293) T. T. Puck, A. Garen, and J. Cline, *J. Exptl. Med.* **93**, 65 (1951).

(294) E. Goldwasser and F. W. Putnam, *J. Phys. & Colloid Chem.* **54**, 79 (1950).

(295) A. E. Mirsky, *Advances in Enzymol.* **3**, 1 (1943).

reveals complex formation between α- and β-caseins even at pH values where both bear like charges.[263,288] Furthermore, opposite charge does not insure combination. Thus in protamine–protein interactions, cationic clupein does not precipitate anionic native serum albumin (at pH 7) but does precipitate the heat-denatured protein.[89] Evidently the configuration of the native albumin rules out interaction with the protamine.

In other protein–protein interactions exhibiting strong specificity, e.g., interaction of trypsin with trypsin inhibitor,[296] attempts have been made to delineate the specific sites involved by reacting the proteins with group-specific reagents.[297] Some success has been attained in identifying the essential groups involved in the interaction, but the problem has also become more complicated since the observation that inhibitor from different sources, e.g., soybean versus egg white, interacts with trypsin through different groups.[297] Care must also be exercised in the interpretation of the results with group-specific reagents, because the over-all charge on the protein molecule, as well as the chemical character of the side chains, may be altered drastically, which may considerably reduce its affinity even for a specific structure (see Chap. 10).

Examples par excellence of specificity in protein–protein interactions lie, of course, in the field of serological reactions. Antigen–antibody complexes are discussed in Chap. 23. It will suffice here merely to mention again the extensive work of Landsteiner and his co-workers[176] with a variety of antigens containing side chains of known structure. It is from these experimental foundations that the concept of complementariness in configuration[178-180,189] has been developed in molecular terms and has been shown to be the major requirement for interaction in antigen–antibody complexes. Although equal detail can rarely be specified in other protein–protein interactions, it is clear that here too complementariness in configuration must play a major role.

IX. Internal Interactions of Proteins: Association and Dissociation

Special cases of protein–protein interactions are those homogeneous systems in which association or dissociation occurs. One of the earliest examples to be studied extensively is hemocyanin, the oxygen-carrying pigment of numerous invertebrates. It was shown in 1936 by Eriksson-Quensel and Svedberg[298] from sedimentation measurements that for most species a single component is present within a range of pH near the iso-

(296) M. Kunitz, J. Gen. Physiol. **29**, 149 (1946).

(297) H. Fraenkel-Conrat, R. S. Bean, and H. Lineweaver, J. Biol. Chem. **177**, 385 (1949).

(298) I. B. Eriksson-Quensel and T. Svedberg, Biol. Bull. **71**, 498 (1936).

electric point, but that as the pH is changed in either direction, dissociation occurs. The pH–stability diagram is characteristic of each species. With the hemocyanin of *Helix pomatia*, for example, Brohult[298a,299] found that dissociation into halves and subsequently into eighths was obtained at pH values above 7. Calculations of the lengths of these molecules from frictional ratios and from streaming birefringence data indicated that splitting takes place lengthwise.

The importance of electrostatic factors in these dissociation equilibria is clearly indicated by the following observations. Hemocyanin (*Helix pomatia*) usually starts to dissociate at pH 7, but if 0.01 M calcium ion is present, splitting does not begin until pH's above 9. Furthermore even at pH 11.5, with calcium ion, some undissociated molecules are present. Evidently the whole molecule begins to dissociate at a pH at which its charge causes a substantial internal repulsion. At pH values above the isoelectric point, this negative charge may be balanced by the positive charge of bound calcium ions, and thus the internal repulsion may be reduced.

Another protein whose dissociation equilibria have been studied intensively is insulin. Conflicting conclusions over a period of years in connection with molecular-weight determinations have now been largely resolved by a series of experiments which indicate that the common unit of 12,000 molecular weight is normally associated into trimers or tetramers.[300] The first indication that such equilibria may exist seems to be in the ultracentrifugal experiments of Moody.[301] More extensive ultracentrifugal studies by Fredericq and Neurath[72] and by Oncley, Ellenbogen, Gitlin, and Gurd[290] and osmotic measurements of Gutfreund[302] have clearly established the conditions which lead to dissociation of the polymers and have even led to some estimates of the energetics of the process. In this brief discussion it is sufficient to emphasize again that dissociation seems to be produced largely by the internal electrostatic repulsion produced in the molecule at acid pH. A sufficiently large electrostatic repulsion can overcome the specific attractive forces between monomers. Trimers seem to be stable until each 12,000 molecular-weight unit attains a charge of about +6, and dissociation is essentially complete at a charge of +12. In the presence of thiocyanate anions, known to be bound by insulin in acid solution,[72] lower pH's must be

(298a) S. Brohult, *Nova Acta Regiae Soc. Sci. Upsaliensis* [4], **12**, No. 4 (1940).

(299) S. Brohult, *J. Phys. & Colloid Chem.* **51**, 206 (1947).

(300) Fibrils of insulin, involving even higher degrees of association, may be prepared under special conditions; see D. F. Waugh, *J. Am. Chem. Soc.* **68**, 247 (1946).

(301) L. S. Moody, Ph.D. Dissertation, University of Wisconsin, 1944.

(302) H. Gutfreund, *Biochem. J.* **42**, 544 (1948).

attained to dissociate the trimer. Obviously the bound anions reduce the internal electrostatic repulsion in the insulin molecule and hence stabilize the trimer. Recent experiments suggest that even the 12,000 unit may be split in two under favorable conditions,[72] particularly in a buffer whose anions have very little tendency to be bound to proteins, but this observation is still a subject of dispute[72,302a] (see Chap. 7).

Corresponding studies with chymotrypsin and with chymotrypsinogen[303,304] have led to analogous conclusions, except that only monomer-dimer equilibria have been detected and the pH effect is opposite to that of insulin. Similar equilibria have been found for the globulin of the ground nut *Arachic hypogaea*[305] as well as for several other systems[306] including serum albumin.[73]

These dissociation reactions, produced by mild conditions, seem to be completely reversible. Dissociation has also been found with several proteins, including hemoglobin, in concentrated urea solutions.[307] In urea, more extensive structural changes may be produced in these proteins, although Steinhardt[308] has found that dissociation of hemoglobin is at least partially reversed if the urea is removed by dialysis (see Chap. 9).

From all of these phenomena it has become evident that many protein molecules are composed of smaller units linked together by relatively weak bonds. The nature of these bonds, however, is unknown. Various suggestions have been presented in terms of hydrogen bonds, electrostatic linkages, van der Waals' interactions, or even covalent links, the relative contributions of which remain to be determined.

X. Biological Significance of Protein Interactions

The importance of interactions with proteins has been analyzed in greatest detail in connection with pharmacological problems, particularly by Storm van Leeuwen,[309] Bennhold,[38] Davis,[204,310] and Goldstein.[191] Pharmacologists have been concerned with a number of aspects of these interactions. First, there have been problems connected with the effective concentration of a drug in the presence of serum proteins.

(302a) F. Tietze and H. Neurath, *J. Biol. Chem.* **194**, 1 (1952).
(303) G. W. Schwert, *J. Biol. Chem.* **179**, 655 (1949).
(304) G. W. Schwert and S. Kaufman, *J. Biol. Chem.* **190**, 807 (1951).
(305) P. Johnson and E. M. Shooter, *Biochim. et Biophys. Acta* **5**, 361 (1950).
(306) K. O. Pedersen, *Cold Spring Harbor Symposia Quant. Biol.* **14**, 140 (1950).
(307) N. F. Burk and D. M. Greenberg, *J. Biol. Chem.* **87**, 197 (1930).
(308) J. Steinhardt, *J. Biol. Chem.* **123**, 543 (1938).
(309) W. Storm van Leeuwen, *J. Pharmacol. Exptl. Therap.* **24**, 13, 21 (1924).
(310) B. D. Davis, *in* C. M. MacLeod, ed., The Evaluation of Chemotherapeutic Agents, Columbia University Press, New York, N. Y., 1949, Chap. 4.

Secondly, the question of the possible role of protein complexes in transporting substances from one part of the body to another has been raised. Thirdly, the influence of protein binding on the excretion and general persistence of small molecules and ions in tissues has been widely considered.

From numerous studies it is apparent that drugs bound by plasma proteins are pharmacologically inactive. Thus plasma decreases the activity of penicillins.[311] Similarly, albumin reduces the antibacterial activity of oleic acid against tubercle bacilli[44] and the hemolytic action of fatty acids on erythrocytes.[12] Likewise, rabbit serum reduces the toxicity of digitoxin to frog heart[281] because of combination of the drug with albumin.[312] Thus serum proteins can act as a drug "buffer." By decreasing the concentration of free molecule when it becomes excessive, the proteins reduce any toxic action. When the free concentration falls below the level required for drug action, the proteins release more free drug by dissociation.

The role of proteins as carriers for drugs and other molecules in the blood has been emphasized especially by Bennhold.[38] The importance of such interactions in solubilizing water-insoluble compounds such as lipides or steroids cannot be overestimated. A particularly striking case is that of the β_1-lipoprotein of plasma, recently found to have over 75 per cent lipide.[277] Bennhold[38] has also suggested that protein complexes may enter tissue cells as a unit and dissociate there by special mechanisms. It has been shown, for example, by Rosenthal[9] that bile salts may liberate substances bound to proteins. Nevertheless, there are some difficulties with this concept of "vehicle function," as has been pointed out by Rothlin[313] and Goldstein.[191] In particular the evidence that albumin can penetrate cell walls is not convincing.

Numerous demonstrations exist of the importance of protein binding in affecting excretion. Thus the fraction of phenol red filtered at the glomeruli has been shown to correspond to that which can be ultrafiltered in vitro.[314] Similar behavior has been shown with penicillin[315] and with aureomycin.[316] A particularly interesting case occurs with suramin, a large anion with several sulfonate charges, which is retained within an organism sometimes for months, even though there is no selective storage

(311) R. Tompsett, S. Shultz, and W. McDermott, J. Bact. 53, 581 (1947).
(312) G. Fawaz and A. Farah, J. Pharmacol. Exptl. Therap. 80, 193 (1944).
(313) E. Rothlin, Vierteljahrsschr. naturforsch. Ges. Zürich 90, 195 (1945).
(314) E. K. Marshall, Am. J. Physiol. 99, 77 (1931).
(315) H. Eagle and E. Newman, J. Clin. Invest. 26, 903 (1947).
(316) J. H. Sirota, A. Saltzman, and H. Warmbrand, J. Pharmacol. Exptl. Therap. 100, 210 (1950).

in tissues. Binding of this compound to plasma proteins is thus very strong.[317,318]

We have seen that interactions of plasma proteins with drugs produce a number of divergent pharmacological effects. Exaltation of total concentration may be produced by increased solubility and by conservation against kidney excretion. These effects may be balanced, however, by the lowering of the effective concentration due to binding; such decreases interfere with the chemotherapeutic properties of the drug but in turn protect the host against toxic concentrations.

In addition to the pharmacological aspects of serum protein interactions, immunological reactions have also been studied extensively. These have been of interest not only because of their practical importance in connection with immunity against disease but also because they have furnished a sensitive method of differentiating proteins and of probing their molecular structure. A discussion of the salient facts and concepts in this field is given in Chap. 23. Some aspects which bear strongly on the molecular features of protein interactions have been described earlier in this chapter.

From specific serological reactions it is but a short step to specific enzyme–substrate interactions. These have been studied largely by indirect kinetic methods, but several long strides have been made recently in direct methods[54,193] of examination. With increasing success in the isolation of crystalline enzymes, the stage is being set for a thorough investigation of protein interactions in various phases of cellular metabolism.

The most important theoretical development from studies of specific interactions has been the elucidation of the concept of configurational complementariness in protein molecules. As was pointed out by Ehrlich,[319] with this idea we can link conceptually enzyme–substrate complexes with antigen–antibody combinations. With further progress in the interpretation of biological phenomena, interactions due to configurational or electrostatic complementariness have also been recognized in structural proteins such as muscle,[320] in dynamic cellular processes such as in the conversion of chemical energy into mechanical or electrical, and even in the foreign affairs of organisms such as in the interactions of virus particles with host cells.[293] It is thus evident that the principles of protein interactions are establishing the bridge for the introduction of molecular concepts into biological processes.

(317) H. M. Dewey and A. Wormall, *Biochem. J.* **40**, 119 (1946).

(318) A. Spinks, *Biochem. J.* **42**, 109 (1948).

(319) P. Ehrlich, *Münch. med. Wochschr.* **1909**, 217.

(320) A. Szent-Györgyi, Chemistry of Muscular Contraction, 2nd Ed., Academic Press, New York, N. Y., 1951.

CHAPTER 9

Protein Denaturation

By FRANK W. PUTNAM

I. Introduction

1. DEFINITION

Denaturation is the most characteristic property of proteins and so deserves study for the light it may shed on protein structure and function.[1] Polypeptides containing the organic structural features of proteins cannot be denatured.[1a] Polymeric carbohydrates and other natural

(1) Some years ago denaturation was the subject of several important reviews. The most comprehensive one is that of Neurath *et al.*[2] The reader is referred to this article for the development of present concepts of protein denaturation as well as for a guide to the early literature. Anson[3] has retailed the more chemical aspects of denaturation, and Bull[4] has interpreted the results of studies of denaturation in terms of protein structure. Most recently, Haurowitz[5] has presented an interesting and speculative discussion with emphasis on protein structure.

(1a) Elliott[1b] has recently described a transformation in a synthetic polypeptide which simulates a denaturation change. This can be brought about by manipulation at room temperature or in aqueous solution, and is to be contrasted with conditions formerly used, e.g. stretching in steam, or the action of formic acid.

(1b) A. Elliott, *Nature* **170**, 1066 (1952).

(2) H. Neurath, J. P. Greenstein, F. W. Putnam, and J. O. Erickson, *Chem. Revs.* **34**, 157 (1944).

(3) M. L. Anson, *Advances in Protein Chem.* **2**, 361 (1945).

(4) H. B. Bull, *Advances in Enzymol.* **1**, 1 (1941).

(5) F. Haurowitz, Chemistry and Biology of Proteins, Academic Press, New York, 1950, pp. 125–42.

substances of high molecular weight but rather simple structure are not denaturable. Hence, neither macromolecular size nor chemical composition suffice to endow proteins with their characteristic lability. All the evidence indicates that *denaturation is a physical or intramolecular rearrangement rather than a chemical alteration of native protein structure and that it leads to a change in specific spatial configuration without hydrolysis of primary covalent bonds.*

It is difficult to define denaturation more precisely than this because the very aspect of protein structure which is affected is unique and determinative, yet most diversified and unknown. The above definition obviously conveys an interpretation of the phenomenon in terms of a theory of protein structure, a point of view which might be permitted after the past half century of study. Some workers, such as Anson, still prefer a definition confined to experimental observations but admit that any definition must of necessity be complex and vague.

Denaturation is easier to detect than to define. However, just as protein purity can be established only in a negative sense, so the absence of denaturation can be assumed only after the application of numerous tests. The diversity of protein structure and, thus, the multiplicity of possible changes attending denaturation require the application of sufficient criteria to detect subtle though characteristic alterations. Narrow definitions founder on neglect of these points. Both the stepwise and the multiform character of protein denaturation was suspected for some time but first emphasized by Neurath et al.[2] in their inclusive definition: "Denaturation is any non-proteolytic modification of the unique structure of a native protein giving rise to definite changes in chemical, physical, or biological properties." For "non-proteolytic" the more general term "non-hydrolytic" might be substituted since any hydrolysis of the peptide bond was excluded. This definition was further restricted to exclude reversible combinations with hydrogen, hydroxyl, or other ions, as well as organic chemical substitutions since these are primarily reactions of the amino acid side chains rather than of the protein molecule as a whole. The distinction becomes fine in some cases; for example, in the titration of proteins the region of reversible combination gradually merges into a pH of irreversible reactions, and some physical properties change throughout. Similarly, the chemical modification of proteins by reaction with organic compounds even under the mildest conditions must produce changes in physical properties though not necessarily with loss of biological activity or even alteration in the unique stereochemical structure of the protein. However, chemical modification involves the primary covalent bonds of the amino acid side chains. Hence, chemical modification of proteins merits the separate treatment given in Chapter 10.

The definition of denaturation and the restrictions cited above will be understood throughout this chapter.[6] In effect, this limits denaturation to reactions involving only secondary or ionic bonds, but it should be noted that some workers believe that reactive groups such as —SH which become detectable only on denaturation are bound in primary though readily reversible cross linkages between peptide chains of the protein "backbone."

2. Purpose of Study

The chief purpose of the study of denaturation is the elucidation of protein structure. Indeed, it has been said that since denaturation is such a fundamental property of a large group of proteins, a theory of denaturation is essentially a general theory of the structure of native and denatured proteins. Among the various aspects of protein structure are: composition, sequence, stereochemical configuration, and size. Analytical methods are now available to determine total amino acid composition, and more recently methods of sequential analysis have been developed in the organic chemical approach to protein structure. However, physical chemical methods must largely be relied on for the study of the size, shape, and configuration of proteins. In denaturation, proteins may change in size and must change in shape and configuration. Hence, physical chemical methods are most often used for quantitative comparison of the properties of native and denatured proteins.

The native structure may be surmised only by its loss. In this sense, study of denaturation is a qualitative and descriptive aid rather than a quantitative and analytical method. However, by study of this phe-

(6) Nucleic acids invariably undergo some *depolymerization* during isolation from tissues in which they are presumed to exist in the "native" state. This degradation, often called denaturation, is induced by acid or alkali but is also enzymatically catalyzed. Depolymerization may likewise be caused by heat and possibly by protein denaturants used as adjuncts to isolation.[7] Although nucleic acids, like proteins, are susceptible to physical agents such as irradiation,[8] their depolymerization differs from denaturation in a number of respects: (1) Depolymerized nucleic acids always consist of polydisperse fragments. (2) Apart from the decrease in asymmetry measured physically, for example, by viscosity or flow birefringence, no chemical or enzymatic test exists to detect or quantify the altered nucleic acid.   (3) Nucleic acids vary in physical characteristics and chemical composition according to the procedure of isolation. (4) The nature of the primary internucleotide linkage cleaved by enzymes is still uncertain, and no clear distinction has been made between the action of depolymerases and chemical agents.

(7) For discussion see R. Markham and J. D. Smith, Chap. 12 of Vol. II of this series.

(8) B. Taylor, J. P. Greenstein, and A. Hollaender, *Cold Spring Harbor Symposia Quant. Biol.* **12**, 237 (1947).

nomenon information about proteins has been ascertained which remains the primary factual basis for theories of intramolecular protein structure. The most significant finding was the demonstration of the existence of a complex, labile, and specific stereochemical arrangement or "folding" of the polypeptide chains in native proteins. Other important findings concern the existence of subunits in some proteins but not in others, the multiple nature and weak strength of secondary structural bonds in proteins, the correlation of physical, chemical, and biological properties, and the unavailability of some chemically reactive groups in native proteins.

Other purposes of the study of denaturation are to ascertain the best conditions for purification of native proteins, to modify proteins for industrial uses, and to aid in the purification of one protein by denaturation of another. For the latter purpose heat denaturation is most often chosen, but other methods such as surface denaturation have been employed. Differential heat inactivation sometimes aids in the preparation of enzymes. Denaturation is also used in making protein-free biochemical preparations as in the Sevag method for isolation of nucleic acids.[9] Heat inactivation of enzymes is often introduced to minimize proteolysis or hydrolysis of materials isolated from tissues. Further examples of the use of differential denaturation in the purification of proteins are given in Chap. 1.

The practical uses of the denaturation phenomenon are many but will not be detailed. In the laboratory the thermal coagulation of proteins serves as a qualitative test for their presence just as thermolability signifies enzymatic properties. Clinically, the heat coagulation of proteins is an important diagnostic aid in the recognition of proteinuria. Quite a number of serum tests for cancer depend on the difference in thermal coagulation of blood proteins.[10]

3. Historical Development

Historically, numerous qualitative aspects of the denaturation phenomenon were long observed, such as the thermal coagulation of proteins in the boiling of egg white. Denaturation first appeared in the laboratory as an unwanted phenomenon, but its significance was recognized by various workers such as Hardy,[11] Chick and Martin,[12] and Arrhenius[13] whose classical kinetic work is still of interest. Quantitative

(9) M. G. Sevag, D. B. Lackman, and J. Smolens, *J. Biol. Chem.* **124,** 425 (1938).
(10) C. Huggins, G. M. Miller, and E. V. Jensen, *Cancer Research* **9,** 177 (1949).
(11) W. B. Hardy, *J. Physiol.* **24,** 158 (1899).
(12) H. Chick and C. J. Martin, *J. Physiol.* **40,** 404 (1910).
(13) S. Arrhenius, Immuno-chemistry, Macmillan, New York, 1907.

chemical studies of denatured proteins in solution became possible after Hopkins in 1930 observed the nitroprusside reaction of proteins dissolved in urea.[14] The next year Lewis[15] first reviewed protein denaturation just as Kunitz and Northrop[16] and Mirsky and Anson[17] began to make a series of major contributions. These workers established the quantitative basis for investigation of the phenomenon using the more limited definition supplied by Wu in 1931,[18] namely that "denaturation is a change in the natural protein whereby it becomes insoluble in solvents in which it was previously soluble." As the chemical aspects were elaborated by Greenstein[19] and the physical aspects by Neurath[20] and Bull,[21] new stimulus for kinetic and thermodynamic study was given by application of the theory of absolute reaction rates by Eyring and Stearn[22] and by the keen kinetic analysis of Steinhardt.[23] This work was recognized in the Mirsky and Pauling[24] theory of protein structure which is largely a theory of protein denaturation. Most contemporary theories attempt to explain the denaturation phenomenon. However, the recent hypothesis of helical configurations developed from studies of fibrous proteins[25] refers only briefly to the structural implications of the denaturation of corpuscular proteins.

4. CRITERIA OF DENATURATION

Since denaturation is an intramolecular phenomenon, involving changes in an unknown structure, it can be defined, investigated, and described only in terms of these changes, whether physical, chemical, or biological. Lessened solubility is usually the most tangible manifestation of denaturation, but alteration in other characteristic properties may precede, accompany, or follow this effect. Hence, a variety of methods of study have been utilized, and a series of criteria have evolved. As emphasized by Neurath et al.,[2] "Measurement of any single change is an insufficient means to characterize a denatured protein or for that matter, to estimate the extent to which a protein has become denatured." How-

(14) F. G. Hopkins, *Nature* **126**, 328, 383 (1930).

(15) W. C. M. Lewis, *Chem. Revs.* **8**, 81 (1931).

(16) M. Kunitz and J. H. Northrop, *J. Gen. Physiol.* **17**, 591 (1934).

(17) A. E. Mirsky and M. L. Anson, *J. Gen. Physiol.* **18**, 307 (1935).

(18) H. Wu, *Chinese J. Physiol.* **5**, 321 (1931).

(19) J. P. Greenstein, *J. Biol. Chem.* **125**, 501 (1938).

(20) H. Neurath, *Cold Spring Harbor Symposia Quant. Biol.* **8**, 80 (1940).

(21) H. B. Bull, *Cold Spring Harbor Symposia Quant. Biol.* **6**, 140 (1938).

(22) H. Eyring and A. E. Stearn, *Chem. Revs.* **24**, 253 (1939).

(23) J. Steinhardt, *Kgl. Danske Videnskab. Selskab, Mat.-fys. Medd.* **14**, No. 11 (1937).

(24) A. E. Mirsky and L. Pauling, *Proc. Natl. Acad. Sci U. S.* **22**, 439 (1936).

(25) L. Pauling and R. B. Corey, *Proc. Natl. Acad. Sci. U. S.* **37**, 251, 282 (1951).

ever, while no single criterion is both necessary and sufficient, practical considerations often demand selection of but one, especially in kinetic analysis. Not all changes listed below are always observed in the denaturation of proteins, but most occur together. Any criterion may be singly sufficient to establish the fact of denaturation though inadequate to characterize the altered protein.

Among the most important changes occurring in various kinds of denaturation of most proteins are the following which may be evaluated quantitatively: (1) decrease in solubility, (2) loss of biological activity, (3) increased reactivity of constituent groups, and (4) changes in molecular shape or size. The first three of these have proved most useful for rapid kinetic measurements, whereas, the fourth serves for characterization of the denatured protein.

Other phenomena have proved useful in a number of instances and will be illustrated in subsequent sections. For example, increased susceptibility to enzymatic hydrolysis—one token of the greater reactivity of chemical groups—has been observed for denatured serum proteins and hemoglobin, but not for fibrous proteins such as myosin and fibrinogen (sec. II-1e). Shifts in absorption spectra aid in measuring the denaturation of hemoglobin, but in the case of salicylate the interpretation has been questioned.[26] Small changes in isoelectric point and electrophoretic mobility occur (sec. III-2d). Increase in levorotation has recently found favor as a convenient and quantitative criterion of rate and extent of denaturation (sec. III-2f). Loss of crystallizing ability is observed in the denaturation of crystallizable proteins, probably as a result of gross changes in molecular size and shape. It is evident that the complex physical and chemical structure of proteins endows them with a diversity of properties which may be lost or modified during denaturation.

The methods useful for study of the first two criteria are self-evident. Because of convenience, increased reactivity of constituent groups is usually measured by following the appearance of —SH groups. However, phenolic hydroxyl, disulfide, and acidic and basic groups may also become more reactive. For the fourth criterion, physical methods are usually invoked—most often viscosity.

5. Degree of Denaturation

For some time it was believed that denaturation was an "all-or-none" reaction—that the protein could exist only in the natural state or as completely denatured. This concept leads to two logical conclusions: (1) The completely denatured protein should have the same properties regardless of the mode of denaturation—else there are different types or

(26) R. M. Roberts, *J. Am. Chem. Soc.* **64**, 1472 (1942).

degrees of denaturation; (2) the various changes in properties should occur simultaneously or should parallel each other. Neither of these situations occurs. In the first case it is sometimes suggested that the completely denatured protein should have the configuration of a fully extended polypeptide chain. However, such unfolding is found only when proteins are spread as monomolecular films (sec. III-2). Other kinds of denaturation produce less extensive changes in shape and structure, probably because with polar and ionizable side chains, coiling is unavoidable and the state of minimum free energy is not the most extended one. Secondly, there is no obvious correlation between the rate or degree of liberation of sulfhydryl groups and changes in solubility, molecular size or shape, and biological activity of proteins (sec. VI-1b). These facts upon which attention will be focused in succeeding sections have led to the concept that there are various degrees of denaturation depending on the extent to which the structure of the protein is modified by various denaturants or different concentrations of the same agent.

The degree of change in structure and thus in properties depends on the nature of the protein as well as on the kind or concentration of denaturing agent. For example, insulin apparently remains biologically active when denatured by urea or by spreading as a surface film, and liberates disulfide groups only in high concentrations of urea (sec. V-5); yet tobacco mosaic virus is readily inactivated with marked change in size and shape at concentrations of urea too low to liberate sulfhydryl groups (sec. V-4). In view of the variety of temporally unrelated changes which may occur in the denaturation of proteins, and the recognition of intermediate stages, the "all-or-none" hypothesis has generally given way to the concept of the existence of gradation or degree of denaturation,[2] though alternative interpretations still exist.[26a]

II. Denaturing Agents and Protection Against Denaturation

1. DENATURING AGENTS

a. Temperature and pH as Intensity Factors

Because of the complex structure of proteins, the number of denaturing agents is manifold. Although the controlling influence of tempera-

(26a) For example, Anson (personal communication) would agree that the properties of either the native form or of the denatured form of a protein depend on the chemical environment and temperature, and that when a protein is denatured many bonds are broken and that there must be many intermediate forms of the protein. He believes the "all-or-none" theory is wrong in those cases where more than two forms of the protein have been observed experimentally but considers that in some instances the intermediate forms are relatively unstable and are not readily detectable.

ture and pH was recognized, denaturing agents have been classified as physical, chemical, and biological.[2] This convenient but arbitrary grouping has been criticized by Levy and Benaglia[27] on the grounds that temperature and pH are intensity factors which are continuous and not mutually exclusive functions in aqueous solution. Most kinetic studies of thermal denaturation have been made at constant pH. The effect of temperature has been expressed in terms of the Arrhenius equation, and more recently has been interpreted using the theory of absolute reaction rates. Denaturation, including biological inactivation, has often been found to depend upon some power of the hydrogen- or hydroxyl-ion concentration, indicating that acidic equilibria are involved. Steinhardt[23] first proposed the theory explaining the influence of pH on the rate of protein denaturation as the result of the effect on the ionization of critical groups. The general applicability of Steinhardt's theory was pointed out in the review by Neurath et al.,[2] and the theoretical treatment has recently been extended by the important articles by Levy and Benaglia[27] and by Gibbs.[27a] The latter authors emphasize that the stability of a protein is not a separate function of several environmental conditions and that heat denaturation and acid denaturation are not independent processes.

Each protein has a characteristic stability range which is usually at a maximum at the pH of physiological occurrence. The biological activity of enzymes and viruses simplifies measurement of the stability region, but physical chemical properties such as sedimentation constant must be employed with ordinary proteins. Most proteins are denatured below pH 3 and above pH 10, but numerous exceptions exist. Whereas pepsin is rapidly inactivated above pH 6, ribonuclease[28] and lysozyme[29] resist heating at pH 2–3. Lysozyme is also relatively stable at pH 11. Hemoglobin,[27] hemocyanins, and lipoproteins are all markedly susceptible to denaturation at about pH 5.

The high temperature coefficient characteristic of thermal denaturation and the strong pH dependence are not found in all types of denaturation (sec. IV-1b). For example, denaturation by neutral organic solutes and the synthetic detergents is not very sensitive to pH or temperature. The temperature coefficient is unity for surface denaturation[21] and may be negative for the action of urea.[30] On the other hand, the denaturing

(27) M. Levy and R. E. Benaglia, *J. Biol. Chem.* **186**, 829 (1950).

(27a) R. J. Gibbs, *Arch. Biochem. and Biophys.* **35**, 229 (1952).

(28) J. H. Northrop, M. Kunitz, and R. M. Herriott, Crystalline Enzymes, Columbia University Press, New York, 1948.

(29) G. Alderton, W. H. Ward, and H. L. Fevold, *J. Biol. Chem.* **157**, 43 (1945).

(30) M. A. Lauffer, *J. Am. Chem. Soc.* **65**, 1793 (1943).

action of organic solvents such as the alcohols is controlled by the temperature and to a lesser extent by pH. An elegant application of this fact has been made in the blood plasma fractionation program of the Harvard group.[31] As might be anticipated, the irradiation inactivation of enzymes is almost independent of temperature though the quantum yield is greatly affected by pH.[32] Thus, neither the nature of the denaturant nor the effect of pH or temperature will be taken as the paramount consideration; rather an attempt will be made to integrate and interpret the common features in various kinds of denaturation.

b. Physical Methods

(1) *Heat.* This is the first known, most common, and most widely investigated denaturing agent. Coagulation of a protein by heating near the isoelectric point in the presence of a small amount of salt is a familiar qualitative test for proteins,[33] and heat inactivation is a criterion for an enzyme. The thermal coefficient is unusually great, leading to reports of a "coagulation" or "inactivation" temperature. Though heat-denatured proteins readily aggregate, the coagulation is a secondary phenomenon. Diminished solubility is the most familiar criterion of heat denaturation, and measurement either of the amount of soluble protein remaining or of the precipitate serves as a useful quantitative index for rate studies. However, the coagulated protein is unsuited for most physical or chemical analyses.

(2) *Mechanical Forces.* (a) *Freezing.* Little is known about the effect of freezing on proteins. Some qualitative observations were reviewed in 1936 by Nord.[35] Since that time the lyophilization process has been widely adopted for the preservation of proteins because most proteins resist denaturation during and after freeze-drying. However, egg albumin, β_1-lipoprotein, and some enzymes are denatured, probably by the surface effect in the frothing which occurs in the terminal stages.

(31) E. J. Cohn, L. E. Strong, W. L. Hughes, Jr., D. J. Mulford, J. N. Ashworth, M. Melin, and H. L. Taylor, *J. Am. Chem. Soc.* **68**, 459 (1946).

(32) A. D. McLaren, *Advances in Enzymol.* **9**, 75 (1949).

(33) Not all soluble proteins are heat coagulable, in the absence of salt at a pH removed from the isoelectric point. Nor are all enzymes rapidly inactivated on heating at 96–100°, e.g., lysozyme and ribonuclease. Another exception is the Bence-Jones protein, a urinary constituent found in some cases of multiple myeloma. This protein coagulates on heating to 45–55° at pH 5–7 but not outside this pH range. Further heating causes the precipitate to redissolve yielding the specific identification test. Although the electrophoretic pattern of the protein boiled at pH 8 is unaltered, gross changes in sedimentation constant and ultracentrifugal homogeneity result.[34]

(34) F. W. Putnam and P. Stelos, *J. Biol. Chem. In press.*

(35) F. Nord, *Naturwissenschaften* **24**, 481 (1936).

Lipoproteins are especially susceptible to denaturation and dissociation during freezing or lyophilization.[36]

(b) *Sound Waves.* Proteins may be coagulated and denatured by high-frequency sonic or ultrasonic waves. The phenomenon is believed due to the enormous local stresses and accelerations resulting from the collapse of vapor bubbles of dissolved gases in a liquid, a process known as "cavitation."[37] Hemocyanins are dissociated into molecular subunits, and some proteins are denatured by ultrasonic irradiation.[38] Sensitivity is related to morphology and structure, for the large tadpole-shaped bacteriophages T_2, T_4, and T_6 are rapidly disintegrated sonically, whereas the small spherical bacteriophages T_3 and T_7 are remarkably resistant.[39] Sonic denaturation may be a surface reaction, but the generation of sound waves is always accompanied by the development of considerable heat which must be minimized by water cooling. Ultrasonorators may be used with care at a frequency of 9000 cycles/sec. to liberate active enzymes by sonic disintegration of bacteria. The magnetostriction type is to be preferred to the piezoelectric oscillator which generates much heat.

(c) *Surface Forces.* Proteins are denatured by vigorous shaking or stirring or spreading as a surface film. The susceptibility of proteins varies greatly; egg albumin is most labile, botulinus toxin is readily inactivated, but insulin activity is unaffected. Surface denaturation of proteins has been reviewed by Neurath and Bull,[40] and the surface inactivation of bacterial viruses has been treated by Adams.[41] Only a few quantitative studies of mechanically induced surface denaturation exist.[42] However, there is an extensive literature on the properties of protein films formed by spreading on aqueous surfaces using the Langmuir surface trough and film balance. Protein monolayers are thought to be completely denatured proteins. The synthetic detergents do not denature proteins by reduction in surface tension since non-ionic detergents are without adverse effect and no correlation exists between surface-tension reduction and denaturing power in the various classes of detergents.[43]

(d) *Grinding.* Dry grinding of native soluble proteins produces heterogeneous insoluble products, whereas insoluble proteins are partially

(36) J. L. Oncley, F. R. N. Gurd, and M. Melin, *J. Am. Chem. Soc.* **72**, 458 (1950).

(37) K. Sollner, *Chem. Revs.* **34**, 371 (1944).

(38) S. Brohult, *Nature* **140**, 805 (1937).

(39) T. F. Anderson, S. Boggs, and B. C. Winters, *Science* **108**, 18 (1948).

(40) H. Neurath and H. B. Bull, *Chem. Revs.* **23**, 391 (1938).

(41) M. H. Adams, *J. Gen. Physiol.* **31**, 417 (1948).

(42) H. Wu and S. M. Ling, *Chinese J. Physiol.* **1**, 407 (1927).

(43) F. W. Putnam, *Advances in Protein Chem.* **4**, 79 (1948).

solubilized.[44]   Oxidative changes and degradation may occur, especially
in the aromatic amino acids.   Heating of the proteins during grinding is
probably an important factor.   The products are unsuited for further
study.

(e) *Pressure.*   High hydrostatic pressures of the order of 5000–10,000
atm. rapidly coagulate proteins and inactivate enzymes at ordinary
temperatures.   The reaction is complex but generally seems to be of the
first order.   *Staphyloccoccus* bacteriophage and a number of viruses
attacking animals lose their infectivity on exposure to pressures of 2000–
5000 atm., but tobacco mosaic virus is resistant up to about 6000 atm.[45]
Curl and Jansen[45a] observed a great variation with pH in the inactivation
of trypsin and chymotrypsin by high pressures and suggested that these
enzymes may exist in an equilibrium mixture of a reversibly inactive
form (globular) and an active enzyme which is partially unfolded.   The
greater susceptibility to pressure inactivation at pH 8 was attributed to
the predominance of the active unfolded form in the pH range optimum
for proteolysis.

Though high pressures generally cause inactivation of enzymes and
viruses, moderate pressures retard protein denaturation by heat, alcohol,
and other agents, presumably because there is a large volume increase
during the formation of the activated complex.   Thus, pressures up to
10,000 lb./sq. in. (about 700 atm.) decrease the rate of precipitation of
serum globulin on heating at 65° both in the presence and absence of
ethyl alcohol,[46] and likewise diminish the rate of inactivation of *Staphylococcus* antitoxin at the same temperature.[47]   The early work, done primarily at high pressures causing enzyme inactivation, protein coagulation,
etc., has been summarized by several authors,[48] whereas the interrelation
of pressure and other physicochemical factors controlling rate processes
has been reviewed by Johnson *et al.*[49] with regard to the luciferase system.

(3) *Ultraviolet Irradiation.*   Proteins are denatured and coagulated,
and enzymes, hormones, and viruses are inactivated by irradiation with
ultraviolet light.[50]   The threshold is about 3100 A., but longer wavelengths suffice in the presence of photosensitizers.   It is difficult to

(44) H. R. Cohen, *Arch. Biochem.* **2**, 1, 345, 353 (1943).
(45) M. A. Lauffer and R. B. Dow, *J. Biol. Chem.* **140**, 509 (1941).
(45a) A. L. Curl and E. F. Jansen, *J. Biol. Chem.* **184**, 45 (1950).
(46) F. H. Johnson and D. H. Campbell, *J. Biol. Chem.* **163**, 689 (1946).
(47) F. H. Johnson and G. C. Wright, *Proc. Natl. Acad. Sci. U. S.* **32**, 21 (1946).
(48) J. E. Matthews, Jr., R. B. Dow, and A. K. Anderson, *J. Biol. Chem.* **135**, 697
       (1940).
(49) F. H. Johnson, H. Eyring, R. Steblay, H. Chaplin, C. Huber, and G. Gherardi,
       J. Gen. Physiol. **28**, 463 (1945).
(50) L. E. Arnow, *Physiol. Revs.* **16**, 671 (1936).

measure the quantum yield with biologically inactive proteins, but two processes may be demonstrated. The first is the primary photochemical denaturation with a temperature coefficient of about unity; the second is coagulation which is highly sensitive to temperature.[51,52] The biological inactivation of proteins is always monomolecular, yet the quantum yield is very low and has no relationship to molecular weight.[32] The photochemical action is almost always accompanied by the physical and chemical changes characteristic of protein denaturation, for example, by decreased solubility at the isoelectric point and liberation of sulfhydryl groups as for egg albumin,[51] changes in molecular size and homogeneity such as dissociation of the hemocyanins[53] and the aggregation and polydispersity of serum albumin[54] and urease,[55] and the alteration in biological activity already mentioned. However, the prolonged exposure of proteins (and amino acids) to ultraviolet irradiation leads to the liberation of ammonia, photoöxidation, and significant changes in absorption spectrum with rupture of peptide bonds adjacent to chromophoric side chains.[56]

This has led the author of the most comprehensive review of the photochemistry of proteins[32] to conclude that the restriction on primary bond hydrolysis must be removed from the definition of light denaturation. However, ultraviolet light inactivation of tobacco mosaic virus occurs without observable changes in size, shape, optical rotation, viscosity, absorption spectrum, isoelectric point, or serological properties.[57]

The biological effects of ultraviolet irradiation are well known. One of the most important recent developments is the photochemical reactivation of bacteria[57a] and bacteriophages[58] by exposure to visible light of wavelength about 3650 A.

(4) *Ionizing Radiation.* The impact of atomic warfare has spurred a vast study of the mechanism of action of ionizing radiation on living cells and biologically active agents. The mutagenic, carcinogenic, and lethal action of α-, β-, γ- and x-radiation is the subject of much review and some controversy. It would seem unwise to attribute these latter effects to protein denaturation. The mechanism of action and the effects of ionizing radiation on proteins have recently been summarized by

(51) J. H. Clark, *J. Gen. Physiol.* **19,** 199 (1936).
(52) J. H. Clark, *J. Gen. Physiol.* **27,** 101 (1943).
(53) S. Brohult, *Nova Acta Regiae Soc. Sci. Upsaliensis* [4], **12,** No. 4 (1940).
(54) E. B. Sanigar, L. E. Krejci, and E. O. Kraemer, *Biochem. J.* **33,** 1 (1939).
(55) A. D. McLaren, E. Sheppard, and J. Wagman, *Nature* **162,** 370 (1948).
(56) D. C. Carpenter, *J. Am. Chem. Soc.* **62,** 289 (1940).
(57) W. M. Stanley, *Science* **83,** 626 (1936).
(57a) A. Kelner, *J. Bact.* **58,** 511 (1949).
(58) R. Dulbecco, *J. Bact.* **59,** 329 (1950).

Barron[59] who points out that the complexity, size, shape, and side-chain reactivity of proteins permit different actions of ionizing radiation. Two theories of biological action of ionizing radiation exist: the "hit" theory which proposes that ionization directly produces effects within or near the molecule or cell, and the "indirect action" theory which attributes effects to the radiation products of water, e.g., H_2O_2 and H, and the free radicals OH and O_2H produced in the presence of oxygen. Barron points out that "the effect of ionizing radiations differs *qualitatively* when the radiation-dose is changed. Small doses act by indirect action and produce mainly oxidations; large doses act by the two mechanisms."[59]

Many enzymes requiring —SH for activity are reversibly inhibited by oxidation resulting from x-, α-, or β-radiation with doses of only a few hundred roentgens.[60] This inhibition can be partially or completely reversed with glutathione or may be prevented by previous addition of catalase or by protecting the —SH groups with p-chloromercuribenzoic acid and subsequent addition of glutathione.[61] The thiol reversible part of this inhibition is not considered protein denaturation. However, the degree of reactivability diminishes with increasing inhibition, probably owing to denaturation. Enzymes not requiring —SH are irreversibly inactivated by ionizing radiations; for example, carboxypeptidase, pepsin, trypsin, and ribonuclease. Dale[62] first showed with crystalline carboxypeptidase that significant inhibition could be obtained with small doses of radiation if the protein concentration was greatly diminished, thus suggesting an indirect effect of irradiation products of water.

A similar inverse relation of dosage effect and protein concentration is seen on irradiation of biologically inactive proteins such as serum albumin. Only small changes in physicochemical properties such as sedimentation constant and ultracentrifugal homogeneity are observed on irradiation of 1 per cent solutions up to 90,000 roentgens (r), and there is no effect on electrophoretic mobility or acid–base properties.[59] One of the most significant findings is that the changes in absorption spectrum of egg albumin denatured by ionizing radiations differ from the changes produced by heat, acid, alkali, or ultraviolet denaturation.[56]

As with ultraviolet irradiation, proteins denatured by ionizing radiation may precipitate in a secondary step which is highly temperature

(59) E. S. G. Barron, *in* A. Hollaender, ed., High Energy Radiation, McGraw-Hill New York. *In press.*
(60) E. S. G. Barron, S. Dickman, J. A. Muntz, and T. P. Singer, *J. Gen. Physiol.* **32,** 537 (1949).
(61) E. S. G. Barron and S. Dickman, *J. Gen. Physiol.* **32,** 592 (1949).
(62) W. M. Dale, *Biochem. J.* **34,** 1367 (1940); *ibid.* **36,** 80 (1942).

dependent.[51] Proteins such as the hemocyanins which dissociate readily in urea are also split into subunits by irradiation with α-particles.[53]

The enhanced action of ionizing radiation in dilute solution which is due to the activation of water is a secondary reaction which may be separated from the primary effect of an ionizing collision by irradiation of dried samples in vacuum. Pollard[63] has employed a cyclotron deuteron beam for the bombardment of the digestive enzymes, pepsin, trypsin, and chymotrypsin, and of the *Escherichia coli* bacteriophage T_1. Molecular weights calculated from the target volumes indicate that the enzymes are inactivated all at once by a single primary ionization almost anywhere in the molecule, whereas the bacterial virus has many radiation-sensitive spots.

c. Organic Solvents and Solutes

One of the most cogent arguments for present concepts of protein structure is that denaturation is caused not only by acid and alkali or by physical methods imparting energy to the system but is also brought about at room temperature by neutral solvents and solutes. Acetone, alcohol, and other organic solvents; urea, guanidine salts, and related amides; salicylate and the synthetic ionic detergents all denature proteins. However, two differences are to be noted between the organic solvents on the one hand and the organic solutes on the other. Organic solvents coagulate proteins at the isoelectric point, and the rate is governed by a high thermal coefficient; whereas, organic *solutes*—under the usual conditions of pH and concentration—disperse insoluble or coagulated proteins in a process which is relatively independent of temperature, or as with urea, may have a negative temperature coefficient. Most of the organic denaturants are hydrogen-bond-forming compounds with the exception of the synthetic detergents which apparently combine stoichiometrically with the oppositely charged groups of the protein. While the primary mode of attachment of the ionic and non-ionic organic denaturants may differ, competition (stabilization) effects occur and the result of action of either type is a disruption of intramolecular bonds.

It is sometimes suggested that the denaturing action of organic *solvents* is related to their effect on the dielectric constant of the solution (D). The addition of organic solvents decreases the dielectric constant of the solution and thus increases electrostatic forces between charged groups on the same as well as on nearby molecules. However, with organic *solutes* Steinhardt[64] was unable to correlate the effectiveness of

(63) E. Pollard, *Am. Scientist* **39**, 99 (1951).
(64) J. Steinhardt, *J. Biol. Chem.* **122**, 371 (1938).

denaturants with change in D.   For 4 M urea solutions capable of dissociating hemoglobin, D is 90 (greater than that of water which is 80), while equally effective solutions of acetamide have a value of D less than that of water, and saturated (2 M) solutions of glycine ($D = 124$) were without effect.   It is clear that the principal denaturing action of organic substances is unrelated to some common physical property such as contribution to the dielectric constant.

(1) *Organic Solvents.*   At room temperature and above, proteins are irreversibly precipitated from solution by the addition of a water-miscible organic solvent such as acetone, methyl alcohol, or ethyl alcohol. At a critical temperature near 65° much lower concentrations of alcohol are needed.   Nonetheless, the fractionation of protein mixtures may be accomplished without denaturation by the addition of water-miscible organic solvents such as ethyl alcohol, provided the temperature is kept close to the freezing point.   Proteins such as the prolamines which are rich in nonpolar amino acids are most readily soluble in 70 per cent alcohol, but the natural heterogeneity and insolubility of these substances preclude judgment as to whether they are denatured by this process.

(2) *Organic Solutes.*   Three classes of organic solutes have been studied as protein denaturants: (*a*) urea, guanidine salts, urethan, and related amides; (*b*) the ionic detergents; and (*c*) sodium salicylate.   All these compounds are excellent dispersing agents for soluble proteins, denatured proteins, and even gliadin and wheat gluten.   These reagents also disperse keratins if a reducing agent is added.[65]   Because these substances keep the denatured protein in homogeneous solution they allow investigation unimpaired by the secondary process of coagulation or the necessity for heterogeneous titration.   They are thus the most suitable denaturants for investigation with physical chemical methods such as osmotic pressure, ultracentrifugation, and electrophoresis.   Two drawbacks of the use of the amides and salicylate may be cited.   First, the requisite high molar concentrations necessitate large corrections for the viscosity and density of the solvent in molecular kinetic methods and prevent convection-free electrophoresis.   Secondly, although the removal of the denaturant by dialysis yields a precipitate of denatured protein and some soluble "regenerated" material susceptible to study free of the objections just cited,[66] this procedure leads to ambiguity in determining the effect of concentration of the denaturant.

(*a*) *Amides.*   *Urea* and other amides at *low* concentrations cause a large solubility increase in proteins without denaturation.[64]   In dilute protein solutions at *high* concentrations, the amides induce a large viscosity

(65) C. B. Jones and D. K. Mecham, *Arch. Biochem.* **3**, 193 (1943).
(66) H. Neurath, G. R. Cooper, and J. O. Erickson, *J. Biol. Chem.* **142**, 249 (1942).

increase with a lower rate of diffusion and possible liberation of —SH groups, molecular dissociation, or increase in levorotation. However, with concentrated protein solutions the amides form a firm transparent gel.[14,67] Urea produces its maximum effects at only about 8 M, and these are exceeded by several other denaturants.

Guanidine hydrochloride is much more effective at equimolar concentrations. It produces a greater viscosity increase[66,68] and liberates the full complement of —SH groups.[19,69] The greater part of the denaturing effect is exerted rapidly, but the initial rate depends on the protein, and progressive changes may occur up to about 24 hr.[70,71,71a] For both substances hygroscopicity, impurities in the commercial products, and "creeping" of the concentrated solutions must be reckoned with.

Amides such as guanidine hydrochloride, urea, acetamide, and formamide dissociate some proteins into molecular subunits. Other proteins retain their original molecular weight but undergo a large increase in molecular asymmetry (sec. III-2). Though viruses[30] and toxins[72] are readily inactivated by urea, some proteolytic enzymes are resistant[64] (sec. III-3a). Amides have often been used to modify the antigenicity of serum proteins[73-75] (sec. III-3b).

The denaturing action is undoubtedly a property of the amide bond but can be modified or eliminated by structural changes.[14,69] N-Methylurea and O-methylisourea hydrochloride are equally effective as the parent compound, as is methylguanidine hydrochloride, whereas, *as*-dimethylguanidine is less potent, and further substitution diminishes the action. A surprising result of variation of the anion was encountered in the liberation of —SH groups of egg albumin by guanidinium salts. The sulfate, carbonate, and acetate were without effect, whereas the other halides and thiocyanate were more active than the chloride.[69] The action of low concentrations of urea and guanidine hydrochloride (0.15–0.50 M) in abolishing the double refraction of flow and in decreasing

(67) C. Huggins, D. F. Tapley, and E. V. Jensen, *Nature* **167**, 592 (1951).
(68) F. W. Putnam, J. O. Erickson, E. Volkin, and H. Neurath, *J. Gen. Physiol.* **26**, 513 (1943).
(69) J. P. Greenstein, *J. Biol. Chem.* **130**, 519 (1939).
(70) G. G. Wright and V. Schomaker, *J. Biol. Chem.* **175**, 169 (1948).
(71) P. D. Boyer, G. A. Ballou, and J. M. Luck, *J. Biol. Chem.* **162**, 199 (1946).
(71a) W. Kauzmann, R. B. Simpson, M. T. Watson, B. Levedahl, J. Schellman, and H. K. Frensdorff, Abstracts of 120th Meeting, American Chemical Society, 1951, p. 11 P.
(72) G. G. Wright and V. Schomaker, *J. Am. Chem. Soc.* **70**, 356 (1948).
(73) J. O. Erickson and H. Neurath, *J. Exptl. Med.* **78**, 1 (1943).
(74) D. S. Martin, J. O. Erickson, F. W. Putnam, and H. Neurath, *J. Gen. Physiol.* **26**, 533 (1943).
(75) J. O. Erickson and H. Neurath, *J. Gen. Physiol.* **28**, 421 (1945).

the viscosity of myosin is in marked contrast to the effect on globular proteins.[76]

(b) *Ionic Detergents.* When compared on an equimolar basis, the anionic detergents are the most effective denaturants known.[77] However, the maximum amount of —SH liberated in egg albumin and the maximum viscosity increase observed with serum albumin is the same for the alkyl sulfates and guanidine hydrochloride.[78–80] Quantitative study of cationic detergents is lacking. Though some of these agents liberate —SH groups, dodecylamine hydrochloride is ineffective.[81,82] The diverse effects of the interactions of synthetic detergents and proteins have recently been reviewed.[43] In addition to all the criteria listed for denaturation, these include stabilization against urea and heat denaturation, precipitation of proteins of opposite charge with redispersion at higher detergent to protein ratios,[83] and catalyzed hydrolysis of the peptide bond. The many advantages of these compounds have allowed detailed study and have enabled interpretation of the detergent denaturation of proteins in a model system comprising sodium dodecyl sulfate (SDS) and serum albumin.[84] Though interaction and denaturation effects in this system are being explored by many workers, the profound influence of salt on the size and shape of the protein–detergent complex has only recently been reported.[84a] The myriad number of detergents now available should encourage exploration of the relation of structure and action for these increasingly important compounds. Non-ionic detergents are without effect on proteins.

(c) *Sodium Salicylate.* Sodium salicylate denatures methemoglobin at a concentration of 0.5 M—the denatured protein differing from the native in respect to solubility, absorption spectrum, and susceptibility to tryptic digestion.[85] The instance though controversial[26] is important because it has been used to postulate an equilibrium between the native and denatured protein of a type, it was suggested, which may have biological significance. The structure of salicylate suggests that its mode of action is similar to that of the detergents.

(76) J. T. Edsall and J. W. Mehl, *J. Biol. Chem.* **133**, 409 (1940).
(77) M. L. Anson, *J. Gen. Physiol.* **23**, 239 (1939).
(78) M. L. Anson, *J. Gen. Physiol.* **24**, 399 (1941).
(79) A. E. Mirsky, *J. Gen. Physiol.* **24**, 709 (1941).
(80) H. Neurath and F. W. Putnam, *J. Biol. Chem.* **160**, 397 (1945).
(81) S. N. Timasheff and F. F. Nord, *Arch. Biochem.* **31**, 309 (1951).
(82) R. Kuhn and H. J. Bielig, *Ber.* **73B**, 1080 (1940).
(83) F. W. Putnam and H. Neurath, *J. Am. Chem. Soc.* **66**, 692 (1944).
(84) F. W. Putnam and H. Neurath, *J. Am. Chem. Soc.* **66**, 1992 (1944).
(84a) J. A. Friend, B. S. Harrap, and J. H. Schulman, *Nature* **168**, 910 (1951).
(85) M. L. Anson and A. E. Mirsky, *J. Gen. Physiol.* **17**, 399 (1934).

Sodium salicylate also denatures arginase and is somewhat more effective than guanidine hydrochloride, though incomparably less so than Duponol (a mixture of alkyl sulfates).[86] The sigmoid curve relating fractional inactivation to denaturant concentration is similar in character to that obtained for the action of urea on the serum proteins and has been interpreted in terms of the combination of one molecule of enzyme with several molecules of the denaturant. A similar sigmoid curve is seen in the displacement of methyl orange by urea from the binding sites of serum albumin.[87] The mode of action of the organic solutes such as the amides, detergents, and salicylates is best interpreted in terms of binding to key sites. The potency of these agents parallels their affinities. Further clues are afforded by the action of stabilizing agents particularly the detergent dodecyl sulfate (sec. II-2b). While study has been restricted to salicylate, similar organic anions also probably denature proteins. Trichloroacetic acid is an effective protein denaturant[88] but in some cases may be used for purification purposes.

d. Inorganic Electrolytes

It has been long known but little noted that certain anions are capable of acting as denaturing agents, particularly iodide and thiocyanate. On a molar basis these anions may be more potent than urea in affecting the rate of denaturation.[71a] The characteristic property of myosin of producing stream double refraction is abolished in 8 per cent solutions of potassium iodide and thiocyanate.[89] Although potassium chloride and bromide have no effect on egg albumin, iodide and thiocyanate from 2 to 6 molal precipitate the protein without freeing —SH groups, and above 6 molal the protein is precipitated with simultaneous release of these groups.[69] In this connection the effect of the guanidinium anion has already been noted. Thiocyanate also completely inhibits arginase.[86] The denaturing action of these anions is to be contrasted to the protective effect of other electrolytes (sec. II-2b) and indicates caution in interpreting the general rule that proteins are more stable in salt solutions.

e. Proteolytic Enzymes

The increased susceptibility of denatured proteins to proteolytic fission is a useful criterion of denaturation and one of the most convincing signs of the exposure of internal peptide bonds in the latter proc-

(86) A. Hunter and C. E. Downs, *J. Biol. Chem.* **173**, 31 (1948).
(87) I. M. Klotz, H. Triwush, and F. M. Walker, *J. Am. Chem. Soc.* **70**, 2935 (1948).
(88) A. E. Mirsky, *J. Gen. Physiol.* **19**, 559 (1936).
(89) A. L. von Muralt and J. T. Edsall, *J. Biol. Chem.* **89**, 351 (1930).

ess.[90-92] It has also led to the widely held notion that proteolysis is preceded by enzymatically induced denaturation.[93] Linderstrøm-Lang[94] has suggested that the slow action of trypsin on native proteins and the rapid decomposition of individual molecules of denatured protein indicate that the substrate must undergo an initial reaction by which it is prepared for the attack of the enzyme. This initial reaction may be a denaturation or may involve the splitting of a few strategically located peptide bonds. The enzymatic hydrolysis of proteins is accompanied by a large volume decrease greater than that attributable only to the electrostrictive effect of the new charged groups. This decrease, measurable dilatometrically, is similar to the large volume contraction observed in the denaturation by urea. Other considerations, such as the initial increase in optical rotation in urea or when native but not denatured protein is attacked by trypsin, also indicate that the tryptic digestion of β-lactoglobulin may first produce a denatured protein similar to that formed by urea.[95] Linderstrøm-Lang assumes trypsin catalyzes a process of the type

$$Q_s' \rightleftarrows (Q_d')$$

where Q_s' is an equilibrium form of native lactoglobulin and Q_d' a form of the type produced by rapid reversible denaturation with urea and capable of being split enzymatically. In this view the resistance of many globular proteins to enzymes is a matter of steric hindrance. In principle this picture is similar to the earlier one of Lundgren and Williams[96,96a] ($N \rightleftarrows \alpha \rightarrow D$, where α is an intermediate unfolded form).

2. PROTECTION AGAINST DENATURATION

a. Optimum Conditions for Storage

The prevention of denaturation has long been of practical importance in the purification of proteins and recently has assumed significance in interpreting the mode of protein denaturation. Three aspects may be considered. The first, covered below, concerns the choice of conditions

(90) H. Lineweaver and S. R. Hoover, J. Biol. Chem. 137, 325 (1941).
(91) F. Bernheim, H. Neurath, and J. O. Erickson, J. Biol. Chem. 144, 259 (1942).
(92) F. Haurowitz, M. Tunca, P. Schwerin, and V. Göksu, J. Biol. Chem. 157, 621 (1945).
(93) K. Linderstrøm-Lang, R. D. Hotchkiss, and G. Johansen, Nature 142, 996 (1938).
(94) K. Linderstrøm-Lang, Cold Spring Harbor Symposia Quant. Biol. 14, 117 (1950).
(95) L. K. Christensen, Nature 163, 1003 (1949).
(96) H. P. Lundgren, J. Biol. Chem. 138, 293 (1941).
(96a) J. W. Williams and H. P. Lundgren, J. Phys. Chem. 43, 989 (1939).

that avoid denaturation; the second involves the addition of substances that protect against the action of denaturants; and the third involves the use of denaturants such as urea[14] or detergents,[77] of the sulfhydryl reagent, iodoacetic acid,[97] or thymus nucleate[98] to prevent the heat coagulation of proteins. Since the latter is inhibition of coagulation rather than of denaturation, it will not be considered further.

General rules for avoiding denaturation have already been elaborated in Chap. 1 but may be summarized again. In brief, proteins should be prepared and kept in the cold, and should be lyophilized or stored in concentrated solution in the presence of salts at a benign pH. Exceptions and additions to these rules may be found by study of the properties of each protein. Proteins are best kept at the pH of their natural environment but remain native over a characteristic pH stability range. Dilute salt solutions usually favor the stability of proteins, and in some cases specific cations or anions are required. Viruses, in particular, are sensitive to the ionic environment; some of the bacteriophages require bivalent cations such as Ca^{++} for stability.[99] Needless to say, organic solvents employed in fractionation should be used cautiously and removed completely.

(1) *Desiccation and Low Temperature.* Purification should be attempted and preparations maintained at the lowest temperature possible above freezing. This not only avoids thermal denaturation by taking advantage of the high temperature coefficient of this process but also prevents the action of enzymes and bacterial growth. Proteins are more stable when dry than when in solution, but lyophilization is not always feasible. Storage in the frozen state is often employed for serum because only minor electrophoretic changes are detectable after freezing. This method is unsuitable if careful lipoprotein analysis is to be made.

(2) *Protein Concentration.* Proteins are much more stable in concentrated than in dilute solution. Sterile concentrated solutions of serum albumin (about 25% protein) have been kept almost water-clear for years without apparent change in physical properties or increase in pyrogens. This principle must be observed in biological work where great dilutions of viruses and toxins must often be made for assay. The addition of inert protective proteins such as gelatin, egg albumin, and even serum, nutrient broth, or peptones is common practice and is usually necessary to obtain the maximal titer. Clearly, the protective effect is nonspecific. It has been variously ascribed to the increase in dielectric

(97) E. V. Jensen, V. D. Hospelhorn, D. F. Tapley, and C. Huggins, *J. Biol. Chem.* **185**, 411 (1950).

(98) J. P. Greenstein and M. L. Hoyer, *J. Biol. Chem.* **182**, 457 (1950).

(99) M. H. Adams, *J. Gen. Physiol.* **32**, 579 (1949).

constant contributed by the protein[100] and to the avoidance of surface
denaturation by the addition of enough protein to form a continuously
replaceable[41] surface film. In a few instances protection is due to the
binding of toxic metals or protein denaturants by the added protein.
Protection of viruses against inactivation by ultraviolet irradiation may
be conferred by the addition of proteins, nutrient broth, or other light-
absorbing substances.

b. Chemical Inhibitors

(1) *Neutral Organic Solutes.* In saturated solutions of sugars and
sugar alcohols the heat coagulation of egg albumin is averted,[101] and the
formation of the characteristic electrophoretic "C" component found
only in heated serum is prevented.[102] At much lower concentrations
(about 0.25 M), the liberation of —SH groups in heated egg albumin
solutions is partially inhibited.[103] The protective ability varies among
sugars—glucose, fructose, and sucrose being most efficient. The effect
may be due to the osmotic property of the added solute because it appears
somewhat related to the solubility of the sugar. The possibility of the
formation of sugar–protein complexes has been discounted, and no satisfactory explanation of this effect has yet been offered.

(2) *Long-Chain Organic Ions.* One of the most significant examples
of protection against denaturation is the stabilization of serum albumin
by long-chain organic anions against the effects of heat, urea, and guanidine hydrochloride. Boyer, Ballou, Luck, and co-workers[71,104] found
that low concentrations of fatty acid anions, anionic detergents, or other
anions with large nonpolar groups retard the heat coagulation of bovine
serum albumin and prevent the viscosity increase in heated solutions,
in 6 M urea or 2.5 M guanidine hydrochloride, but not in 6 M guanidine
hydrochloride or 1.2 per cent sodium dodecyl sulfate. The prevention of
the viscosity rise demonstrates that the anions stabilize the native, not
the denatured protein. The protective effect, not given by cations with
nonpolar groups, is observed on both sides of the isoelectric point, and
increases with chain length up to 12 carbon atoms at low anion concentrations. However, at higher concentrations maximum stabilization is
produced by C_7 or C_8 fatty acids. At very low mole ratios, sodium
dodecyl sulfate is the most effective stabilizer both in raising the cloud

(100) E. J. Cohn *in* E. J. Cohn and J. T. Edsall, Proteins, Amino Acids and
        Peptides, Reinhold Publishing Corp., New York, 1943, pp. 571–2.
(101) A. Beilinsson, *Biochem. Z.* **213,** 399 (1929).
(102) C. R. Hardt, I. F. Huddleson, and C. D. Ball, *J. Biol. Chem.* **163,** 211 (1946).
(103) C. D. Ball, C. R. Hardt, and W. J. Duddles, *J. Biol. Chem.* **151,** 163 (1943).
(104) P. D. Boyer, F. G. Lum, G. A. Ballou, J. M. Luck, and R. G. Rice, *J. Biol.
        Chem.* **162,** 181 (1946).

point and in preventing the viscosity rise in urea denaturation, but at higher ratios it produces the large viscosity increase already reported.[80] Acetyltryptophan, phenylacetate, and mandelate were used during the war for the stabilization of concentrated solutions of human plasma and of serum albumin. Sodium dodecyl sulfate also combines with β-lactoglobulin to form a crystalline complex containing two equivalents per mole protein. This complex is more resistant to heat and alkali denaturation than is the native protein.[105]

The protective effect of the fatty acids and similar substances is undoubtedly related to the binding of the anions by the positively charged groups of the protein. Four circumstances favor this view: (1) The binding of the effective anions has been demonstrated in other connections; (2) the protective ability parallels the affinity or binding energy of the ion; (3) serum albumin is stabilized and is highest on the scale of anion-binding ability (Chap. 8), whereas, γ-globulin is low on this scale and is not protected;[105a] and (4) denaturants of the organic solute type, such as urea, urethan, and salicylate compete with other anions such as methyl orange for the binding sites on proteins.[87]

The dependence of the stabilizing efficacy on chain length probably results from interaction of the hydrocarbon moieties with nonpolar amino acid residues of neighboring polypeptide chains, thus preventing separation. Although organic denaturants compete for the same sites on proteins, competition is not the sole stabilizing factor since thermal denaturation is also prevented. Protection is dependent on the anion to albumin ratio. At a caprylate concentration sufficient for maximum protection, about nine molecules of caprylate are bound per molecule of protein. A minimum in the curve relating relative viscosity to dodecyl sulfate concentration indicates that eight molecules of the anion combine with one of the protein to form a stable complex.[106] As emphasized by Putnam,[43] in discussion of the mode of detergent denaturation of proteins, it would appear that certain areas or groups play an essential role in maintaining structure. These may be protected against thermal disorder and hydrogen-bond-breaking substances by combination and crosslinking with anions of high affinity and dual structure. However, excess binding of the same anions may lead to structural disorder, disorientation, and denaturation. This idea of a "zipper" type structure with many

(105) M. L. Groves, N. J. Hipp, and T. L. McMeekin, *J. Am. Chem. Soc.* **73**, 2790 (1951).

(105a) The difference in behavior in urea of serum albumin, lactoglobulin, and egg albumin is likewise paralleled by the affinity of these proteins for dyes and other anions.[71a]

(106) E. L. Duggan and J. M. Luck, *J. Biol. Chem.* **172**, 205 (1948).

groups or bonds exposed only after the breaking of a critical few will be considered further in the discussion of the kinetics of hemoglobin denaturation and the accessibility of reactive groups in proteins.

(3) *Inorganic Electrolytes.* The effect of inorganic anions on proteins appears to follow the lyotropic or Hofmeister series, ions on the thiocyanate end denaturing, those on the sulfate end inhibiting denaturation:

$$CNS^- > I^- > Br^- > NO_3^- > Cl^- > CH_3COO^- > SO_4^{--} > CO_3^{--}.$$

This is true of the liberation of titratable —SH groups in egg albumin dissolved in urea, studied by Burk,[107] and in a solution of the corresponding guanidinium anions investigated by Greenstein.[69] A comparable effect of salts on the rate of change of optical rotation by urea has recently been reported.[71a] A similar lyotropic series for cations exists. It is highly significant that a similar series holds for the combination of anions with proteins as measured by the shift in the isoionic point, with even greater and tighter binding for large organic anions such as trichloroacetate which serve as protein precipitants (Chap. 8). These facts emphasize the common features of the action of amides, ionic detergents, organic anions, and inorganic electrolytes on proteins: (1) Though the affinity varies, all are bound to the charged groups of proteins; (2) low concentrations of denaturing agents of high affinity protect against heat and competitively against the binding of agents of low affinity even when the latter are in nearly saturated solutions; (3) low concentrations of some of these agents precipitate proteins without evident signs of denaturation; (4) high concentrations redisperse denatured proteins, except that iodide and thiocyanate salts, though excellent "peptizing" agents for proteins at low concentration, do not redissolve proteins at high molarities; and (5) the effectiveness of the denaturants, when measured on an equimolar basis, is directly related to their binding energy, dodecyl sulfate being most potent. These facts clearly indicate that the action of all these denaturing agents is largely based on combination with specific groups in proteins rather than by contribution to some physical property of the medium such as dielectric constant or surface tension.

III. Properties of Denatured Proteins

1. Liberation of Chemically Reactive Groups

a. Chemically Reactive Groups Liberated in Denaturation

Since Arnold[108] in 1911 first demonstrated the appearance of nitroprusside-reactive groups[109] during the heat coagulation of egg white,

(107) N. F. Burk, *J. Phys. Chem.* **47**, 104 (1943).

(108) V. Arnold, *Z. physiol. Chem.* **70**, 300, 314 (1911).

(109) The nitroprusside test is a deep-violet unstable color obtained on addition

protein chemists have sought to explain the position and function of these and similar latent but demonstrable groups. Although some proteins contain freely reactive —SH or other polar side-chain groups, the number does not always correspond to the analytical composition. The latent groups revealed only on denaturation have been called "hidden," "masked," "inaccessible," and "unavailable." Whether they are masked sterically by the folded configuration of the native protein, by intramolecular hydrogen bonding or salt linkages, or by readily dissociable covalent cross bonds is still uncertain.[110] The inactivity is relative, the distribution of free and masked groups differs among proteins, and the number liberated depends on the denaturing agent. Their rate of appearance on denaturation is gradual, not discontinuous. Their liberation is not necessarily paralleled by loss of biological activity or increased molecular asymmetry.

Owing to the ease and specificity of measurement, —SH groups have figured most prominently in the literature on denaturation. There is no reason to assume that their role is more significant than that of other masked groups such as disulfide, phenolic, and indolyl on which less information is available. The structural significance of masked groups has been assessed only for disulfide which has a cross-linking function.

The groups liberated are all polar and represent the amino acid side chains which are uncombined in the peptide linkage but are presumably involved in secondary bondings. Specific methods of measurement are lacking for nonpolar side chains and also for aliphatic hydroxyl groups in proteins. The polar groups most frequently investigated do not contribute significantly to the amphoteric properties of proteins. However, discrepancies exist in the comparison of the number of amino, guanidyl, imidazolyl, and carboxyl groups as determined by electrometric titration and from total analysis. Recently other evidence has been presented for the occurrence of unreactive acidic[113,113a] and basic

---

of a drop of sulfhydryl-containing compound to a drop of 5% sodium nitroprusside ($Na_2Fe(CN)_5NO$) and a drop of 1 M NH_4OH. Nitroprusside is suitable only for qualitative tests or as an end-point indicator.

(110) For hypotheses about structural mechanisms see Anson.[3] The theory of inaccessibility and hydrogen bonding was proposed by Mirsky and Pauling.[24] Linderstrøm-Lang and Jacobsen[111] suggested that the inapparent —SH groups are combined in thiazolidine rings which open on denaturation. This concept has been investigated by several authors.[2,112]

(111) K. Linderstrøm-Lang and C. F. Jacobsen, Compt. rend. trav. lab. Carlsberg 23, 289 (1940).

(112) E. Fredericq and V. Desreux, Bull. soc. chim. biol. 29, 100 (1947).

(113) J. Steinhardt and E. M. Zaiser, J. Biol. Chem. 190, 197 (1951).

(113a) J. Steinhardt and E. M. Zaiser, Abstract of Papers, 120th Meeting, American Chemical Society, 1951, p. 12 P.

groups in proteins.[114-116] The methods described in the following sections are those useful and specific for determining masked groups; general group reactions are discussed in Chapter 10.

b. Quantitative Measurement of Sulfhydryl Groups

The liberation, measurement, and significance of the sulfhydryl and disulfide groups of proteins has been treated in reviews by Neurath et al.[2] and by Anson.[3] Barron[117] has detailed the chemistry and biological importance of thiol groups. Barron and Hellerman et al.[118] have classified the thiol residues of proteins into three types: (1) *freely reacting —SH groups* (type "a" of Hellerman) present in the native protein, possibly surface-situated and thus reacting readily with nitroprusside and with mild oxidizing agents such as ferricyanide and porphyrindin as well as with mercaptide-forming agents and iodoacetamide; (2) *sluggish —SH groups* (type "b") which are less available for structural or other reasons and thus do not give a nitroprusside test nor reduce ferricyanide or porphyrindin but are accessible to p-chloromercuribenzoate; and (3) *masked —SH groups* which react with all reagents but only after denaturation of the protein. No rigid categories exist, and Anson emphasizes that —SH groups of very different degrees of reactivity are found in different native proteins. For example, though none of the —SH groups of native egg albumin are oxidized by ferricyanide or porphyrindin or combine with silver in the amperometric titration, all react with iodine in KI at pH 7 and can be titrated in guanidine hydrochloride solutions. At pH 9, 40 per cent combine with iodoacetamide. All three types of groups were first distinguished by Hellerman and associates in a study of crystalline urease. Oxidation of the freely reacting groups had no effect on enzyme activity, whereas oxidation or substitution of the second type ("b") resulted in complete inactivation. Additional groups were exposed by denaturation with guanidine hydrochloride. However, some doubt has arisen as to the number of —SH groups in native urease and whether types "a" and "b" are both present. Ambrose, Kistiakowsky, and Kridl[118a] report that urease is totally inhibited by combination of one molecule with three to four silver ions, the Ag^+ apparently combining with identical and mutually independent groups in the enzyme.

(114) R. R. Porter, *Biochim. et Biophys. Acta* **2**, 105 (1948).

(115) R. R. Porter, *Biochem. J.* **46**, 304 (1950).

(116) J. Roche and M. Mourgue, *Bull soc. chim. biol.* **26**, 1206 (1944); *ibid.* **28**, 34 (1945); *ibid.* **30**, 322 (1948).

(117) E. S. G. Barron, *Advances in Enzymol.* **11**, 201 (1951).

(118) L. Hellerman, F. P. Chinard, and V. R. Deitz, *J. Biol. Chem.* **147**, 443 (1943).

(118a) J. F. Ambrose, G. B. Kistiakowsky, and A. G. Kridl, *J. Am. Chem. Soc.* **73**, 1232 (1951).

The number of groups measurable depends on the protein and the denaturing agent as well as the titrating reagent. Liver nucleoproteins contain only freely reacting —SH groups. All the —SH groups of some proteins are masked in the native state, e.g., egg albumin, serum albumin, edestin, excelsin, tobacco mosaic virus, and horse globin. Other proteins, such as amandin and insulin, give no test for —SH either before or after denaturation. Myosin and urease contain both types.

The —SH groups of proteins were first measured quantitatively by Mirsky and Anson[17] in 1935 using cystine as an oxidizing agent in a study of coagulated egg albumin. Greenstein[19] introduced a new oxidant, porphyrindin, and titration in homogeneous media, such as concentrated solutions of amides. Anson[78] and Mirsky[79] later employed ferricyanide and tetrathionate and also the mercaptide-forming agent, p-chloromercuribenzoic acid, to estimate the maximum number of —SH groups liberated in amides or in Duponol. Table I summarizes the results for denatured egg albumin in homogeneous media.

Although unrelated denaturing agents such as guanidine hydrochloride and Duponol produce the same increase in chemical reactivity,

TABLE I

MAXIMUM PROPORTION OF SULFHYDRYL GROUPS OF DENATURED EGG ALBUMIN
LIBERATED IN HOMOGENEOUS SOLUTION

Denaturing agent	Sulfhydryl reagent	Protein sulfhydryl liberated[a]	Reference
Urea	Porphyrindin	1.00	Greenstein[19]
	Ferricyanide	0.96	Mirsky[79]
	Iodoacetate	0.87	Rosner[119]
Guanidine HCl	Porphyrindin	1.28	Greenstein[19]
	Ferricyanide, tetrathionate, or p-chloromercuribenzoate	1.24	Anson[78]
	o-Iodosobenzoate	1.29	Hellerman et al.[118]
	Ferricyanide	0.96	Mirsky[79]
	p-Chloromercuribenzoate	0.96	Benesch and Benesch[120]
	p-Chloromercuribenzoate	1.07	MacDonnell et al.[120a]
Duponol	Ferricyanide, tetrathionate, or p-chloromercuribenzoate	1.24	Anson[78]
	Ferricyanide	0.96	Mirsky[79]
	Amperometric	0.90	Benesch and Benesch[120]
Ethanol	Amperometric	1.34	Benesch and Benesch[120]

[a] Expressed as per cent cysteine.

(119) L. Rosner, J. Biol. Chem. **132**, 657 (1940).
(120) R. Benesch and R. E. Benesch, Arch. Biochem. **19**, 35 (1948).
(120a) L. R. MacDonnell, R. B. Silva and R. E. Feeney, Arch. Biochem. and Biophys. **32**, 278 (1951).

not all agents are as effective. Heat and surface denaturation produce a coagulated protein with only half the —SH groups detectable, and urea liberates only 80 per cent (but see Anson[3]). Proof that the methods measure the same groups is offered by the fact that with egg albumin similar maximum values are obtained for a given denaturing agent whatever —SH reagent is employed. The figure 1.3 per cent —SH groups (expressed as cysteine) seems most reliable. Hess and Sullivan[121] have reported 1.41 per cent cysteine in egg albumin but titrated the unhydrolyzed protein with iodine at 20° in the presence of 2 per cent HCl and KI. Hughes (cited by Fevold[122]) has recently confirmed the value of 1.28 per cent. This corresponds to about 4.75 equivalents of —SH per mole protein, but some workers believe there are 4 equivalents per mole.[120a] The reason for deviation from an integral molar value (and perhaps also for the finding of 0.96 per cent cysteine by some workers) may lie in the heterogeneity of egg albumin.

Though a number of methods exist for estimation of protein —SH, most have been criticized.[2,3,117] Except for cystine, which has other disadvantages, the oxidizing agents are not wholly group specific but also act on tyrosine or tryptophan if conditions are not ideal.[117,123,124] It is claimed that porphyrindin, ferricyanide, and o-iodosobenzoate react only with —SH under the conditions recommended. The alkylating agents (iodoacetate and its amide) are also unspecific, but may be used to estimate protein —SH from the decrease in cysteine content of the hydrolyzed alkylated protein. Because of its high specificity, p-chloromercuribenzoic acid has been strongly recommended,[117,118] but it reacts with —SH groups not attacked by mild oxidizing reagents. Its advantage of reversibility renders it more suited for the study of —SH-activated enzymes than of denatured proteins. A rapid, accurate, specific method recently adapted to proteins is amperometric titration of —SH with $AgNO_3$.[120] The first excess of Ag^+ is indicated by a sharp rise in the diffusion current. The high concentration of ammonium hydroxide used is a disadvantage. Another new —SH reagent is CH_3HgNO_3.[125] It is desirable to employ more than one procedure for the estimation of protein —SH, one reason being that oxidizing agents require the proximity of two —SH groups, whereas alkylating and mercaptide-forming agents react with single —SH groups.

An important study of methods for the characterization of sulfhydryl groups has recently been conducted by Larson and Jenness[125a] who used

(121) W. C. Hess and M. X. Sullivan, J. Biol. Chem. **151**, 635 (1943).
(122) H. L. Fevold, Advances in Protein Chem. **6**, 187 (1951).
(123) R. M. Herriott, Advances in Protein Chem. **3**, 169 (1947).
(124) H. S. Olcott and H. Fraenkel-Conrat, Chem. Revs. **41**, 151 (1947).
(125) W. L. Hughes and R. Straessle, J. Am. Chem. Soc. **72**, 452 (1950).
(125a) B. L. Larson and R. Jenness, J. Am. Chem. Soc. **74**, 3090 (1952).

TABLE II
Specificity, Stoichiometry and Method of Analysis for Common Reagents Used for Quantitative Estimation of Protein —SH Groups

A. Oxidizing agents

1. *Ferricyanide:* Specific at pH 6.8, reacts with phenol and indole at higher pH.[79,126]

$$2[Fe(CN_6)]^{---} + 2RSH \rightarrow 2[Fe(CN)_6]^{----} + R—S—S—R + 2H^+$$

Colorimetric measurement of Prussian blue formed in reaction.

2. *Porphyrindin:* Rapid, stoichiometric, but expensive and unstable.[19]

End point is disappearance of nitroprusside reaction of the denatured protein.

3. *Iodosobenzoate:* Specific at pH 7, quite satisfactory.[118,127]

Iodimetry—excess of standard added is reduced by iodide, and the iodine liberated is titrated with standard thiosulfate.

B. Alkylating agents

1. *Iodoacetate:* Unspecific irreversible combination with single —SH group.[17]

$$ICH_2COO^- + RSH \rightarrow R—S—CH_2COO^- + HI$$

C. Mercaptide-forming agents

1. *p-Chloromercuribenzoate:* Highly specific reversible combination with single —SH groups.[118]

Titration to negative nitroprusside end point.

(126) M. L. Anson, *J. Gen. Physiol.* **23**, 247 (1939).
(127) L. Hellerman, F. P. Chinard, and P. A. Ramsdell, *J. Am. Chem. Soc.* **63**, 2551 (1941).

the liberation of these groups for following the kinetics of the heat denaturation of lactoglobulin.

The specificity, stoichiometry, and method of analysis is given in Table II for a number of the more commonly used —SH reagents. Oxidizing agents are generally added stepwise to minimize oxidation of other groups, and the end point is determined by the disappearance of the nitroprusside reaction. Among oxidizing agents used but not listed in Table II are iodine, cystine, tetrathionate, 2,6-dichlorophenolindophenol, and the Folin uric acid reagent.

c. Other Reactive Groups

(1) *Disulfide Groups.* As Walker[128] first demonstrated, some proteins, such as serum albumin,[17] reveal only a fraction of their disulfide groups while in the native state, and others such as egg albumin show none;[129] but the full quota of —S—S— becomes detectable on denaturation. The disulfide groups are reduced with thioglycolic acid (mercaptoacetic acid) or cyanide, the excess reducing agent is removed, and the increase in —SH is measured as just described or cysteine is determined on the denatured hydrolyzed protein. Neutral thioglycolate is far more effective than alkaline cyanide which is actually not a reducing agent since it adds to the disulfide bond to give one —SH group and one thiocyanate group.[124] Although the effect of reduction on biological activity has frequently been studied, the disulfide groups of only a few proteins have been estimated before and after denaturation. According to Mirsky and Anson,[17,129] the number of —SH and —S—S— groups in a denatured but unhydrolyzed protein is equivalent to the quantity of cysteine and cystine found in the hydrolyzed protein. A number of studies on the sulfur balance in proteins support this view (see, for example, the summary in Table 5 of Ref. 2). The first clear-cut indication that the —SH and —S—S— groups of intact denatured proteins belong quantitatively to the respective cysteine and cystine components was given by the sulfur distribution analyses of Hess and Sullivan.[121] However, the difficulties in accurate determination of the cysteine of hydrolyzed proteins were later realized (as discussed in Chap. 3), and some authors have suggested that the good agreement between the cysteine content of intact denatured proteins with the cysteine present in acid hydrolyzates is fortuitous and the result of compensating errors.[130] Since there is both formation and destruction of cysteine during acid hydrolysis, determination of sulfhydryl groups by titration of the intact

(128) E. Walker, *Biochem. J.* **19**, 1082 (1925).
(129) A. E. Mirsky and M. L. Anson, *J. Gen. Physiol.* **19**, 427 (1936).
(130) H. S. Olcott and H. Fraenkel-Conrat, *J. Biol. Chem.* **171**, 583 (1947).

denatured protein has been recommended as the procedure least subject to error or artifact. The total cystine plus cysteine may be obtained by prior reduction.

There is much evidence that the —SH groups of native proteins exist preformed instead of arising by reduction of the disulfide bond. This consists of (a) the difference in reactivity of the —SH groups of an individual protein with various reagents, (b) the difference in distribution of free and masked —SH and —S—S— groups among various proteins, (c) the approximate agreement of total —SH and —S—S— content of intact denatured proteins with the sulfur balance, (d) the inertness of synthetic peptides of cystine towards neutral protein denaturants, and (e) the fact that sulfhydryl groups are actually determined by oxidation in the presence of protein denaturants.

(2) *Phenolic and Indole Groups.* Ferricyanide is not reduced by native egg albumin which contains —SH and tyrosine both of which react in the free state. Hence, phenolic groups as well as —SH may be masked within proteins. Measurements of the reactivity of phenolic hydroxyl groups of tyrosine in proteins, however, have given somewhat obscure results for three reasons. First of all, it is recognized that both phenol and indole groups react with the phenol reagent. Secondly, the chromogenic value of all proteins examined with the Folin phenol reagent by the method of Herriott is substantially less than the sum of the tyrosine and tryptophan content, the values ranging from 42 to 73 per cent. This discrepancy is partially attributable to the fact that peptides of tyrosine and other derivatives give less color with the Folin reagent than do equivalent quantities of free tyrosine. Though the disadvantages and optimum conditions for application of the Folin reagent to the measurement of protein phenol groups are a matter of discussion,[123,124] there is no doubt that maximal color values are obtained only after proteins are denatured.[131,132] Finally, most of the tyrosine phenol groups of proteins are not detected by titration unless the protein is iodinated.

The best evidence for the masking of phenolic groups in some proteins is given by a spectrophotometric method introduced by Crammer and Neuberger.[133] The ionization of tyrosine is accompanied by a shift of the ultraviolet spectrum to longer wavelengths allowing a spectroscopic estimation of the concentration of the phenoxide ion and the phenolic dissociation constant. The pK of free tyrosine is 10.1 and the corresponding phenolic pK of insulin is only slightly shifted (pK about 11) indicating that most of the tyrosyl groups are dissociated at pH 12.

(131) R. M. Herriott, *J. Gen. Physiol.* **21**, 501 (1938).
(132) G. L. Miller, *J. Biol. Chem.* **146**, 339 (1942).
(133) J. L. Crammer and A. Neuberger, *Biochem. J.* **37**, 302 (1943).

However, with egg albumin a marked change in absorption spectrum for wavelengths above 285 mμ occurred only on exposure to pH 13. The shift was irreversible and attributed to alkali denaturation because it was also produced by acid, urea, and heat. Since these results indicated that few or none of the phenolic groups of egg albumin were free to ionize, Crammer and Neuberger postulated that in native proteins hydrogen bonds may exist between the phenolic groups of tyrosine and the carboxyl groups of other amino acid residues and may be one of the most important structural features endowing the native configuration of the protein with stability. Subsequently, Sizer and Peacock[133a] compared the ultraviolet absorption of tyrosine and bovine serum albumin as a function of pH, also observing a shift toward the red with increasing pH. At pH 12, a sharp maximum attributed to the phenoxide ion appears at 240 mμ for free tyrosine, but there is only a plateau for the protein. Since hydrolysis increased the absorption in alkali at 240 mμ, it was concluded that the tyrosine groups of the intact protein are not free to ionize. Sizer and Peacock likewise suggested that the phenolic groups of tyrosine were combined in the protein but proposed a hydrogen bond with a basic amino group as the most plausible linkage. The phenolic groups of insulin were more reactive than those of serum albumin. It is remarkable that 60 per cent of the phenolic groups of native egg albumin react with the complex Folin reagent[131] under the same conditions where only 20 per cent can be detected by the spectrophotometric method.

(3) *Carboxyl Groups.* Since the titration curves of denatured proteins differ but little from those of native proteins, and since the titration curve of a protein such as β-lactoglobulin is fully reversible between pH 2 and 10, the liberation of acidic or basic groups on denaturation would be unexpected. Yet such groups are presumed to be involved in intramolecular bonding and appear inaccessible to complex anions if not to protons. The first instance of the masking of acid-binding groups was recently reported by Steinhardt and Zaiser[113] for carbonylhemoglobin (COHb). It was known that the titration curve of hemoglobin was irreversible below pH 4 and that spectroscopic changes indicative of denaturation occurred simultaneously in this region. By determining the acid segment of the instantaneous titration curve of COHb and subtracting the number of milliequivalents of acid bound from that found for the back titration curve, Steinhardt and Zaiser found a maximum difference corresponding to about 36 groups liberated per mole. These were tentatively identified to be half carboxylate and half imidazole—or what appears more likely—all carboxylate but of varying strength. The authors concluded that the liberation was an "all-or-none" effect,

(133a) I. W. Sizer and A. C. Peacock, *J. Biol. Chem.* **171**, 767 (1947).

the combination of acid with two carboxylate groups being responsible for the unfolding process that liberates all 34 to 36.[113a] The dependence of the initiating reaction on the square of the hydrogen-ion activity recalls an earlier analysis of the kinetics of acid denaturation of hemoglobin which was attributed to the addition of two protons and the breaking of two hydrogen bridges (Ref. 2, pp. 202–205).

(4) *Basic Groups.* The unreactive amino groups of proteins have been investigated by Porter[114] by measurement of the number of groups combining with Sanger's 1,2,4-fluorodinitrobenzene (FDNB) reagent to yield a dinitrophenyl (DNP) derivative in the native and denatured protein. No protein was found in which the number of α-amino groups reacting with FDNB was changed by denaturation. Since these are terminal groups, this result is not surprising. However, with β-lactoglobulin all the amino groups in the native protein were acetylated by ketene, but 12 of the 31 ϵ-amino groups due to lysine did not react with FDNB. The fact that all of the amino groups in this protein are titratable in aqueous solution and can be acetylated under conditions avoiding denaturation but that only some of the ϵ-amino groups can form DNP derivatives in the native protein suggested a steric effect which prevented the approach of FDNB but allowed access to ketene or a proton. For serum globulins all three classes of ϵ-amino groups were found in the native protein, i.e., those reacting (a) with both ketene and FDNB, (b) only with ketene, and (c) only with FDNB; the latter two sets were not the same. Unreactive amino groups were absent in bovine serum albumin. Denaturation by acid, heat, ethanol, and guanidinium ion exposed all the amino groups in both lactolgobulin and the serum globulins.

The titration data of Steinhardt and Zaiser[113] suggested the presence of masked imidazole groups due to histidine in carbonylhemoglobin, but Porter,[115] again using FDNB, found no evidence for increased reactivity of imidazole groups in hemoglobin, egg albumin, bovine serum albumin, or globin as the result of denaturation by heat, ethanol, or guanidine hydrochloride. However, two of the four histidine residues in β-lactoglobulin failed to react unless the protein was first denatured. Roche and Mourgue[116] have presented evidence that the guanidyl groups of proteins vary greatly in reactivity.

2. Physical Properties

a. Solubility

Globular proteins always become less soluble on heat denaturation, but this change may not be observed unless the protein is adjusted to its isoelectric point. Neutral organic denaturants such as urea and the detergents render the denatured protein soluble and even prevent heat coagulation. However, removal of the denaturant by dialysis or other methods results in the precipitation of some irreversibly denatured protein no longer soluble even in concentrated urea. The physicochemical properties of the remaining soluble fraction have been carefully studied by Neurath and associates.[66,68,73,74,134] The soluble protein, designated by various authors as "regenerated," "renatured," "reversibly denatured," or "reversed," closely resembles the native form in molecular kinetic properties, in crystallinity, and in serological specificity but it differs in electrophoretic properties, in susceptibility to enzymatic digestion, and in antigenicity.

The observations on the solubility of denatured and regenerated proteins are essentially qualitative, referring to solubility at the isoelectric point or in solutions of ammonium sulfate rather than to phase-rule solubility diagrams. Thus, whereas solubility must often be used as an index for measuring the rate or amount of denaturation of a biologically inactive protein, the criterion is arbitrary and in some cases insufficient. It is not feasible to distinguish between solubility as a property of the denatured protein and that due to reversible or incomplete denaturation.

b. Molecular Weight

The molecular-kinetic properties of proteins, due to their size and shape, change upon denaturation. Since proteins occur naturally with definite molecular weights and may be isolated with a high degree of homogeneity, changes either in physical constants or in the degree of homogeneity may result from denaturation. As a consequence, supplementary methods must be used for characterization of altered protein. Methods most frequently employed are: (a) osmotic pressure, (b) sedimentation and diffusion, (c) diffusion and viscosity, and (d) more recently, light scattering and other optical methods. Of these, the first method gives a *number-average* molecular weight with no information on molecular shape or heterogeneity. The second and third procedures yield *weight-average* molecular weights and also the frictional ratio which is a parameter of molecular shape, but the sedimentation–diffusion method is more reliable and alone reveals differences in molecular homogeneity. Optical methods which also give *weight-average* molecular weights are particularly convenient for following molecular changes during the course of denaturation but are inordinately sensitive to the presence of small amounts of impurities or aggregates. Despite recent developments in the ultracentrifuge and in optical methods, the physicochemical characterization

(134) H. Neurath, G. R. Cooper, and J. O. Erickson, *J. Biol. Chem.* **142**, 265 (1942).

of denatured proteins has not been extended much in the past decade. The methods have been useful for establishing the presence of molecular subunits in some proteins and their apparent absence in others, for ascertaining the identity of native and regenerated proteins, and for revealing the progressive nature and variety of changes occurring with different protein denaturants. Most of the measurements have been made in 6–8 M urea solution, generally by the osmotic-pressure method. In some instances the soluble product remaining after heat, acid, or alkali denaturation has been studied. The accuracy of the data is subject to some scrutiny because the osmotic-pressure and light-scattering methods do not detect heterogeneity, and large viscosity corrections must be introduced for the other methods. However, it is clear that proteins may react in three ways on denaturation: (1) no alteration in molecular weight despite change in shape, (2) dissociation into subunits of definite uniform size, and (3) aggregation.

To a degree the effect of denaturation on molecular weight is characteristic of a protein. Proteins which are readily dissociated by the mild denaturing agent, 6 M urea, are also split by other methods. However, proteins such as egg albumin and serum globulin which resist this reagent are dissociated by other denaturants. β-Lactoglobulin is split into half-molecules when spread as a surface film; egg albumin is not, but both are aggregated on heating.[135–137]

Because of the few additions to the data it is unnecessary to repeat the extensive tabulation given by Neurath et al.[2] for the effect of denaturation on the molecular weights of proteins—the more so inasmuch as the accepted values for the molecular weights of native proteins have since undergone gradual revision. In summary it may be said that urea (usually 6.66 M but in some instances 4, 6 or 8 M) causes no change in the molecular weight of egg albumin,[138–140] horse and bovine serum albumin,[66,68,141] serum globulin,[134,142] and sheep and dog hemoglobin or globin,[143] and does not change the average molecular weight of the heterogeneous prolamines, gliadin[144] and zein,[145] nor the sedimentation

(135) H. B. Bull, J. Am. Chem. Soc. **68**, 745 (1946).

(136) D. R. Briggs and R. Hull, J. Am. Chem. Soc. **67**, 2007 (1945).

(137) C. F. C. MacPherson, M. Heidelberger, and D. H. Moore, J. Am. Chem. Soc. **67**, 578 (1945).

(138) W. T. Astbury and R. Lomax, J. Chem. Soc. **1935**, 846.

(139) T. Huang and H. Wu, Chinese J. Physiol. **4**, 221 (1930).

(140) A. Rothen, Ann. N. Y. Acad. Sci. **43**, 229 (1942).

(141) N. F. Burk, J. Biol. Chem. **98**, 353 (1932).

(142) N. F. Burk, J. Biol. Chem. **121**, 373 (1937).

(143) H. Wu and E. F. Yang, Chinese J. Physiol. **1**, 277 (1927).

(144) N. F. Burk, J. Biol. Chem. **124**, 49 (1938).

(145) C. C. Watson, S. Arrhenius, and J. W. Williams, Nature **137**, 322 (1936).

constant of pepsin.[146] On the other hand, the same urea concentration splits myogen[147,148] and horse and beef hemoglobins[139,146] into halves; the plant seed globulins, edestin,[138] excelsin,[149] and amandin,[149] into units approximately one-sixth the native size; cleaves *Limulus* hemocyanin[150] and "myosin"[151] into much smaller units; and degrades tobacco mosaic virus.[152] Hydrochloric acid produces more profound changes than urea, cleaving edestin into even smaller particles[153,154] and splitting off the prosthetic group and denaturing the globin moiety of hemoglobin,[155] but causing aggregation of egg albumin.[137]

These dissociation reactions first suggested the presence of molecular subunits in some proteins. The number of such units should correspond to the minimum number of peptide chains (or some multiple thereof) and to some integral multiple of the minimum molecular weight based on chemical analysis. Insufficient analytical data are available to confirm this viewpoint; however, the agreement is good in the case of hemoglobin, edestin, human serum albumin, and insulin. It is noteworthy that the "reversible dissociation" theory of protein structure cannot apply to all proteins; for serum albumin has not been reported to be split by any denaturant, and in confirmation, apparently has only a single polypeptide chain and a single —SH group per molecule. By contrast, insulin has four peptide chains per molecular weight subunit of 12,000, which is obtained by adjustment of the pH either below 4 or above 7.5. Recently Fredericq and Neurath[156] have calculated from sedimentation and diffusion measurements that insulin may dissociate into units of 6000 but Tietze and Neurath have been unable to confirm these findings (personal communication). Harfenist and Craig[156a] have reported a minimum molecular weight of 6500 as determined by counter current distribution, and Fredericq[156b] has confirmed the existence of sub-molecules of the order of molecular weight 5000–6000 using Bull's mono-layer technique described later in Sec. III-2e. A molecular weight of this magnitude would correspond to a sub-unit containing one each of the A and B

(146) J. Steinhardt, *J. Biol. Chem.* **123**, 543 (1938).

(147) N. Gralén, *Biochem. J.* **33**, 1342 (1939).

(148) H. H. Weber and R. Stöver, *Biochem. Z.* **259**, 269 (1933).

(149) N. F. Burk, *J. Biol. Chem.* **120**, 63 (1937).

(150) N. F. Burk, *J. Biol. Chem.* **133**, 511 (1940).

(151) H. Wu, *Chinese J. Physiol.* **1**, 81 (1927).

(152) W. M. Stanley and M. A. Lauffer, *Science* **89**, 345 (1939).

(153) G. S. Adair and M. E. Adair, *Biochem. J.* **28**, 199 (1934).

(154) K. Bailey, *Biochem. J.* **36**, 140 (1942).

(155) N. Gralén, *Biochem. J.* **33**, 1907 (1939).

(156) E. Fredericq and H. Neurath, *J. Am. Chem. Soc.* **72**, 2684 (1950).

(156a) E. J. Harfenist, and L. C. Craig, *J. Am. Chem. Soc.* **74**, 3087 (1952).

(156b) E. Fredericq, *Biochim. et Biophys. Acta* **9**, 601 (1952).

polypeptide chains described by Sanger (see Chap. 3). Further information on the number of peptide chains in proteins is required before it can be determined how generally these coincide with the sub-units produced by denaturation.[156c]

As seen above, typical denaturation may occur without alteration in molecular weight, and it is not always certain that dissociation or depolymerization as of the hemocyanins is accompanied by denaturation. Aggregation of proteins, however, most commonly occurs as the result of heating and is averted by the presence of denaturants such as the amides or detergents. The aggregation process is difficult to control and is sensitive to environmental factors such as pH, ionic strength, and solvent composition, and also depends on the time and rate of heating but does not give a linear time–dosage response. In other words, aggregation is a secondary phenomenon dependent on the electrokinetic potential of the denatured protein particles. Although heat coagulation of proteins is the most commonly noted denaturation phenomenon, few quantitative studies exist because of the insolubility of the denatured protein. When horse serum albumin is heated, the mean molecular weight of the somewhat polydisperse product varies from two to nine times the original depending on the pH of the solution.[157] Heat denaturation of β-lactoglobulin involves a first stage with an approximately fourfold increase in particle weight without change in electrophoretic mobility, and a second stage recognizable by change in electrophoretic mobility and accompanied by further increase in particle weight.[136] Denaturation of egg albumin by heat, alkali, or acid causes large increases in the particle weight which vary with the conditions and also with the time of standing after denaturation.[137] Most of these products probably are polydisperse and difficult to reproduce. Because of their apparent electrophoretic homogeneity and their high viscosity with corresponding skewness in their diffusion curves, it is difficult to estimate their molecular uniformity.

An interesting exception is the unique case of the Bence-Jones protein

(156c) Weber,[156d] introducing the method of depolarization of the fluorescence of protein conjugates, has obtained evidence suggesting that bovine serum albumin reversibly dissociates into sub-units in acid or alkali but now considers that this phenomenon may be explained by an internal molecular rotation or other effect (personal communication). He also found that egg albumin exhibits an increased relaxation time attributable to aggregation after denaturation by acid, urea, or heat. This result is in accord with the report that egg albumin contains no detectable N-terminal groups (see Chap. 3) and that this protein is not split by urea[138–140] or by spreading on a surface, but that it is aggregated by heat or acid denaturation (see later).

(156d) G. Weber, Biochem. J. 51, 155 (1952).

(157) G. R. Cooper and H. Neurath, J. Phys. Chem. 47, 383 (1943).

found in the urine of some patients with multiple myeloma. Careful heating to 55–60° near the isoelectric point causes complete coagulation of the protein; higher temperatures bring about redispersion but with precipitation on cooling. When either product is brought into solution by dialysis against pH 8.6 buffer, it is found to migrate as a single boundary in electrophoresis. However, the heat-coagulated protein exhibits unchanged ultracentrifugal properties, whereas the product which dissolved at 100° is ultracentrifugally heterogeneous, containing material with both greater and lower sedimentation constants than the original.[34]

c. Molecular Shape and Hydration

There is no doubt that the hydrodynamic properties of soluble proteins change greatly on denaturation. With globular proteins such as serum albumin[66,68,80,158] and globulin,[134] myogen,[147] egg albumin,[159] and β-lactoglobulin[136] various denaturants such as heat, urea, guanidine hydrochloride, and sodium dodecyl sulfate (SDS) all produce a large increase in specific viscosity. There is a corresponding increase in frictional ratio and in streaming birefringence, a decrease in diffusion constant, or a similarly significant change in whatever property is used to estimate the length, shape, or degree of hydration of proteins. However, with initially asymmetric proteins such as (acto-)myosin[76] or tobacco mosaic virus[152] the relative viscosity and double refraction of flow diminish upon denaturation, with a concomitant decrease in sedimentation constant and particle weight. It is probable that the changes in the latter initially asymmetric proteins are due to the fact that they are complex molecules composed of subunits held together by relatively weak forces. In this case the different behavior of these proteins, compared with others just mentioned, would be related to differences in molecular structure rather than molecular shape.[159a] Hemoglobin[155] and hemocyanin[53] are apparently cleaved along the major axis by acids without undergoing further elongation.[20] Some shape changes accompanying protein denaturation have previously been tabulated (Table 2 of Ref. 2), and the myriad experimental details which must be specified—together with the general lack of information about homogeneity—make further compilation unprofitable. The phenomenon is well illustrated by Table III containing data on the diffusion constant of serum albumin

(158) H. Neurath, and A. M. Saum, *J. Biol. Chem.* **128**, 347 (1939).

(159) H. B. Bull, *J. Biol. Chem.* **133**, 39 (1940).

(159a) Urea establishes an equilibrium between globular and fibrous actin, which depends upon urea concentration in the range 0–15%. At higher concentrations urea depolymerizes actin irreversibly in the absence of adenosine triphosphate and related nucleotides.[159b]

(159b) A. J. Szent-Györgyi and R. Joseph, *Arch. Biochem. and Biophys.* **31**, 90 (1951).

in urea solutions taken from the early study of Neurath and Saum.[158] Figure 1 shows the relative viscosity of horse serum albumin in 8 M urea and 8 M guanidine HCl (taken from Neurath, Cooper, and Erickson[66]) together with a dashed curve for 8 per cent SDS (0.28 M) (taken from Neurath and Putnam[80]). The viscosity of serum albumin in 8 M urea has been reinvestigated by several workers using the crystalline bovine albumin but with essentially similar results. Since it has just been noted that there is no change in the molecular weight of serum albumin in 8 M urea, the fall in diffusion constant and rise in intrinsic viscosity must be interpreted in terms of increased molecular asymmetry or hydration or adsorption of solute.

TABLE III

DIFFUSION CONSTANTS AND SHAPE FACTORS OF HORSE SERUM ALBUMIN IN UREA SOLUTIONS[158]

Molecular weight 67,100; $D_0{}^{25} = 8.22 \times 10^{-7}$ cm.^{2} sec.$^{-1}$

Urea	$D' \times 10^7$	D_0/D'	a/b
M	cm.^{2} sec.$^{-1}$		
0	6.85	1.20	4.3
0.5	6.20	1.33	6.1
1.5	6.08	1.35	6.5
3.0	5.69	1.44	8.0
4.5	4.45	1.85	16.5
6.0	4.27	1.93	18.3
6.66	4.15	1.98	19.4

a/b = ratio of the long to the short axis of a prolate ellipsoid of revolution, neglecting hydration.

As discussed by Edsall in Chap. 7, no simple reliable indirect methods exist for determining the shape of proteins, and the direct (electron microscope) method has not yet been satisfactorily applied to most low molecular weight proteins. Accordingly, estimates of the shape of native and denatured proteins are based on the frictional ratio (f/f_0) calculated from sedimentation and diffusion constants or from viscosity. More recently, quantitative measurements have been made on denatured proteins by the theoretically less ambiguous method of flow birefringence, and attempts have been made to apply light-scattering techniques to this problem. The limitations of all these methods have already been considered in a discussion which emphasized that f/f_0 is a composite function of molecular shape and hydration. It was also pointed out that where the particles are sufficiently asymmetric and homogeneous the lengths can be calculated from birefringence data without serious error due to assumptions about axial ratio or degree of solvation or choice of ellipsoidal shape model.

It is now quite generally agreed that the increased frictional resistance of denatured proteins, exhibited as higher viscosity, etc., is due to
greater anisometry which is attributed to an unfolding or uncoiling of
the main polypeptide chains from their specific native configuration.

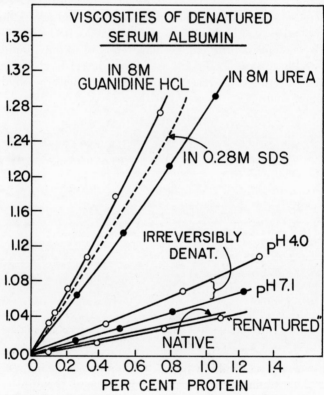

FIG. 1.   Relative viscosities of serum albumin plotted against the protein concentration in weight per cent.   The curves refer to, in order of decreasing slopes, the
denatured serum albumin in 8 M guanidine hydrochloride, in 0.28 M sodium dodecyl
sulfate, and in 8 M urea, the irreversibly denatured protein at pH 4.0 and pH 7.1, the
native serum albumin, and the "reversibly" denatured ("renatured") serum albumin.
(Figure redrawn.)

In the past, some workers interpreted the viscosity increase as resulting from increased hydration or from aggregation; but several of the
original proponents no longer advocate this theory.   However, Doty
and Katz[160,161] have concluded that "the principal change undergone by
the serum albumin molecule in concentrated urea solutions is that of

(160) P. Doty and S. Katz, *cited by* P. Doty and J. T. Edsall, *Advances in Protein
        Chem.* **6,** 35 (1951).
(161) S. Katz, Ph. D. Thesis, Harvard University, 1950.

approximately isotropic swelling." It is clear from the preceding section that denaturation may often occur without change in molecular weight and thus that aggregation cannot be a general explanation of the changes in physical properties on denaturation. Moreover, the character of the protein determines the alteration so that hemoglobins and hemocyanins may be cleaved lengthwise whereas anisometric molecules such as myosin and tobacco mosaic virus are dissociated into small heterogeneous units, but the majority of globular proteins undergo a viscosity increase.

Despite the challenging concept offered by Doty and Katz, a large number of arguments can be marshaled to support the view that denaturation of globular proteins is accompanied by an increase in asymmetry rather than just by greater hydration, or solvation:

(1) To account for the increase in intrinsic viscosity of serum albumin solely in terms of adsorption of urea, 4.2 g. urea per gram protein or about 5000 molecules of urea per molecule of protein would have to be bound in 8 M urea. Klotz et al.[87] have reported that the binding constant of this protein for urea, as measured by the displacement of methyl orange, is the smallest yet observed. However, Doty and Katz,[160,161] from light-scattering measurements of serum albumin in 8 M urea, report that 2000 molecules of urea were *preferentially* bound at pH 8, that about 3000 molecules of water were preferentially bound at pH 3, and that neither water nor urea was preferentially adsorbed at the isoelectric point. This is important as the first proof that large quantities of urea are bound to proteins. However, no explanation of the pH difference is offered nor of the fact that irreversibly denatured serum albumin obtained after the removal of all dialyzable urea has a significantly higher viscosity than the native or the soluble regenerated protein. Moreover, the binding of such large amounts of urea by proteins is at variance with conclusions based on the analysis of the kinetics of urea denaturation. For example, Deutsch[161a] has reported that only four molecules of urea are bound per molecule of catalase when the enzyme is inactivated, and other workers have given evidence that even fewer urea molecules are bound in the denaturation of other proteins.

(2) Similarly for the effects of detergents on proteins, it can be calculated that insufficient detergent ions are bound by the protein to account for the viscosity increase in buffered solutions. In this instance it is known that most of the detergent is combined with the protein up to an albumin/SDS weight ratio of about one.[43] The dissymmetry ratio of light scattering of this complex is greatly diminished by the presence of salt but reaches a value of 1.5 to 1.6 in the absence of salt.[84a] This suggests that an even greater uncoiling of the protein molecule may occur than was indicated by the viscosity measurements in buffered solutions.

(161a) H. F. Deutsch, *Acta Chem. Scand.* **5**, 1074 (1951).

(3) The viscosity increase of proteins in concentrated detergent solutions is accompanied by the development of positive flow birefringence indicative of rod-shaped particles and by visible fiber formation upon extrusion into coagulating solutions.[162,163] Proteins denatured by urea likewise may be spun into fibers as was shown by Astbury, Dickinson, and Bailey[164] who first described the conversion of corpuscular proteins to a fibrous form.

(4) Spreading on a surface produces a monomolecular film with a thickness of about 9.5 A. corresponding to the side-chain spacing observed in x-ray diffraction studies of fibrous proteins with the β-keratin structure and of proteins denatured by heat, urea, and detergents.[165]

(5) Streaming birefringence measurements of egg albumin denatured in acid media[166] and of heat-denatured horse serum albumin[167] have shown large increases in apparent particle length. Fredericq[166] has attributed the increased birefringence to unfolding of the protein molecules with some aggregation, whereas Joly and Barbu[167] concluded that the effect was largely due to aggregation. Foster and Samsa[168,169,169a] investigated the polydispersity of urea- and heat-denatured ovalbumin by study of the dependence of the calculated length and the apparent intrinsic birefringence on the velocity gradient. They concluded that *both* unfolding and aggregation of the molecules occur except at pH values far removed from the isoelectric point. However, under certain conditions of heat or urea denaturation at extreme pH the particles were nearly homogeneous in molecular length, the values always lying in the range 500–700 A. This suggests that intramolecular unfolding is the essential feature of denaturation, and that aggregation is a secondary effect.

(6) There is a loss of hydrophilic properties on denaturation which is incompatible with the concept of increased hydration. The solubility of proteins is lower in the denatured state than in the native. The density of native and heat- and surface-coagulated proteins is the same when measured with hydrogen, but the coagulated proteins are more dense when xylene is used as a displacing agent.[21] Volume-contraction measurements show that water is liberated on heat denaturation.[170]

(162) H. P. Lundgren, *J. Am. Chem. Soc.* **63**, 2854 (1941).
(163) H. P. Lundgren, *Advances in Protein Chem.* **5**, 305 (1949).
(164) W. T. Astbury, S. Dickinson, and K. Bailey, *Biochem. J.* **29**, 2351 (1935).
(165) W. T. Astbury, *Advances in Enzymol.* **3**, 63 (1943).
(166) E. Fredericq, *Bull. soc. chim. Belges* **56**, 223 (1947).
(167) M. Joly and E. Barbu, *Bull. soc. chim. biol.* **31**, 1642 (1949).
(168) J. F. Foster and E. G. Samsa, *J. Am. Chem. Soc.* **73**, 3187 (1951).
(169) E. G. Samsa and J. F. Foster, *J. Am. Chem. Soc.* **73**, 3190 (1951).
(169a) J. F. Foster and E. G. Samsa, *J. Am. Chem. Soc.* **73**, 5388 (1951).
(170) E. Heymann, *Biochem. J.* **30**, 126 (1936).

(7) Increased hydration, the binding of more solvent molecules by protein, is an association reaction which should lead to a decrease in entropy. Actually, large increases in entropy are found in the denaturation of proteins, and these can best be interpreted in terms of a more random molecular structure. Indeed, the binding of the first few SDS ions by serum albumin is accompanied by an entropy increase of 24 cal./mole/degree, though denaturation is assumed not to occur. The positive entropy for this reaction can be explained only by the *release* of fixed water molecules from the protein.[171]

(8) Organic solvents such as alcohol and acetone which are denaturing agents are also dehydrating agents. It might be expected that these substances as well as concentrated amides might compete with the protein for solvent molecules.

It should be emphasized that the unfolding or elongation of the protein molecule suffered on denaturation is moderate since it only corresponds to a maximum increase in axial ratio of four- to fivefold for serum albumin in concentrated amides or in detergents. Axial ratios corresponding to formation of a completely unfolded, rigid, single polypeptide chain are never obtained. However, the polypeptide chain is flexible; most proteins contain a number of chains probably in a layer structure. The peptide chains are cross-linked and may be internally linked both by stable disulfide bonds which are liberated but not split by denaturation and by labile hydrogen bonds. In the helical configuration theory of protein structure, Pauling and Corey[25] have assigned the "pleated-sheet" structure to β-keratin and to denatured proteins and the "α-helix" to native globular proteins. The conversion of the α-structure to the pleated sheet corresponds to an extension of only about 117 per cent. It is not necessary for all of the hydrogen bonds to be broken for the conversion to occur.

It should be noted that any postulated *isotropic* swelling which accounts for the changed hydrodynamic properties of the denatured protein without admitting increase in axial ratio must be accompanied by an elongation of the protein molecule about equivalent to that calculated assuming no change in hydration. Thus, the question is not whether elongation and unfolding occur, but whether in addition hydration is increased.

d. Electrochemical Properties

Despite the widespread adoption of the Tiselius electrophoresis apparatus, there has been little new investigation of the effect of denaturation on the electrochemical properties of proteins. The reason is

(171) I. M. Klotz, *Cold Spring Harbor Symposia Quant. Biol.* **14**, 97 (1950).

threefold: (1) Denatured proteins are less soluble and are often coagulated at the isoelectric point; (2) concentrated denaturing agents such as urea or sodium salicylate which keep protein in solution are unsuitable for electrophoretic investigation because of the risk of thermal convection and anomalous effects; (3) in general, only small changes in electrochemical properties are observed despite the liberation of significant numbers of reactive groups or large alterations in molecular kinetic properties. The types of investigation which have proved most suitable are study of the irreversible segments of titration curves; electrophoretic analysis of dialyzed, soluble, reversibly denatured proteins; and electrophoretic analysis of detergent–protein interaction. In addition there is one electrophoretic study of the kinetics of heat denaturation.

(1) Titration Curves. Historically, the first measurements of the effect of denaturation on the amphoteric properties of proteins consisted of comparison of the titration curves before and after treatment with acid, alkali, and heat. The insolubility of the denatured proteins often necessitated heterogeneous titration, and in any event maximum acid- and base-binding capacity can be measured only at extreme acidity or alkalinity where irreversible changes may occur.[172] The results do not merit detailed analysis because of the contradiction in the literature even regarding the portion of the titration curve which lies in the pH-stability region, and secondly because the curves for native proteins are sometimes inconsistent with results of more recent investigation. Suffice it to say that the changes in amphoteric properties which occur on denaturation are of a small order of magnitude. This poses the dilemma already noted in discussion of the liberation of reactive groups: namely, there are basic groups in β-lactoglobulin which are freely and reversibly titratable but which do not react with certain reagents prior to denaturation. With this exception, however, the masked groups so far uncovered are of a type which are never titratable under ordinary conditions.

The titration curve of hemoglobin serves as a good example. The considerable and discordant literature on the variation of this curve with denaturation has been resolved by the recent careful analysis of Steinhardt and Zaiser.[113] As shown in Fig. 2, these workers unearthed a unique effect of rapid liberation of acid-binding groups on exposure to dilute acid. How common this phenomenon is remains to be determined. Significant changes in the titration curves but not in the acid- and base-binding capacity of heat denatured collagen have also been observed.[173]

(2) Isoelectric Point and Electric Mobility. The small change in amphoteric properties of proteins produced by denaturation is generally

(172) R. K. Cannan, *Chem. Revs.* **30**, 395 (1942).
(173) E. R. Theis and T. F. Jacoby, *J. Biol. Chem.* **148**, 105 (1943).

revealed as a slight alkaline shift in the isoelectric point and pH-mobility curves. This is illustrated by the data of Moyer[174] who showed that the isoelectric point of surface-denatured egg albumin is pH 5.02 instead of pH 4.55 as in the native state. The mobility of egg albumin in the

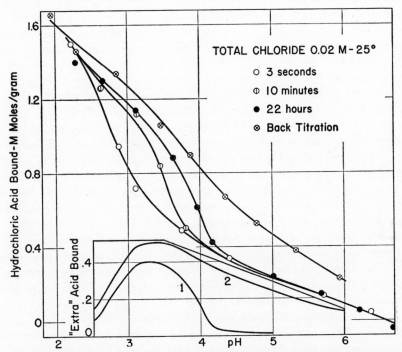

FIG. 2. The amounts of hydrochloric acid combined with twice recrystallized COHb (0.04 per cent) in solutions of constant chloride concentration as a function of pH and time. The two curves in the inset are obtained by difference: Curve 1, by subtracting the 3-second data from the 24-hour data; Curve 2, by subtracting the 3-second data from the back-titration data. (Taken from Steinhardt and Zaiser.[113])

range pH 6.8–10.3 is also only slightly lowered by heat and acid denaturation.[137,175] It is noteworthy that a pH increase is observed on surface, heat, and urea denaturation of this protein.[21]

The mobility curve of acid-denatured thyroglobulin is also transposed about 0.4 pH unit toward the alkaline side at the isoelectric point.[176] Similar results were obtained for heat-denatured serum albumin; the

(174) L. S. Moyer, *J. Phys. Chem.* **42**, 71 (1938).
(175) L. G. Longsworth, *Ann. N. Y. Acad. Sci.* **41**, 267 (1941).
(176) M. Heidelberger and K. O. Pedersen, *J. Gen. Physiol.* **19**, 95 (1936).

mobility curve remained parallel to that for native protein, but the isoelectric point was raised from pH 4.88 to pH 5.1–5.3.[177] The early results on the alkaline mobility shift of heated serum albumin were obtained by the microelectrophoretic method, but have been confirmed in the Tiselius apparatus by Cooper and Neurath.[157] However, the latter workers found that ionic strength and time of heating altered the electrophoretic patterns. This effect has perhaps discouraged more frequent electrophoretic study of the pH-mobility curves of denatured proteins. The isoelectric point of heat-denatured collagen is also shifted toward the alkaline side.[173]

In agreement with results for heat-treated horse serum albumin, the mobility at pH 7.6 of bovine serum albumin irreversibly denatured with 8 M guanidine HCl is less than that of the native protein.[178] However, bovine serum albumin regenerated from the same agent has a mobility identical to that of native protein, and regeneration of urea- or detergent-treated horse serum albumin[83,179] or of urea-treated bovine serum albumin leads to an increase in mobility at pH 7.6. On the other hand, urea-regenerated horse serum pseudoglobulin has a lower mobility on the alkaline side of the isoelectric point.[180]

The available evidence suggests that the changes in amphoteric properties of denatured proteins result from the liberation of paired acidic and basic groups upon the rupture of structure-determining hydrogen or electrostatic bonds. In consequence of the assumed freeing of equal numbers of amino and carboxyl groups, the Mirsky and Pauling theory[24] predicts that the isoelectric point of the denatured protein should be shifted toward neutrality. This is in accord with fact. The rearrangement in molecular configuration allows for a spatial redistribution of polar groups and reformation of some salt linkages and hydrogen bonds. It is unnecessary that new titratable groups be liberated and that the acid- and base-binding capacity increase, for the pK's of dissociable groups may alter owing to steric and interaction effects.

(3) *Electrophoretic Homogeneity.* It is always surprising that such small changes in electrophoretic homogeneity occur as the result of denaturation as compared to the striking changes in molecular homogeneity that may develop concomitantly. The case of the Bence-Jones proteins already mentioned upholds this point. Indeed, protein mixtures often undergo an increase in electrophoretic homogeneity owing to com-

(177) K. O. Pedersen, *Nature* **128,** 150 (1931).
(178) F. W. Putnam and H. Neurath, *J. Biol. Chem.* **160,** 239 (1945).
(179) D. G. Sharp, G. R. Cooper, J. O. Erickson, and H. Neurath, *J. Biol. Chem.* **144,** 139 (1942).
(180) D. G. Sharp, G. R. Cooper, and H. Neurath, *J. Biol. Chem.* **142,** 203 (1942).

plex formation on heating. Thus, the heating of serum at 65°[181] and ultraviolet irradiation[182] both cause the progressive formation of a denatured electrophoretic component at the expense of the albumin and globulins, but the effects of heat on the electrophoretic pattern of bovine serum can be repressed by prior saturation with glucose.[102]

All the regenerated proteins described in the above section approach the native protein in electrophoretic homogeneity, and so do serum albumin and β-lactoglobulin irreversibly denatured in guanidine HCl. However, heating of serum albumin produces two components, the proportion of which depends on pH and ionic strength.[157] Heat denaturation of β-lactoglobulin brings about two processes recognizable by the difference in electrophoretic mobility and particle weight of the products. In a unique investigation, Briggs and Hull[136] were able to determine the kinetic and thermodynamic constants of the two reactions by means of electrophoretic analysis. Heat- and acid-denatured egg albumin are unchanged in electrical homogeneity from pH 6.8 to 10.3, but alkali gives rise to two components.[175] The change in electrophoretic pattern on aging of egg albumin, however, is attributable to enzymatic action (for summary see Fevold[122]). Electrophoretic studies of the interaction of proteins with detergents are described elsewhere[43,183] and in Chap. 8. The formation of a new electrophoretic component of intermediate mobility also occurs when serum is exposed to acetic acid at pH 3.[184]   In this case the phenomenon appears due to the splitting of lipide–protein linkages and subsequent complex formation of albumin and globulins.

e. Internal Structure

(1) X-Ray Diffraction Studies of Fibrous and Denatured Proteins. The clearest direct evidence that the primary effect of denaturation is an intramolecular rearrangement of protein structure is furnished by x-ray diffraction measurements. The changes in chemical and physical properties just discussed concern primarily the soluble globular proteins. While certain generalities could be made, for example about the types of groups liberated, increasing asymmetry, etc., the details must be specified for each protein and type of denaturation. However, wherever investigated, all denatured globular proteins have, on orientation, produced a single type x-ray diffraction pattern. This photograph, called the β-keratin type, is almost identical with that obtained from stretched

(181) J. van der Scheer, R. W. G. Wyckoff, and F. L. Clarke, J. Immunol. 40, 39 (1941).
(182) B. D. Davis, A. Hollaender, and J. P. Greenstein, J. Biol. Chem. 146, 663 (1942).
(183) F. W. Putnam and H. Neurath, J. Biol. Chem. 159, 195 (1945).
(184) G. E. Perlmann and D. Kaufman, J. Biol. Chem. 179, 133 (1949).

fibrous proteins of the keratin–myosin group. Thus, though crystalline globular proteins such as β-lactoglobulin, insulin, etc., in the undenatured state give sharp, highly detailed, and characteristic x-ray diffraction patterns with hundreds of clearly resolvable spots, denaturation with the formation of oriented fibers produces the β-pattern. This is evidence that all proteins are structurally related, for the fully denatured state is a fibrous state.

The β-keratin pattern has already been described and interpreted (Chap. 4). Astbury[138,164,165,185] first recognized the alteration in diffraction pattern in the transition from unstretched keratin or myosin to the stretched fiber and called the normal form the α-configuration and the stretched form the β-configuration. While numerous structures have been proposed and discarded for the two patterns, there is general agreement that the β-configuration represents elongation of a coiled polypeptide chain and that the α-form is somehow folded or coiled into about half the length of the β-chain.[25,186,187] Thus the theoretical "repeat distance" or length per residue in a fully extended polypeptide chain is 3.63 A.[188] The maximum distance observed in proteins is 3.5 A.

TABLE IV

X-Ray Diffraction Spacings of Some Native and Denatured Proteins

Protein	Denaturing agent	Side-chain spacing A.	Backbone spacing A.	Diagonal spacing A.	Reference
Egg albumin	Native	10.65	4.75		192
	Heat	10.2	4.75	3.67	192
	Heat	10.2	4.66	3.75	189
	Heat	9.8	4.65	3.75	190
	Heat	9.8	4.65	3.75	191
	Alkyl benzenesulfonate	10.3	4.65	3.76	189
Serum albumin	Native	9.7	4.6		148
	Heat	9.6	4.5	3.6	148
Lactoglobulin	Heat	9.7	4.68	3.72	191
Edestin	Urea	10.0	4.5	3.7	164
β-Keratin		9.8	4.65	3.75	148

(185) W. T. Astbury, *Trans. Faraday Soc.* **29**, 193 (1933).

(186) M. L. Huggins, *Chem. Revs.* **32**, 195 (1943).

(187) H. Neurath, *J. Phys. Chem.* **44**, 296 (1940).

(188) R. B. Corey, *Advances in Protein Chem.* **4**, 385 (1948).

(189) K. J. Palmer and J. A. Galvin, *J. Am. Chem. Soc.* **65**, 2187 (1943).

(190) F. R. Senti, C. R. Eddy, and G. C. Nutting, *J. Am. Chem. Soc.* **65**, 2473 (1943).

(191) F. R. Senti, M. J. Copley, and G. C. Nutting, *J. Phys. Chem.* **49**, 192 (1945).

(192) W. T. Astbury and F. Bell, *Tabulae Biol.* (*Haag*) **17**, 90 (1939) (through Ref. 2).

This value is found in silk fibroin (which undergoes little reversible stretching and is believed to be a nearly fully extended polypeptide chain). For maximally elongated hair keratin, the residue distance is about 3.3 A., and the same fiber repeat reflection is prominent in well-oriented denatured proteins. Some selected results on the x-ray diffraction spacings of native and denatured proteins are given in Table IV.

(2) *Surface-Film Measurements.* The status and significance of surface-film measurements on proteins have been reviewed by Neurath and Bull,[40] by Bateman,[193] by Bull,[194] and by Rothen.[195] The decline in effort in this field has been marked in past years. As a result the method, while demonstrating the unfolding of spread proteins, has not recently contributed much that is new to the understanding of the nature of the folding in native proteins. However, there exists a substantial body of information about spread and deposited protein films which any theory of protein structure must be able to interpret before it can be called a success. Neurath and Bull[40] concluded that under the influence of surface forces protein molecules unfold when spread on water, and under suitable conditions form a monolayer of fully extended polypeptide chains of the β-configuration. In the compressed state the side chains are oriented vertically to the surface with hydrophobic residues on the air side and hydrophilic in the water. However, Bull[194] now doubts the formerly expressed view that at low film pressures the side chains lie flat on the surface. It is to be noted that mere spreading does not denote unfolding of a protein and that determination of the film thickness is the only criterion.[195]

It is a striking phenomenon that complex soluble protein molecules become insoluble when spread on a surface and form films that have a thickness of about 9.5 A., corresponding to that of a fully expanded polypeptide chain. The structure of the films is thus fibrous and similar to that of compressed keratin in which the side chains are oriented. It is only natural that the predominantly hydrophilic-hydrophobic alignment of the films as well as their monolayer nature has led to suggestions of a layer structure for native globular proteins.[196] Such theories demand a nearly equal partition between polar and nonpolar amino acids and a corresponding alternation of such residues to provide a cleavage plane within the protein. Insulin forms a monolayer[197] and is

(193) J. B. Bateman, *in* Höber, Physical Chemistry of Cells and Tissues, Blakiston Co., Philadelphia, Pa., 1945.
(194) H. B. Bull, *Advances in Protein Chem.* **3**, 95 (1947).
(195) A. Rothen, *Advances in Protein Chem.* **3**, 123 (1947).
(196) H. B. Bull, *J. Am. Chem. Soc.* **67**, 8 (1945).
(197) H. A. Dieu and H. B. Bull, *J. Am. Chem. Soc.* **71**, 450 (1949).

the sole example for which extensive sequential analysis has been performed.   There is no obvious type of periodicity in either the A chain or the B chain of insulin (see Chap. 3).

The monolayer technique for the determination of molecular weights is simple and rapid and is suggested as the method of preference for proteins under 25,000 molecular weight and for polypeptides.   Film molecular weights of proteins may be calculated from the intercept of the force–area versus force curves to determine the effect due to spreading as a monolayer.[197a]   However, under certain conditions the plots are not linear, making the extrapolation ambiguous.   In explanation it has been suggested that protein molecules can exist on a surface in a compact form and in an expanded state, and probably also in intermediate expanded states.   The film molecular weights of egg albumin and bovine serum albumin agree with those observed in solution, but pepsin, chymotrypsinogen, chymotrypsin, and rabbit γ-globulin appeared to be associated under some conditions of spreading.   Previous experiments had suggested that both β-lactoglobulin and insulin may dissociate in monolayers as they do in urea and acid solution, respectively, but that the molecular dissociation was repressed by the presence of cupric ion.[135,197,198]

The biological activity of films of proteins has become a subject of controversy with regard to the possible operation of long-range forces.[195]   However, there is no doubt that true monolayers of proteins can still combine specifically with antibodies and that monolayers of antibodies are capable of specific fixation of the corresponding antigens.[199]   Monolayers of certain of the pituitary hormones are nearly inactive, but insulin retains full activity and the evidence argues against a reversible inactivation process.[200]   Trypsin and urease become inactive on spreading, but work with other enzymes has been criticized on the grounds that a true monolayer and thus unfolding was not realized.[195]   The significance of the persistence of activity of the immunological properties of antibodies and antigens after spreading and transfer to slides will be discussed later (sec. III-3).

f. Optical Properties

In addition to flow birefringence and light scattering, which measure the size and shape of denatured proteins, optical properties such as the rotation of polarized light or absorption spectra which are influenced by structural changes may be studied.   For the most part these have been

(197a) H. B. Bull, *J. Biol. Chem.* **185,** 27 (1950).
(198) H. B. Bull, *J. Am. Chem. Soc.* **67,** 4 (1945).
(199) A. Rothen and K. Landsteiner, *J. Exptl. Med.* **76,** 437 (1942).
(200) A. Rothen, B. Chow, R. O. Greep, and H. B. van Dyke, *Cold Spring Harbor Symposia Quant. Biol.* **9,** 272 (1941).

surprisingly neglected.   The spectroscopic method used by Crammer and
Neuberger[133] to follow the liberation of phenolic groups represents the
first important example of such application.   The method might be
applicable to the study of other aromatic amino acids.   Recently, Goldfarb[201] reported a large generalized increase in ultraviolet light absorption
spectra down to 205 mμ as the result of heat denaturation of serum albumin under special conditions.   The spectra at 205 mμ are correlated with
peptide structure, and if it can be shown that light scattering can be
neglected, this method may prove useful in the study of denaturation.
Barron[59] has also begun investigation of the change in absorption spectra
of proteins denatured in various ways.   Infrared absorption studies are
restricted by the requirements for specimen preparation.

Only recently has change in optical rotation been introduced as a
method for measuring the rate of protein denaturation.   Like viscosity it
can be used in the presence of a denaturant such as urea, but has the
advantages of greater rapidity and simplicity.   The optical rotation
depends on interactions which extend over only relatively short distances
and are therefore sensitive to local changes at the asymmetric centers.[71a]
Since no clear relationship between optical rotation and protein structure
is known, a change in rotation signifies an alteration in structure without
revealing its nature.   Christensen[95] found that there is a rapid increase
in optical rotation when β-lactoglobulin is denatured by urea or by alkali
at pH 9.3 and also when the native but not the urea-denatured protein is
attacked by trypsin.   The specific rotations of lactoglobulin denatured
by pH, heat, dodecyl sulfate, urea, and guanidine hydrochloride differ
when measured under the same conditions, being respectively −72.9,
−79.7, −59.6, −107, and −114.   The increase in guanidine hydrochloride is instantaneous but is slow in urea.   The difference in values
obtained is noteworthy but unexplained.   Kauzmann et al.[71a] used this
rapid method in a comparative study of the kinetics of urea denaturation of several proteins.   With serum albumin the entire increase in
levorotation occurred immediately, but the change with egg albumin was
gradual.   Since one might expect optical rotation to be a sensitive
measure of changes in molecular configuration, further study of this
convenient method is indicated.

3. BIOLOGICAL PROPERTIES

a. Inactivation of Enzymes, Hormones, Viruses, Etc.

Though a loss of specific biological properties is regarded as a criterion
of denaturation and in many instances closely accompanies other char-

(201) A. R. Goldfarb, Science 114, 177 (1951).

acteristic effects, it is by no means a necessary phenomenon.   A number
of exceptions may be noted: for example, the retention of insulin activity
despite urea denaturation or spreading as a monomolecular film; the lack
of inactivation of some proteolytic enzymes, urease and saccharase, on
spreading as a monolayer; the stability of proteolytic enzymes such as
trypsin, papain, and pepsin in urea; and the heat resistance of ovomucoid,
ribonuclease, and lysozyme.   Indeed, the latter enzymes are hardly
affected by boiling in dilute acid.

b. Immunological Properties

Immunological activity is a characteristic in varying degree of all
proteins and has the two parameters of antigenicity and specificity.   It
has been known for half a century that denaturation diminishes the
antigenicity of some proteins, and it was long considered that denaturation also alters specificity.   This was the basis of one avenue of search
for plasma substitutes.   Chemical degradation due to the attack of acid
and alkali, insolubility, complex formation, and aggregation resulting from
heat, and toxicity associated with the detergents led to the choice of
amides for this type of investigation.   After treatment of serum albumin
with concentrated urea or guanidine hydrochloride followed by removal
of the amide by dialysis, a soluble "regenerated" product of the original
molecular weight is obtained.   The regenerated protein retains the
immunological specificity of the native protein but has a greatly reduced
capacity to incite antibody formation.[73,74]   Although these experiments
with purified proteins demonstrated that no new specificity arose as a
result of denaturation and revealed a contribution of the intact native
structure to the antigenic complement of the serum albumins, further
work with native and with irreversibly denatured antipneumococcal
horse serum antibody (type I) and with the normal globulin showed that
denaturation with guanidine hydrochloride provoked no significant differences in the antigenic activity of these proteins when injected into rabbits.[75]   This was interpreted to mean that the specific configuration of
this protein does not determine serological activity.

In addition to the finding that the irreversibly denatured antibody was
antigenically active, Erickson and Neurath showed that both the soluble
and insoluble (regenerated and irreversibly denatured) fractions remained
precipitable by the specific polysaccharide.   Although the extent of type
I specific precipitation differed, this was attributable to a change in molecular weight or other properties.   Somewhat similar results have been
reported by Campbell and Cushing[202] for urea-treated rabbit antiovalbu-

(202) D. H. Campbell and J. E. Cushing, Jr., *Science* **102**, 564 (1945).

min. Wright[203] has shown that the activity of diphtheria antitoxin is reduced by denaturation with 7.5 M urea despite the earlier report of Pappenheimer, Lundgren, and Williams[204] that urea (about 3 M) is without effect on the antitoxin property.

Egg albumin denatured incident to extensive deamination showed a specificity different from that of the native protein, but partial deamination without denaturation did not affect serological specificity.[204a]

The uncertainty about the effects of denaturation on the serological properties of proteins prompted MacPherson and Heidelberger[205] to undertake a careful investigation of egg albumin denatured in various ways and characterized by physical criteria of homogeneity and molecular weight. It was found that egg albumin denatured by acid, alkali, or heating exhibited remarkably uniform serological behavior and appeared to be identical in the region of antibody excess. Alkali-denatured egg albumin showed serological properties dependent on the degree of degradation, and if severely degraded gave practically no reaction toward antiserum prepared with the native protein. This explains various statements in the literature about the effect of alkali on the serological properties of proteins. In general, ten times as much denatured egg albumin as the homologous native protein was required to give comparable precipitation in the precipitin test. This was considered to be a reflection of a change in immunological specificity and to be a more sensitive measure of such a change than the study of serological reactions in films which reported equivalent reactions for films of native and denatured egg albumin.[199]

The alteration in the immunological properties of purified proteins is in a different category from the effects observed on heating or irradiating antigen or antibody in the presence of nonspecific protein. In such cases, as Bawden and Kleczkowski[206] have shown, the variation in immunological properties can be attributed to complex formation and is partly dependent on the nature of the antigen or antibody so treated. Irradiation or heating of sera produces physicochemical changes indicative of complex formation as well as changes in typical antibody reactions.

If denaturation with amides produces only small changes in the immunological properties of *antibodies* and alters *antigenic activity* to a variable degree, it might be expected that surface denaturation producing

(203) G. G. Wright, *J. Exptl. Med.* **79**, 455 (1944).
(204) A. M. Pappenheimer, Jr., H. P. Lundgren, and J. W. Williams, *J. Exptl. Med.* **71**, 247 (1940).
(204a) P. H. Maurer and M. Heidelberger, *J. Am. Chem. Soc.* **73**, 2076 (1951).
(205) C. F. C. MacPherson and M. Heidelberger, *J. Am. Chem. Soc.* **67**, 585 (1945).
(206) F. C. Bawden and A. Kleczkowski, *Brit. J. Exptl. Pathol.* **22**, 192 (1941); *ibid.* **23**, 178 (1942).

a monomolecular film of about 10 A. thick might have a more profound effect—if serological properties depend on the native protein configuration. Although the first experiments are to be criticized on the ground that true monomolecular films were not formed, Rothen[195] did produce monolayers of about 10 A. thickness. Rothen and Landsteiner[199] first reported the ability of a monolayer of egg albumin to combine with the specific antiserum, and subsequently Rothen[195] has made numerous studies demonstrating antigen–antibody combination in surface films or transferred monolayers for various proteins. Thus, Neurath and associates have concluded that serological activity appears to be largely independent of native protein structure and to reside in structures which are among the last to be affected by denaturation.[73,74] This interpretation has been criticized by proponents of Pauling's theory of antibody formation.

IV. Kinetics and Thermodynamics of Protein Denaturation

1. KINETICS

The kinetics of protein denaturation and biological inactivation are marked by certain features sufficiently distinct and characteristic to serve as criteria of denaturation. In the general case, denaturation is characterized by an extremely high temperature coefficient and by a correspondingly large energy of activation "which cannot be accounted for by any known process for the redistribution of energy between molecules in gases or in solutions."[23] Yet denaturation and enzyme inactivation are often stated to be regularly first order with regard to protein concentration.[22,207] Now denaturation is a reaction unique to proteins and hence must be related to their typical structure. Accordingly, one school[22,207,208] has pictured the process of denaturation as the simultaneous breaking of many weak bonds leading to loss of a specifically restricted structure and thus to greater randomness. As Eyring and Stearn[22] have remarked: "The fact of finite rates coupled with large heats of activation necessarily implies a large increase of entropy of activation." However, it has already been pointed out that the reaction-rate constant is not only a function of temperature and pressure but also of pH. The extraordinary pH dependence of some types of protein denaturation is not due to an acid–base type catalytic effect but results from a preliminary ionization process in the transition to the activated state. Temperature affects the ionization and thus the activity of the ionized species. Accordingly, the customary method of calculating the activation energy by comparison of the velocity at two different tem-

(207) A. E. Stearn, Advances in Enzymol. 9, 25 (1949).
(208) A. E. Stearn, Ergeb. Enzymforsch. 7, 1 (1938).

peratures but at the same pH is incorrect insofar as temperature influences the concentration of the reactive ionic species.   Steinhardt[23] and La Mer[209] first pointed out that this method of calculation leads to erroneous values of the energy of activation unless the heat of dissociation of all the ionization steps in preparing the activated complex is subtracted.

a. Order of the Reaction

It is of importance to establish the order of reaction for protein denaturation for two reasons.   First, the a priori acceptance of a first-order law has led to or perhaps been based on the assumption of a unimolecular process of denaturation; that is to say, it is assumed that each act of decomposition involves only one protein molecule as would be expected if denaturation produced an intramolecular change in the specific configuration.   Secondly, the computation of the thermodynamic functions such as the free energy and entropy of activation has, for convenience, been based on first-order constants, whether real or simulated. If in many cases the reaction kinetics can be proven to be unsteady and the order indeterminate, the values calculated from first-order "constants" will lose significance.

Although denaturation has generally been regarded to be first order with regard to protein concentration, and thus a unimolecular process, numerous discrepancies exist in the literature.   The kinetics of denaturations and inactivations studied up to a recent date have been reviewed,[2] and it was found that deviations from first order were reported in about one-third of the cases.   Critical analysis shows that up to the last decade there were few kinetic studies with highly purified proteins or by adequate experimental methods.   It is now well known that the presence of impurities may affect even the order of the reaction, and it must be realized that the experimental quantity measured may be a property of one of the numerous secondary reactions attending protein denaturation. For example, measurements based on turbidity or the amount of soluble or insoluble protein remaining involve the tacit assumption that flocculation is not the rate-limiting step.   In these cases the salt concentration may be critical.   Where biological activity or function is examined, the possible reversal of inactivation must be taken into account.   It should be unnecessary to reiterate that denaturation consists of a series of concomitant or consecutive changes, any one of which may be used to determine the velocity.   Enzyme inactivation and the abolition of activity of viruses, toxins, and protein hormones is classified as denaturation not only because of the usually demonstrable change in physical properties and structure but also because of the characteristically high temperature

(209) V. K. La Mer, Science 86, 614 (1937).

coefficients and critical increments. While first-order kinetics are often
followed in the denaturation of proteins by acid, alkali, heat, alcohol, and
urea, it is to be noted that surface denaturation appears to be zero
order.[210] The complications of the kinetics of photochemical inactivation have been considered by McLaren[211] who concludes that the loss of
identity of the native material is characterized by (pseudo) first-order
kinetics. The presence of two stages in thermal and surface denaturation is, of course, well known. The first of these is the initial denaturation conforming to criteria already described; the second is flocculation
of the insoluble protein.[51]

A number of more recent kinetic studies may be mentioned. In two
important investigations of reversible denaturation it was found that both
the forward and the reverse reaction obey the first-order law, i.e., the
reversible heat denaturation of crystalline soybean trypsin inhibitor
protein (Kunitz[212]) and of chymotrypsinogen (Eisenberg and Schwert[213]).
However, the irreversible denaturation of the soybean protein was close
to second order. The increase in levorotation of ovalbumin in urea does
not follow a simple first-order law.[7a] The thermal destruction of bacterial luminescence is first order,[49] and so is the denaturation of ricin.[27]
The urea inactivation of influenza A virus is first order,[214] but the thermal
destruction of the hemagglutinin activity of this virus seems to follow
the course of a reaction of the three-halves order.[215] The urea inactivation of serum and chorionic gonadotropins was first order under all
conditions studied, although evidence was obtained for intermediate
reaction products.[216] Deviations from simple first-order kinetics
encountered in the inactivation of diphtheria and equine *Staphylococcus*
antitoxins[70] could be explained by a mechanism involving two competing
reactions of the native protein. Evidence for a second-order reaction
was found when the heat denaturation of lactoglobulin was studied by
changes in electrophoretic mobility,[136] but the reaction was first order
when followed by the liberation of sulfhydryl groups.[125a] In this instance
the two investigations were made in the same laboratory but no fruitful
comparison of the rates could be made when they were determined by
different methods. A similar situation obtains for the kinetics of the
denaturation of egg albumin. Early investigators[12,15] did not establish

(210) H. B. Bull, and H. Neurath, *J. Biol. Chem.* **125**, 113 (1938).
(211) A. D. McLaren, *Arch. Biochem. and Biophys.* **31**, 72 (1951).
(212) M. Kunitz, *J. Gen. Physiol.* **32**, 241 (1948).
(213) M. A. Eisenberg and G. W. Schwert, *J. Gen. Physiol.* **34**, 583 (1951).
(214) M. A. Lauffer, M. Wheatley, and G. Robinson, *Arch. Biochem.* **22**, 467
         (1949).
(215) M. A. Lauffer and H. L. Carnelly, *Arch. Biochem.* **8**, 265 (1945).
(216) F. Bischoff, *J. Biol. Chem.* **165**, 399 (1946).

whether the reaction was of the first or the second order. After a careful reinvestigation, Gibbs, Bier, and Nord[216a] decided that the denaturation was first order over a wide range of protein concentrations and other conditions. Simultaneously, Haurowitz *et al.*[216b] concluded that the heat denaturation, as measured by the increase in dye-binding, was first order with respect to protein concentration, but that the reaction order with respect to time was of a high and variable order. In study of the effect of heat and urea on horse erythrocyte catalase Deutsch[161a] observed that the inactivation did not obey a first order law, and he suggested that the nature of the process indicated the presence of molecules of widely varying reactivities in the crystalline and supposedly pure enzyme.

It is noteworthy that nearly all the recent studies were made with highly purified proteins, but reversible or secondary reactions were observed in most instances and in some cases the apparent order depended on the method of estimating the velocity. This is a clear demonstration that there are numerous stages in the denaturation process. Some of these depend in a different manner on pH, concentration, temperature etc., and it is thus not surprising that different over-all orders of reaction result when different properties of the protein are used as criteria for evaluating the kinetics of denaturation. This emphasizes the need for isolating the reaction being studied.

(1) Heat Inactivation of Pepsin. The heat inactivation of pepsin serves as a typical example of a case which some workers considered to be a first-order unimolecular process and for which others found deviations from simple kinetics. The discrepancies in the literature led Casey and Laidler[217] to an important reinvestigation of the order of this reaction, using the method of measuring the initial rate, v as a function of both concentration, c, and temperature. They found a marked variation of initial rate and of the Arrhenius activation energy, E, with initial enzyme concentration. Thus, E dropped from 147 kcal. at 0.004 per cent pepsin to 56 kcal. at 0.5 per cent enzyme. Similarly, the reaction was not of simple order; it was first order at pepsin concentrations above 0.5 per cent but extrapolated to fifth order at 0.004 per cent. They interpreted the facts that the apparent order of the reaction and the energy of activation both vary with enzyme concentration to mean that strong intermolecular forces act between the pepsin molecules. These forces are presumably electrostatic and certainly repulsive. Casey and

(216a) R. J. Gibbs, M. Bier, and F. F. Nord, *Arch. Biochem. and Biophys.* **35,** 216 (1952).

(216b) F. Haurowitz, F. DiMoia, and S. Tekman, *J. Am. Chem. Soc.* **74,** 2265 (1952).

(217) E. J. Casey and K. J. Laidler, *J. Am. Chem. Soc.* **73,** 1455 (1951).

Laidler formulated the final rate expression given below in which k_0, K, and n are constants, n signifying the order of the reaction:

$$v = \frac{k_0 K c^n}{c_{H^+}{}^5 (1 + n^2 K c^{n-1})}. \tag{1}$$

This equation is in accord with the facts that good first-order constants are given in the high concentration region, as found for example by Northrop[218] and reported by Arrhenius,[13] but that earlier workers found drifting constants. Quite apart from the admittedly unusual interpretation accorded these results is the significance of the finding that both n and E may vary with enzyme concentration. Similar data have not yet been obtained for other denaturations, and it is to be noted that most authorities deem reactions higher than the third order as being most unlikely.[219] However, by use of the same method of kinetic analysis, Haurowitz et al.[216b] arrived at the conclusion that the heat denaturation of egg albumin is "first-order with respect to protein concentration, but of higher order with respect to time." Since the reaction order was as high as 6.5 at 65° but dropped to 1.85 at 75°, these authors suggested that the mechanism of denaturation differed at the higher temperature from that at the lower temperature.

b. Effect of Temperature on the Rate of Protein Denaturation

In general the effect of temperature on the rate of protein denaturation is so marked and the corresponding activation energy is so high, that the result cannot be interpreted by classical kinetics, and the phenomena have been designated as the "abnormalities" of protein denaturation kinetics. The very nature of the phenomena suggests that they have import for protein structure and has stirred much speculation and investigation. There is no need to assume that the kinetics are abnormal if recognition is made that proteins possess many mutually sustaining labile bonds and that prototropic groups are involved in maintaining structure. Either of two processes will suffice to explain the observations: (1) the simultaneous breaking of many bonds or (2) the ionization steps taken in preparation of the activated complex for breaking of a few critical bonds.

(1) The Temperature Coefficient. Whereas the velocity of ordinary homogeneous gas reactions approximately doubles or trebles for each ten-degree rise in temperature, the rate of thermal denaturation is

(218) J. H. Northrop, J. Gen. Physiol. 13, 739 (1930).

(219) S. Glasstone, Textbook of Physical Chemistry, 2nd. Ed., D. Van Nostrand, New York, 1946, pp. 1044–1118.

extraordinarily accelerated. Temperature coefficients $\left(Q_{10} = \dfrac{k'_{t+10}}{k'_t} \right)$ in excess of 600 have been reported for protein denaturation, and values up to 100 are common. This behavior limits the kinetic study of denaturation to a narrow temperature range, often only 2–3°, and is the cause of the characteristic "coagulation" or "cloud-point" temperature used in the study of the thermal stability of proteins.

The high temperature coefficient of denaturation is real and consequently has prompted physical chemists to seek an explanation of this anomalous kinetic phenomenon. Such temperature coefficients can be obtained only with reactions of large complex molecules and their elucidation clearly is of importance in the study of protein structure. Historically this phenomenon is one of the first observations made on proteins and is the origin of the idea that enzymes are proteins as well as the basis for the thermal destruction of microorganisms.

Not all denaturants have the same high temperature coefficient. Acid denaturation has a lower coefficient which may approach the normal value. The effect of temperature on urea denaturation is complex; the coefficient may be positive or negative. If increasing temperature elevates the action of urea at all, the effect is small. On the other hand, a number of instances have been reported where urea denaturation has a negative temperature coefficient. In an exhaustive investigation of the kinetic aspect of urea denaturation of tobacco mosaic virus, Lauffer[30] found that the rate decreased as temperature increased between 0 and 23° but that above 23° the rate increased with temperature. This effect was explained by assuming that the denaturation of the virus can proceed by several parallel reactions with temperature coefficients of opposite sign. Clark[220] has also interpreted the negative temperature coefficient for urea denaturation in terms of two reactions, both of which are assumed to have positive coefficients but of different magnitude. One of these reactions is supposed to split the egg albumin molecule, though no evidence was offered, and earlier results indicate that urea has no effect on the molecular weight of this protein. Eyring and Stearn[22] consider the behavior of urea denaturation in terms of the entropy change (see later) and of binding of solute by the protein.

(2) *Activation Energy.* The activation energy (*E*) calculated from the Arrhenius equation is the most commonly used measure of the effect of temperature on reaction rate.[13] Despite the ease and precision with which *E* may be measured, the advances made through use of the activation energy have been somewhat disappointing. Activation energies recorded for protein denaturation have ranged from about −7000

(220) J. H. Clark, *J. Gen. Physiol.* **28**, 539 (1945).

cal./mole for the action of urea on egg albumin to about 200,000 cal./mole for the thermal destruction of goat hemolysin. Tabulations of ΔH^* (which for practical purposes may be assumed equal to E) may be found in several references[22,207,208,221] for all the important denaturation reactions studied prior to 1940. Typical values range from 40,000 to 100,000 cal./mole. At 50°C. these figures correspond to temperature coefficients of 7 and 125, respectively. Such reactions should not have measurable velocities at 50–100°C. according to simple collision theory of molecular reactions. For example, Getman and Daniels[222] show that gas reactions having the usual frequency factor and thus low entropy of activation go measurably at 300°C. only if E is in the range below 25,000 cal./mole, the magnitude common for chemical reactions. Yet protein denaturation is generally too rapid for kinetic study at temperatures above 65°.

In collision theory the velocity constant k' is given by the equation

$$k' = PZe^{-\frac{E}{RT}}. \tag{2}$$

where P is the probability factor or steric factor, Z the number of collisions per second, and R the gas constant. P is an empirical factor correcting for unfavorable or unfruitful collisions and varies from 10^{-8} to unity for most chemical reactions. La Mer[209] first pointed out that the activation energy for the denaturation of egg albumin (140,000 cal./mole) calls for the astronomical value of the steric factor equal to 10^{72}. There is no theory for P; intuitively one can rationalize all cases where it is less than unity, but there is no way to account for higher values for simple reactions. Obviously, either the calculated values of E for protein denaturation are erroneous or the energy of activation is not the factor dominating the reaction rate.

2. Application of the Theory of Absolute Reaction Rates to Protein Denaturation

a. Theory of Absolute Reaction Rates

The kinetic paradox posed by the high energies of activation of protein denaturation has been attacked by application of the theory of absolute reaction rates developed particularly by Eyring and invoked in this case chiefly by Stearn.[207,208] In this theory the equilibrium constant K^* for the formation of the activated complex $(A + B + \cdots \rightarrow X^* \rightarrow$

(221) I. W. Sizer, *Advances in Enzymol.* **3**, 35 (1943).

(222) F. H. Getman and F. Daniels, Outlines of Physical Chemistry, 7th Ed., J. Wiley & Sons, New York, 1943.

products) is expressed in terms of the free energy of activation in the standard state, ΔF^*

$$-\Delta F^* = RT \ln K^*. \tag{3}$$

Since $\Delta F^* = \Delta H^* - T\Delta S^*$ where ΔH^* and ΔS^* represent the increase in heat content and entropy, respectively, when the activated complex is formed from the reactant, all in the standard state

$$K^* = e^{\frac{-\Delta F^*}{RT}} = e^{\frac{\Delta S^*}{R}} e^{\frac{-\Delta H^*}{RT}}. \tag{4}$$

It has been shown[219] that k', the specific reaction-rate constant, is given by

$$k' = \left(\frac{kT}{h}\right) \frac{C^*}{C_A C_B} = \left(\frac{kT}{h}\right) K^*. \tag{5}$$

In this expression kT/h is a universal frequency for the flying apart of the complex and is composed of the Boltzmann constant k, the Planck constant h, and the absolute temperature T (the transmission coefficient being taken as unity). Hence, if the standard states are taken correctly

$$k' = \left(\frac{kT}{h}\right) e^{\frac{-\Delta F^*}{RT}} = \left(\frac{kT}{h}\right) e^{\frac{-\Delta H^*}{RT}} e^{\frac{\Delta S^*}{R}}. \tag{6}$$

Thus the rate constant is seen to be determined by the free energy of activation. Since $\Delta H^* = E - RT$, it is apparent that both the heat of activation and the entropy of activation affect the reaction rate. In general, ΔS^* has a small positive or negative value for simple molecules corresponding to only about ± 5 entropy units (E.U.) (cal./deg./mole); thus ΔH^* is usually rate determining. However, for complex molecules considerable entropy changes are possible. Comparison with Eq. 2 shows that PZ (the frequency factor of the rate equation based on collision theory) is approximately equal to $\frac{kT}{h} e^{\frac{\Delta S^*}{R}}$. Since Z is nearly constant and kT/h is constant at given temperature, the probability or steric factor P is equal to $e^{\frac{\Delta S^*}{R}}$ and thus is related to the entropy of activation. If P is unity, ΔS^* is zero; if less than unity, ΔS^* is negative, and the reaction will be "slow." However, if P is much greater than unity, there must be a considerable increase in entropy during the activation process. *Hence, protein denaturation is distinguished by large entropy changes both for the over-all reaction and for the activation step.* The large increase in entropy is sufficient to make the reaction go despite the high energy of activation. Thus, in the Eyring theory it is the free energy of activation not the heat of activation which is the determining factor in reaction velocity.

b. Magnitude of the Thermodynamic Functions

Only the influence of temperature on the rate constant need be determined in order to calculate ΔH^*, ΔF^*, and ΔS^*. ΔH^* is equal to $E - RT$ where E is obtained from the Arrhenius plot of log k' vs. $1/T$ in the usual manner. ΔF^* and ΔS^* are found by substitution in Eq. 6. Most of the kinetic data on protein denaturation existing before 1940 have been collected and thermodynamic functions calculated and interpreted in a series of reviews.[2,22,207,208,221] Some of the substances studied are hardly recognizable to the present-day biochemist, and with the exception of crystalline pepsin not one of the proteins studied was subjected to modern criteria of purity. Temperature data on rate processes are valuable for obtaining ΔH^* even with crude preparations, provided the kinetics are explicit. However, some of the reactions were studied even before the introduction of the concept of pH and most before the significance of the pH dependence of reaction rate was recognized. Some of the abnormally large activation entropies of protein reactions are admittedly due to the failure to include the hydrogen-ion concentration properly in calculating the specific reaction rate constants.[22]

In addition to the magnitude and range of ΔH^* already mentioned, some generalizations may be made. In general, the activated complex of a unimolecular process will have a looser or more random structure and thus will be formed with an increase in entropy, but small negative changes in entropy are possible if the structure becomes more rigid. The entropy of activation of ordinary unimolecular gas reactions is about $+2$ to 10 E.U.,[219] for the ionization of acetic acid is -3 E.U., and for the splitting of the peptide bond there is a negative ΔS^* of -20 to -30 E.U.[22] With protein denaturation, by contrast, there is a large entropy increase during the activation process—commonly running from $+50$ to as high as 500 units. This must be interpreted in terms of a considerable "opening up" of protein structure during the activation process, although the appearance of new molecular species (water, ions) may contribute to the entropy change. The large increase in entropy explains the abnormal values of the steric factor P and permits rapid reaction rates despite the large activation energies. For example, a ΔS^* of 537 E.U. explains why the heat inactivation of goat hemolysin with $\Delta H^* = 198,000$ cal. proceeds at 50° at a rate comparable to the thermal destruction of "pancreatic proteinase" where ΔH^* is only 38,000 cal. and ΔS^* is 40.6 E.U. (see Eyring and Stearn[22]). For conveniently measurable reaction rates $\Delta F^*/T$ cannot vary much, and ΔF^* (except for cases of dry heating) was in the range of 22,000–27,000 cal. $T\Delta S^*$, however, varied over a range of more than 150,000 cal. It is noteworthy that the general order of increasing relative effectiveness of denaturants, as measured by the order of increasing values of ΔS^*, ΔH^*, and $T\Delta S^*$, was urea, acid, alcohol, and heating in water or salt solution.

c. Thermodynamics of Reversible Denaturation

There are only three cases where the free energy and entropy changes of the equilibrium reaction of protein denaturation are known. The first, already discussed elsewhere,[22,207,208,221] is the reversible inactivation of trypsin; the second, the reversible heat denaturation of the crystalline soybean trypsin inhibitor;[212] the third, the reversible heat denaturation of chymotrypsinogen.[213] For the trypsin inactivation it was necessary to use Pace's data on the kinetics of the irreversible inactivation of crude trypsin at pH 6.5 together with Anson and Mirsky's figures on the equilibrium between (crystalline) native and denatured trypsin at pH 2–3.[223] Kunitz[212] has provided complete data on the kinetics and thermodynamics of the reversible denaturation of the soybean protein at constant pH (about pH 3), but he has made no attempt to investigate the effect of pH on the rate and reversal of the reaction. Eisenberg and Schwert[213] chose chymotrypsinogen to avoid complications due to enzymatic digestion and determined the kinetic and thermodynamic constants for the reversible reaction at pH 2 and 3. The thermodynamic constants are summarized in Table V. Because of their sensitivity to experimental error, the figures represent orders of magnitude rather than exact data.

TABLE V

THERMODYNAMICS OF REVERSIBLE HEAT DENATURATION AT 50°C.

	ΔH	ΔH_1^*	ΔH_2^*	ΔS	ΔS_1^*	ΔS_2^*	ΔF
	cal./mole			cal./deg./mole			cal./mole
Trypsin[208,223]	67,600	40,000	−27,000	213.1	44.7	−168.4	−1270 (50°)
Trypsin inhibitor[212]	57,000	55,000	− 1,900	180	95	− 84	− 900 (50°)
Chymotrypsinogen[213]							
pH 2.0	99,600	84,550	−15,700	316	202	−116	−1200 (46.4°)
pH 3.0	143,000	80,200	−63,700	432	178	−258	− 247 (58.2°)

From Table V it can be seen that the three reactions have some common features. At 50° the free-energy change is negative except for chymotrypsinogen at pH 3. Since $-\Delta F$ is equal to $RT \ln K$, the reversal is aided by cooling. This is also indicated by the unusual fact that the heat of activation of the reverse reaction is negative in all cases. How-

(223) M. L. Anson and A. E. Mirsky, *J. Gen. Physiol.* **17**, 393 (1934).

ever, there is a large loss of entropy in going from denatured protein to the activated complex which slows up the reverse reaction. The fact that ΔS is greater than ΔS^* indicates that the opening up in protein structure begun in forming the activated complex increases in the decomposition which forms the denatured protein. These large entropy changes suggest why reversal of denaturation is accomplished only under certain conditions and why irreversibly denatured protein is often obtained. They are explicable only in terms of a substantial disorientation at many points in the structure of the protein.

d. Nature and Number of Bonds Broken in Activation and Denaturation

On the basis of certain assumptions, the number of bonds broken in activation and denaturation can be calculated. However, the nature of these bonds cannot be determined from the thermodynamic data. The heat and entropy changes are too great to be interpreted in terms of the breaking of any one known protein covalent bond. Moreover, chemical evidence for the rupture of such covalent bonds is lacking. Accordingly, the large values of ΔH and ΔH_1^* have therefore had to be ascribed to the breaking of many different bonds. Mirsky and Pauling[24] first attributed protein denaturation to rupture of side-chain hydrogen bonds between amino and carboxyl groups of adjacent layers. They calculated the number of bonds broken by dividing E by 5000 cal., the average value assigned for the energy of the hydrogen bond. Eyring and Stearn[22] have proposed that specific configuration is maintained by disulfide bonds as well as by salt linkages between amino and carboxyl groups. They also have attempted to calculate the number of bonds broken using 5 kcal. as the average bond strength. Stearn[207,208] has considered the possible variation in bond strengths and has compared the measured entropy increase (ΔS_{meas}^*) with the calculated entropy increase (ΔS_{calc}^*) using the value of 12 cal./degree as the net gain in entropy per bond broken. With increasing activation energy the ratio $\Delta S_{meas}^*/\Delta S_{calc}^*$ approached unity indicating that most of the bonds broken were weak and of the hydrogen bridge type. According to this interpretation, the energy required for the thermal destruction of cross linkages which do not "pay their way" (total $T\Delta S^* < \Delta H^*$) is compensated for by the large increase in entropy associated with the opening up of the structure upon the breaking of the last few bonds which more than pay their way (total $T\Delta S^* \gtrless \Delta H^*$, so $\Delta F^* \gtrless 0$). Clearly, upwards of 20 hydrogen bonds are destroyed in the activation step of the denaturation of many proteins provided this interpretation is correct. This, of course, is a net value since some hydrogen bonds may be reformed at new points in the unfolded structure.

(The bonding of water has no net effect since for every new water–protein H bond formed, a water–water bridge of equivalent strength is broken.)

According to Stearn about eight bonds $\left(\dfrac{\Delta H^*}{5000} = \dfrac{40,000}{5,000}\right)$ are broken when native trypsin forms activated trypsin, and about six more, when activated trypsin forms denatured trypsin (67,000/5,000). A much greater increase in entropy is associated with the second process (28 cal./deg. vs. 5.5 cal./deg.) suggesting that critical bonds are broken. The latter bonds do not differ essentially in type, but their fission allows opening up of the molecule as a whole. Analogous behavior is shown by chymotrypsinogen, but the situation is entirely different for the denaturation of the soybean protein. Here a large increase in entropy in the second process occurs without the apparent further breaking of bonds. This result is difficult to interpret. A different interpretation is accorded their data by Eisenberg and Schwert who suggest that the reversible heat denaturation of chymotrypsinogen consists largely of a dehydration of the protein molecule rather than an intramolecular change. In their work, the contribution of the heat of ionization to the heat of activation is negligible because only three groups with a pK_a of 2.5 are involved. Presumably these are carboxyl groups with only a small temperature coefficient for dissociation. On the other hand, these workers point to the high heat of hydration of (dry) proteins and the large entropy changes occurring in the fusion of ice, which is similar in structure to water of hydration. In this viewpoint it would appear that at pH 2 about 69 moles of water must be removed from each mole of chymotrypsinogen and at pH 3 about 99 moles of water to account for the heat changes of the reaction.

3. Ionization Steps in the Denaturation of Proteins

a. pH Dependence of Kinetic Constants

Though k' and ΔS^* for a unimolecular reaction are independent of the standard states, i.e., the concentration units, the change in activities due to pH must be considered. Since Steinhardt and La Mer pointed out the necessity for rate comparison at constant concentration of reactive ionized species instead of at different temperatures and the same pH, it has been recognized that many of the large values for ΔH^* are illusory. Steinhardt in his paper on the alkaline inactivation of pepsin showed that the rate was inversely proportional to the fifth power of the H-ion activity. He suggested that the initial protein molecule, P_0 in the general case undergoes n ionization steps to give P_n. Ascribing a unique instability to the product of the n-fold ionization, the activation step becomes

$P_n \rightarrow P_n{}^*$. Increasing the temperature promotes the ionization to form P_n as well as the transition to the activated complex. Hence, the activation energy measured by the customary method of rate comparison at constant pH and different temperature leads to a composite value of E which includes the heat of dissociation in the n steps as well as the true heat of activation. The extraordinary pH dependence is revealed by plotting of log k' against pH; n is the slope of the line. To the experimental points a theoretical curve was fitted corresponding to the equation

$$\log (P_n/P_0) = n(\log K_0 - \log a_H) \qquad (7)$$

in which K_0 is the postulated dissociation constant, assumed identical for each step. In this manner K_0 is determined and Δ pH corresponding to Δ pK may be calculated. Substitution in the equation

$$\Delta H = 2.3\Delta \text{ pH} \times \frac{RT_2T_1}{T_2 - T_1} \qquad (8)$$

enables calculation of the heat of dissociation of each group. The true energy of activation equals the measured E minus $n\Delta H$. In this way it was found that the experimentally observed E had to be corrected for five dissociations each with a heat of 9040 cal. Subtraction gave 18,300 cal. and thus quite a normal value for the true heat of activation. Steinhardt ascribed the pH dependence to the successive dissociation of a proton from each of five primary amino groups in the initial molecule. The change in velocity of 10,000 times for one pH unit suggests why proteins appear to have sharp almost discontinuous pH-stability ranges.

A paucity of data at first prevented the further application of Steinhardt's method. However, Putnam and Neurath (quoted in Ref. 2) using data of Cubin showed that over a limited pH range, the denaturation of hemoglobin gave a rate dependent on the square of the hydrogen-ion activity. Subsequently, a number of workers have noted that the rate of protein denaturation depends on some power of the hydrogen-ion activity, and the data of Cubin and of Lewis have been recalculated by Gibbs et al.[27a,216a]

From pH 2 to 3 the amount of denatured chymotrypsinogen is a function of the third power of the hydrogen-ion activity.[213] The rate of alkaline denaturation of egg albumin is proportional to the fourth power of the hydroxyl-ion activity.[172] In the thermal denaturation of tobacco mosaic virus the rate varied inversely with about the third power of the hydrogen-ion activity,[224] and for urea denaturation of the same protein log k' depended on the reciprocal of the 1.5 power.[30] About 3.5 protons per molecule are involved in the extinction of luminescence.[49]

(224) M. A. Lauffer and W. C. Price, *J. Biol. Chem.* **133**, 1 (1940).

However, when log k' was plotted against pH for the destruction of influenza A virus, hemagglutinin, a minimum was found.[215] This was taken to indicate that activation may proceed by two processes, one involving H^+, the other OH^-. The rate of denaturation of lactoglobulin is dependent on $(H^+)^{1.1}$, but the lack of temperature effect was inconsistent with the ionization of amino groups.[105] Two dissociations are involved in the acid denaturation of egg albumin, but in this case, too, the groups could not be identified with types known to exist along the polypeptide chain.[216a]

b. Prototropic Steps in the Denaturation of Ricin

Although all the above investigations confirm the significance of ionization processes in denaturation, most of the work was done over a limited pH or rate range. Also, fractional powers of (H^+) were involved, and deviations from the simple ionization theory were reported. The most extensive study is that of Levy and Benaglia[27] on the influence of temperature and pH upon the rate of denaturation of crystalline ricin, the toxin of the castor bean. From the postulates of Steinhardt these workers developed a generalized theory with equations that satisfactorily described the behavior of ricin from pH 1 to 12 and also explained the denaturation of hemoglobin over an extended pH range.

TABLE VI

THERMODYNAMIC ANALOGS OF ACTIVATION REACTIONS IN THE DENATURATION OF RICIN[27]

Equation		Constant	ΔH^*, kcal.	ΔS^*, cal./°C.	ΔF_{338}^*, kcal.
a.	$P^\circ + 2H^+ \rightleftharpoons P^{*2+}$	K_1^*/K_1K_2	79	173	20.5
b.	$P^\circ + \ H^+ \rightleftharpoons P^{*+}$	K_2^*/K_2	81	161	26.4
c.	$P^\circ \ \rightleftharpoons P^*$	K_3^*	89.3	168.5	32.3
d.	$P^\circ \ \rightleftharpoons P^- + H^+$	$K_3 (338°)$	30.0	54	11.7
e.	$P^- \ \rightleftharpoons P^{*-}$	K_4^*	53	41.6	38.9
f.	$P^- \ \rightleftharpoons P^{*2-} + H^+$	$K_5^*K_4$	62.7	58.2	42.8
g.	$P^- \ \rightleftharpoons P^{*4-} + 3H^+$	$K_7^*K_4K_5K_6$	86.4	32.6	75.4

Table VI contains the values for the thermodynamic analogs of the activation reactions postulated to occur in the denaturation of ricin. A fundamental modification of Steinhardt's concept lies in the conclusion that each of a number of prototropic steps is accompanied by a change in the stability of the protein, not just the last ionization. This and the fact that the stability may be increased or decreased by the dissociation of protons is indicated by the equations of Table VI. A resulting limitation is that a great many mixed constants are required to describe the data (col. 2). On the other hand, such complex parameters are necessary to derive equations fitting the experimentally observed pH dependence of log k'. In the most acid region the plot is linear with a slope of -2. Close to the isoelectric point at pH 5, the curve goes through a minimum corresponding to maximum stability. In the alkaline region, as predicted, the plot of log k' vs. pH shows successive slopes of 0, 1, 2, and 3. A similar generalized expression was found which fitted the thermal denaturation of hemoglobin.

Of all the reactions formulated in Table VI only d is nonactivating, but this has a surprisingly large ΔH^* and ΔS^*. The generally high values of ΔS^* are evidence for a considerable loosening in the structure of the protein. ΔS^* is about the same for the three processes, a, b, and c, but is much greater than for the reactions at alkaline pH. It can be seen that of the 50-odd prototropic groups in ricin only 6 are involved in the denaturation. (The equations of Table VI are presented formally without regard to the net charge of the protein.) Of the six, only three have a pK attributable to well-recognized titrating groups; i.e., K_4–K_6 are possibly due to the guanidinium of arginine. However, all six are presumed to reside in side chains of the protein which are involved in proton-sensitive hydrogen bonds (prototropic chelations). Thus, most of the titratable groups in proteins though capable of forming salt bridges are not of primary importance in maintaining specific structure. Breaking of the six prototropic chelations in ricin does not necessarily lead to denaturation but decreases the thermal energy required to break open the metastable native configuration. In this view denaturation may be reversible despite the statistical improbability of recombination to give the original six chelations, that is, provided treatment is mild and local regions still exist which are capable of guiding the folding back into the native form.

Recently, Gibbs[27a] has reviewed the effects of pH on the rate of protein denaturation and has proposed that different velocities obtain for different states of the protein. Thus, each molecular type has its own rate of denaturation. In this view the effects of pH are readily explainable in terms of equilibrium systems in which there are certain dissociation states of greater or less stability. From studies on egg albumin[216a] he concluded that there are also reactions not connected with interactions of hydrogen ions which play a role in determining the over-all velocity of protein denaturation. However, there was no evidence for these unknown pathways in the kinetics of ricin inactivation and thus they did not appear to be general in the phenomenon of protein denaturation. Gibbs also pointed out that since there are many paths by which a protein can be denatured, the apparent heat of activation of protein denaturation can vary over wide ranges. Indeed, as Steinhardt first suggested, the apparent heat of protein denaturation is not a true value but a composite figure for many reactions.

While the importance of ionization steps in protein denaturation is now established, these do not suffice to explain all the large heats of activation. True, for hemoglobin and pepsin a case may be made, but not for chymotrypsinogen or ricin. In ricin half the ionizing groups are not identifiable; in chymotrypsinogen they appear to be carboxylate which has a negligible heat of dissociation.

4. THE HEAT OF REACTION

The heat of a reaction, ΔH, is equal to the difference in the energy of activation of the forward and reverse reactions but unrelated to their magnitude. In addition to the values given in Table V for chymotrypsinogen and the soybean protein for which ΔH and ΔH^* were determined from measurements under the same conditions, there are a number of instances where ΔH has been determined calorimetrically. At constant quantity of alkali, the heat of denaturation of methemoglobin is 138 kcal./mole, about twice the value reported for trypsin or its inhibitor.[225] At constant pH, ΔH drops to 100 kcal./mole for methemoglobin. The heat of the reaction of salicylate with methemoglobin or carboxyhemoglobin increased with the concentration of the denaturant after passing through a hiatus at about 0.2–0.3 M salicylate.[26] The heat of alkaline denaturation of pepsin fell off with pH from 85 kcal./mole of pepsin at pH 4.3 to a negligible value at pH 6.8.[226] Unfortunately, the calorimetric experiments are not comparable with Steinhardt's kinetic data. The heat of denaturation of pepsinogen is 31 kcal./mole as calculated from the van't Hoff equation.[131]

V. Denaturation of Representative Physiologically Important and Biologically Active Proteins; Reversibility of Denaturation

This section will present a summary and interpretation of the results of study of the denaturation of a number of important proteins and will emphasize the question of reversibility of the process. Numerous workers have shown that some soluble proteins, such as serum albumin, lactoglobulin, and the proteolytic enzymes, are capable of reverting from a denatured state either on cooling or removal of the denaturing agent.

(225) J. B. Conn, G. B. Kistiakowsky, and R. M. Roberts, *J. Am. Chem. Soc.* **62,** 1895 (1940).
(226) J. B. Conn, D. C. Gregg, G. B. Kistiakowsky, and R. M. Roberts, *J. Am. Chem. Soc.* **63,** 2080 (1941).

The regenerated protein is soluble and resembles the parent protein in one or more properties. The question has arisen whether this connotes the reversibility of denaturation. It may be said a priori that the question of reversibility cannot be answered positively and categorically because it is presently impossible to demonstrate the point-to-point reformation of the native protein configuration or the regain of all the many original properties. Some changes perhaps may be too subtle for us yet to discern. By demonstration of any single irreversible change the question can be answered negatively. The general approach has been to show that any one or more of a number of physical, chemical, or biological properties is restored by cooling or by removal of the denaturant.

There is no doubt that in many instances an equilibrium exists between two forms of a protein, one possessing, the other lacking a specific property such as enzymatic activity or characteristic solubility. Most instances where the rates and equilibria are suitable for careful study concern reversible heat inactivation of enzymes. In these cases it must be postulated that moderate heating produces a metastable configuration capable of reverting slowly to an active form after rapid cooling, but that more drastic heating produces a stable irreversibly denatured form. Thus, a number of examples are known in which both reversible and irreversible inactivation occur on heating. Organic denaturants such as concentrated urea can be removed only slowly by dialysis, and the kinetics of reversal cannot readily be studied. Anson[3] has suggested that the most favorable conditions for reversal are denaturation for the minimum time at the least concentration of denaturant and lowest temperature feasible followed by a rapid and cautious procedure for reversal which avoids aggregation.

1. SERUM ALBUMIN

A number of investigations in Neurath's laboratory on the regeneration of horse and bovine serum albumin (and globulins) have already been mentioned. In these cases the maximum effect possible was achieved by long standing in concentrated amides followed by removal of the denaturant by dialysis. This procedure yields a soluble and an insoluble fraction, the first called "regenerated," the second "irreversibly denatured." In this type of experiment it is important to demonstrate that all of the molecules are affected to the same extent by the denaturing agent. Diffusion experiments on solutions of the denatured proteins indicated that the latter were monodisperse within the sensitivity of the method.[226a] Increasing concentrations of urea or guanidine HCl exerted

(226a) Ultracentrifugal studies of serum albumin in the presence of increasing

increasing effect on the protein according to a sigmoidal curve. The higher the concentration the greater was the percentage of total protein which was denatured, both for serum albumin or pseudoglobulin, and either in urea or guanidine HCl.

Both of the fractions recovered after dialysis differed in properties from the original albumin. The irreversibly denatured protein was molecularly but not electrophoretically heterogeneous; it was more asymmetric and far less soluble. Its susceptibility to proteolytic fission was increased but its antigenicity diminished. The regenerated protein closely resembled the native protein in molecular kinetic properties, in crystallinity, and in serological specificity. However, it was equally susceptible to proteolysis as the fully denatured protein and likewise had attenuated antigenicity. The electrophoretic mobility of the regenerated protein was generally greater than that of the native, although an effect of species or of denaturing agent was found. Similarly, the protein obtained after removal of detergent closely resembled native albumin but differed significantly in several properties. Essentially the same result was found after denaturation of pseudoglobulin with concentrated amides. Since restoration of the original properties was never quantitative, denaturation of serum albumin was considered to be an irreversible process. A detailed reinvestigation of the urea denaturation of serum albumin is now in progress in several laboratories. In one instance, Weber[156d] by the method of depolarization of fluorescence has found in agreement with earlier studies[68] that the molecular weight of bovine serum albumin is the same in the native state and after regeneration from urea; however, there appeared to be an increase in the rotational freedom of the regenerated protein.

2. β-Lactoglobulin

Other crystalline proteins which have been well studied with regard to kinetics and change in properties on denaturation are egg albumin and lactoglobulin. It is unfortunate that these proteins, as well as serum albumin, have not proved to be electrophoretically homogeneous. The

---

concentrations of urea and guanidine hydrochloride would be valuable in determining whether aggregation occurs, as postulated by Kauzmann et al.[71a] Preliminary measurements of bovine serum albumin in 8 M urea have revealed a single sedimenting boundary both in the presence and absence of reducing agents. When reducing agents are absent, the boundary is quite diffuse indicating heterogeneity (F. W. Putnam and E. Jensen, unpublished experiments). In the presence of mercaptoethanol or thioglycolic acid the sedimentation rate is halved and the boundary spreading indicates that the homogeneity is comparable to that of the native protein (E. Jensen).

denaturation of egg albumin has been well summarized by Fevold.[122] This protein appears less capable of regeneration than most others studied. Some aspects that bear on the reversibility of denaturation of lactoglobulin follow.

According to Linderstrøm-Lang,[94] lactoglobulin may exist in two forms that are in mutual equilibrium and readily transformable. One of these which predominates at low temperature is quite susceptible to urea denaturation. The denaturation apparently proceeds in two steps, one rapid and reversible, the other irreversible. Trypsin forms a product similar to that of the reversible denaturation step. No reversion of lactoglobulin denatured by alkali occurs as measured by changes in optical rotation, solubility, or crystallizability.[105] However, apparent reversal after amide denaturation can be demonstrated by means of the identity of the native and regenerated protein in crystal form, optical rotation, solubility, and electrophoretic and antigenic properties. It is significant that heating of lactoglobulin brings about two processes, one irreversible but repressed above 75°, the other increasing in rate up to 99°.[136] On the other hand, the heat denaturation of lactoglobulin followed simple first order kinetics over the temperature range of 64° to 75°, when followed by the reactivity of sulfhydryl groups.[125a]

3. HEMOGLOBIN

The kinetics and the reversal of the denaturation of hemoglobin have provided a continuing spur for experiment. The variation in E with pH and salt concentration was widely studied, and an explanation of the remarkably low activation energy of acid denaturation was sought in the dependence of the rate on $(H^+)^2$ over a limited pH range. The more generalized concept of Levy and Benaglia extended the pH region over which the kinetics can be interpreted. With hemoglobin, as with the hemocyanins, it is necessary to distinguish between the products of dissociation and denaturation.[227]

Regeneration of hemoglobin has been attempted following denaturation by amides, acid, or sodium salicylate. Concentrated amides cause

(227) Dissociation into subunits is a property characteristic of many respiratory proteins, notably the hemocyanins. Brohult's dissertation[53] details the many factors affecting the composition of the solution which influence the reversible dissociation reaction. These include: pH, protein concentration, salt concentration and composition, and the presence of such diverse non-electrolytes as urea and sugars. In addition to the reversible dissociation reactions caused by change in composition of the solution, irreversible splitting into subunits may occur as the result of exposure to ultrasonic waves, ultraviolet light and α-rays.

dissociation of (horse) hemoglobin into half molecules containing both heme (HE) and globin (Gl)[146]

$$HE_4Gl_2 \rightleftarrows 2HE_2Gl.$$

The amides do not cause the formation of denatured globin or even split the heme from the globin moiety as does acid in a further reaction:

$$HE_2Gl \rightarrow HE_2 + Gl.$$

Nor is there liberation of —SH groups or change in absorption spectrum characteristic of acid denaturation.[228] However, after removal of the amide-dissociating agent, only a portion of the protein remains soluble; the degree of regeneration diminishes with increasing urea concentration and depends on the nature of the amide. The soluble regenerated protein is less homogeneous in the ultracentrifuge.

The action of urea is not a mere dissociation, though by contrast with acid it goes only one step toward denaturation. In urea solutions of 5–6 M the initial rate of digestion of hemoglobin by papain is 100–6000 times greater than in the absence of urea.[90] The increase in digestibility with urea concentration closely parallels the decrease in solubility. Also, the protein is equally rapidly attacked whether denatured by neutral urea, alkaline urea, or heat.

In a series of investigations, Mirsky and Anson and others studied the acid denaturation of hemoglobin and its reversal.[229,230,231] Acid denaturation which begins at about pH 4 produces denatured globin with liberation of —SH. Neutralization yields a precipitate which when dissolved in alkali will combine with heme to form hemochromogen. This pigment is incapable of combining reversibly with oxygen and differs from native hemoglobin in absorption spectrum.

Regeneration of acid-treated carbonylhemoglobin gives a material devoid of free sulfhydryl groups and a spectrum identical to that of the undenatured protein.[230] Though the regenerated hemoglobin has the same molecular kinetic properties as the original, it differs in susceptibility to dissociation by alkali, in electrophoretic mobility, and in the shape of the oxygen dissociation curve. Regeneration of heat-coagulated hemoglobin[229] yields a protein identical with the native in respect to crystal form, coagulation temperature, spectrum, and reversible com-

(228) A. E. Mirsky and M. L. Anson, *J. Gen. Physiol.* **19**, 439 (1936).

(229) A. E. Mirsky and M. L. Anson, *J. Gen. Physiol.* **13**, 133 (1929); *ibid.* **13**, 477 (1930).

(230) H. F. Holden, *Australian J. Exptl. Biol. Med. Sci.* **14**, 291 (1936); *ibid.* **15**, 43 (1937).

(231) J. Roche and M. Chouaiech, *Bull. soc. chim. biol.* **22**, 263 (1940).

bination with oxygen and CO. The irreversible aspects of the reaction have been attributed to the denaturation of the globin rather than to the first dissociation phase.

The effect of salicylate on hemoglobin has frequently been cited as an example of a completely reversible denaturation in which the equilibrium is shifted toward the denatured form with increasing concentration of salicylate.[3,85,230] The denatured protein differs from the native in solubility, in absorption spectrum, and in other properties, but the color change was found most useful for measuring the equilibrium. However, sodium benzoate later proved to cause the same spectral shift as salicylate though the heat of the reaction with benzoate is nearly zero. Roberts[26] concluded that colorimetric estimation of the reaction of salicylate with methemoglobin is unreliable and suggested hydrogen-bond formation between salicylate and side chains in the protein molecule. Haurowitz (Vol. II) discusses some further aspects of hemoglobin denaturation.

4. Tobacco Mosaic Virus

Relatively few quantitative studies on the inactivation of animal or bacterial viruses exist except for Lauffer's studies on influenza virus.[232] This is the more remarkable because of the ease of measurement and also because of the practical importance such information might have in the preparation of vaccines as well as in the understanding of virus action. Tobacco mosaic virus may be chosen as an example of a group of highly purified plant viruses which have been studied quite extensively. The literature on the inactivation of plant viruses has been reviewed by Bawden and Pirie[233] and the kinetics by Lauffer, Price, and Petre.[234] A variety of agents inactivate the plant viruses: heat, high pressure, certain types of radiation, formaldehyde, urea, SDS, and acids and bases. Whenever tobacco mosaic virus is inactivated, the rodlike particles are broken down with loss of nucleic acid into fragments which are no longer soluble in dilute salt solutions. The loss of infectivity (or the disintegration of the virus particles) when due to heat, formaldehyde, or concentrated urea is a first-order process. The energy of activation for heat denaturation is high—153,000 calories—but the temperature coefficient for urea denaturation of tobacco mosaic virus and other plant viruses goes through a minimum. It is known that tobacco mosaic virus activity may be inhibited reversibly by combination with ribonuclease or basic polypeptides, but this appears to be more of an interaction effect.

(232) Attention is directed to recent studies of the *photoreactivation* and *multiplicity reactivation* phenomena in the *E. coli* bacteriophages.[58]
(233) F. C. Bawden and N. W. Pirie, *Biochem. J.* **34**, 1258 (1940).
(234) M. A. Lauffer, W. C. Price, and A. W. Petre, *Advances in Enzymol.* **9**, 171 (1949).

Schramm[235] has reported that dissociation of tobacco mosaic virus under moderate conditions (pH 9 at 0°) yields two components, one devoid of nucleic acid. The two products are homogeneous in sedimentation and electrophoresis and have a molecular weight of about 360,000. Adjustment to pH 5 causes reassociation yielding a crystallizable material similar in size and shape to the original rodlike particles but lacking infectivity.

5. INSULIN

Insulin is remarkable among proteins in its resistance to the common denaturing agents. Its very method of preparation using acidified ethanol testifies to this fact. However, insulin is readily and reversibly dissociated into smaller units at pH below 4 and above 7.5 (see Li, Vol. II). Its apparent molecular weight depends on concentration as well as on hydrogen-ion activity. The exact figure for the minimum molecular weight is still a matter for scrutiny. Just when general agreement was reached that the submultiple had a molecular weight of 12,000 with trimers and tetramers possible in solution, Fredericq and Neurath[156] presented evidence based on the effect of thiocyanate on the equilibrium which indicated that the minimum molecular weight was 6000, and this is supported by counter current distribution studies etc. Insulin remains active after exposure to dilute acid, concentrated urea, and ethanol, and even when spread as a monomolecular film. However, Greenstein (quoted as Ref. 167 of Ref. 2) found that disulfide groups become apparent in concentrated amides and that dialysis of such solutions results in a precipitate. Nonetheless, the insoluble protein (and the protein dissolved in urea) retained the original activity. When insulin is heated in acid solution at 100° it forms highly asymmetric inactive fibrils which subsequently aggregate to form spherocrystals or spherites.[236] The fibrils of the heat precipitate can be demonstrated by flow double refraction or by use of the electron microscope. Waugh[237] has discussed the reversibility of this phenomenon with reactivation by alkali. He concluded that the fibrils represent endwise linkage of unfolded units of the protein and not aggregates of fibrous and denatured molecules. The crystallizable product regenerated from the fibrils could not be distinguished from untreated insulin by physical, chemical, and biological tests. Moreover, on addition of seeding fibrils to native insulin at 37°, the fibrils elongate and quantitatively remove the native insulin from solution in a fibrous form.[237a] The dissociability of insulin must be

(235) G. Schramm, *Naturwissenschaften* **31**, 94 (1943).
(236) D. F. Waugh, *J. Am. Chem. Soc.* **68**, 247 (1946).
(237) D. F. Waugh, *J. Am. Chem. Soc.* **70**, 1850 (1948).
(237a) D. F. Waugh, R. E. Thompson, and R. J. Weimer, *J. Biol. Chem.* **185**, 85 (1950),

related to its stability toward denaturing agents. The lack of antigenicity precludes immunological investigation of the modified protein.

6. PROTEOLYTIC ENZYMES

The reversible inactivation of proteolytic enzymes and denaturation
of their zymogens offers the most challenging evidence that at least some
initial stages of protein denaturation are reversible. This work, largely
pursued at the Princeton Laboratories of the Rockefeller Institute, has
been conveniently summarized by Northrop, Kunitz, and Herriott.[28]
Subsequently, the field lay dormant for a decade until the study by
Kunitz[212] on the soybean inhibitor and that of Eisenberg and Schwert
on the reversible heat denaturation of chymotrypsinogen.[213]

Chymotrypsin heated to 100° in 0.0025 HCl is rapidly and completely
inactivated and becomes insoluble in 1 M NaCl, but the activity and
solubility are slowly restored on standing at 20°. *Pepsinogen* can be
heated to boiling but recovers full potential activity on cooling in the
absence of salt. It is also reported to be denatured at pH 9.0, but this
reaction is likewise reversible. *Pepsin*, which loses activity at pH 10.5,
recovers some proteolytic capacity on standing at pH 5.4. The most
extensive studies have been on *trypsin*. This enzyme may be heated to
boiling many times without loss of activity if afterwards rapidly cooled.
The enzyme does not digest casein at elevated temperatures but does so
if the mixture is cooled to 37°. Anson and Mirsky were the first to
interpret this phenomenon in terms of an equilibrium between native and
denatured protein. The large value of ΔH (see Table V) emphasizes the
fact that a small temperature rise causes a great increase in the percentage
of denatured enzyme and that rapid cooling favors reactivation. The
inactivation of trypsin in alkaline solution is also supposed to be reversible. Within a restricted range of pH and protein concentration, *chymotrypsinogen* undergoes thermal denaturation which is wholly reversed on
cooling. As with trypsin and the other enzymes, irreversible denaturation sets in on longer heating. Prolonged exposure to acid or alkali likewise causes irreversible inactivation of the proteolytic enzymes. Inactivation of trypsin by high pressures is not reversed by pH adjustment.

The kinetics and the thermodynamics of the reversible denaturation
of several of the proteolytic enzymes have already been discussed.
Though the phenomenon of reversible denaturation has been most
thoroughly explored for the proteolytic enzymes, there is no reason to
suppose it is limited to these proteins. Lactoglobulin and trypsin
inhibitor serve as other examples. It is to be noted that in most cases
altered solubility, not diminished enzymatic activity, has been used as
the criterion of denaturation. This is of interest in view of the suggestion

that dehydration rather than intramolecular rearrangement is responsible for the reversible heat denaturation of chymotrypsinogen.[213]

7. LUCIFERASE

The kinetics of denaturations so far studied are mostly for: (1) the heating of purified proteins—generally an irreversible process because of aggregation, or (2) the inactivation of crystalline hydrolytic enzymes—a reaction reversible in the early stages only. The oxidative luminescent system, comprising the enzyme *luciferase* and the dialyzable substrate luciferin, also undergoes a reversible denaturation. The heat inactivation of the partially purified luciferase from the crustacean *Cypridina* has been analyzed kinetically by Chase.[238] The reversible inhibition of bacterial luminescence in *Vibrio phosphorescens* and *Photobacterium phosphoreum* is the subject of a monograph by Johnson *et al.*[49] Since the latter work was of necessity done with intact cells and has been so well reviewed, this section will deal only with *Cypridina* luciferase.

If solutions of *Cypridina* luciferase of pH 6.8 are heated at 40–55° for varying times up to 24 hr., then cooled and their activity measured, the form of the curve relating activity to time of exposure is compound, indicating that at least two inactivating reactions occur. There is a considerable pH effect, but this was investigated only superficially. About 60 per cent recovery of lost activity can be demonstrated if, after brief exposure to 48° at pH 6.8, luciferase is cooled rapidly and allowed to stand at room temperature. Since E for inactivation was about 57,000 cal./mole, the reaction appears to be a typical denaturation. A mathematical analysis of the kinetics was undertaken in terms of the three mechanisms given below.

(1)
$$N \text{ (active)} \begin{array}{l} \xrightarrow{k_1} I \text{ (inactive)} \\[1em] \xrightarrow[k_3]{k_2} P \text{ (``protected'' and active)} \end{array}$$

(2)
$$N \text{ (active)} \underset{k_2}{\overset{k_1}{\rightleftarrows}} \text{ (inactive)} \xrightarrow{k_3} I \text{ (inactive)}$$

(3)
$$N \text{ (active)} \begin{array}{l} \xrightarrow{k_1} I \text{ (inactive)} \\[1em] \xrightarrow[k_3]{k_2} \alpha \text{ (inactive)} \end{array}$$

(238) A. M. Chase, *J. Gen. Physiol.* **33**, 535 (1950)

N represents native protein, I inactive and irreversibly denatured protein, and α an inactive but reversibly denaturable form. Except for nomenclature, these three equations denote the principal features of all the important mechanisms proposed for reversible denaturation or for complications in kinetics associated with denaturation. (The equilibrium *native* $\rightleftarrows$ *denatured* is considered insufficient since it does not express the irreversible phase.) Mechanism (1) invoked by Wright and Schomaker[70,72] formally accommodates for the deviation of antitoxin inactivation from simple first-order behavior. Though it fits the inactivation data for luciferase, it could be discarded because it does not account for the recovery on cooling. Mechanism (2) is similar to that suggested by Lundgren[96] for the papain denaturation of thyroglobulin. Except for changed symbols it is essentially the reaction chain postulated by Linderstrøm-Lang for the reversible denaturation of lactoglobulin.[94] Unlike Lundgren, the other workers have no evidence for an unfolded intermediate form of the protein. The chymotrypsinogen data suggest this consecutive reaction series but also might be explained by Chase's third mechanism. The luciferase results were best described by mechanism (3) where all the constants are first order. It is to be noted that (1) and (3) differ only in that α the intermediate compound is inactive in the latter case.[239]

It is instructive to note again that kinetics can be used only to favor or reject mechanisms, not to prove them. Nonetheless, it is implicit in these hypotheses that reversible and irreversible denaturation differ either in mechanism or in the distance gone toward a common end. To avoid semantic dispute, all the processes involving temporary or permanent loss of intrinsic properties may be called denaturation provided all molecules are statistically affected and that prolonged exposure ultimately destroys the equilibrium. Where a single criterion such as solubility is used, it is not to be expected that kinetics based on other criteria will yield the same data except in the unlikely event that all denaturative changes run in parallel.

VI. Protein Denaturation and Protein Structure

The paucity of detailed information relating structure to function which has been gained by exhaustive study of protein denaturation is at first thought disappointing. In this respect, however, it is no less so than the vast effort expended in amino acid analysis, the onerous calcula-

(239) A repetition of the heat inactivation experiments with a considerably more highly purified *Cypridina* luciferase preparation almost exactly duplicated the results described above.[239a]

(239a) W. D. McElroy and A. M. Chase, *J. Cellular Comp. Physiol.* **38**, 401 (1951).

tion of x-ray diffraction data, the tabulation of physical constants, or even the recent brilliant results of sequential analysis. Perhaps this is to be expected from the complexity and diversity of proteins. Each requires an atlas for topography, a treatise for properties, and a tabulator for index of composition, sequence, and steric structure. From studies of denaturation, certain basic facts emerge which apply generally to the structure of proteins, and other items appear which mark each protein as an entity. Thus far, the latter have been given prominence. In conclusion, more general relationships will be stressed.

1. CHEMICALLY REACTIVE GROUPS

a. Accessibility Versus Role in Maintaining Structure

In any complete theory of protein structure a place and a role must be found for chemically reactive groups liberated on denaturation as well as for freely accessible groups. Present theories postulate two types of hydrogen bonding to occur in proteins. In one type the peptide nitrogen and oxygen atoms of adjacent polypeptide chains or of complementary amino acid residues in a single chain are presumed to be joined: —N—H · · · · · O—C—. If these peptide hydrogen bonds are between adjacent chains as in the Huggins structure, they hold the "backbone" together in a plane layer with alternate chains oppositely oriented; if between reciprocating residues of a single chain, they band the helical configurations of Pauling and Corey. Conversion of the helices to the pleated sheet configuration also gives a hydrogen-bonded layer structure but with all chains similarly oriented.

A second possible type of hydrogen bond is that between side-chain amino and carboxyl groups of adjacent layers. Unlike peptide hydrogen bonds in which all the peptide groups—or at least regularly repeating peptide groups—are presumed to be involved, side-chain hydrogen bonds will be formed only between a few appropriately spaced residues within the protein molecule. Mirsky and Pauling suggested that such bonds will usually be between an amino and a carboxyl group, the nitrogen atom forming a hydrogen bond with each of two oxygen atoms and holding also one unshared hydrogen atom. Thus two hydrogen bonds would be formed for each pair of amino and carboxyl groups. Eyring and Stearn write of electrovalent salt bridges between groups such as $-NH_3^+$ and $-COO^-$. Since the hydrogen bond is electrostatic in nature, there is no great difference between the two points of view. (However, though Stearn uses 5 kcal./mole as the bond strength in calculating numbers of bonds broken, Pauling and Corey conclude that 7.5 kcal./mole is a better value for peptide hydrogen bonds, and Edsall (p. 437, Ref. 100) suggests that the separation of an $-NH_3^+$ and a $-COO^-$ group would involve a large amount of electrostatic work.)

It is a peculiarity that the chemically reactive groups liberated in denaturation are not the ones proposed in hydrogen-bond formation above. Various suggestions have been made for the masking of phenolic, sulfhydryl, and other groups. These range from steric inaccessibility to formation of nonpeptide, covalent cross-linkages. Hydrogen bonds are possible between phenolic hydroxyl groups and adjoining carboxyl groups and possibly with amino groups. Because of the weak electronegativity of sulfur, hydrogen bridges are rarely formed with this element as a partner. Chibnall[240] has proposed three possible covalent cross-bridges between peptide chains: (a) An ester linkage R.CO.O.R' may be formed with the hydroxyl group of serine, threonine, and tyrosine, but little can be said for or against this hypothesis; (b) the imide linkage R.CO.NH.COR' may be formed with the amide group of asparagine or more probably of glutamine; and (c) the thiol ester linkage R.CO.S.R' may be formed with the thiol group of cysteine. The lability of the last linkage might permit its disruption during denaturation and the consequent appearance of $-SH$. Thiazolidine ring formation involving cysteine and rupture during denaturation has been considered as a possibility by other authors.[111,112,166]

In this connection the heterogeneity of the binding sites of serum albumin and the disparity in anion-binding ability of different proteins is of interest. It has been shown both for small numbers of anions[87,171] and for the stoichiometric equivalent[178] that the positively charged groups are the loci of combination. Binding is not purely statistical for the first 25 dodecyl sulfates taken up, and successive complexes are formed and intramolecular changes occur when much higher numbers are bound; yet the binding of the first dozen protects against heat and urea denaturation. To explain some aspects of this behavior, Karush[241] has advanced the concept of configurational adaptability. "By this is meant that there exist a number of sites on the protein, each associated probably with several side-chains, which to a varying extent can assume a large number of configurations in equilibrium with each other and of approximately equal energy. In presence of an organic anion, for example, that configuration is stabilized which by virtue of its structural relation to the anion permits the various portions of the anion to interact with appropriate groups of the protein." This leads to the conclusion that in aqueous solutions of serum albumin—but not of poor anion-binding proteins—there are a large number of configurations of approximately

(240) A. C. Chibnall, *Proc. Roy. Soc.* (London) **B131**, 136 (1942).

(241) F. Karush, *J. Am. Chem. Soc.* **72**, 2706 (1950).

equal energy and in thermodynamic equilibrium with each other. With proteins such as γ-globulin, which are not stabilized against denaturation by long-chain anions, it is not unavailability of the cationic loci which prevents binding at positive sites, but rather the rigid configuration of the site. How far the concept of configurational adaptability can be pressed to explain the unavailability of phenolic or sulfhydryl groups is uncertain. In anion binding, electrostatic forces are primarily involved though aided by van der Waals' interactions; however, covalent bonds are formed in the estimation of masked groups in proteins with the usual chemical reagents. Moreover, the charged groups are generally available to titration or other means of analysis.

This summary of postulated intramolecular bonds and of the concept of adaptable configuration in proteins illustrates the variety of possibilities and suggests the difficulty of establishing the nature of the bonds. Moreover, there is the probability of recombination or of formation of new bonds to give the many possible configurations indicated by the increased entropy of the denatured protein. Cohn et al.[242] have postulated that additional salt bonds are formed and stabilize the denatured protein. Transition from the α-helix to the pleated (β-keratin) configuration is accompanied by a reshuffling of hydrogen bonds. Perhaps the electrostatic repulsion of similarly charged groups has been generally too much neglected in this type of discussion.

In interpretation of protein denaturation kinetics, two apparently opposing but reconcilable views prevail: (1) When emphasis is placed on ΔH^* or ΔS^* it is concluded that many weak bonds are broken—be they called hydrogen bonds or salt bridges—and that only the last few pay their way. The number cannot be accurately estimated because of the uncertainty of the H-bond energy for proteins, and the number must vary as does ΔH^* with pH and salt concentration. (2) Where prototropic changes are emphasized, it is concluded that only a few ionization processes are required to prepare the activated complex—five for pepsin, six for ricin, two for hemoglobin, and only one for egg albumin, according to a recent note.[243] These groups are identifiable through their pK's, but only a few correspond to recognized titratable groups and none to phenolic OH or to —SH. The ease of denaturation after the breaking of so few critical bonds suggests a zipper type of structure for proteins.[243a]

(242) E. J. Cohn, T. L. McMeekin, J. T. Edsall, and M. H. Blanchard, J. Biol. Chem. 100, xxviii (1933).

(243) R. J. Gibbs, M. Bier, and F. F. Nord, Arch. Biochem. and Biophys. 33, 345 (1951).

(243a) Comparative study of the changes in optical rotation, viscosity, and solubility of ovalbumin and bovine serum albumin have revealed large differences in the stability of these proteins.[71a] The behavior of lacto-

The role of the charged groups in proteins is difficult to assay. With rare exceptions these groups are freely and reversibly titratable and accessible to most chemical reagents. Yet enhancement or suppression of the dissociation of a few is a critical stage in denaturation. Evidence previously summarized indicates that many denaturants such as detergents, salicylate, thiocyanate, and probably the amides combine with the positively charged groups of the protein. On the other hand, urea, alcohol, and salicylate are known hydrogen-bond formers and in high concentration are capable of interacting with the peptide N and O. Even detergents can combine with the peptide bonds of proteins. Clearly, a new approach is needed in which combination of denaturants with proteins is studied at the effective concentrations of these agents.

b. Correlation of the Appearance of —SH with Other Criteria of Denaturation

In presenting evidence for the "all-or-none" character of protein denaturation, Anson[3] stated that when a protein is half denatured by one criterion, it is half denatured by another. For example, several proteolytic enzymes when half denatured by the solubility test are half inactivated. He emphasized that the ideal experiment for testing the all-or-none character of protein denaturation by measurement of different properties in the same solution had not yet been presented. However, there are now a number of examples of a lack of correlation of the appearance of the several criteria of denaturation. Fredericq[166] has concluded that there is no correlation between the unfolding of polypeptide chains and the activation of —SH groups. Concentrations of dodecyl benzene sulfonate and other detergents which produced strong double refraction of flow and a fibrous character in egg albumin liberated only about one-half the potentially active —SH groups. Yet alkyl sulfates which caused only feeble double refraction liberated the maximum —SH complement. Significant differences exist in the rate of pH denaturation of β-lactoglobulin when measured at intermediate pH by optical rotation compared to insolubility at the isoelectric point, but the rate constants are the same at pH 8.0 and 10.1. Moreover, no measurable —SH was revealed by pH denaturation though all of the —SH groups were activated in guanidine HCl.[105] With both ovalbumin and the serum albumin in urea, the viscosity continues to change after the optical rotation has

---

globulin is intermediate. For all three proteins the stability of the native configuration paralleled the anion-binding tendency. The rapidity of the denaturation of serum albumin and the ease of renaturation suggested a flexibility on structure or "looseness" in the folding analogous to the concept of "configurational adaptability" derived from binding studies.

reached equilibrium.[71a] Differences in the kinetics of heat denaturation of lactoglobulin and of egg albumin when measured by different methods is further evidence for the existence of a number of stages in protein denaturation (see Sec. IV-1a).

There is no obvious correlation between the effect of urea on the liberation of groups in proteins and on the changes in molecular weight that occur. Where molecular weight is decreased, the effect generally takes place at urea concentrations inadequate to liberate the maximum number of —SH groups. The same may be said for a number of agents such as thiocyanate which diminish the double refraction of flow of myosin without affecting the number of titratable groups. Moreover, guanidine HCl alters the physical properties of myosin at concentrations of 0.3 M as well as at 6 M but only liberates the maximum —SH complement at higher concentrations. Comparative studies of the effect of denaturants on the viscosity of proteins and the freeing of —SH are lacking, but for both phenomena there is a correlation between the greater efficacy of guanidine HCl as opposed to urea. Since diffusion measurements indicate serum albumin is homogeneous in solutions of concentrated amides, the sigmoidal curve relating viscosity to concentration is interpreted in terms of increasing average asymmetry of the molecules rather than as an all-or-none effect. The variation in susceptibility of enzymes, hormones, and viruses to inactivation has already been summarized. In a number of instances the changes in physical or chemical properties did not parallel the rate of inactivation.

2. PHYSICAL PROPERTIES

The changes in physical properties induced on denaturation indicate the various aspects of protein structure. The increased molecular asymmetry is not at all comparable to that expected for a single polypeptide chain of the β-keratin form. The apparent axial ratio for urea-denatured egg albumin is about twice that for the native protein but only one-tenth that calculated for an isolated polypeptide chain.[159] In part this may be explicable by a layer structure of the protein and in part is attributable to a high degree of internal cohesion which causes a recoiling into a condensed state. The renaturation of proteins also indicates such elasticity though the original properties are not exactly regained. The dissociation of many proteins by denaturing agents offers strong support for the concept of molecular subunits held together by labile bonds. Additional evidence for the layer-type structure is proffered by study of surface monolayers. The actual structure of such monolayers, however, is not much better known than the internal structure of the natural protein.

Electrophoretic evidence is in accord with the finding that most dissociable groups in proteins are freely titratable.   The small shift in isoelectric point accompanying denaturation favors the conclusion that only a few electrostatic bonds break in this reaction.   The prediction of Eyring and Stearn that proteins with approximately equal numbers of acidic and basic groups will be most stable at the isoelectric point seems generally to be met.   Certainly, this is true in several cases where the effect of pH on rate of inactivation has been carefully investigated.

The entropy changes occurring in denaturation support the hypothesis that the native protein has a unique configuration and that the denatured protein has many accessible configurations and a more open structure. (This view has to be somewhat modified in Karush's concept which assigns a large configurational entropy to certain dissolved proteins.) Biological specificity is assumed in large part to be associated with the unique configuration.   It has been calculated that the value of 100 E.U. between the native (active) state of trypsin and the denatured (inactive) state corresponds to 10^{20} for the number of accessible configurations of the inactive enzyme.[244]   Entropy increases of up to 300 units have been found for the activated state in the heat denaturation of egg albumin at pH 6, but in concentrated urea at the same pH ΔS^* is -90 E.U. according to Eyring and Stearn.   These authors emphasize that the entropy change for the breaking of a particular bond is the sum of three contributing terms: (a) that involved in the freeing of the side chains that form the bridge; (b) that involved in freezing solvent molecules to the free side chains; and (c) that due to the effect of the breaking of the bridge on the opening up of the protein molecule.   The behavior of urea thus must be interpreted in terms of strong bonding of solute molecules by the activated complex.   The magnitude of the entropy change is not so great when considered in terms of the vast number of vibrational frequencies in such large molecules.   An entropy increase of 100 units per mole corresponds to a change of only 0.5 per cent in the vibrational frequency for a molecule with 10,000 internal degrees of freedom.[244]

The volume change in denaturation has been measured dilatometrically and also by means of the pressure effect.   The dilatometric method indicates that in proteolytic denaturation there is an initial volume contraction of about 700 ml./mole greater than that attributable to electrostriction.   This contraction occurring to form a reversibly denaturable product is partly offset by a volume increase during the irreversible phase of denaturation.[94]   Dilatometry has indicated that heat denaturation of several proteins is accompanied by an increase in volume.[170]   A number of studies of the effect of hydrostatic pressure on the reactivity of proteins

(244) H. Neurath, G. R. Cooper, and J. O. Erickson, *J. Phys. Chem.* **46**, 203 (1942).

have shown that large volume increases may accompany the activation process or the over-all reaction. This is true of the heat precipitation of egg albumin and serum globulin,[46] the temperature inactivation of anti-toxin[47] and invertase,[245] and the phenomenon of bacterial luminescence.[49] The volume change of the activation or of the reaction can be obtained by plotting the logarithm of the velocity constant or of the equilibrium constant, respectively, against pressure. The values obtained range from 60 to 100 ml./mole and are interpreted in terms of an unfolding of the molecule. Thus moderate pressures retard denaturation, but very high pressures disintegrate tobacco mosaic virus and denature other proteins.

3. BIOLOGICAL SIGNIFICANCE OF DENATURATION

In conclusion, brief consideration may be given to the biological significance of denaturation. The phenomenon of reversible denaturation early suggested to various authors the possibility that this process might be a factor controlling some reactions *in vivo*. Among the specific phenomena that have been proposed to involve reversible denaturation are the contraction of muscle, the interconversion of visual purple and visual yellow, and bacterial luminescence and its inhibition by drugs. The latter subject is most thoroughly covered by a recent review.[49] Muscle contraction is discussed by Bailey (Vol. II).

Addendum

In a valuable new treatment of the hydrodynamic properties of proteins discussed in Chapter 7, Scheraga and Mandelkern[246] have represented the configuration of the protein molecule in terms of an *effective* hydrodynamic ellipsoid described by a function β. Using the data of Neurath and Saum,[158] they calculated β for horse serum albumin in urea solution. For the native protein β corresponded to an effective prolate ellipsoid of axial ratio 5:1, but in urea solution its value fell to an almost constant figure somewhat lower than the theoretical quantity for a sphere. The latter may suggest that the data are not of the required precision. The radii of the effective hydrodynamic spheres were also calculated for the denatured molecules, though these should not be identified with the actual shapes. The calculated dimensions correspond to non-isotropic alterations in native configuration more drastic than hitherto conceived; for example 6.66 M urea causes an effect equivalent to an eight-fold increase in volume. On the basis of this single instance Scheraga and Mandelkern have concluded that "the denaturation process thus appears

(245) H. Eyring, F. H. Johnson, and R. L. Gensler, *J. Phys. Chem.* **50**, 453 (1946).
(246) H. A. Scheraga and L. Mandelkern, *J. Am. Chem. Soc.* **75**, 179 (1953).

to involve an increased effective volume due to swelling instead of uncoiling of polypeptide chains." Clearly, accurate new physical data on a number of proteins denatured by different agents are needed before the value of this new treatment can be exploited. Moreover, any interpretation must consider effects owing to the topography of the disorganized protein structure and should be related to the mechanism of denaturation.

CHAPTER 10

The Chemical Modification of Proteins

By FRANK W. PUTNAM

893

I. Introduction

1. Purpose of Study

The chemical modification of proteins has been investigated for three main purposes: (1) to alter the activity or physical properties of proteins in order to render them more suitable for medical or industrial use; (2) to determine the nature of the structures responsible for the biological action of proteins; and (3) to prepare specific protein derivatives for comparative study of the physical or biological properties of the unmodified substance, particularly for immunological investigation. Of these, the first—the practical approach—is historically important and still plays an important role in the preparation of biologicals and in protein technology. Some aspects of the preparation and properties of toxoids and vaccines will be considered in chapters of the second volume of this treatise. The use of formaldehyde for this purpose has been summarized by French and Edsall.[1] Cross-linking processes in industrial protein chemistry have been treated by Bjorksten,[2] and the protein–chemical aspects of tanning are reviewed by Gustavson.[3] The modification of proteins for industrial use is similar in principle to protein reactions described below except for more exhaustive treatment and less regard for specificity and mildness of reaction. Despite the practical importance of these problems, they will not be considered further here.

Chemical modification to determine the nature and number of amino acid groups essential for biological action gained impetus with the refinement of methods of purification and the advent of new techniques for characterization of proteins. Its development paralleled and its achievements supported the evidence that such activity was due to intact proteins rather than to prosthetic groups. A significant recent development

(1) D. French and J. T. Edsall, *Advances in Protein Chem.* **2**, 277 (1945).
(2) J. Bjorksten, *Advances in Protein Chem.* **6**, 343 (1951).
(3) K. H. Gustavson, *Advances in Protein Chem.* **5**, 354 (1949).

has been the introduction of radioactive substituent groups into proteins for study of immunological properties.[4–8] The blocking of reactive groups and the substitution of known antigenic groups are discussed in Chap. 11 in a general summary of the relation of biological activity to chemical structure of the proteins. The chemistry and properties of modified proteins will be considered in this section.

A fourth purpose of chemical modification of proteins not mentioned above but of increasing interest in recent years has been to aid in sequential and end-group analysis of proteins. This work—so greatly stimulated by the introduction of Sanger's method[9] and so vigorously pursued by the British biochemists—differs from the preparation of a protein derivative or a modified protein in the sense that the product is afterward hydrolyzed and the amino acids are isolated. Often, not only the intact protein but partial enzymatic and acid hydrolyzates or oxidized fragments are studied in this type of structural analysis. The technique of breaking cystine cross linkages (—S—S—) by oxidation to cysteic acid groups (—SO$_3$H), which was also introduced by Sanger,[10] splits the protein molecule into separate polypeptide chains. Tristram[11] (Chap. 3) and Fox[12] have evaluated the analytical findings of this important work.

2. DEFINITION AND RESTRICTIONS

This chapter will primarily be concerned with the substitution reactions of proteins in connection with their composition, structure, and function. Conditions of reaction which suffice for amino acids may lead to denaturation or degradation of proteins, and so some emphasis will be laid on choice of conditions for the modification of native proteins. Enzymatic alteration of proteins will be considered only for significant cases such as the egg albumin–plakalbumin transformation or the tyrosinase oxidation of proteins, which produce a few specific changes rather than extensive hydrolysis. All other reactions resulting in peptide-bond hydrolysis will be excluded.

(4) H. N. Eisen and A. S. Keston, *J. Immunol.* **63,** 71 (1949).
(5) T. E. Banks, J. C. Boursnell, H. M. Dewey, G. E. Francis, R. Tupper, and A. Wormall, *Biochem. J.* **43,** 518 (1948).
(6) J. C. Boursnell, H. M. Dewey, G. E. Francis, and A. Wormall, *Nature* **165,** 111 (1950).
(7) T. E. Banks, G. E. Francis, W. Mulligan, and A. Wormall, *Biochem. J.* **48,** 180 (1951).
(8) E. F. Jansen, M. D. F. Nutting, and A. K. Balls, *J. Biol. Chem.* **179,** 201 (1949).
(9) F. Sanger, *Biochem. J.* **39,** 507 (1945).
(10) F. Sanger, *Biochem. J.* **44,** 126 (1949).
(11) G. R. Tristram, *Advances in Protein Chem.* **5,** 84 (1949).
(12) S. W. Fox, *Advances in Protein Chem.* **2,** 156 (1945).

In the same vein, protein salt derivatives obtained by electrostatic interaction of acidic or basic groups with cations or anions will not be treated. Some aspects of this subject have been taken up in the chapters on the isolation and interactions of proteins. However, it should be noted that a variety of crystalline stoichiometric complexes of proteins may be prepared including egg albumin metaphosphate,[13] lactoglobulin dodecyl sulfate,[14] and most notably, the scores of crystalline forms of serum albumin and mercaptalbumin prepared by Lewin.[15]

Undoubtedly there are many biological applications of the principles of protein reactions which must be neglected. This is particularly so in the bacteriological literature where one finds studies of the effect of esterification of protein carboxyl groups on the staining reactions of bacterial cells,[16] the chemical alteration of the bacterial surface with regard to the effect on agglutination or electrophoretic mobility,[17] the inhibition of fermentation by alkylating reagents, or the search for mutagenic agents.

The expanding field of the introduction of radioactive isotopes into proteins and viruses, though of utmost interest, is not properly considered here since the normal atom is merely replaced by a tracer atom. However, the chemical introduction of radioactive substituent groups, such as mustard sulfones containing S^{35} or the preparation of I^{131} iodinated or P^{32} phosphorylated proteins, deserves special emphasis.

The principles and criteria accepted herein for treatment of the chemical reactions of proteins are largely based on those proposed in two fundamental reviews which appeared almost simultaneously, the one by Herriott,[18] the other by Olcott and Fraenkel-Conrat.[19] *Only non-ionic reactions which involve the primary bonds of the amino acid side chains will be considered.* Hydrolysis of the peptide bond and simple ionization processes will be excluded. Denaturation has already been defined as an intramolecular change resulting from rupture of labile electrostatic linkages (hydrogen bond or ionic bond). To be sure, denaturation may also ensue from drastic treatment with protein reagents, but emphasis will be placed on mild procedures which do not cause irreversible structural changes. Otherwise, the biological significance of chemical modification would be lost in the sequence of denaturative steps. Group substitution will necessarily alter the physical properties of a protein, primarily the solubility and electrochemical behavior, but biological activity is sometimes retained. Herriott has emphasized the desirability of using many criteria to compare the protein derivative with the native form. He suggests that the best proof that the change in the protein

(13) G. Perlmann, *Biochem. J.* **32**, 931 (1938).
(14) T. L. McMeekin, B. D. Polis, E. DellaMonica, and J. H. Custer, *J. Am. Chem. Soc.* **71**, 3606 (1949).
(15) J. Lewin, *J. Am. Chem. Soc.* **73**, 3906 (1951).
(16) J. F. Danielli, *Cold Spring Harbor Symposia Quant. Biol.* **14**, 32 (1950).
(17) S. S. Cohen, *J. Exptl. Med.* **82**, 133 (1945).
(18) R. M. Herriott, *Advances in Protein Chem.* **3**, 169 (1947).
(19) H. S. Olcott and H. Fraenkel-Conrat, *Chem. Revs.* **41**, 151 (1947).

results from the chemical reaction rather than from denaturation is to be found in a demonstration of reversibility and restoration of the properties of the original protein. This ideal condition has seldom been met, but in a number of cases removal of bound reagent has been accomplished with restoration of biological activity.[20-25] Occasionally, too, chemical modification of an enzyme, virus, or hormone has resulted in a derivative which retains activity though generally it is less soluble.[20,26-30] Crystalline derivatives of quite a number of proteins have been obtained.[20,26,31-33] Hence, a number of criteria are available to judge whether a protein has been denatured during modification. It should be noted that the retention of activity after chemical modification is often relative; for example, the crystalline acetylated pepsin had only 60 per cent the proteolytic activity of the original enzyme, and solubility phase-rule diagrams indicated the presence of several derivatives.

3. Principles and Criteria for Study

In the choice of a system for study, certain general principles should be followed. Obviously, a highly purified protein should serve as a starting material, preferably one characterized as homogeneous by one or more methods. In this discussion, emphasis will be placed on the modification of purified proteins rather than on treatment of mixtures such as serum. Since protein reagents may be classed as group specific or nonspecific, a specific reagent should be sought.

Criteria suggested[19] for ideal specific reagents are:

"(1) The amount of reagent introduced or used up should be measurable.

(2) The protein group to be reacted should be measurable.

(20) R. M. Herriott and J. H. Northrop, *J. Gen. Physiol.* **18,** 35 (1934).
(21) C. R. Harington and A. Neuberger, *Biochem. J.* **30,** 809 (1936).
(22) L. Hellerman, F. P. Chinard, and V. R. Deitz, *J. Biol. Chem.* **147,** 443 (1943).
(23) C. E. Weil and M. L. Caldwell, *J. Am. Chem. Soc.* **67,** 214 (1945).
(24) W. F. Ross and A. Tracy, *J. Biol. Chem.* **146,** 63 (1942).
(25) A. F. Ross and W. M. Stanley, *J. Gen. Physiol.* **22,** 165 (1938).
(26) E. F. Jansen, A. L. Curl, and A. K. Balls, *J. Biol. Chem.* **189,** 671 (1951).
(27) H. Fraenkel-Conrat, R. S. Bean, and H. Lineweaver, *J. Biol. Chem.* **177,** 385 (1949).
(28) M. B. Glendening, D. M. Greenberg, and H. Fraenkel-Conrat, *J. Biol. Chem.* **167,** 125 (1947).
(29) P. Agatov, *Biokhimiya* **6,** 269 (1941) (through Ref. 18).
(30) G. L. Miller and W. M. Stanley, *J. Biol. Chem.* **146,** 331 (1942).
(31) B. H. Shahrokh, *J. Biol. Chem.* **151,** 659 (1943).
(32) W. L. Hughes, Jr., *Cold Spring Harbor Symposia Quant. Biol.* **14,** 79 (1950).
(33) K. G. Stern and A. White, *J. Biol. Chem.* **122,** 371 (1938).

(3) The amount of reagent introduced or used up should be equivalent to the number of protein groups reacted.

(4) The reaction should proceed under mild conditions and, preferably be reversible by mild treatment."

If under the conditions described above, biological activity is lost on
treating a chosen group with a specific reagent and restored by unblocking that group, it may be considered essential for activity. This is not
to say that the activity may be ascribed wholly to that group or equally
to all members of that group. Furthermore, it is desirable to verify the
essentiality of a group by use of more than one specific reagent. It
should be emphasized that balance studies on the amount of reagent
introduced into a group and that disappearing from solution have seldom
been performed.

Such rigid criteria are not needed for all purposes to which chemical
modification of proteins is put. Specificity not reversibility is required
in the preparation of protein derivatives for the study of structural or
physical properties, or for analytical use, and not even specificity in some
instances. Modification of proteins for industrial purposes may be
intended to achieve irreversible changes.

II. Chemically Reactive Groups in Native Proteins

1. Nature and Availability of the Chemically Reactive Groups

The general reactions of the carboxyl and amino groups of the amino
acids have already been considered by Desnuelle (Chap. 2); likewise some
of the special reactions of the acidic, basic, aromatic, hydroxyamino, and
sulfur-containing amino acids. The chemical reactions of proteins are
obviously those characteristic of these groups and are only slightly modified by the structure of the protein. Many model reactions with amino
acids for determining the specificity of protein reagents thus will not be
mentioned in this chapter. The abundance of the functional groups in
various proteins has been tabulated by Tristram (Chap. 3) and will be
compared with the amount of reagent introduced. The origin and chemical structure of these groups need hardly be repeated at this point.

Though the reactions of the side-chain polar groups of proteins are
similar to those of the corresponding amino acids, the reactivity toward
specific reagents is often significantly reduced. As described in Chap. 9,
denaturation increases the reactivity of proteins by liberating "masked"
groups. The first evidence for such chemical groupings was Arnold's
demonstration in 1911 of the appearance of a positive nitroprusside reac-

tion after heat coagulation of egg white.[33a] This reaction, characteristic of mercaptans, was attributed to the —SH group of cysteine. Harris[33b] later showed that denaturation of egg white with HCl, alcohol, mechanical shaking, or ultraviolet irradiation also produced nitroprusside-reactive groups. In 1930 Hopkins[33c] found that egg albumin liberated —SH groups in urea solution and thus he laid the way for quantitative measurement by methods already described in Chap. 9. Disulfide linkages were the next masked groups to be discovered. These were also measured in proteins denatured in homogeneous media. Suggestive evidence for the masking of phenolic and indolyl groups in proteins was derived from their diminished chromogenic power with the Folin reagent. Though the Folin color increased when the proteins were denatured, low values were also given by tyrosine peptides and derivatives.[18,19] This obscured interpretation until Crammer and Neuberger[33d] introduced the spectrophotometric method for measuring the degree of ionization of the phenolic OH of tyrosine in native and denatured proteins. Other workers have shown that this group, like —SH, may vary greatly in reactivity among proteins, for, in insulin[33d] and lysozyme,[33e] tyrosine ionization is similar to that of the amino acid but is greatly shifted in egg albumin[33d] and bovine serum albumin.[33f]

In the past the inaccessibility of sulfhydryl and phenolic groups has been emphasized because acidic and basic groups appear to be freely titratable over the range of pH 2–10. However, the titration curve of hemoglobin and the slow reaction of proteins with nitrous acid suggested the masking of acid- and base-binding groups. The identification of masked acidic groups was made possible by the instantaneous titration method described in Chap. 9. Study of the differential reactivity of proteins with ketene and fluorodinitrobenzene, described below, has revealed the masking of basic groups. The increased reactivity of such groups in denatured proteins can be explained by assuming that they are accessible to hydrogen and hydroxyl ions but not to larger reagents, or that they are involved in secondary bonding which is not very dependent on pH. Hydrogen bonding is possible with both the ionized and uncharged forms of protein groups containing electronegative atoms.

The availability of protein groups to chemical reagents has been extensively discussed in connection with denaturation. Since this sec-

(33a) V. Arnold, Z. physiol. Chem. **70**, 300, 314 (1911).

(33b) L. J. Harris, Proc. Roy. Soc. (London) **B94**, 426 (1923).

(33c) F. G. Hopkins, Nature **126**, 328, 383 (1930).

(33d) J. L. Crammer and A. Neuberger, Biochem. J. **37**, 302 (1943).

(33e) C. Fromageot and G. Schnek, Biochim. et Biophys. Acta **6**, 113 (1950).

(33f) I. W. Sizer and A. C. Peacock, J. Biol. Chem. **171**, 767 (1947).

tion will cover only reactions of intact proteins, and preferably only reactions of purified native proteins, the question recurs. In the past, relatively drastic conditions were employed for the modification of proteins, resulting in denaturation and often in a concomitant increase in reactive groups. Modern methods of substitution are designed to avert this effect. However, in *measuring* the apparent degree of substitution, it may be important to secure complete denaturation. An example of this is furnished by Miller's study of the role of denaturation of tobacco mosaic virus in the measurement of the phenolic groups in various derivatives of the virus.[34] To minimize turbidity it was necessary to add urea in determining the chromogenic power, but it was found that the normal and the acetylated virus were more susceptible to urea denaturation than the phenylureido virus and the carbobenzoxy, *p*-chlorobenzoyl, and benzenesulfonyl derivatives. Sodium dodecyl sulfate achieved a uniform rate of denaturation and revealed a much smaller proportion of substitution of some of the derivatives than had been indicated by the urea method. These observations accentuate the question about the reliability of the color methods for estimating phenolic groups; this problem was raised in the preceding chapter and has been discussed by several authors.[18,19,35]

The rare occurrence of unreactive groups in the serum proteins is of some importance because of the frequency with which these proteins have been modified for immunological investigation. No —SH groups are detectable in either normal or immune rabbit γ-globulin,[36] and only one per mole in serum albumin.[32] All the α-NH_2 and imidazole groups of these proteins reacted with fluorodinitrobenzene (FDNB) whether the protein was native or denatured.[37] However, not all the ϵ-amino groups of the native serum globulins reacted with ketene or FDNB. This led Porter to the interesting suggestion that during isolation of the globulins breaking of labile bonds such as are responsible for the unreactivity of polar groups and the association of molecules in solution may be responsible for the apparent physical chemical heterogeneity.

Many instances of incomplete substitution are available. This is notably true for acetylation of amino groups with ketene where determination of the number of acetyl groups introduced has often been neglected. Extensive treatment with ketene does not acetylate all the amino groups of tobacco mosaic virus[38] equally readily, and the amino

(34) G. L. Miller, *J. Biol. Chem.* **146**, 339 (1942).

(35) M. L. Anson, *Advances in Protein Chem.* **2**, 361 (1945).

(36) R. R. Porter, *Biochem. J.* **46**, 473 (1950).

(37) R. R. Porter, *Biochim. et Biophys. Acta* **2**, 105 (1948).

(38) G. L. Miller and W. M. Stanley, *J. Biol. Chem.* **141**, 905 (1941).

groups of diptheria toxin[39] and the serum globulins differ in reactivity. Fortunately, the chemical reactions generally appear to proceed in a statistical fashion so that the introduction of a few groups on one molecule does not alter the reactivity of the molecule with regard to unsubstituted groups. The frequent homogeneity of protein derivatives thus favors interpretation of their biological and chemical properties. Chemical methods for measuring the amount of reagent introduced into a protein will be mentioned only briefly. Where possible, the efficiency of different reagents will be compared.

The ease of reaction of the same group may differ in several proteins owing to their nature as well as to a masking of the type described above. Most studies of the modification of proteins that have attracted interest because of the connection between structure and biological activity or function deal with the soluble globular proteins. However, much important work has been done on the oxidation of the fibrous proteins such as wool keratin and on the introduction of cross-linkages into these substances. Coverage of this will be limited because of the inapplicability of the criteria of ideal reactions and because of the lack of biological activity. Thus to the protein chemist, accessibility of groups most generally refers to measurements on soluble corpuscular proteins. Insoluble fibrous proteins react much less readily. Alexander and associates[40] have shown that the number of carboxyl groups in wool available for esterification by alcohols varies with the molecular weight of the latter. Not all the carboxyl groups of wool are accessible even to such a small molecule as methanol which was earlier shown by Fraenkel-Conrat and Olcott[41] to esterify completely a number of proteins.[41a] Likewise, epoxides other than epichlorhydrin failed to react with the carboxyl groups in wool, an effect not observed for other proteins.[42] Bailey[43] has pointed out that procedures such as the FDNB method have been applied for the most part to proteins of the soluble corpuscular type. He extended it to the soluble asymmetric proteins tropomyosin, myosin, and fibrinogen, and with others carried on a collateral physical chemical study of the proteins. All the lysine side chains of myosin, but only about 85 per cent of those of tropomyosin, were fully reactive. Unexpectedly, these proteins appeared to be cyclic polypeptides as there was no evidence of a

(39) A. M. Pappenheimer, Jr., *J. Biol. Chem.* **152**, 385 (1944).
(40) P. Alexander, D Carter, C. Earland, and O. E. Ford, *Biochem. J.* **48**, 629 (1951).
(41) H. Fraenkel-Conrat and H. S. Olcott, *J. Biol. Chem.* **161**, 259 (1945).
(41a) P. E. Wilcox, Abstracts of Papers, XIIth International Congress of Pure and Applied Chemistry, New York, N. Y., September 10–13, 1951, pp. 60–61.
(42) H. Fraenkel-Conrat, *J. Biol. Chem.* **154**, 227 (1944).
(43) K. Bailey, *Biochem. J.* **49**, 23 (1951).

free terminal amino group. A similar finding had been earlier reported for ovalbumin but in this case might be ascribed to linkage with a carbohydrate prosthetic group.[36] These provocative results should be investigated by further end-group analysis, particularly for carboxyl groups.

In discussing the reactivity of proteins a word should be said about the stability of the linkages. A number of instances of a slow, spontaneous loss of substituent groups have been reported. It is well known that formaldehyde may be both reversibly and firmly bound to proteins,[1] and Ross and Stanley[25] have even described the reactivation of formalin-treated tobacco mosaic virus after prolonged dialysis. Though this could not be confirmed by some authors,[44] it has been substantiated by others.[45] There is evidence that the acetylated phenolic groups of tobacco mosaic virus (but not the phenylureido derivative) are hydrolyzed on long standing,[34] and likewise, malonyl substituent groups on the phenolic hydroxyl of serum albumin are lost by spontaneous hydrolysis.[46] Unlike natural phosphoproteins, phosphorylated serum albumin readily undergoes partial dephosphorylation on standing.[47] This behavior must always be considered in estimating the proportion of reactive groups.

2. Group-Specific Versus Nonspecific Reagents

Specific group reagents have been defined as those which under suitable conditions affect only one type of group in a protein.[19] The number of such reagents is quite limited, and in most of the older literature, little effort was made to determine either the specificity or degree of substitution. Few new reagents have been introduced in the past decade, but conditions most favorable for specificity of reaction have been investigated, largely by the group at the Western Research Laboratory. In their review Olcott and Fraenkel-Conrat have placed greatest emphasis on specific group reagents.

As a class the most highly selective reagents are those involving the sulfhydryl group, and these include several examples of fully reversible reactions. However, practically all protein reagents react with —SH groups to some extent. Mercaptide reagents such as p-chloromercuribenzoate are among the most specific, and their combination can be reversed by adding excess mercaptan.

As discussed in Chap. 9, mild oxidizing agents such as iodosobenzoate,

(44) B. Kassanis and A. Kleczkowski, *Biochem. J.* **38**, 20 (1944).
(45) M. A. Fischer and M. A. Lauffer, *Arch. Biochem.* **23**, 291 (1949).
(46) A. H. Tracy and W. F. Ross, *J. Biol. Chem.* **142**, 871 (1942).
(47) M. Mayer and M. Heidelberger, *J. Am. Chem. Soc.* **68**, 18 (1946).

porphyrindin, ferricyanide, and iodine are highly specific under certain conditions. Reducing agents act only on the disulfide bond converting it to sulfhydryl. However, most other protein reagents attack more than one grouping unless conditions most favorable for specificity are employed. For example, ketene which is often used as an acetylating agent for amino groups acts also on phenolic and sulfhydryl groups. Indeed, Li and Kalman[48] found that 75 per cent of the tyrosine groups of the pituitary lactogenic hormone were acetylated while only 35 per cent of the amino groups were covered by ketene, though previously Herriott and Northrop[20] had shown that the amino groups of crystalline pepsin were the first to be acetylated; Stern and White[33] found the same to be true for insulin. This indicates that studies on the behavior of one protein toward a specific reagent cannot be used to infer a corresponding behavior on the part of another protein. In later work, however, Herriott[49] was able to demonstrate that it was the acetylation of the tyrosine phenolic groups that caused the inactivation of pepsin. In brief, acetylation of the phenolic group and inactivation of pepsin are more rapid at pH 5.5 than at pH 4, but the phenyl acetate linkage is split both in molar acid or in alkali at pH 10. Treatment with acid gave a 100 per cent active acetyl pepsin with loss of all "pH 10 labile" acetyl groups and the original number of tyrosine phenols. Alkali treatment of the ketenized preparation can also be used to give selective acetylation of the amino groups (but in this case not an active pepsin because of the alkali liability of both the normal and acetylated enzyme). This summary of one example serves to illustrate the necessity for the choice of conditions most favorable for specificity and for the investigation of each protein with several reagents. Table I, taken from Olcott and Fraenkel-Conrat,[19] lists the effects of reagents on protein groups under conditions most favorable for specificity. The details must be sought in the literature.

Table I may be used as a guide in the selection of specific reagents if it is realized that the conditions most suitable for specificity and for avoiding denaturation must be verified for each protein. A brief consideration of the reactions of proteins by functional groups, rather than by classes of reagents will first be given, references being found in later sections. Conditions most suitable for specificity are assumed.

The free amino groups of proteins are the ϵ-amino groups of lysine and the N-terminal or α-amino groups, the latter corresponding in number to the polypeptide chains in the molecule. Differentiation between free α-amino and free ϵ-amino groups with regard to their essentiality

(48) C. H. Li and A. Kalman, *J. Am. Chem. Soc.* **68**, 285 (1946).
(49) R. M. Herriott, *J. Gen. Physiol.* **19**, 283 (1935).

TABLE I
Effects of Reagents on Protein Groups under Conditions Most Favorable for Specificity*

Reagents	Amino	Guanidyl	Imidazole	Indole	Aliphatic hydroxyl	Amide	Thioether	Disulfide	Sulfhydryl	Phenol	Carboxyl
Oxidizing agents:											
Iodosobenzoate, porphyrindin, ferrocyanide, iodine[a]	−	−	−	−	−	−	−	−	3+	−	−
Hydrogen peroxide[b]						−	2+		3+		−
Reducing agents:											
Cysteine, thioglycolic acid, thioglycol, cyanide, sulfite[c]	−	−	−	−	−	−	−	3+	−	−	−
Alkylating agents:											
Iodoacetate, iodoacetamide[d]	±					−	−		2+	±	−
Dinitrofluorobenzene[e]	3+	−	+			−	−		3+	3+	−
Acylating agents:											
Ketene[f]	3+	−	±	±	−	−	−		+	2+	−
Acetic anhydride[g]	3+	−	−	−	−	−	−		−	±	
Phenyl isocyanate[h]	3+	±				−	−	−	3+	?	−
Carbon suboxide[f]	2+	−	−			−	−	−	3+	2+	−
Azides, benzoyl, carbobenzoxy, benzenesulfonyl chlorides, etc.[i]	3+					−	−		+	±	−
Phosphorus pentoxide[j]	−	−	−	−	3+	−	−	−			−
Concentrated sulfuric acid[k]	−	−	−	−	3+	−	−	−	3+	+	−
Nitrous acid[l]	3+	−		+?	−	−		−	3+	2+	−
Iodine[m]	−	−	±	+?	−	−			3+	3+	−
Formaldehyde (pH 7–8)[n]	(3+)[n]	+	−	−	−	−			±	−	
Formaldehyde (pH 11)[n]	(3+)[n]	3+	−	3+	−	3+			+	−	
Epoxides[o]	+					−	−		2+	2+	3+
Mustard gas[p]	−	−	+			−	+	−	3+	?	2+
Acid–alcohol[q]	−	−	−	−	−	−		−	−	−	3+
Methyl diazoacetate, diazoacetamide[r]	−	−	−	−	−	−			2+	−	3+
p-Chloromercuribenzoate[s]	−	−	−	−	−	−			3+	−	−
Mercuric chloride, other mercurials[t]	−	−	−	−	−	−			3+	−	?
Diazonium compounds[u]		−	3+	+	−	−	−			2+	−
o-Methylisourea[v]	3+	−	−	−	−	−		−	−	−	−

* The symbols used have the following significance: 3+, 2+, and + indicate the relative rapidity or extent of reaction, with 3+ denoting the most rapid reaction. ± indicates reactions that may or may not occur under the conditions suggested. Minus (−) indicates those reactions either that have been shown not to occur or that appear improbable from organic chemical considerations. Question mark (?) indicates those reactions for which more information is required. Spaces have been left

TABLE I. (*Continued*)

blank where there is a possibility of reaction but no evidence is available. Allocation of the proper symbols for each reaction is difficult because of the differences between proteins. The choices are arbitrary.

The conditions of the reaction given in the following footnotes are those suggested by users of these reagents. For references to the original literature, see reference 19 and the text. Table has been slightly modified.

  [a] pH 7, 0.001–0.01 M, 0–25°C., 5–30 min. The specificity of *iodine* as an oxidizing agent requires a high concentration of iodide ions, pH 1–7.

  [b] pH 6.6, 0.005 M, 25°C., 0.5–40 hr.

  [c] pH 7–8, 0.001–0.1 M, 25°C., 0.5–4 hr.

  [d] pH 7–8, 0.05–0.1 M, 0–25°C., 0.5–2 hr.

  [e] pH 7–8, 0.17 M, 25°C., 2 hr.

  [f] pH 5–8, 0–25°C., 5–30 min.

  [g] pH 7–8, 0°C., 30 min.

  [h] pH 7–8, 0–25°C., 0.5–2 hr., reagent–protein ratio, 0.5–2.5:1.

  [i] pH 7–9, 0–25°C., 0.5–2 hr., limited amounts of reagent.

  [j] In 100 % phosphoric acid for several days, 25°C.

  [k] −18° to 0°C. 10–30 min.

  [l] pH 4, 1 M, 0°C., 30 min.

  [m] pH 5–11, −5 to 25°C., 0.5–3 hr., limited amount of iodine, low iodide concentration. See also footnote *a*.

  [n] 25°C., 1–2 M, at pH 7–8, 1 hr.; at pH 11, 10 min. Amino groups react rapidly but reversibly. After isolation by dialysis, amino groups are essentially free.

  [o] pH 5–6, 1–2 M, 25°C., 1–4 days.

  [p] pH 5–6, 25°C., 0.5–4 hr.

  [q] 0.01–0.1 M mineral acid in absolute alcohol, 0–25°C., 1–2 days.

  [r] pH 5 for the ester, pH 6 for the amide, 0°C.; —SH can be blocked with mercurials.

  [s] pH 7, 10^{-5} to 10^{-2} M, 25°C., 5–30 min.

  [t] —SH only combines with mercurials on addition of stoichiometric amount.

  [u] pH 7–9, limited amounts of reagent, 25°C., 30 min.

  [v] pH 10.5–11. 0.5 M, 0°C. for 3 days.

for bioactivity is just now being attempted.[49a]   The ϵ-amino groups vary in reactivity or accessibility to ketene and FDNB, but all N-terminal groups in proteins so far examined react freely with both reagents.   The FDNB reagent is not specific.   However, in end-group or sequence analysis advantage is taken of the fact that the derivatives of the amino group are colored, thus allowing identification after hydrolysis and chromatographic separation.   Except for specific sulfhydryl reagents, P_2O_5, concentrated sulfuric acid, and esterifying agents, all substances

(49a) Reid[49b] recently introduced selective acetylation of free α-amino groups followed by progressive reaction of ϵ-amino groups with FDNB as a means of distinguishing the functions of the two types. He found that both the growth-promoting activity and the diabetogenic activity of the growth hormone depend on the integrity of the ϵ-amino groups but not on the terminal α-amino groups.

(49b) E. Reid, *Nature* **168**, 955 (1951).

listed in Table I react readily with amino groups.   For a time a number
of acylating agents were commonly used to block amino groups, but
none were truly specific.   Acetic anhydride, just recently introduced, is
the reagent of choice.   Guanidination—the conversion of lysine residues
to homoarginine residues by use of O-methylisourea—has also just
been developed and is included in the modified table.   This method
appears specific for amino groups, possibly converting only lysine residues.   It holds promise for studies of the effect of charge and configuration on the physical and biological properties of proteins.

No specific reagents are listed for the guanidyl group of arginine or
the imidazole group of histidine—the other basic residues of proteins.
Neither has yet been clearly implicated in biological activity.   The evidence on their availability or reactivity in proteins is likewise meager.
However, all the imidazole groups of a number of native proteins, except-
ing lactoglobulin, react with FDNB.

Likewise, no specific method exists for blocking the indolyl group of
the tryptophan residue.   This reacts weakly with quite a few protein
reagents and strongly with formaldehyde at pH 11.   The tryptophan
residue interferes in the Folin method for the estimation of unsubstituted
tyrosyl groups.   Amide groups also react strongly with basic formaldehyde but are otherwise inert.   Neither indolyl nor amide groups have yet
been found essential for bioactivity.

The lack of selective methods for certain groups just listed above
(guanidyl, imidazole, indolyl, and amide) has prevented the accumulation
of evidence about their role in bioactivity.   The fact that they have not
yet been implicated does not warrant the conclusion that they are not
essential groups in some proteins.

The aliphatic hydroxyl group of the hydroxy amino acids is due chiefly
to serine and threonine, at least in the globular proteins.   Concentrated
sulfuric acid in the cold is said to be selective for these groups, but the
reaction conditions are probably too severe for most proteins.   Phosphorylation with $POCl_3$ is not specific and introduces labile linkages.
However, phosphorylation with P_2O_5 at room temperature, which is indicated in the modified table, has been developed as a method apparently
specific for the aliphatic hydroxyl group.   This treatment is likewise
probably injurious to proteins.   Though the aliphatic hydroxyl groups
of insulin are apparently not essential for hormonal activity, they seem
involved in the action of crotoxin.   Periodate oxidation of terminal
serine or threonine is being explored.   The aliphatic hydroxyl residues
are largely inert with most of the group reagents listed; they react
slightly with ketene.

The thioether linkage of methionine has received no attention in specificity studies, but several suggestions for modification of this group have been advanced.[19,49c]

Reduction of the disulfide groups is a specific process, no side reaction being known. The masking of disulfide groups has been discussed in Chap. 9; the relative efficiency of reducing agents will be considered later. Olcott and Fraenkel-Conrat[19] emphasize that proteins containing much cystine are particularly sensitive to reducing agents. The disulfide groups are presumed to be involved in cross-linkages. Although the reaction is readily reversible by careful oxidation, the recovery of biological activity has seldom been established.

The sulfhydryl groups of cysteine are the most widely reactive groups of proteins; they combine with virtually all reagents listed in Table I. They have been the most frequently studied protein functional groups because of the early discovery of their liberation during protein denaturation, the requirement of —SH for many enzymes, and their ease of detection and measurement. A number of group-specific methods have been developed that involve oxidation, alkylation, or mercaptide formation; these have been described in the section on protein denaturation. The masking of —SH has perhaps been overemphasized compared to that of other functional groups, and the avidity of —SH for protein reagents has not received sufficient attention. However, the sulfhydryl groups may be protected during reactions by prior oxidation or by blocking with p-chloromercuribenzoate.

Like —SH, the phenolic OH groups of tyrosine residues are widely reactive and have incurred much study both with regard to their masking and their requirement for biological activity. The alkaline lability of the acylated residue is of some advantage in specificity studies. In their investigation, ultraviolet-light-absorption spectra might more profitably be employed than the classical Folin color test. The question whether tyrosyl residues of intact proteins can be oxidized enzymatically has been actively investigated.

The free carboxyl groups of proteins arise from nonamidized residues of aspartic and glutamic acids and also from the C-terminal residues of the polypeptide chains. Recently, the specific esterification of protein carboxyl groups has been explored, and several rather satisfactory methods have been found. The acid-alcohol reagent (Table I) demands that conditions of treatment be separately worked out for each protein

(49c) One reaction of methionine not covered in this chapter but recently of commercial importance is the transformation of the thioether group to the toxic sulfoximine group by reaction with NCl_3. This occurs with some of the methionine groups of the prolamines during treatment of flour with Agene (NCl_3).

and involves some risk of denaturation. Diazoacetic acid derivatives may prove more selective and benign. It is noteworthy that carboxyl groups react only with the esterifying agents, although the possibility of combination with heavy-metal ions should be remembered. The determination of carboxyl end groups by methods involving reduction prior to hydrolysis is in a state of rapid development, and carboxypeptidase is proving useful for the same purpose.

III. The Chemical Reactions of Proteins

This section will treat the chemical reactions of proteins, stating where possible the conditions, time, or degree of completion of the reaction; specificity; lability of linkage; stoichiometry; and methods of estimation of reacting groups for important examples. No attempt will be made to review the literature which is already excellently covered.[18,19] This section necessarily derives from these reviews and will follow Table I in organization. A preference will be given to selective reagents and conditions for specificity and lack of denaturation, and much of the older literature will be disregarded on this account. Reactions will be discussed only for aqueous solvents, and the introduction of cross-linkages will only be mentioned. For details of the reactions or measurement of the amount of reagent introduced, the original literature must be consulted.

The most favorable conditions for specificity and for avoiding denaturation are given in the stoichiometric equation. These are based on reports in the literature and on the opinions of various reviewers. However, it has already been emphasized that the behavior of one protein toward a reagent or toward conditions of denaturation is not necessarily reflected by another. In general, the most favorable conditions are short reaction periods at low concentrations of reagents at temperatures of 0 to 25°. Lower temperatures are preferred because the temperature coefficient for protein denaturation is so much greater than for ordinary chemical reactions. The importance of controlling the pH is emphasized by the conditions prescribed in the footnotes to Table I and in the equations. Most of the reactions take place near neutrality, and the system must be adequately buffered. In a number of instances to be cited, the specificity of a group reagent breaks down if the pH is altered. Moreover, low molecular weight products liberated in some cases may catalyze new reactions, denature the protein, or otherwise affect an unbuffered system. The time of reaction indicated varies from a few minutes to several days. If complete blocking of one group without alteration of another is desired, experience is required with each protein to determine the optimum conditions. Usually this information is obtained by following the course of reaction by analytical methods for the functional groups. In controlling the specificity and degree of reaction, pH is often the most useful variable.

1. OXIDATION

a. Oxidation of —SH, Availability, Reversibility

Perhaps more attention has been paid to the oxidation of the —SH group and to the reversibility and specificity of this reaction than to the treatment of any other protein group. This subject has already been fully covered in Chap. 9 on protein denaturation and moreover, is the subject of a number of reviews.[35,50,51] The classification of the —SH groups into three types (freely reacting, sluggish, and masked) has already been described, as has the measurement of these groups. Many enzymes requiring —SH groups for activity are known (sulfhydryl-activated enzymes, thiol enzymes). These have been reviewed by several authors[50,52] and will be further described by Porter in Chap. 11. Barron[50] has emphasized that in no case has it been demonstrated that *only* the —SH groups are necessary for enzyme activity and that masked groups are, in general, not connected with enzyme activity since they are liberated only on denaturation which usually connotes enzyme inactivation. Under proper conditions, inactivation of an enzyme by oxidation of sulfhydryl groups can always be overcome by reduction. Alkylating and mercaptide-forming reagents, as well as oxidizing agents, should be used to substantiate the requirement for the —SH group, and reversibility of the latter two should be demonstrated.

b. Oxidation of Other Groups

The degree of oxidation of a protein is limited only by the severity of the conditions and the choice of reagent. A variety of oxidizing methods and agents have been used in addition to those mentioned as specific or nearly so for the —SH group. These include hydrogen peroxide; catalyzed oxidation by certain heavy metals such as cupric ion; air oxidation; a number of inorganic oxidants such as bromine, permanganate, and dichromate; strong oxidizing acids, such as perbenzoic, and periodic acids; and even photochemical oxidation in the presence of light sensitizers such as eosin. Ultraviolet and ionizing radiations also appear to oxidize proteins. None of these last mentioned methods are specific, but, after —SH, phenolic and indolyl groups seem to be first affected. This is illustrated by a study of the effect of permanganate on the ultraviolet

(50) E. S. G. Barron, *Advances in Enzymol.* **11**, 201 (1951).
(51) H. Neurath, J. P. Greenstein, F. W. Putnam, and J. O. Erickson, *Chem. Revs.* **34**, 157 (1944).
(52) L. Hellerman, *Physiol. Revs.* **17**, 454 (1937).

absorption spectra of aromatic amino acids and proteins.[52a] Tyrosine and tryptophan are susceptible, but phenylalanine is resistant to permanganate oxidation. Permanganate also induces somewhat parallel changes in the fine structure of the spectra of insulin and pepsin but without any actual increase in absorption. Sizer[53,54] has studied the inactivation of chymotrypsin, invertase, and other enzymes as a function of the oxidation–reduction (redox) potential of the digest with a wide variety of inorganic compounds to poise the potential. Above 540 mv., chymotrypsin was progressively inactivated by a partially reversible oxidation of tyrosyl groups. This approach deserves further investigation. The oxidative cleavage of disulfide bonds with performic acid has already been mentioned. Periodate seems to react with the hydroxylsine groups of proteins.[55] It has been suggested as a reagent for determination of terminal hydroxy amino acids.[19] Jansen et al. found acetaldehyde corresponding to terminal threonine in periodate oxidized preparations of α-chymotrypsin.[56] However, the precursor of the acetaldehyde was shown to be an impurity in the α-chymotrypsin, and Desnuelle et al.,[56a] using the dinitrophenyl (DNP) method have reported that alanine and leucine, and probably phenylalanine, are the N-terminal residues in this enzyme. Nonprotein nitrogen is formed in the periodate oxidation of chymotrypsin, but no significant decrease in molecular weight was detected.[26] Though hydrogen peroxide is suggested as a reagent for the thioether group in Table I, the evidence is meager. At higher concentrations cysteine–H_2O_2 treatment causes an increase in the electrophoretic mobility and heterogeneity and a decrease in serological activity of normal and digested human γ-globulin.[57]

c. Enzymatic Oxidation of Protein Groups

Very few validated instances exist of the modification of the side chains of intact proteins by enzymatic action.[58] Enzymatic oxidation

(52a) W. J. Haas, I. W. Sizer, and J. R. Loofbourow, *Biochim. et Biophys. Acta* **6,** 601 (1951).

(53) I. W. Sizer, *J. Biol. Chem.* **160,** 547 (1945).

(54) I. W. Sizer, *J. Gen. Physiol.* **25,** 399 (1942).

(55) P. Desnuelle and S. Antonin, *Helv. Chim. Acta* **29,** 1306 (1946).

(56) E. F. Jansen, M. D. F. Nutting, R. Jang, and A. K. Balls, *J. Biol. Chem.* **185,** 209 (1950).

(56a) P. Desnuelle, M. Rovery, and C. Fabre, *Compt. rend.* **233,** 1496 (1951).

(57) H. F. Deutsch, *J. Am. Chem. Soc.* **68,** 2625 (1946).

(58) Harris[59] has identified a phosphatase in frog's eggs capable of hydrolyzing the serine phosphate groups of trichloroacetic acid-precipitable casein, and this work has been confirmed and extended by others. The enzyme appears to have a wide distribution.

(59) D. L. Harris, *J. Biol. Chem.* **165,** 541 (1946).

of protein side chains—as opposed to prosthetic groups—is a moot point. In a series of papers Sizer[60,61] has claimed that a variety of proteins containing tyrosine could be oxidized by tyrosinase either directly or after a preliminary treatment with crystalline trypsin. The evidence was based on the marked oxygen consumption measured manometrically during the course of the reaction, on the formation of a pigment absorbing strongly in the blue–violet, the increase in ultraviolet light absorption, and also on chemical determinations of the decrease in tyrosine. The most reactive proteins were the proteolytic enzymes, pepsin, trypsin, and chymotrypsin (also casein which is now known to contain a proteolytic enzyme under the usual conditions of commercial and laboratory preparation).[60-62] The activity of the enzymes was apparently unaffected by tyrosinase oxidation. Although Herriott had earlier shown that extensive acetylation or iodination of the tyrosine groups of pepsin resulted in decreased activity,[49,63] Fraenkel-Conrat did not find tyrosyl groups essential for tryptic activity. This suggested that a large part of the tyrosine residues were inaccessible to tyrosinase. However, Edman[62] pointed out, and Sizer later agreed, that the interpretation of the effect of tyrosinase on the activity of the proteolytic enzymes is obscured by the fact that pepsin is immediately denatured and trypsin undergoes autolysis under the conditions of the experiment. After a repetition of Sizer's manometric experiments, Edman[62] attributed the oxygen consumption and other effects to the reaction of the nonprotein nitrogen impurities always present in proteolytic enzymes rather than to a direct reaction of tyrosinase with tyrosine in the proteins themselves. Sizer[61,64,65] repeated the original work as well as that of Edman and maintained that the manometric and spectroscopic data, as well as the tyrosine analyses, could not be accounted for by oxidation of impurities normally accompanying the protein and were only in part due to oxidation of dialyzable products of autolysis liberated during the reaction.

In later work the proteins of the blood-clotting system, thrombin, fibrinogen, and fibrin also appeared susceptible to oxidation by tyrosinase,[65a] though fibrinogen was previously reported to be relatively resistant.[60] Thrombin and fibrinogen were extensively inactivated, as measured by the increase in clotting time. All three proteins showed an

(60) I. W. Sizer, *J. Biol. Chem.* **163**, 145 (1946).
(61) I. W. Sizer, *J. Biol. Chem.* **169**, 303 (1947).
(62) P. Edman, *J. Biol. Chem.* **168**, 367 (1947).
(63) R. M. Herriott, *J. Gen. Physiol.* **20**, 335 (1937).
(64) I. W. Sizer and J. F. Fennessey, *J. Biol. Chem.* **188**, 351 (1951).
(65) W. J. Haas, I. W. Sizer, and J. R. Loofbourow, *Biochim. et Biophys. Acta* **6**, 589 (1950/1951).
(65a) I. W. Sizer and P. F. Wagley, *J. Biol. Chem.* **192**, 213 (1951).

increased absorption in the ultraviolet. Fibrin formed from fibrinogen previously extensively oxidized by tyrosinase was decreased in amount and appeared amorphous when studied with the electron microscope. Fibrin treated with tyrosinase changed from a fibrous to an amorphous form.

The inactivation of yeast invertase by tyrosinase, studied by Sizer,[65b] had puzzling features such as the fact that tyrosinase preparations from different sources varied greatly in activity without regard to purity. Further investigation revealed that the inactivation of the invertase by tyrosinase could be greatly accelerated by the addition of certain phenolic compounds which were converted by tyrosinase to quinones which in turn inactivated the invertase.[65c] $FeCl_3$ can satisfactorily replace tyrosinase in this system.   Moreover, the oxidation in the presence of phenols was not specific, as primary amino and sulfhydryl groups as well as tyrosyl were involved, and since pepsin, trypsin, chymotrypsin, and insulin could be readily inactivated by tyrosinase plus phenolic compounds.

The possible role of metal ions as activators of tyrosinase for the oxidation of invertase and pepsin was also studied.[64] Only copper and gold appeared to accelerate the inactivation of invertase by tyrosinase. However, "both metals by themselves inhibit invertase, and at concentrations lower than those which produce partial inhibition of invertase these metals do not facilitate the action of tyrosinase on invertase." The maximum acceleration of tyrosinase activity was observed at 3×10^{-7} M $CuCl_2$, at which concentration 30 per cent of the invertase activity was destroyed as compared with the control which contained inactive tyrosinase. Gold was much less satisfactory because it also strongly inhibits the tyrosinase. Copper ions accelerated the oxidation of pepsin without effecting inactivation, although even without added copper the pepsin was extensively oxidized by tyrosinase.

Many proteins are very resistant to oxidation by tyrosinase. Serum albumin is refractory, insulin is relatively resistant, and egg albumin is not at all attacked.[60,65] Pepsin, though very susceptible to tyrosinase oxidation, appears to be attacked more readily in the denatured form, although at pH 5.6 in the native state it is also oxidized.[64] It has been suggested that "the relative resistance of most proteins to attack by tyrosinase may be related to steric unavailability of the tyrosyl groups at the surface of the molecule or to phenolic hydrogen bonding to the side chains of other amino acids, or both."[65] Tyrosine, in which the amino and carboxyl groups are combined, as in a polypeptide chain, is

(65b) I. W. Sizer, Science 108, 335 (1948).

(65c) I. W. Sizer and C. O. Brindley, J. Biol. Chem. 185, 323 (1950).

oxidized by tyrosinase in a manner more closely resembling the oxidation of proteins than the oxidation of free tyrosine.[65] It has already been pointed out (sec. II-1) that the reactivity of the phenolic hydroxyl varies greatly among proteins. Though spectroscopic studies reveal that this group is free to ionize in insulin but is largely masked in serum albumin and egg albumin, all three proteins are quite resistant to tyrosinase oxidation, although insulin is more susceptible than the others.[60,65]

The inactivation of anti-Rh agglutinins by peroxidase in the presence of H_2O_2 is another example of enzymatic oxidation of proteins.[65d] The peroxidative inactivation was accompanied by a decrease in ratio of maximum to minimum in the ultraviolet absorption spectrum, by manometric evidence for oxidation, and by a decrease in microbiologically available tyrosine groups. The results suggested that intact and unaltered tyrosine residues are required for the agglutinin activity. A preliminary report indicates that peroxidase oxidizes other proteins and affects their biological activity.[65e]

2. REDUCTION

The reduction of the disulfide bond is one of the mildest, most specific, and most readily reversible reactions of proteins. It is generally accomplished in neutral or slightly alkaline solution using an excess of any one of a variety of thiol compounds such as cysteine, gluthathione, thioglycolic acid, monothioglycol, the lower alkyl mercaptans, hydrogen sulfide or sodium sulfide, and BAL (British Anti-Lewisite or 2,3-dimercapto-1-propanol).

$$\text{protein}\begin{array}{c} S \\ | \\ S \end{array} + 2RSH \underset{\text{pH 7-8}}{\overset{25°}{\rightleftharpoons}} \text{protein}\begin{array}{c} SH \\ \\ SH \end{array} + R-S-S-R$$

The amount of sulfhydryl compound consumed can be measured and also the number of protein thiol groups formed. Under conditions avoiding denaturation only the disulfide bond is affected. The efficacy of the reagents varies greatly. Thioglycolate has been claimed to be most effective, and, indeed, reduces the lactogenic hormone 50 times more readily than does cysteine.[66]

In reactions proceeding beyond the reversible process pictured above: (1) Cyanides have been used as "reducing agents," their action on the

(65d) P. F. Wagley, I. W. Sizer, L. K. Diamond, and F. H. Allen, *J. Immunol.* **64,** 85 (1950).

(65e) I. W. Sizer, *Federation Proc.* **6,** 202 (1947).

(66) H. Fraenkel-Conrat, M. E. Simpson, and H. M. Evans, *J. Biol. Chem.* **142,** 107, 119 (1942).

disulfide linkage being one of addition; (2) bisulfite has been employed with the keratins to yield equimolar quantities of sulfhydryl groups and S-cysteinyl sulfonate groups; (3) catalytic hydrogenation has been utilized for the removal of the carbobenzoxy moiety from substituted protein[67] or to remove iodine from iodinated insulin;[21] and (4) reduction with zinc or tin in acid, sodium amalgam, sodium in liquid ammonia, and so forth has been applied but is most suitable for proteins such as insulin, which withstand inactivation by the acid or other treatment.

Though small amounts of reducing agents have most often been used in the study of —SH enzymes, extensive reduction of proteins has been applied to demonstrate the requirement of disulfide groups for the activity of enzymes, hormones, and crotoxin and for the dispersion of the fibrous proteins. Unlike the ease of reversible inactivation due to oxidation of essential —SH groups, the regeneration of activity of reduced proteins by means of oxidation is seldom successful. This is because of the low probability of reunion of the original pairs of —SH to form the essential disulfide group. The dispersion of keratins, such as feathers, tortoise shell, etc., is usually accomplished by reduction in the presence of denaturing agents such as urea or detergents.[68] A method for determining the terminal carboxyl groups of proteins by reduction with $LiAlH_4$ under nitrogen has been described by Fromageot et al.[68a] The protein is treated at 55° with the double hydride in a suspension of N-ethylmorpholine, and the free carboxyl groups only are reduced to primary alcohol groups. After hydrolysis of the protein, the amino alcohols are extracted and are identified by paper chromatography. A related method of determining free carboxyl groups of proteins by esterification, then reduction with $LiBH_4$, is described in sec. III-4c (3).

3. Mercaptide Formation

Mercurials and arsenicals have been used increasingly in the study of protein reactions. They have the advantages of highly specific, reversible, and avid combination with single —SH groups under mild conditions. The stoichiometry for p-chloromercuribenzoate has already been presented in a discussion of the utility of this reagent for the detection and estimation of groups in proteins which appeared masked to oxidizing agents. This specific —SH reagent, introduced by Heller-

(67) R. F. Clutton, C. R. Harington, and M. E. Yuill, *Biochem. J.* **32**, 1111, 1119 (1938).

(68) W. H. Ward, L. M. High, and H. P. Lundgren, *J. Polymer Research* **1**, 22 (1946).

(68a) C. Fromageot, M. Jutisz, D. Meyer, and L. Penasse, *Biochim. et Biophys. Acta* **6**, 283 (1950/1951).

man,[22,52] has been most widely applied by Barron and Singer[69,70] in a study of the essentiality of —SH groups in a large number of enzymes. Because it combines at low concentrations with single —SH groups and can readily be removed by the addition of thiols, p-chloromercuribenzoate has been most strongly recommended for this purpose. Almost invariably, inhibition by this compound is relieved by this treatment. The same property makes it useful for protecting sulfhydryl groups during the modification of proteins with other reagents.

Barron takes the specificity of p-chloromercuribenzoate toward protein —SH as established despite the report that $HgCl_2$ can react with carboxyl and amino groups of proteins.[71] A crystalline derivative of native egg albumin and p-chloromercuribenzoate has been prepared containing about 3 moles of mercury per mole protein. Dialysis against excess cysteine restores the original protein.[71a]

Singer[72] has found that the extent of inhibition of wheat germ lipase by reagents such as p-chloromercuribenzoate varies with the substrate used for assay. Since the extent of inhibition increased with the molecular size of the substrate molecule, he suggested that in this case —SH reagents interfered sterically with the approach of large substrate molecules. The inhibition of D-amino acid oxidase was independent of the size of the substrate, indicating that —SH groups were directly involved in the activation of the substrate.

Mercuric salts combine with carboxyl and amino groups of proteins, according to Haarman,[71] but first react stoichiometrically with the —SH group to form mercaptides. Recently, Hughes[32] has reported an elegant study of the equilibrium of mercaptide formation between $HgCl_2$ and a fraction of serum albumin which has a single —SH per mole. On addition of an amount of mercuric chloride just equivalent to the total sulfhydryls, a crystalline mercaptide was obtained which had precisely one-half atom of mercury per albumin molecule. Ultracentrifugal analysis showed it to be a dimer, and, together with light-scattering measurements, revealed the equilibria expressed below:

$$AlbSH + HgCl_2 \rightleftarrows AlbSHgCl + HCl$$
$$AlbSHgCl + AlbSH \rightleftarrows (AlbS)_2Hg + HCl$$

On standing, some of the dimer dissociates to form the monomer, and this reaction is expedited by addition of the stoichiometric amount of

(69) E. S. G. Barron and T. P. Singer, J. Biol. Chem. 157, 221 (1945).

(70) T. P. Singer and E. S. G. Barron, J. Biol. Chem. 157, 241 (1945).

(71) W. Haarman, Biochem. Z. 314, 1 (1943).

(71a) L. R. MacDonnell, R. B. Silva, and R. E. Feeney, Arch. Biochem. and Biophys. 32, 288 (1951).

(72) T. P. Singer, J. Biol. Chem. 174, 11 (1948).

mercuric chloride. The mercaptalbumin can be regenerated by dialysis or by ethanol precipitation in the presence of cysteine. Though crystalline mercuric salts of enzymes have previously been reported, this work lays the foundation for other interesting studies. It has already been followed by the demonstration that copper, zinc, and other metal ions preferentially form mercaptides with the sulfhydryl group of serum albumin before interaction with other side chains.[72a]

Hughes has also investigated the reaction of proteins with methyl mercury iodide.

$$CH_3HgI + \text{protein SH} \rightleftarrows CH_3HgS \text{ protein} + H^+ + I^-$$

It is noteworthy that proteins differ in their rate of reaction with this compound.

Though mercury compounds have been most used for the formation of specific —SH derivatives of proteins and for the blocking or estimation of —SH groups, arsenic-containing compounds and heavy metals inhibit many enzyme systems *in vitro* and cause arsenical or metal intoxication in living systems. Inhibition of the pyruvate oxidation system is one of the outstanding biochemical changes. Stocken and Thompson[72b] have reviewed the historical background of the work which established the connection between the reaction of arsenite and arsenical vesicants with protein thiol groups and the inactivation of enzymes or vesication. Although monothiols afforded protection against the toxic effects of "arsenoxide," and to a lesser extent against the effects of sodium arsenite, the simple thiols were ineffective against more toxic arsenicals such as lewisite [dichloro(2-chlorovinyl)arsine]. The British workers suggested "It seemed possible that the arsenic had combined with two —SH groups closely placed on the same molecule to form a large relatively strainless ring. From these considerations it followed that, in order to displace arsenic from its cyclic combination with proteins such as kerateine, the presence of competing dithiols, which could form even more stable cyclic compounds than the protein, would be necessary."[72b] A number of dithiols were prepared to test this hypothesis, and they proved protective. Of these 2,3-dimercapto-1-propanol (British Anti-Lewisite, BAL) was selected for therapy in man. Though BAL prevents vesication of human skin by lewisite, it is an efficient inhibitor of metal-containing enzymes and may inactivate proteins by reduction of disulfide groups. It is useful for combating arsenical and other metal intoxications.

(72a) I. M. Klotz, J. M. Urquhart, and H. A. Fiess, *J. Am. Chem. Soc.* **74**, 5537 (1952).
(72b) L. A. Stocken and R. H. S. Thompson, *Physiol. Revs.* **29**, 168 (1949).

4. ALKYLATION, ARYLATION, ESTERIFICATION

a. —SH Alkylating Agents

Since Lundsgaard's rediscovery of the iodoacetate poisoning of muscle and the inhibition of fermentation in yeast, great interest has attached to the use of this reagent in physiological experimentaion. Though iodoacetate was once considered a specific reagent for sulfhydryl groups, it is now known that its action is not confined to —SH[73] except under mild conditions of reaction.[73a] Both iodoacetic acid and its amide can react with amino, phenolic, or indolyl groups at alkaline pH, but, under the conditions recommended, these reagents can be used to estimate the —SH groups of proteins by comparing the cysteine content of the hydrolyzates of the original and the alkylated protein. Besides being unspecific, these reagents combine irreversibly and with only a single —SH group. Some of the latent —SH groups of native egg albumin react with iodoacetamide, though not with other reagents. It is noteworthy that iodoacetate leaves a charged residue, whereas, iodoacetamide does not. This appears to be the reason why iodoacetate inhibits heat coagulation of the serum proteins, and iodoacetamide does not. This phenomenon forms the basis for a popular blood test for cancer.[74]

$$ICH_2COO^- + \text{protein SH} \xrightarrow[\text{pH 7-8}]{0-25°} \text{protein—S—CH}_2COO^- + H^+ + I^-$$

$$ICH_2CONH_2 + \text{protein SH} \xrightarrow[\text{pH 7-8}]{0-25°} \text{protein—S—CH}_2CONH_2 + H^+ + I^-$$

b. Fluorodinitrobenzene

Reaction with 1,2,4-fluorodinitrobenzene (FDNB) is an alkylation reaction introduced by Sanger[9] which has assumed great importance for end-group and sequence analysis, as is illustrated in examples already mentioned. However, this reagent has not been found useful for modifying proteins in the study of their biological activity or properties. FDNB reacts quantitatively with the free amino groups of proteins to form a dinitrophenyl- (DNP-)protein. The reaction is carried on in a bicarbonate solution under mild conditions which do not bring about hydrolysis of peptide bonds. For terminal amino acid analysis the DNP-protein is wholly hydrolyzed in strong acid liberating the stable DNP-amino

(73) L. Michaelis and M. Schubert, *J. Biol. Chem.* **106**, 331 (1934).
(73a) H. Fraenkel-Conrat, A. Mohammed, E. D. Ducay, and D. K. Mecham, *J. Am. Chem. Soc.* **73**, 625 (1951).
(74) E. V. Jensen, V. D. Hospelhorn, D. F. Tapley, and C. Huggins, *J. Biol. Chem.* **185**, 411 (1950).

acids which can be identified by their yellow color, fractionated by chromatography, and estimated colorimetrically. In sequence analysis the protein is only partially hydrolyzed by acid or by enzymes, and the peptides must be made to react with FDNB. The FDNB reaction is not specific for free α-amino groups. Fluorodinitrobenzene also combines with the ϵ-amino groups of lysine giving rise to ϵ-DNP-lysine which can be identified. In addition, sulfhydryl groups, the phenolic hydroxyl groups of the tyrosine residues, and the imidazole groups of the histidine residues form DNP products. However, these do not interfere with the estimation since they are colorless.[37] Further information on the use of the FDNB reagent for the determination of the arrangement of amino acids in proteins can be found in Chaps. 2 and 3 and in the review by Sanger.[74a]

c. Methylation

(1) *Miscellaneous Alkylating Agents.* The methylation of proteins can easily be accomplished by use of reagents such as dimethyl sulfate $[(CH_3)_2SO_4]$, methyl iodide and methyl bromide, and diazomethane (CH_2N_2) by treatment at room temperature and slightly alkaline pH. Methylation is rather general, and both O- and N-methyl derivatives are formed. Carboxyl, amino, and phenolic hydroxyl groups, and sometimes the sulfhydryl group, react readily. Even the hydroxy amino acids are methylated in strongly alkaline solution. Methoxyl is often said to be introduced in amounts corresponding to the free carboxyl groups; such methyl esters are readily saponified by alkali at low temperature. The procedures employed in the use of these reagents by various authors have varied widely, and little can be stated about the conditions most favorable for specificity. Besides standard techniques for the determination of free amino and free phenolic groups, several methods are available for estimating the site and degree of alkylation, for

(74a) F. Sanger, *Advances in Protein Chem.* **7**, 1 (1952).

example: titration, dye binding (suitable only for the esters of higher alcohols), alkaline hydrolysis of labile O-methyl groups, and the Zeisel methoxyl method.

For the most part these miscellaneous alkylating agents have been applied to the methylation of fibrous proteins such as wool, silk fibroin, and gelatin[75-77] in a study of structure or a search for useful derivatives. Considerable work has been done on insulin.[78] Charles and Scott[79] obtained nearly complete inactivation of the crystalline hormone by reaction with methyl iodide. Incubation with dilute alkali at 0° restored 30 per cent of the activity. Though the authors did not attribute inactivation to esterification, others have since pointed out that conditions were favorable for esterification and have noted the alkaline lability of the ester linkage[18,19] (see also below). Jensen et al.[80] have reported a decrease in the cystine content of insulin after treatment with diazomethane and methyl iodide and also a loss of amino nitrogen with diazomethane. Both of these reagents reversibly inactivate insulin. It is probable that both esterification and methylation take place. In addition to these studies, Haurowitz[81] has extensively methylated hemoglobin and egg albumin by treatment with dimethyl sulfate, and Herriott[18] mentions the inactivation of pepsin by introduction of 15 methoxyl groups per mole of protein.

(2) *Esterification with Acid–Alcohol.* Although the esterification of proteins with acid–alcohol has long been employed and much used for insulin,[78] only recently have procedures been introduced for the selective and quantitative methylation of the carboxyl groups of proteins without perceptible modifications of other groupings.[41,41a] In early work, Felix[82] used methyl alcohol saturated with hydrogen chloride to form the methyl esters of such atypical proteins as protamines, histones, and gliadin; however, some degradation must have been induced by the strong acid. In 1945 Fraenkel-Conrat and Olcott[41] reinvestigated the conditions for obtaining selective and complete esterification of the carboxyl groups of a number of proteins and developed a more specific and less drastic method. For maximal esterification the procedure calls for suspension of the dry protein in a 100-fold amount of alcohol which is made 0.1 N with concentrated HCl. The dilute acid acts as a catalyst, and the derivative is obtained after one to several days standing at room temperature. It can be isolated by precipitation or by lyophilization after

(75) S. Blackburn, E. G. H. Carter, and H. Phillips, *Biochem. J.* **35**, 627 (1941).
(76) S. Blackburn, R. Consdon, and H. Phillips, *Biochem. J.* **38**, 25 (1944).
(77) H. A. Rutherford, W. I. Patterson, and M. Harris, *J. Research Natl. Bur. Standards* **19**, 467 (1937).
(78) H. Jensen and E. A. Evans, Jr., *Physiol. Revs.* **14**, 188 (1934).
(79) A. F. Charles and D. A. Scott, *J. Biol. Chem.* **92**, 289 (1931).
(80) H. Jensen, E. A. Evans, Jr., W. D. Pennington, and E. D. Schock, *J. Biol. Chem.* **114**, 199 (1936).
(81) F. Haurowitz, *Z. physiol. Chem.* **256**, 28 (1938).
(82) K. Felix and H. Reindl, *Z. physiol. Chem.* **205**, 11 (1932).

dialysis. Primary alcohols other than methanol reacted sluggishly and incompletely, but methanol gave quantitative agreement between the carboxyl content of the untreated proteins and the methoxyl content of the methylated proteins. No other groups were detectably affected. Of course, many proteins cannot withstand even dilute acid. Indeed, egg albumin is methylated but denatured. Moreover, the conditions with respect to time, temperature, and composition of the esterifying agent must be worked out individually for each protein.

$$\text{protein COOH} + CH_3OH \xrightarrow[0.1 \ N \ HCl]{0-25°} \text{protein CO.OCH}_3 + H_2O$$

The method is suitable only for study of the effect of esterification on the biological activity of proteins which are resistant to denaturation by acid and alcohol. It has recently been applied to insulin and the pituitary lactogenic hormone. In the case of the lactogenic hormone it was concluded[83] that carboxyl groups are essential for the biological activity, although it was recognized that the esterification may have induced physical changes in the nature of the molecule through rupture of hydrogen or ionic bonds or change in net charge. In a study of insulin methyl ester, Mommaerts and Neurath[84] confirmed the specificity of the reaction, finding that under suitably modified conditions, the carboxyl groups of the hormone were exclusively and completely esterified. The biological activity was diminished only after the first two-thirds of the carboxyl groups had been esterified, but incorporation of a few more methoxyl groups completely abolished the activity. Considerable reactivation was achieved by alkaline hydrolysis of the ester groups. Though others have also regenerated insulin activity by this procedure, the potency of the lactogenic hormone was not restored by hydrolysis with alkali at pH 11. It should be emphasized again that there are very few proteins that can withstand the acid, alcohol, and alkali required in the inactivation–reactivation treatment. Moreover, prolonged exposure to the acid–alcohol at room temperature or more brief treatment at elevated temperatures causes introduction of methoxyl in excess of the number of original carboxyl groups, probably through the hydrolysis of amide groups.[41,84]

(3) *Esterification with Diazo Derivatives.* The serious risk of denaturation introduced by use of methanol–hydrochloric acid prompted a search for a milder group-specific methylating agent. Wilcox[41a] has reported that methyl diazoacetate and diazoacetamide, which convert the carboxyl group to a glycolic acid derivative, satisfy many of the criteria of ideal protein-group reagents. The diazoacetic acid derivatives

(83) C. H. Li and H. Fraenkel-Conrat, *J. Biol. Chem.* **167**, 495 (1947).
(84) W. F. H. M. Mommaerts and H. Neurath, *J. Biol. Chem.* **185**, 909 (1950).

react under mild conditions in aqueous or alcohol–water media (pH 5–6, 0°). The reaction is completely reversible, the glycolic residue being removed by hydrolysis at pH 10 and 0°. Only the carboxyl and sulf-hydryl groups react, and the reaction can be made specific by temporarily blocking the —SH with mercurials. The number of glycolic residues introduced equals the number of carboxyl groups covered. Application of this method to human serum albumin did not produce any perceptible change in size or shape of the molecules. A single component was obtained upon electrophoresis, but the boundary spreading indicated some statistical heterogeneity of modification when 25 carboxyl groups were esterified.

In a preliminary communication Chibnall and Rees[85] have described a new method for the determination of the amide and free carboxyl groups in proteins. Insulin dissolved in 0.03 N 85 per cent (v/v) ethanolic HCl was treated in the cold with an excess of diazomethane in ether to esterify the free γ-carboxyls of the glutamyl residues, the free β-carboxyls of the aspartyl residues, and the free α-carboxyls. The ester groups are reduced with an excess of LiBH$_4$ in tetrahydrofuran to form the corre-sponding hydroxyls. The terminal amino acids form β-amino alcohols which react with periodic acid, and the aldehydes so formed can be identified after allowance is made for serine and threonine.

d. Epoxides

Epoxides have been investigated as reagents for the esterification of protein carboxyl groups in aqueous solution at room temperature. Fraenkel-Conrat[42] found that over the course of several days ethylene oxide, propylene oxide, and epichlorohydrin reacted with a number of proteins to yield less soluble derivatives with isoelectric points shifted as much as 3 pH units to the alkaline side. These facts, as well as the electrophoretic behavior and estimation of the amphoteric groups by the dye-binding method, indicated that the carboxyl groups were largely esterified, but that the basicity of the amino groups was unaffected. The reaction, however, proved to be unspecific. Phenolic and sulfhydryl groups formed ethers and thio ethers, respectively, with the epoxide reagents. The amino groups were preferentially alkylated at pH 8 to form secondary amines without suppression of their basic nature, thus giving the physical properties of selectively esterified proteins. The reaction was carried out in neutral, acid, alkaline, and urea solution, and the proportion of the different functional groups reacting depended some-what upon the conditions. The four possible reactions have been for-mulated as follows:

(85) A. C. Chibnall and M. W. Rees, *Biochem. J.* **48**, xlvii (1951).

$$\text{protein}\overset{\overset{\displaystyle COOH}{\diagup}}{\underset{\underset{\displaystyle SH}{\diagdown}}{\bigcirc}}OH + \underset{\underset{\displaystyle O}{|}}{CH_2}\!-\!CHR \rightarrow \text{protein}\overset{\overset{\displaystyle COOCH_2\!-\!CHOH\!-\!R}{\diagup}}{\underset{\underset{\displaystyle S\!-\!CH_2\!-\!CHOH\!-\!R}{\diagdown}}{\bigcirc}}O\!-\!CH_2\!-\!CHOH\!-\!R$$

e. Mustard Gas and Related Compounds

Since World War II much has been revealed about the action of mustard gas, the nitrogen mustards, and related war gases on biological systems, and many new investigations have been initiated. Particular emphasis has been placed on the reaction of war gases with enzymes, on nucleoproteins, in nucleic acid synthesis and general tissue metabolism, and as chemical agents for inducing mutations in microorganisms. Most of this work is outside the scope of this chapter. Much attention has been focused on the reaction of the sulfhydryl group with mustard gas and other vesicant and lachrymatory war gases. Indeed, the inhibition of enzymes has been attributed by a group of Belgian workers (Bacq, Fischer, Desreux, and Fredericq[86,87]) to combination of mustard with —SH. In support of this concept many investigators have found that war gases such as the mustards, chloroacetophenone, bromopicrin, chloropicrin, and phosgene react with the —SH groups of proteins, as summarized in several reviews.[50,88] However, these reagents are not specific for the sulfhydryl group, since they also combine with the carboxyl, amino, and imidazole groups and even affect the phenol color of proteins. Despite many attempts, the reactions have not been reversed under physiological conditions.[50] The purity of the mustard is important in studying the reaction with —SH.

The reaction of mustard gas [bis (2-chloroethyl) sulfide] with purified soluble proteins has been investigated by a number of authors, notably Herriott, Anson, and Northrop[88,89] and Davis and Ross.[90] The former found that thirteen different proteins, including six crystalline enzymes, rapidly combined with liquid mustard gas on stirring at 25° at pH 6–8. The rate of inactivation of the enzymes was studied kinetically and found to vary characteristically. All were inactivated in contrast to the cited conclusion of Dixon, Van Heyningen, and Needham[88] to the effect that the potency of some ezymes is unaffected by mustards. At pH 6 the carboxyl groups were largely esterified, as indicated by the fact that the decrease in free acidic groups

(86) Z. M. Bacq, *Enzymologia* **10**, 48 (1941).

(87) V. Desreux, E. Fredericq, and P. Fischer, *Bull. soc. chim. biol.* **28**, 7 (1946).

(88) J. H. Northrop, M. Kunitz, and R. M. Herriott, Crystalline Enzymes, Columbia University Press, New York, 1948.

(89) R. M. Herriott, M. L. Anson, and J. H. Northrop, *J. Gen. Physiol.* **30**, 185 (1946).

(90) S. B. Davis and W. F. Ross, *J. Am. Chem. Soc.* **69**, 1177 (1947).

equaled the number of alkali-labile mustard residues bound. When crystalline horse oxyhemoglobin and serum albumin were treated with mustard gas under controlled pH conditions, the greatest reduction in titrable groups occurred in the region pH 2–5.5 where carboxyl is normally titrated, indicating that free carboxyl groups were esterified.[90] However, a further loss of titrable groups occurring at pH 5.5–8.5 suggested that imidazole groups also react with mustard gas. This brief summary must neglect studies of the effect of mustards on skin proteins, the inactivation of viruses, etc. The use of S^{35}–mustard gas sulfone-treated proteins in studies of the antigen–antibody reaction is an interesting application.[5] The reactions with protein functional groups have been written in terms of the sulfonium or imonium ions.[91] The reactions resemble those of epoxides.

The reaction of bromopicrin and chloropicrin with egg albumin, myosin, and sylfhydryl enzymes has been investigated by Fredericq and Desreux.[87,92] From a study of the titration curve and electrophoretic mobility of chloropicrin-treated egg albumin, these workers concluded that the principal action of this toxic agent was the oxidation of the —SH groups. This conclusion was based on the fact that the titration curve was shifted in the region pH 8–11 by an amount corresponding exactly to the four —SH groups known to be in egg albumin, and by the effect of denaturation on the rapidity of the reaction. However, iodine which also oxidizes the —SH groups of egg albumin shifted the titration curve in a different manner. It was suggested that 1 mole of chloropicrin oxidizes 3 moles of cysteine, according to the following equation, but the products of the transformation of the radical —CNO_2 have not been identified.

$$6HS—CH_2—CHNH_2—COOH + 2CCl_3NO_2 \rightarrow$$
$$3HOOC—CHNH_2—S—S—CHNH_2—COOH + 6HCl$$

(91) H. Fraenkel-Conrat *in* D. M. Greenberg, Amino Acids and Proteins, C. C. Thomas, Springfield, Ill., 1951, Chap. 9.

(92) E. Fredericq and V. Desreux, *Bull. soc. chim. biol.* **29**, 100, 105 (1947).

924 FRANK W. PUTNAM

5. ACYLATION

Acylating agents are among the most common chemicals employed for the modification of proteins, though as seen from Table I, none of these reagents are specific for a functional group. All acylating agents react with the amino group, sometimes preferentially but never selectively, and most also form derivatives of phenolic hydroxyl and —SH and sometimes of other functional moieties. Among the acylating reagents employed with a single protein, tobacco mosaic virus, have been: ketene, phenyl isocyanate, carbobenzoxy chloride, *p*-chlorobenzoyl chloride, and benzenesulfonyl chloride.

a. Acetylation

(1) *Ketene.* Ketene has been perhaps the most frequently used reagent for the determination of protein group specificity and ranks next to nitrous acid and formaldehyde for frequency in use for the modification of serum proteins, antigens, and antibodies. About 20 enzymes, hormones, toxins, and viruses have been ketenized. Because of this multiplicity of applications, reviews must be consulted as a guide to the original literature.

Ketene ($H_2C\!=\!C\!=\!O$) is an extremely toxic gas generated by passing acetone vapor over an electrically heated filament. Several ketene generators suitable for use with proteins have been described.[93,94] The gas is usually bubbled into the protein solution through a sintered-glass disk, suggesting another disadvantage for proteins susceptible to surface denaturation. Acetylation is carried out at 0–25° and pH 4–8 with a rapid flow of gas for periods no longer than 20–30 min. Free amino groups are measured as usual with the Van Slyke nitrous acid reaction. The extent of acetylation of tyrosine groups is estimated by the procedure of Herriott[49] by comparison of the Folin color value at pH 8 and 11, a method based on the fact that acetyl groups attached to the phenolic hydroxyls are removed by short hydrolysis at pH 11. Ketene reacts with —NH, —OH, and —SH groups, but owing to the behavior of pepsin[20,88] and insulin,[33] an erroneous impression has developed that amino groups always react more rapidly than phenolic groups. This subject and other facts pertinent to the ketene reaction have already been discussed in the introductory remarks focused on acetylation with ketene as an example of the potentialities and pitfalls in the formation of protein derivatives.

Neuberger[95] has concluded from model studies with amino acids that when proteins are treated with ketene in alkaline solution, acetylation may take place at amino, thiol, and phenolic groups while guanidino and aliphatic —OH groups are unaffected. Olcott and Fraenkel-Conrat[19] summarize the disadvantages of ketene as a good protein reagent as follows: "(1) Its action is not sufficiently specific for amino groups. (2)

(93) R. M. Herriott, *J. Gen. Physiol.* **18**, 69 (1934).
(94) C. H. Li, *Science* **90**, 143 (1939).
(95) A. Neuberger, *Biochem. J.* **32**, 1452 (1938).

It does not generally attack this type of grouping to completion. (3) As an unstable gas it needs special equipment for its preparation, is difficult to employ in accurately known amounts, and tends to surface-denature sensitive proteins. As an additional disadvantage, ketene appears to be extremely toxic. It has been suggested that it might racemize some of the asymmetric carbon atoms of proteins if reaction is carried out in acid solution."

$$\text{protein} \begin{pmatrix} NH_2 \\ SH \\ \\ \\ OH \end{pmatrix}\!\!-\!OH + O\!=\!C\!=\!CH_2 \xrightarrow[\text{pH 5-8}]{0-25°} \text{protein} \begin{pmatrix} NH\!-\!CO\!-\!CH_3 \\ S\!-\!CO\!-\!CH_3 \\ \\ \\ O\!-\!CO\!-\!CH_3 \end{pmatrix}\!\!-\!O\!-\!CO\!-\!CH_3$$

(2) *Acetic Anhydride.* Acetic anhydride has been recommended as the superior reagent for acetylating proteins. From Table I it can be seen that its action is far more specific than that of ketene; besides, it lacks some of the obvious disadvantages of that toxic, unstable gas. Although acetic anhydride has often been used under severe conditions such as anhydrous solution at high temperatures, a recent technique is said to produce acetylation without denaturation. This method attributed to Hughes[18] consists of reaction by slow addition of acetic anhydride to the protein dissolved or suspended in a concentrated cooled solution of sodium acetate. Hemoglobin acetylated by this method has unchanged oxygen-combining capacity, and egg albumin retains its masked —SH group, is heat-coagulable, and remains soluble at its iso-electric point. According to data of Olcott and Fraenkel-Conrat,[19] the number of acetyl equivalents introduced into bovine serum albumin, egg albumin, and insulin corresponds closely with the original number of amino groups and with the loss in amino groups as measured in the nitrous acid reaction. Lysozyme and crotoxin, however, did not react to completion. Extensive acetylation of crystalline trypsin by this procedure did not abolish its enzymatic activity, but the acetylated derivative was completely resistant to inhibition by ovomucoid (the egg white trypsin inhibitor). On the other hand, acetylation of most of the amino groups did not destroy the trypsin-inhibiting property of the ovomucoid.[27] Acetylated bovine serum albumin has been used by Klotz[96] in a study of the groups responsible for ion interactions.

$$\text{protein } NH_2 + O\!\!\begin{array}{c} \diagup COCH_3 \\ \diagdown COCH_3 \end{array} \xrightarrow[\text{pH 7-8}]{0°} \text{protein}\!-\!NHCOCH_3$$

(96) I. M. Klotz, *Cold Spring Harbor Symposia Quant. Biol.* **14,** 97 (1950).

b. Aromatic Isocyanates

Phenyl isocyanate readily forms phenylureido (phenylcarbamido, phenylcarbamino) derivatives with a large number of proteins at pH 8 and 0°. It was long assumed that under these conditions the amino groups were principally attacked, and probably also the tyrosine hydroxyls.[97] The decrease in amino nitrogen agreed well with the number of p-bromo-phenyl isocyanate residues introduced into casein, horse serum albumin, and insulin,[98,99] and the amino nitrogen of insulin almost completely disappeared on reaction with phenyl isocyanate.[97] However, phenyl-ureido tobacco mosaic virus showed an increase in chromogenic power in Herriott's pH 11 method for measurement of the phenolic groups, whereas other acylated derivatives exhibited a decreased color.[38] In order to explain this effect, Miller[100] studied the determination of phenolic groups in the various virus derivatives by means of model experiments with derivatives of tyrosine. He concluded that the effect was due to the greater rate of saponification of the phenylureido derivative at pH 11 and to the formation of aniline in this reaction. Consequently, as indicated in Table I, it is still uncertain whether tyrosine couples with phenyl isocyanate. However, Fraenkel-Conrat[101] reported that phenyl isocyanate reacts rapidly with the amino groups of proteins, and Fraenkel-Conrat and Olcott (unpublished experiments[19]) have found that the —SH groups of native egg albumin react even more readily at 0° with m-chloro-phenyl isocyanate than do the amino groups.

The reaction of phenyl isocyanate and related compounds with insulin marks one of the earlier and more interesting studies of the formation of a protein derivative. Jensen and Evans[78] found that when insulin was treated with phenyl isocyanate, a product is obtained which retains approximately 5 per cent of the original activity of the hormone, and almost all of the amino nitrogen disappears. Hopkins and Wormall[98,99] also noted the inactivation of insulin by this reagent and suggested that the free amino groups were attacked. In further study of an acid

(97) H. Jensen and E. A. Evans, Jr., J. Biol. Chem. 108, 1 (1935).
(98) S. J. Hopkins and A. Wormall, Biochem. J. 27, 740, 1706 (1933).
(99) S. J. Hopkins and A. Wormall, Biochem. J. 28, 2125 (1934).
(100) G. L. Miller, J. Biol. Chem. 146, 345 (1942).
(101) H. Fraenkel-Conrat, J. Biol. Chem. 152, 385 (1944).

hydrolyzate of phenyl isocyanate–insulin, Jensen and Evans[97] isolated the phenylhydantoin of phenylalanine, an amino acid not previously found in crystalline insulin.   Similar treatment of insulin with α-naphthyl isocyanate yielded the naphthylhydantoin of phenylalanine.   Some of the free amino groups of insulin evidently were due to phenylalanine. This work not only served to establish a terminal group of a relatively pure protein at an early date but also provided the first evidence for the occurrence of phenylalanine in insulin.   This technique has been applied to several other proteins[102] and has been discussed earlier (Chap. 3) and elsewhere.[12]   Some years later, Sanger,[9,10] using the FDNB method, confirmed that phenylalanine was the terminal amino acid of one of the polypeptide chains of insulin.   As described in Chap. 3, phenyl isothiocyanate has more recently been used to identify the N-terminal amino acid residue and has been applied in the stepwise degradation of peptides.[102a]   Both phenyl isocyanate and the thio analog have proved useful as blocking agents in a subtractive microbiological method for the determination of N-terminal residues.[102b]   The microbiologically recoverable amino acids of the treated and hydrolyzed protein are compared with those of the complete hydrolyzate of the untreated protein.   The sequence of a tripeptide was established by selective hydrolysis.

Edman's method of stepwise degradation of peptides[102a] has recently been adapted to proteins by Fraenkel-Conrat and Fraenkel-Conrat.[102c] Phenyl isothiocyanate reacts with the terminal amino group under conditions similar to other protein end-group reagents.   The thiohydantoin of the terminal amino acid is then split off with aqueous HCl under conditions which do not hydrolyze the protein (ca. 1 N, 36°).   Identification of the terminal amino acid is done chromatographically after regeneration by hydrolysis of the thiohydantoin with baryta.   The method has already been applied in a preliminary study to insulin and a number of other proteins with results that accord with findings obtained by the DNP method.   The phenyl isothiocyanate method holds promise for the complete elucidation of the amino acid sequence of proteins, but, as attempts to apply the successive degradation to insulin have shown,[102d] the appearance of extra reactive groups and of degradative products may limit its application.

Isocyanates have largely been employed for the coupling of proteins

(102) J. Roche, R. Michel, and J. Schiller, Compt. rend. **219**, 38 (1944).

(102a) P. Edman, Acta Chem. Scand. **4**, 277, 283 (1950).

(102b) S. W. Fox, T. L. Hurst, and K. F. Itschner, J. Am. Chem. Soc. **73**, 3573 (1951).

(102c) H. Fraenkel-Conrat and J. Fraenkel-Conrat, Acta Chem. Scand. **5**, 1409 (1951).

(102d) H. N. Christensen, Compt. rend. trav. Lab. Carlsberg **28**, No. 7–8 (1953).

to carcinogenic hydrocarbons related to anthracene.[103] Several enzymes have been reacted with phenyl isocyanate to demonstrate the requirement for amino groups. Sizer[53] concluded that phenyl isocyanate added at 0.5 mg./mg. chymotrypsin had relatively little effect in inactivating the enzyme and hence that primary amino groups are not essential for activity. However, when ten times as much reagent was added, rapid inactivation was produced. This suggests the need for establishing the nature and number of groups reacting with a nonspecific substituting agent.

c. Malonylation with Carbon Suboxide

Carbon suboxide (C_3O_2) is a gas with many of the properties, reactions, and disadvantages of ketene. It combines with amino, sulfhydryl, and tyrosyl groups to form half-amides and half-esters of malonic acid, the —SH being attacked most readily.[101] For proteins lacking —SH, carbon suboxide can be made specific for amino groups by virtue of the slow hydrolysis of the O-malonyl group in acetate buffer, pH 4.0.[104] The use of carbon suboxide instead of ketene introduces a polar carboxyl group instead of a neutral aliphatic side chain into the molecule. Consequently, the malonyl derivatives are more acidic. Because of the symmetry of the compound, there are two equally reactive loci, and dimerization may conceivably take place. At pH 5–8 and at room temperature or in the cold, addition of carbon suboxide blocks more than 75 per cent of the amino and tyrosyl groups of a number of proteins, as was shown in a series of investigations by Tracy and Ross.[24,46] The possible reactions are given below.

$$\text{protein}\overset{\displaystyle \text{NH}_2}{\underset{\displaystyle \bigcirc\!-\!\text{OH}}{\overset{\diagup}{\underset{\diagdown}{\text{—SH}}}}} + \text{O}=\text{C}=\text{C}=\text{C}=\text{O} + \text{H}_2\text{O} \rightarrow$$

$$\text{protein}\overset{\displaystyle \text{NH—CO—CH}_2\text{—COOH}}{\underset{\displaystyle \bigcirc\!-\!\text{O—CO—CH}_2\text{—COOH}}{\overset{\diagup}{\underset{\diagdown}{\text{—S—CO—CH}_2\text{—COOH}}}}}$$

protein—NH$_2$ + O=C=C=C=O + H$_2$N—protein →
protein—NH—OC—CH$_2$—CO—NH—protein

One of the most important uses of malonylation concerns an inquiry into the specificity of pepsin. In confirmation of Herriott and Northrop's[20] elegant study of the acetylation of pepsin by ketene, Tracy and

(103) H. J. Creech and W. R. Franks, Am. J. Cancer 30, 555 (1937).
(104) A. H. Tracy and W. F. Ross, J. Biol. Chem. 146, 63 (1942).

Ross[104] showed that loss of activity was associated with blocking of the phenolic hydroxyls. Half of the activity was lost when one-fourth of these groups had reacted, and almost complete inactivation occurred when three-fourths had disappeared. Though a higher percentage of the amino groups reacted simultaneously, hydrolysis of the O-malonyl linkage resulted in partial reactivation. The N-malonylpepsin so formed had the same specificity toward proteins and a synthetic substrate as did native pepsin. Thus, the specificity of pepsin was not altered by the presence of carboxyl groups in positions normally occupied by the basic lysyl residues, indicating that these basic groups were both unessential for activity and without influence on the specificity of the enzyme. Surprisingly, both the native and the N-malonyl enzyme hydrolyzed malonyl serum albumin to a greater extent than the unmodified protein. Discussion of the physical properties of malonylated proteins will be reserved till later.

d. Benzoylation, Carbobenzoxylation, Etc.

(1) Benzoyl Chloride. Benzoylation with this reagent (the Schotten-Baumann reaction) has been used for the preparation of protein derivatives—particularly antigens, for the investigation of the active groups in tobacco mosaic virus, and has been suggested for determination of terminal amino groups of peptides. When limited amounts of benzoyl chloride are added to the protein in weakly alkaline solution, the amino groups are largely acylated, as was shown by Mellon, Korn, and Hoover[105] in a study of casein. A number of earlier inquiries had indicated that the ε-amino groups of lysine were attacked but had also suggested the involvement of other basic groups. Benzoylated tobacco mosaic virus possessing full biological activity has been described by Agatov,[29] and Miller and Stanley[30] prepared the p-chlorobenzoyl virus. With up to 70 per cent of the amino groups substituted and only 11 per cent of the phenol plus indole, the p-chlorobenzoyl derivative retained full activity on one host, Nicotiana glutinosa, but was only half as infectious on another, Phaseolus vulgaris. The varied response of different hosts to virus derivatives was also found for the acetyl, carbobenzoxy, and benzenesulfonyl virus, but no significant difference in host susceptibility was encountered with the DNP-virus.[106] The true extent of phenolic group blocking in these derivatives seems in doubt, since the apparent degree of substitution depended on the denaturing agent employed.[34]

(105) E. F. Mellon, A. H. Korn, and S. R. Hoover, J. Am. Chem. Soc. 69, 827 (1947).
(106) C. A. Knight, J. Biol. Chem. 192, 727 (1951).

The chief reaction undergone by proteins with the addition of minimum quantities of benzoyl chloride is given below.

$$\text{protein—NH}_2 + \text{Cl—C} \overset{O}{\diagdown} \bigcirc \xrightarrow[\text{pH 8}]{0-25°} \text{protein—NH—CO—} \bigcirc$$

(2) *Carbobenzoxylation.* Carbobenzoxy chloride, a reagent frequently relied on for peptide synthesis, has also been successfully applied to the modification of proteins to give both the carbobenzoxy derivative and also *O-β-glucosido-N-carbobenzoxytyrosyl* proteins.[67] Its chief advantage should be the possibility of removal of the group by catalytic hydrogenation with regeneration of the protein. This feature has not been sufficiently exploited as yet, and the difficulty of preparing this reagent is a drawback. The reaction takes place readily at pH 8, chiefly with the amino group. There was some evidence that carbobenzoxy chloride was more selective for amino groups than the other acylating agents tried on tobacco mosaic virus.[30] The electrophoretic homogeneity of these derivatives was important in establishing that virus activity was exhibited by the acylated virus rather than by a small amount of contaminating normal virus. Insulin, however, was inactivated by combination with carbobenzoxy chloride.[107]

$$\bigcirc \text{—CH}_2\text{—O—C—Cl} + \text{H} \diagdown \underset{\text{H}}{\overset{}{\diagup}} \text{N-protein} \xrightarrow[\text{pH 8}]{0-25°}$$

$$\bigcirc \text{—CH}_2\text{—O—C—NH-protein}$$

(3) *Benzenesulfonic Acid.* 2-Napthalenesulfonyl chloride and benzenesulfonyl chloride have both been widely applied for the determination of terminal amino acids and sequence studies of peptides, particularly the former compound, but this application was largely before the discovery of Sanger's FDNB reagent. Although a number of protein derivatives have been formed, including those of gelatin[108] and tobacco mosaic virus,[30] there is not much to recommend this over other acylating agents already discussed. Gurin and Clarke[108] succeeded in isolating the ε-aminobenzenesulfonyl derivative of lysine from gelatin and compared the titration curves of the normal and arylsulfonated proteins.

(4) *Azides and Azlactones.* Azides and azlactones have served for the purpose of introducing complex moieties into proteins, often in a study of

(107) W. E. Gaunt and A. Wormall, *Biochem. J.* **33**, 908 (1939).
(108) S. Gurin and H. T. Clarke, *J. Biol. Chem.* **107**, 395 (1934).

antigenicity. A group of English workers[67] have used O-β-glucosido-N-carbobenzoxytyrosyl azide to link glucose to proteins, reducing the carbobenzoxy group after the reaction. Though they think the reaction is specific for α-amino groups, this conclusion has been questioned.[19] Proteins modified by reaction with azlactones have been studied by the anaphylactic reaction, but Timasheff and Nord[109] present the first evidence for the change in chemical and physical properties. The combination of a thiophene-2-azlactone [2-phenyl-4-(2-thenal)-5-oxazolone] with egg albumin is not group specific, as shown below:

protein—(—XH)$_n$ + n [structure] $\xrightarrow[\text{pH 8}]{25°}$

protein— { —X—Ö—C=CH— } X=NH, O, S, =N

The principal reactive groups are the primary amino groups of the protein, but other types of reaction must have occurred because the light absorption increased after all the free amino groups reacted. The acidic protein derivative was electrophoretically homogeneous but had a correspondingly altered mobility.

6. THE FORMALDEHYDE REACTION

Formaldehyde is probably the simplest, most frequently used, and least understood protein reagent. The vast literature on this subject has been surveyed by French and Edsall.[1] The influence of formaldehyde on the titration curves of amino acids and proteins is familiar and has been described in Chap. 6. This is the oldest and most common of the titrations in mixed solvents, but its interpretation awaited many years of experience. Levy[110-113] provided the first systematic treatment

(109) S. N. Timasheff and F. F. Nord, *Arch. Biochem. and Biophys.* **31**, 320 (1951).
(110) M. Levy, *J. Biol. Chem.* **99**, 767 (1933).
(111) M. Levy, *J. Biol. Chem.* **105**, 157 (1934).
(112) M. Levy, *J. Biol. Chem.* **109**, 361, 365 (1935).
(113) M. Levy and D. E. Silberman, *J. Biol. Chem.* **118**, 723 (1937).

of the rapid effect on dissociation curves of proteins or amino acids caused by addition of formalin at room temperature. In their comprehensive review, French and Edsall[1] have summarized Levy's conclusions as follows: "(1) Only the uncharged amino or imino group reacts with formaldehyde, (2) the formaldehyde addition products are such weak bases that their basicity may be neglected in considering the equilibria involved, (3) amino groups can combine, rapidly and reversibly, with either one or two molecules of formaldehyde; imino groups with only one." The chief reactions are probably those shown below:

$$RNH_2 + HCHO \rightleftarrows RNHCH_2OH$$
$$RNHCH_2OH + HCHO \rightleftarrows RN(CH_2OH)_2.$$

However, numerous other reactions have been postulated to occur with glycine and other amino acids. It is important to recognize that the reactions given above are largely reversible as can be shown by the fact that formaldehyde can be removed from proteins by dialysis or dilution if the exposure is short and at moderate temperature. Unbound and reversibly bound formaldehyde can also be determined by precipitation with dimedone (5,5-dimethyl-1,3-cyclohexanedione) and weighing the precipitate.

Upon long standing in dilute solutions of formaldehyde at 37°—the usual procedure for the formation of toxoids and vaccines—slow irreversible reactions take place leading to the formation of stable derivatives of attenuated potency but of high antigenicity. Preliminary experiments with purified toxins indicated the disappearance of amino groups and the possible formation of methylene cross bridges. References to the formol treatment of toxins and viruses may be found in the review cited above.[1]

The reaction of formaldehyde with proteins is also of importance in the tanning of leathers, the fixing of tissues, and in the formation of fibers and plastics. Gustavson[3] has reviewed this field, and in past years Fraenkel-Conrat and his associates have added greatly to the understanding of the tanning reaction of proteins with formaldehyde.

In addition to the primary reversible reaction with amino groups to give methylol amines, formaldehyde has either been shown or postulated to react with virtually every protein side-chain group as well as with the peptide linkage. It has been stated[114] that "The identity of the protein groups involved in this reaction has been more frequently the object of conjecture than of exhaustive study." The contrasting interpretations of various investigators have been described, and the possible reactions

(114) H. Fraenkel-Conrat, M. Cooper, and H. S. Olcott, *J. Am. Chem. Soc.* **67,** 950 (1945).

have been elucidated in a series of papers by Fraenkel-Conrat, Olcott, and co-workers.[114–118] Using a variety of soluble and fibrous proteins, protein derivatives, synthetic polypeptides, and other model substances, these workers demonstrated that, at pH 3–7 and 70°, formaldehyde combined with both the primary amino and the primary amide groups of proteins but not with the secondary amide linkages of the peptide chain or with the phenolic groups. Gramicidin, the polypeptide antibiotic, contains no polar groups other than indole and aliphatic hydroxyl groups but was found to bind in alkaline solution an amount of formaldehyde equivalent to its tryptophan content.[115] The tanning or hardening reaction of formaldehyde is not supposed to be due to its primary addition to the amino or other type of protein group but rather to a secondary condensation reaction which transforms the methylol ($-CH_2OH$) groups into cross-linking methylene ($-CH_2-$) bridges. The workers at the Western Regional Laboratory were able to show that at room temperature and within the range of pH 3–9, methylene cross-links can be formed between amino groups on the one hand and amide, guanidyl, indolyl, phenolic, or imidazole groups on the other.[117] These secondary reactions probably account for much of the irreversible binding of formaldehyde by proteins and apparently occur under the conditions of pH and temperature suitable for tanning and for the preparation of vaccines and toxoids. Intermolecular cross-linking was demonstrated by the increase in molecular weights (as measured by osmotic pressure) of such products as were water soluble.[118] This is in accord with the decreased solubility and resistance to swelling of formaldehyde-tanned proteins. However, cross-linking could be forestalled by addition of low molecular weight amides such as acetamide or of secondary amines and did not take place with amino-acetylated proteins.

This discussion indicates that a great variety of reactions may take place between proteins and formaldehyde. Some occur rapidly but are reversible by dialysis or dilution. Others require weeks at room temperature or 37° to achieve the desired biological effect, and are only partially reversible. Irreversible reactions go on at elevated temperatures and alkaline pH. Clearly, the conditions of formaldehyde treatment must be carefully described, and conclusions about the function of any group, especially in biological activity, should be corroborated by use of another and more specific derivative.

(115) H. Fraenkel-Conrat, B. A. Brandon, and H. S. Olcott, *J. Biol. Chem.* **168,** 99 (1947).

(116) H. Fraenkel-Conrat and H. S. Olcott, *J. Am. Chem. Soc.* **70,** 2673 (1948).

(117) H. Fraenkel-Conrat and H. S. Olcott, *J. Biol. Chem.* **174,** 827 (1948).

(118) H. Fraenkel-Conrat and D. K. Mecham, *J. Biol. Chem.* **177,** 477 (1949).

It would be exhausting to attempt to tabulate all the effects of formaldehyde on the activity of enzymes, hormones, toxins, and viruses. A number of references may be found in the reviews by French and Edsall and by Herriott. One of the most thorough recent studies deals with the kinetics of the reaction of tobacco mosaic virus with formaldehyde.[45,119] In this work Fischer and Lauffer determined the kinetics of the decrease in infectivity and the increase in electrophoretic mobility and measured the free amino groups by the ninhydrin color reaction. The results were interpreted in terms of three types of free amino groups: a fraction reacting reversibly with formaldehyde, and two classes of amino groups which reacted irreversibly but at different rates.

The reaction of proteins with other aldehydes, such as acetaldehyde, and with glucose and other sugars, the so-called "browning" reaction, is now being widely studied because of its significance in the food industry. Like formaldehyde, acetaldehyde can react with primary amino groups and with indole groups.   However, this is an aspect of protein reactions outside the realm of this chapter.

7. DEAMINATION WITH NITROUS ACID

Deamination with nitrous acid is the basis of the well-known Van Slyke method for the determination of amino groups; this has been described in an earlier chapter. When the limitations of this standard method are recognized and the reaction conditions carefully controlled, it serves as the most useful procedure for measurement of the free amino groups of proteins. The α-amino (N-terminal) groups react most readily, the ϵ-amino groups somewhat more slowly, and the guanidyl groups very gradually liberate nitrogen. The excess of free amino groups found by the Van Slyke reaction over the analytical content of lysine was one of the first indications of N-terminal groups in proteins. The reaction is rapid and quantitative and has found great application in estimating the degree of substitution of amino groups in chemically modified proteins. Recently the ninhydrin method has come into favor.

The optimum conditions for the deamination of proteins to yield soluble derivatives have been worked out by Philpot and Small[120] in the case of pepsin. The protein is treated in 0.5 M acetate buffer at pH 4 with M NaNO$_2$ for varying periods of time at 0°:

$$\text{protein—NH}_2 + \text{HONO} \xrightarrow[\text{pH 4}]{0°} \text{protein—OH} + \text{N}_2\uparrow + \text{H}_2\text{O}$$

(119) M. A. Fischer and M. A. Lauffer, *J. Am. Chem. Soc.* **71**, 3800 (1949).
(120) J. St. L. Philpot and P. A. Small, *Biochem. J.* **32**, 542 (1938).

The reaction can be stopped by neutralization, and the mixture is dialyzed to remove the excess nitrite. Under these conditions the reaction of the amino groups is rapid, and secondary reactions such as the formation of nitroso and diazo derivatives of phenolic groups is minimal. Other unwanted reactions that may occur on extensive deamination involve the indolyl, imidazole, guanidyl, and disulfide groups of proteins. The kinetics of deamination have been studied by a number of authors.[53,120,121] They believe that the deamination can be distinguished from the diazotization in two respects: the former proceeds very much more rapidly and is of the second order (pseudo-bimolecular) in the presence of excess nitrite, whereas the reaction with tyrosine is of the first order (pseudo-unimolecular). Thus, Sizer[53] found that the inactivation of chymotrypsin by HNO_2 at pH 4.6 and 0° was first order, and accordingly concluded that neither amino nor sulfhydryl groups are required for chymotryptic activity but that tyrosine is an essential group. However, Fraenkel-Conrat and Olcott mention unpublished experiments which indicate that in the treatment of egg albumin with nitrous acid at pH 4 most of the —SH groups were oxidized though the amino and phenolic groups were only slightly affected, while serum albumin showed a partial loss of both of the latter type groups. These observations add to the previous emphasis that the reactivity of a given side chain may vary among proteins, and caution must be used in interpreting the extent of tyrosine involvement as measured by the color reaction.

Lately a series of papers have appeared on the deamination of crystalline egg albumin with the purpose of determining whether this labile protein can be deaminated without being denatured. Maurer and Heidelberger[122–124] used the deamination procedure of Philpot and Small and afterwards reduced any —S—S— formed by addition of thioglycolate, subsequently removed by dialysis. A soluble and an insoluble fraction were formed under all conditions tested and could be separated by precipitation at the common isoelectric point (shifted to about pH 4). Complete deamination was never achieved. The soluble fraction (B) had lost 27–36 per cent of the amino groups, and the extent of deamination was always greater in the insoluble fraction (A). Physical and chemical study of the two deaminated protein fractions indicated that the B fraction with only a third of its amino groups removed had an

(121) J. E. Little and M. L. Caldwell, J. Biol. Chem. 147, 229 (1943).
(122) P. H. Maurer and M. Heidelberger, J. Am. Chem. Soc. 73, 2070 (1951).
(123) P. H. Maurer, M. Heidelberger, and D. H. Moore, J. Am. Chem. Soc. 73, 2072 (1951).
(124) P. H. Maurer and M. Heidelberger, J. Am. Chem. Soc. 73, 2076 (1951).

optical rotation, viscosity, molecular weight, and frictional ratio similar to that of the native protein and hence could be called an undenatured, deaminated protein.   The insoluble, more extensively deaminated fraction A differed in all these properties from native egg albumin and was therefore considered to be denatured.   The immunochemical properties of the deaminated fractions supported this interpretation.   The authors ascribed denaturation to deamination of structurally important amino groups which reacted only after the more easily available groups had been modified.   However, as indicated above, and later acknowledged by Maurer and Heidelberger,[124a] the reaction of nitrous acid with proteins is quite nonspecific.   The deaminated fractions were always yellow owing to the introduction of chromophoric nitroso, azo, or diazo groups into the aromatic amino acid residues.   Moreover, the acetylation of considerably more amino groups of egg albumin with acetic anhydride had none of the denaturing effects of the incomplete deamination observed by Maurer and Heidelberger (i.e., the acetylated egg albumin remained heat-coagulable, was soluble at the isoelectric point, and retained its masked —SH group).[19]   Consequently, the conclusions about the role of amino groups in maintaining the native structure of egg albumin are in doubt.

8. Iodination

Iodinated proteins represent a unique case where physiological activity can be incorporated by chemical modication of an inert protein. The study of iodinated proteins, begun more than half a century ago, has been thoroughly summarized from the biochemical viewpoint by Roche and Michel.[125]   These authors have emphasized the natural iodoproteins, which include the thyroglobulins and the iodinated scleroproteins of invertebrates, and have discussed the formation and activity of artificially iodinated proteins.   The physiological action and comparative biochemistry of these compounds is outside the scope of this volume.   Direct iodination of proteins has been carried out in the laboratory (a) to obtain metabolically active derivatives for therapeusis or for study of the mode of action, (b) to modify enzymes or hormones in order to ascertain the essential groups, and (c) to prepare derivatives of altered physical properties suitable for study of the side chains involved in titration or interaction and for projected study of x-ray diffraction patterns of proteins with heavy atoms in known positions.   In addition, iodinated radicals have been introduced into proteins either for modifying antigenicity or for amino acid analysis and end-group assay.   A complete

(124a) P. H. Maurer and M. Heidelberger, J. Am. Chem. Soc. **74**, 1088 (1952).

(125) J. Roche and R. Michel, Advances in Protein Chem. **6**, 253 (1951).

documentation of work on the iodination of proteins will be found in the review mentioned above.

Iodine may be added to proteins as the solid element, in alcoholic solution, in aqueous solution in the presence of KI—and thus containing the triiodide ion (I_3^-)—and as hypoiodide. The known reactions of iodine are oxidation of the —SH group and substitution. As previously described in Chap. 9, Anson[35] has selectively and completely oxidized the sulfhydryl groups of egg albumin by addition of iodine in the presence of 1 N KI at 0°. Though the stoichiometry was good in this case, more than stoichiometric amounts of iodine and the absence of KI were required for oxidation of the —SH of tobacco mosaic virus.[126] The abolition of the —SH groups of the virus did not destroy infectivity, and this represents the first instance of chemical modification of a virus without inactivation. Many —SH enzymes are inactivated by oxidation with iodine. Selective oxidation is best accomplished in acid solution with a high concentration of iodide ions.

All the verified substitution reactions of iodine with proteins involve tyrosine or tyrosine derivatives. At low iodide concentrations and at neutral or alkaline pH, iodine preferentially substitutes at phenolic groups giving little oxidation. Three iodinated amino acids, 2-iodotyrosine, 3,5-diiodotyrosine, and thyroxine, have been isolated both from natural and artificial iodoproteins. The isolation of thyroxine from iodinated casein[127] is now accepted as a fact, but the mechanism of its formation remains unexplained. In work that has been disputed,[128] Herriott[129] isolated monoiodotyrosine from pepsin treated with dilute iodine until only two iodines per molecule of pepsin had been introduced. However, usually iodine transforms all accessible phenolic groups into 3,5-diiodotyrosine. When 35–40 iodine atoms are absorbed per molecule of pepsin, the enzyme is inactive. At least 82 per cent of the iodine appeared to be in diiodotyrosine, and 53 per cent could be isolated in the form of the crystalline amino acid.[63]

The occurrence of appreciable amounts of monoiodotyrosine in iodinated proteins remained disputed until recently. In a study of the kinetics of the iodination of tyrosine, Li[129a] concluded that the rate-determining step was the formation of the monoiodo compound. This implies that as soon as the first iodine atom enters the benzene ring, the second one reacts instantaneously. However, more and more evidence has

(126) M. L. Anson and W. M. Stanley, *J. Gen. Physiol.* **24**, 679 (1941).
(127) W. Ludwig and P. Mutzenbecher, *Z. physiol. Chem.* **258**, 195 (1939).
(128) C. R. Harington and R. V. Pitt Rivers, *Biochem. J.* **38**, 320 (1944).
(129) R. M. Herriott, *J. Gen. Physiol.* **25**, 185 (1941).
(129a) C. H. Li, *J. Am. Chem. Soc.* **64**, 1147 (1942).

accumulated against this mechanism. Fraenkel-Conrat[129b] showed by chromatography after hydrolysis of iodinated lysozyme that stably bound iodine is present as diiodotyrosine and to a lesser extent as mono-iodotyrosine. Final proof has recently come from Roche et al.[125,129c,129d] that monoiodotyrosine is a stable intermediate in the iodination of tyrosine, whether as the free amino acid, or in proteins. The formation of monoiodotyrosine as the first iodinated derivative in the biosynthesis of thyroxine seems well established.

Li[130] has studied the kinetics of the iodination of proteins and shown that not all the tyrosine residues react at the same rate. In urea solution the phenolic groups reacted more readily with iodine than in the absence of the denaturant, suggesting a greater availability of these groups after denaturation.

Diiodotyrosine gives only half the color at pH 8 in the Herriott modification of the Folin method that tyrosine does, so the method is unsuited for application to this problem. However, diiodotyrosine gives a negative test in the Millon reaction, and precedures based on this test may be employed to measure the amount of 3,5-unsubstituted tyrosyl groups in iodinated proteins. In a pure substitution reaction half the amount of iodine consumed should be bound. Thus the extent of oxidation and substitution can be determined by comparing the iodine consumed with the iodine organically bound by the protein. Iodimetry is used to follow the rate of uptake, and organically bound iodine is determined by the method of Herriott.[63] The reaction is written:

$$\text{protein}\langle\bigcirc\rangle\text{OH} + 2\text{I}_2 \xrightarrow[\text{pH 5-10}]{0°} \text{protein}\langle\overset{\text{I}}{\underset{\text{I}}{\bigcirc}}\rangle\text{OH} + 2\text{H}^+ + 2\text{I}^-$$

Characteristic changes in ultraviolet absorption spectrum and titration curves occur which are related to the number of iodine atoms bound per molecule of protein.

When iodine is taken up in small amounts by proteins lacking —SH, or under favorable conditions with other proteins, oxidation does not occur and only tyrosyl groups react. However, minor oxidative side reactions often precede tyrosyl substitution even at low concentrations of iodine. At high concentrations, more than the tyrosine equivalent of

(129b) H. Fraenkel-Conrat, Arch. Biochem. 27, 109 (1950).

(129c) J. Roche and R. Michel, Biochim. et Biophys. Acta 2, 97 (1948).

(129d) J. Roche, S. Lissitzky, O. Michel, and R. Michel, Biochim. et Biophys. Acta 7, 439 (1951).

(130) C. H. Li, J. Am. Chem. Soc. 67, 1065 (1945).

iodine is bound. The sequence of reactions with human serum albumin has been carefully investigated by Hughes and Straessle.[131] Though the iodination of horse or human serum albumin had previously been studied by a number of workers[31,130] and crystalline derivatives had been obtained in some cases, Hughes and Straessle[131] re-examined the conditions for specificity and used a number of analytical and physical methods to follow the reaction and characterize the derivatives obtained. They found that the sulfhydryl group could be completely oxidized with only negligible simultaneous substitution reactions. Following this, about 70 per cent of the 3,5-positions in the tyrosyl residues took up iodine before other substitution reactions began. However, concomitant substitution of other groups occurred before complete iodination of the phenols. Presumably, these were histidyl residues since previous work had implicated the imidazole ring in the uptake of excess iodine. Tryptophan was oxidized in highly iodinated preparations.

Though the above sequence of reactions with iodine is probably followed by many proteins, Fraenkel-Conrat[129b] has found an interesting exception in lysozyme which substantiates the previous warning that the relative reactivity of groups varies among proteins. The phenolic groups of lysozyme are very unreactive compared with those of most other proteins. The single histidine residue of lysozyme participates in the reaction with iodine, causing a reversible inactivation. Only half the phenolic groups react under the same conditions, and they appear to have only a minor role in the activity of the enzyme.

The preparation of radioactive iodinated proteins has already been mentioned. The biosynthesis of I^{131} thyroglobulins has been accomplished in connection with metabolism studies. The immunochemical behavior of iodoproteins obtained either by direct iodination or by the fixation of iodinated radicals has been investigated in several laboratories.[67] The radioactive iodinated proteins have proved useful in the study of antibody formation in relation to the persistence of antigen in the tissues.[4,7,31,131a]

At first, proteins obtained by the fixation of iodinated radicals were prepared only for immunochemical purposes, but recently such derivatives have been successfully applied to the characterization of free amino groups. Radioactive derivatives of amino acids are obtained by reaction with p-iodophenylsulfonyl chloride (pipsyl chloride) containing I^{131} or S^{35}. When applied to a protein hydrolyzate this serves as the basis

(131) W. L. Hughes, Jr. and R. Straessle, J. Am. Chem. Soc. 72, 452 (1950).
(131a) F. Haurowitz, C. F. Crampton, and R. Sowinski, Federation Proc. 10, 560 (1951).

for the pipsyl method of isotope-derivative analysis.[131b,131c] However, since the free amino groups of proteins can also be made to react with pipsyl chloride and since the sulfonamide derivatives so formed are resistant to acid hydrolysis, the method was suggested for end-group analysis.[132] The procedure, developed by Udenfriend and Velick,[132a] in principle resembles the amino end-group method of Sanger.[9] An I^{131}-labeled pipsyl chloride reagent is employed with the protein, and an indicator S^{35}-labeled pipsyl amino acid is added to the protein before hydrolysis. The pipsyl N-terminal amino acids and ϵ-N-pipsyllysine are identified chromatographically. By use of the indicator principle the terminal amino acids and lysine can be determined quantitatively (without the necessity of quantitative isolation) by comparison of the ratio of $I^{131}:S^{35}$ in pure bands of the chromatogram. The end-group identifications on insulin and hemoglobin were in qualitative agreement with the results reported by the DNP method. However, the pipsyl method gave a smaller number of residues in each case. This discrepancy might mean that some of the terminal amino acids are inaccessible to pipsyl chloride but not to dinitrofluorobenzene.

9. Phosphorylation, Sulfation, Nitration

Phosphorylation, sulfation, and nitration are among the more rigorous and less specific procedures for the modification of proteins. They lead to acidic products with a marked change in physical properties, and under the conditions usually applied in the past must have resulted in denaturation. Only a few recent applications will be cited to illustrate the reactions.

a. Phosphorylation

The importance of phosphorylation in biological synthesis and energy transfer has stimulated interest in the preparation of phosphorylated proteins.[47] Though studies of peptide- and amide-bond synthesis in model systems have demonstrated a requirement for adenosine triphosphate (ATP), no evidence for the direct phosphorylation of a substrate by ATP has yet been presented. Moreover, early methods of phosphorylation of proteins were nonspecific resulting in the introduction of a high proportion of labile phosphoryl residues.

In Rimington's method[133] for the phosphorylation of proteins, phos-

(131b) S. F. Velick and S. Udenfriend, J. Biol. Chem. 190, 721 (1951).

(131c) A. S. Keston, S. Udenfriend, and R. K. Cannan, J. Am. Chem. Soc. 71, 249 (1949).

(132) A. S. Keston and S. Udenfriend, Cold Spring Harbor Symposia Quant. Biol. 14, 92 (1950).

(132a) S. Udenfriend and S. F. Velick, J. Biol. Chem. 190, 733 (1951).

(133) C. Rimington, Biochem. J. 21, 272 (1927).

phorus oxychloride ($POCl_3$) dissolved in chloroform or carbon tetrachloride is added dropwise to a protein solution at 0° and the pH is maintained at 8.5–9 by dropwise addition of strong NaOH. In contrast to natural phosphoproteins, the linkage of much of the phosphorus introduced is labile. Egg albumin was phosphorylated by this procedure[134] and the titration curve examined. Since this protein appeared to be denatured, Mayer and Heidelberger[47] studied the conditions for phosphorylation of serum albumin, hoping to avoid this complication. Solid potassium or sodium borate was used to buffer the reaction mixture. Phosphorylation was less complete, but products of the same N:P ratio had the same viscosity and antigenic specificity whether strong alkali or borate was used. The most notable chemical difference between the artificially phosphorylated proteins and the natural phosphoproteins lies in the stability of the linkage. Phosphorylated serum albumin loses much of its P spontaneously in the cold but some resists splitting by 1 per cent alkali at 37° for 24 hr. In natural phosphoproteins the P is stably combined but is completely lost on the prolonged alkali treatment. In casein and vitellin the P is attached to the aliphatic hydroxy groups and phosphoserine can be isolated. Though such groups may also react with $POCl_3$, Mayer and Heidelberger presented evidence that at least half of the phosphoryl radicals of phosphorylated serum albumin were either coupled to amino groups or shielded them from reaction with nitrous acid. The decrease in color in the Folin reaction was taken as qualified evidence for esterification of the tyrosine residues.

Phosphorylation by treatment at room temperature for several days with phosphorus pentoxide (P_2O_5) dissolved in 100 per cent phosphoric acid has been developed as a method apparently specific for the aliphatic hydroxyl groups of proteins.[135] Because of the stability of insulin in acid, the hormonal activity as might be expected is not lost by this treatment.[136] Exposure of ovomucoid to 85 per cent sulfuric or phosphoric acid results in partial loss of the property of trypsin inhibition.[27] Since the reaction proceeds at room temperature in acid, most proteins would be denatured by this treatment.

$$P_2O_5 + protein-OH \xrightarrow[H_3PO_4]{25°} O{=}P{-}O{-}protein$$

(134) M. Heidelberger, B. Davis, and H. P. Treffers, *J. Am. Chem. Soc.* **63**, 498 (1941).

(135) R. E. Ferrel, H. S. Olcott, and H. Fraenkel-Conrat, *J. Am. Chem. Soc.* **70**, 2101 (1948).

(136) J. Fraenkel-Conrat and H. Fraenkel-Conrat, *Biochim. et Biophys. Acta* **5**, 89 (1950).

b. Sulfation

The sulfation of proteins can be accomplished by treating them at low temperature with concentrated sulfuric acid.[137] Nearly all the aliphatic hydroxyl groups form very stable acid sulfate esters. Some of the phenolic groups of tyrosine also react, as does —SH. If the reaction mixture is kept cold throughout, phenol sulfate esters form. Some sulfonation of the ring results if the mixture is allowed to warm. Sulfation yields very acidic derivatives and is useful for the transformation of waste protein products.[138] The biological activity of insulin sulfate, the neutral salt of the acid sulfate ester of insulin, is similar to that of the crystalline hormone if sulfonation is avoided.[28] It would be surprising, however, if other proteins withstood this treatment.

$$\text{protein} \overset{\displaystyle OH}{\underset{\displaystyle SH}{\diamond}} \!\!-OH + H_2SO_4 \xrightarrow[\text{conc. acid}]{-18° \text{ to } 0°}$$

$$\text{protein} \overset{\displaystyle O-SO_3H}{\underset{\displaystyle SO_3H \atop S-SO_3H}{\diamond}} \!\!-O-SO_3H + H_2O$$

c. Nitration

The xanthoproteic reaction is familiar to every student beginning chemistry, and nitrated proteins have often been prepared more deliberately. It is believed that nitration of the benzene ring occurs, but with many concomitant effects. Attention has been called[18] to the use of tetranitromethane as a more suitable nitrating agent, though this has been only infrequently applied.[139,140]

10. DIISOPROPYL FLUOROPHOSPHATE

The fluorophosphates comprise the diesters of fluorophosphoric acid (such as diisopropyl fluorophosphate), the substituted diamidophosphoryl fluorides, and such related substances as alkylamido-substituted phosphoric acid, the esters of alkanephosphoryl fluoride, and some thionyl derivatives. Among these substances are some of the most

(137) H. C. Reitz, R. E. Ferrel, H. Fraenkel-Conrat, and H. S. Olcott, J. Am. Chem. Soc. 68, 1024 (1946).

(138) H. C. Reitz, R. E. Ferrel, and H. S. Olcott, Ind. Eng. Chem. 36, 1149 (1944).

(139) A. Wormall, J. Exptl. Med. 51, 295 (1930).

(140) L. Ehrenberg, I. Fischer, and N. Löfgren, Nature 157, 730 (1946).

toxic war gases (the so-called "nerve gases") developed in World War II. Their chemistry is reviewed by Sartori.[140a] The diesters of fluorophosphoric acid are the most powerful and specific enzyme inhibitors known. Of these, diisopropyl fluorophosphate has been the most thoroughly investigated.

The equimolar reaction between chymotrypsin and diisopropyl fluorophosphate (DFP) to give a crystallizable inhibited enzyme is one of the clearest and most important examples of the study of the nature of enzymic activity by chemical modification of a protein. When Jansen, Nutting, Jang, and Balls[8,56,141] undertook an investigation of the inhibition of trypsin and chymotrypsin by DFP, it had been known for some time that organic phosphates such as this and tetraethyl phosphate selectively and generally irreversibly inhibited certain esterases such as true and pseudo cholinesterases. These authors discovered the simultaneous inhibition of the esterase and proteinase activities of chymotrypsin by minute concentrations of DFP (8×10^{-6} M), thus supporting previous indications that the two activities probably resided in the same active center of the molecule.[141a] Chymotrypsinogen was unaffected and after treatment with DFP could be converted to the active enzyme by recrystallization and the usual activation with trypsin. Trypsin was inhibited by somewhat larger amounts of DFP (4×10^{-4} M), but both the esterase and proteinase activities likewise were decreased progressively at an equal rate. Acetyltrypsin required higher amounts of DFP and lost only proteinase activity.

The reaction has been most extensively investigated for α-chymotrypsin, but the nature of the single active group is still unknown.[141b] When a slight excess of DFP is added to α-chymotrypsin in pH 7.7 buffer, 1 mole of the inhibitor combines with 1 mole of the enzyme to form a crystallizable, dialyzable, and lyophilizable enzyme–inhibitor complex. By use of radioactive DFP it was found that 1.1 moles of phosphorus were introduced per mole of enzyme, and by chemical analysis it was determined that two isopropyl groups were incorporated but

(140a) M. F. Sartori, *Chem. Revs.* **48**, 225 (1951).

(141) E. F. Jansen, M. D. F. Nutting, R. Jang, and A. K. Balls, *J. Biol. Chem.* **179**, 189 (1949).

(141a) G. W. Schwert, H. Neurath, S. Kaufman, and J. E. Snoke, *J. Biol. Chem.* **172**, 221 (1948).

(141b) A recent abstract reports the isolation of radioactive serine phosphoric acid from chymotrypsin reacted with DFP[32]. The authors conclude that the ultimate, but not necessarily the immediate, site of attachment of DFP to chymotrypsin is through an —OH group of one of the serine moieties of the enzyme [N. K. Schaffer, S. C. May, Jr., and W. H. Summerson, *Federation Proc.* **11**, 282 (1952)]. See also *J. Biol. Chem.* **202**, 67 (1953).

no fluorine. None of the amino acids known to occur in chymotrypsin reacted with DFP, and the crystalline inhibited enzyme had the same amino nitrogen content as the active protein, but the latter results are attributable to the insensitivity of the methods. Accordingly the reaction has to be written:

$$\text{xt—H} + \text{F—P}\overset{\displaystyle \overset{O}{\|}}{\underset{\displaystyle OC_3H_7}{\diagup}}\underset{OC_3H_7}{\diagdown} \xrightarrow[\text{pH 7.7}]{25°} \text{xt—P}\overset{\displaystyle \overset{O}{\|}}{\underset{\displaystyle OC_3H_7}{\diagup}}\underset{OC_3H_7}{\diagdown} + \text{HF}$$

where H represents some essential active hydrogen, and xt, chymotrypsin. The results agree with the postulate that only one type of group is responsible for both the esterase and proteinase activities of chymotrypsin (and trypsin) but suggest that the activity depends on some special configuration of the protein.

Further study has shown that a number of analogs of DFP similarly inhibit α-chymotrypsin, forming crystallizable inert enzyme derivatives.[141c] Although the concentration of inhibitor required to produce 50 per cent inhibition under standard conditions differed greatly, analysis of five analog derivatives showed that in each case about 1 mole of phosphorus was introduced per mole of enzyme. These inhibitors were diphenyl chlorophosphate, diethyl thionofluorophosphate, tetraisopropyl pyrophosphate, diethyl p-nitrophenyl phosphate, and tetrapropyl dithionopyrophosphate. It is assumed that the stoichiometry is similar to that given above with a dialkyl or diaryl phosphate being introduced into the protein.

Other esterolytic proteinases likewise form crystalline DFP inhibition products.[142] The proteinase and esterase activities of α-chymotrypsin, β-chymotrypsin, and γ-chymotrypsin and of trypsin in each case are inhibited about equally at a given concentration of DFP. In all the derivatives approximately one mole of phosphorus was introduced by the inhibition reaction.

Compound formation in the inhibition reaction with DFP has been demonstrated for several other enzymes with esterase activity. Boursnell and Webb[142] used DFP containing radioactive phosphorus (P^{32}) to study the inactivation of horse liver esterase which was 80 per cent pure electrophoretically. Complete loss of activity resulted from the combination of one mole of inhibitor with 96,000 g. of esterase. Michel and Krop[143] also used DFP^{32} to study the combination between

(141c) E. F. Jansen, A. L. Curl, and A. K. Balls, *J. Biol. Chem.* **190**, 557 (1951).

(142) J. C. Boursnell and E. C. Webb, *Nature* **164**, 875 (1949).

(143) H. O. Michel and S. Krop, *J. Biol. Chem.* **190**, 119 (1951).

an enzyme and this inhibitor. With electric eel cholinesterase, they found that the labeled phosphorus was bound in amounts proportional to the degree of inhibition. Though ultracentrifugal analysis had indicated a molecular weight of about 3,000,000 for a more active preparation of eel cholinesterase, the equivalent weight of the enzyme calculated from the DFP binding and the highest activity attained for the enzyme was 63,000.

Many other organic phosphates are potent cholinesterase inhibitors, and, *in vivo,* because of penetration to all parts of the nervous system, they produce both the muscarinic and nicotinic actions of acetylcholine, leading to rapid death. Thus their toxic properties are ascribed to the inhibitory effect on acetylcholine-hydrolyzing enzymes. Hexaethyl tetraphosphate has been most commonly studied pharmacologically, but it is a mixture of phosphates of which tetraethyl pyrophosphate is the most active agent. The latter reagent inhibits α-chymotrypsin[56] but at such a slow rate that inactivation was not at first observed.[141] The amount of phosphorus and alkoxy units bound per unit weight of enzyme is the same whether inhibition occurs with DFP or tetraethyl pyrophosphate.[143a] In the reaction of human plasma cholinesterase with P^{32}-labeled hexaethyl tetraphosphate, it first appeared that radioactive phosphorus was not incorporated into the enzyme.[143b] However, it is now known that only a minor component of this organic phosphate is active, and the enzyme preparation was quite impure. When hexaethyl tetraphosphate was labeled with C^{14}, a definite measurable uptake of radioactive carbon by the enzyme was observed.[143c] This only corresponded to 3.45×10^{-2} mole hexaethyl tetraphosphate per mole protein, but it was suggested that the protein contained only 3 per cent active enzyme and thus that the 1 mole of the inhibitor combined with 1 mole of the enzyme.

The action of the alkyl phosphates *in vitro* has generally been considered irreversible in contrast to the effects of other types of enzyme inhibitors. However, in sublethal doses the effects of hexaethyl tetraphosphate are rapidly overcome in animals. Recently, evidence has been presented for the slow reactivation of eel acetylcholinesterase on standing in water solution, and more rapid reactivation by addition of choline or hydroxylamine.[143d]

These observations indicate that the reaction may be the same for

(143a) J. H. Fleisher, B. J. Jandorf, W. H. Summerson, and D. P. Norton, *Federation Proc.* **9,** 171 (1950).

(143b) R. W. Brauer, *J. Pharmacol. Exptl. Therap.* **92,** 162 (1948).

(143c) R. W. Brauer and R. L. Pessotti, *Science* **110,** 395 (1949).

(143d) I. B. Wilson, *J. Biol. Chem.* **190,** 111 (1951).

all DFP-susceptible enzymes and that analogous alkyl and aryl phosphate esters inhibit in a like manner. Though systemic insecticidal analogs of DFP had no effect on chymotrypsin, their lethal action may be attributed to hydrolysis after ingestion or absorption. The acid anhydride nature of the fluorophosphate derivatives is probably important in determining the nature and strength of the inhibitor–enzyme bond.

In a review of the reaction between DFP and enzymes Balls and Jansen[143e] conclude that it is the most general inhibitor of the phosphate esters commonly available. However, they also point out that there is no record that DFP is an outstanding inhibitor of any enzyme other than esterases. For example, it has no inhibitory action on crystalline β-amylase from sweet potato, crystalline hog pepsin, or urease. Crude papain is only slightly inactivated. Nor are all esterases inhibited by DFP; for example, pectinesterase and carboxypeptidase (which splits esters of carbobenzoxy- or hippuryl-glycine with β-phenyllactic acid). This permits the use of DFP to remove endopeptidase (tryptic and chymotryptic) activity from carboxypeptidase.[143f] DFP derivatives of trypsin[143g] and of chymotrypsin[143f,143h] have also been used in a study of the C-terminal groups in relation to the activation of the zymogens and in the analysis of the sedimentation behavior of the enzymes (see later).

11. Diazotization and Coupling with Diazo Compounds

a. Direct Diazotization

The primary deamination of proteins by nitrous acid is accompanied by a secondary reaction involving the phenolic groups, possibly also the indolyl and imidazole rings. Tyrosine is diazotized in the *ortho* position, presumably by way of a nitroso derivative. The yellow or reddish diazo proteins formed couple readily with phenolic derivatives to give colored compounds. The reaction is clearly not specific, and little is known about the nature and number of groups participating except for a study of pepsin by Philpot and Small.[120] The latter workers diazotized crystalline pepsin by treatment with dilute $NaNO_2$ and found that only half of the tyrosine groups would react—the same number as could be iodinated.[130] The yellow diazo pepsin formed had an absorption maximum at 412 mμ and only half the activity of the unmodified enzyme. Chymotrypsin[53] and pancreatic amylase[121] also form yellow derivatives on reac-

(143e) A. K. Balls and E. F. Jansen, *Advances in Enzymol.* **13**, 321 (1952).
(143f) J. A. Gladner and H. Neurath, *Biochim. et Biophys. Acta* **9**, 335 (1952).
(143g) E. W. Davie and H. Neurath, *J. Am. Chem. Soc.* **74**, 6305 (1952).
(143h) H. Neurath and J. A. Gladner, *Federation Proc.* **12**, 251 (1953).

tion with nitrous acid, and are progressively inactivated. Although the paucity of amino groups and the activity of acetylated pepsin made the interpretation clear for this enzyme, in the other cases kinetic analysis had to be resorted to in order to distinguish whether the inactivation with nitrous acid was due to deamination or diazotization.

b. Coupling with Diazo Compounds

The coupling of proteins with diazonium compounds has found extensive use in the study of the immunological reactions of proteins and the nature of haptens. The advantages of this method are that diazo derivatives of a great variety of compounds can be prepared and these can then be linked to the protein and that the reaction proceeds readily at 0° to room temperature at pH 7–9 so that denaturation is avoided. Probably thousands of azoproteins have been prepared in a vast study which derives from the classical experiments of Landsteiner. This is described in the texts by Landsteiner[144] and Boyd,[145] in Chap. 11 by Porter, and again in more detail in Volume II by Boyd.

As indicated in Table I, both the imidazole and the phenolic groups combine with diazonium compounds as do the indolyl groups to a lesser extent. A typical reaction is given below.

The most important application of azoproteins has been in the demonstration that the serological specificity of proteins is associated with chemical groups on the molecule. This finding of the chemical basis for

(144) K. Landsteiner, The Specificity of Serological Reactions, 2nd Ed., Harvard University Press, Cambridge, 1945.

(145) W. C. Boyd, Fundamentals of Immunology, Interscience Publ., Inc., New York, 1943.

antigenicity resulted from the conjugation of organic compounds to proteins via the azo linkage and using the modified protein as antigen. The antiserum obtained after injection of such a coupled protein contained antibodies to the azoprotein with a specificity conferred by the prosthetic group, as well as antibodies to the carrier protein. Cross reactions are obtained in the precipitin test when the antiserum is mixed with a heterologous protein conjugated to the same azo group. In addition, the synthetic organic azo compound (the hapten) inhibits the antigen–antibody precipitation, and complex compounds such as dyes containing two or more haptenic groups form a precipitate with the antiserum though they are incapable of eliciting antibodies. Considerable evidence on the nature and valence of the antibody-combining sites and on the factors determining specificity has been amassed by experiments with azoprotein antigens. The several theories of antigen–antibody combination are largely based on this work.

The serological specificity of the artificially conjugated antigens is largely determined by the nature of the *polar* determinant groups introduced. Acidic groups have been most effective and most used, e.g., $-COOH$, $-SO_3H_2$ and $-AsO_3H_2$. Phenylarsonic acid is a favorite $\left(\langle\rangle AsO_3H_2\right)$. The theory of complementariness in the antigen–antibody reaction has been advanced in Pauling's laboratory on the basis of study of the effect of hundreds of haptens and stereochemically related compounds on the precipitation reactions of antisera prepared against a number of azoprotein derivatives. Besides use for serological studies, diazonium salts have been widely employed for the introduction of compounds of physiological or pharmacological interest. Despite the popularity of the coupling of proteins with diazonium compounds, not much can be said about the physical properties of the modified proteins, although spectroscopic methods would often have been applicable. In many cases whole serum rather than a purified protein was conjugated with the azo salt.

12. Guanidination—Interconversion of Protein Groups

Very few reactions have been developed for the interconversion of protein groups. The most successful is the conversion of the amino groups to guanidino groups recently described by Hughes, Saroff, and Carney.[146] Whereas most methods for preparing protein derivatives involve a radical change in the nature of one or more substituent groups—

(146) W. L. Hughes, Jr., H. A. Saroff, and A. L. Carney, *J. Am. Chem. Soc.* **71**, 2476 (1949).

often a marked alteration in charge or acidity—this procedure merely replaces the amino group by the somewhat more basic guanidino group.

For guanidination of crystalline human serum albumin, Hughes and co-workers allowed a solution containing 20 per cent protein in 0.5 M O-methylisourea to stand at 0° for 3 days. The guanidinated derivative was crystallized directly from this solution in 90 per cent yield after dilution and addition of acetate buffer. The rate of reaction increased rapidly with pH in the range pH 8.5–10.5, and the extent of conversion of amino groups was most readily controlled through adjustment of this variable. At pH 10, both reactants are only partially ionized and the reagent itself acts as a buffer. On a balance basis per mole protein, there was good correlation between the number of amino groups disappearing, as measured in the Van Slyke reaction, and the moles of reagent used up. Exhaustive reaction with methylisourea led only to the conversion of 54–57 of the 68 free amino groups in the serum albumin, but this was practically equivalent to the number of lysyl groups. Previous investigation by Greenstein[147] and other workers had indicated that O-methylisourea reacts readily with the ϵ-amino group of lysine and lysine peptides. Because the reaction occurs at pH 10 near the pK of both O-methylisourea hydrochloride and the ammonium groups of the protein, Hughes et al. wrote the equation as follows:

$$\text{CH}_3\text{O}\text{—C(NH}_2)_2{}^+ \quad + \text{prot—NH}_3{}^+ \rightarrow \text{prot—NH—C(NH}_2)_2{}^+ + \text{CH}_3\text{OH} + \text{H}^+$$
$$\text{CH}_3\text{O—C(NH)NH}_2 + \text{prot—NH}_2 \ \rightarrow \text{prot—NH—C(NH}_2)_2{}^+ + \text{CH}_3\text{OH} - \text{H}^+$$

The preparation of a crystallizable guanidinated derivative of human serum albumin in a form as homogeneous as the unmodified protein and having the same molecular weight and shape as the original (within experimental error) marks a real achievement in the chemical modification of proteins.

The transformation of carboxyl groups to hydroxylamido groups (—CO—NHOH) has been studied by Fraenkel-Conrat[147a] in an attempt to determine whether the iron-binding protein, conalbumin, is a hydroxylamidoprotein. Esterification of proteins with 0.1 N methanolic HCl followed by reaction with hydroxylamine, or direct treatment with hydroxylamine led to the conversion of —COOH to —CO—NHOH. The hydroxylamidoproteins gave colored complexes with iron similar to those given by the natural iron-binding proteins, conalbumin and siderophilin. However, marked differences were found in the behavior of the chromogenic property of the natural proteins and the artificial

(147) J. P. Greenstein, *J. Biol. Chem.* **109**, 529, 541 (1935).
(147a) H. Fraenkel-Conrat, *Arch. Biochem.* **28**, 452 (1950).

iron-binding proteins after denaturation, modification with group reagents, and enzymatic degradation. A search failed to reveal evidence for hydroxylamino or hydroxylamido groups in conalbumin, and it was concluded that the iron-binding property is not mediated by such groups.

13. COUPLING OF AMINO ACIDS TO PROTEINS BY THE PEPTIDE LINKAGE

One of the most provocative methods of modifying proteins which is now in the process of development is the addition of amino acids and peptides by reaction with N-carboxyamino acid anhydrides at neutral pH and 0°. This was introduced by Stahmann and Becker[147b] who caused N-carboxyglycine anhydride to react with bovine serum albumin and with chymotrypsin. Glycine was incorporated to the extent that both proteins were increased in molecular weight by about 12 per cent. The glycine content of the albumin was increased about ten-fold, and that of the chymotrypsin was raised about four-fold. Despite the large increase in glycine content both proteins remained soluble; the chymotrypsin derivative showed no loss in enzymatic activity, and the poly-glycyl albumin was precipitated by an antiserum prepared against normal plasma albumin. Titration curves indicated that only about one third of the amino groups had reacted with the anhydride, and that on the average the glycine was attached as polypeptides. This appears to be the first time that unsubstituted amino acids or peptides have been coupled to native proteins to form peptide bonds under such mild conditions that denaturation does not occur.

Fraenkel-Conrat[147c] has investigated the mode of attachment of N-carboxy-L-leucine anhydride labeled with C^{14} in the chain. He prepared derivatives of a number of proteins and ascertained the location of the leucine by means of the FDNB method, by the Edman degradation, and by use of the radio-activity. The reaction appeared to be specific for amino groups, but in all proteins tested the ϵ-amino groups of lysine were only partially blocked and in most instances the N-terminal groups were only partly substituted. Excess of the reagent favored polymerization onto the protein. Tobacco mosaic virus modified by addition of about 1000 leucine residues was unchanged electrophoretically and retained full activity. The progeny were not distinguishably different from the original virus. These preliminary results suggest that this method holds promise for the study of the biological activity of enzymes and viruses.

(147b) M. A. Stahmann and R. R. Becker, *J. Am. Chem. Soc.* **74**, 2695 (1952).
(147c) H. Fraenkel-Conrat, *Biochim. et Biophys. Acta* **10**, 180 (1953).

14. The Ovalbumin–Plakalbumin Transformation

Most of the modifications of proteins discussed thus far result from familiar chemical reactions analogous to those undergone by amino acids and peptides and often established for the different protein groups by comparison with the known reactions of such model substances.   Many proteins have been modified by treatment with proteolytic enzymes, but virtually always in the direction of hydrolytic degradation and the formation of split products.   Even where the products are of high molecular weight and retain immunological activity—as in the papain or pepsin digestion of immune globulins—there is evidence of a reduction in molecular weight.   However, a unique protein transformation discovered in recent years by Linderstrøm-Lang and Ottesen[148,149] yields a modification of ovalbumin which differs from the natural protein in crystalline form, solubility, electrophoretic mobility, and by the absence of several peptides, but has almost identical molecular weight.[149a,b,c]   The study of the transformation of ovalbumin to plakalbumin, the modified form, is complicated by the fact that crystalline ovalbumin is electrophoretically heterogeneous and its phosphorus content does not correspond to an integral number of phosphoric acid residues per mole, when calculated for a molecular weight of 44,000.

Plakalbumin, the modified form of native ovalbumin was crystallized by Linderstrøm-Lang and Otteson[148] from a salt-free solution which had been stored in a refrigerator for several years and gave evidence of microbial contamination, probably with *Bacillus subtilis*.   Whereas ovalbumin sterilized by filtration through a bacteriological filter can be stored unaltered with respect to electrophoretic mobility, P content, and crystalline shape (needles), ovalbumin inoculated with *B. subtilis* as a source of enzymes is transformed to plakalbumin, which crystallizes in plates.   The transformation is accompanied by a decrease in molecular weight of about 300 and the liberation of about 6 atoms of N per protein molecule as nonprotein N due to the loss of peptides (1.2 per cent of the total N).[149a,149c]   No P is split off in the ovalbumin transformation by reasonably pure proteinase from *B. subtilis*.[149a]   The fragments lost by

(148) K. Linderstrøm-Lang and M. Otteson, *Nature* **159**, 807 (1947).

(149) N. Eeg-Larson, K. Linderstrøm-Lang, and M. Otteson, *Arch. Biochem.* **19**, 340 (1948).

(149a) K. Linderstrøm-Lang and M. Otteson, *Compt. rend. trav. Lab. Carlsberg Sér. chim.* **26**, 403 (1949).

(149b) E. Fredericq and K. Linderstrøm-Lang, *Compt. rend. trav. Lab. Carlsberg Sér chim.* **26**, 443 (1949).

(149c) A. V. Güntelberg and K. Linderstrøm-Lang, *Compt. rend. trav. Lab. Carlsberg Sér. chim.* **27**, 1 (1949).

enzymatic fission contained glutamic and aspartic acids but no other residues free to ionize when combined in the peptide bond. The electrophoretic properties of plakalbumin are in accord with the view that two strong carboxyl groups are missing. However, plakalbumin like ovalbumin exists in several electrophoretic forms.[150,150a,150b,151]

The relationship between the plakalbumins and the ovalbumins has been elucidated by Perlmann using electrophoretic mobility, crystal form, and phosphorus content to identify the products of mild enzymatic degradation.[151,151a] Linderstrøm-Lang and Otteson[149a] had suggested that the mobilities of the two components of ovalbumin (designated A_1 and

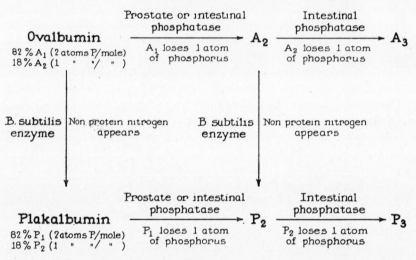

Fig. 1. The relationship between ovalbumin and plakalbumin derivatives.[151a]

A_2)[151b] could be understood on the assumption that A_2 contains only 1 atom of phosphorus per mole while A_1, the major component, contains 2. In a test of this hypothesis Perlmann[150,151] showed that on 14 days' exposure to the bacterial enzyme at 37°, plakalbumin contained two electrophoretic components P_1 and P_2, corresponding in relative abundance to A_1 and A_2 in freshly prepared ovalbumin. On continued incubation the proportion of P_2 increased at the expense of P_1, and a third component appeared which was devoid of phosphorus. Further study

(150) G. E. Perlmann, *Nature* **161**, 720 (1948).

(150a) G. E. Perlmann, *J. Am. Chem. Soc.* **71**, 1146 (1949).

(150b) G. E. Perlmann, *J. Gen. Physiol.* **35**, 711 (1952).

(151) G. E. Perlmann, *Nature* **164**, 961 (1949).

(151a) G. E. Perlmann, *Nature* **166**, 870 (1950).

(151b) L. G. Longsworth, R. K. Cannan, and D. A. McInnes, *J. Am. Chem. Soc.* **62**, 2580 (1940).

of the enzymatic dephosphorylation of ovalbumin and plakalbumin revealed the scheme given in Fig. 1 which is consistent with all the evidence.[151a] The fractions A_1 or P_1 are transformed by purified intestinal or prostate phosphatase (and by impure *subtilis* enzyme containing phosphatases) into A_2 and P_2, respectively, and A_2 and P_2 are further transformed into new components A_3 and P_3 but only by intestinal phosphatase. The failure of prostate phosphatase to remove the second phosphorus of A_1 and P_1 indicates a chemical difference in the nature of the two phosphorus groups in these proteins. The mobility differences within the series A_1, A_2, and A_3 and within the series P_1, P_2, and P_3 probably depend upon the loss of phosphate groups; the mobility differences between A_1 and P_1, and A_2 and P_2 probably depend upon the loss of peptides. However, it must still be established that P_2 obtained by dephosphorylation of P_1 is identical with P_2 obtained by proteolysis of A_2.

The nature of the peptides released in the conversion of ovalbumin to plakalbumin was investigated by Otteson and Villee.[151c] Using starch-column chromatography these workers found three peptides, designated as A, B, and C. A was a hexapeptide containing the amino acids alanine, valine, glycine, and aspartic acid in the ratio 3:1:1:1; B was a tetrapeptide with the same amino acids in equimolar ratio; and C was the dipeptide alanylalanine. The sequence of the two larger peptides was subsequently determined by Otteson and Wollenberger[151d] by a modification of Edman's phenyl isothiocyanate method[102a] with successive removal of the N-terminal amino acids and by the use of carboxypeptidase. The hexapeptide was alanylglycylvalylaspartylalanylalanine, the other two peptides being alanylglycylvalylaspartic acid and alanylalanine. These results support the hypothesis that the three ovalbumin peptides released in the formation of plakalbumin arise from the same site.

It remains to be seen how the three peptides fit into the scheme proposed by Perlmann. The simplest explanation would be that the hexapeptide is liberated in a single step when $A_1 \rightarrow P_1$, or $A_2 \rightarrow P_2$, that the dipeptide and the tetrapeptide arise by later enzymatic fission of the hexapeptide, and that P_2 obtained by dephosphorylation of P_1 is identical with P_2 obtained by proteolysis of A_2. Since ovalbumin is reported to contain no terminal groups,[36] the peptide chain must open on proteolysis,

(151c) M. Otteson and C. Villee, *Compt. rend. trav. lab. Carlsberg. Sér. chim.* **27**, 421 (1951).

(151d) M. Otteson and A. Wollenberger, Abstract submitted to the International Congress of Biochemistry, Paris, July, 1952 (personal communication of K. Linderstrøm-Lang).

accounting for the increased solubility of the plakalbumins. (The first dephosphorylation cannot open the supposedly cyclic polypeptide since the end-group method is sensitive enough to measure the 18 per cent of A_2 usually present; moreover, A_1 and A_2 must have about the same solubility.) However, Otteson and Villee[151c] showed that the rates of appearance of the dipeptide C and the hexapeptide A are rapid and are correlated with the increase in solubility accompanying the transformation of ovalbumin into plakalbumin. In contrast, the tetrapeptide appears at a slower rate uncorrelated with the solubility change. Unfortunately, only the rates of appearance of the peptides, not the exact amounts, could be measured, and even the relative rates differed for two ovalbumin preparations. If a number of assumptions are made this could be reconciled with the loss of the dipeptide in the step $A_1 \rightarrow P_1$, the hexapeptide in the step $A_2 \rightarrow P_2$, and the slow appearance of the tetrapeptide in a step which is rate dependent on the dephosphorylation of $P_1 \rightarrow P_2$ or with the formation of a plakalbumin differing from P_2. The relative rates of appearance of the peptides and relative amounts accord with this interpretation which assumes that the hexapeptide is only slowly attacked by the *subtilis* enzyme and that A_1 forms P_1 more rapidly than A_1 forms A_2 if both *subtilis* enzyme and phosphatase are present.

The suggestions advanced above must be considered tentative, and the full explanation of the ovalbumin-plakalbumin transformation will require more information on the chemical structure of these proteins. Recently, Linderstrøm-Lang[151e] has proposed several models for the structure of ovalbumin which account for the liberation of the two peptides. In one model both ovalbumin and the plakalbumins possess a free carboxyl group but no terminal amino group accessible to the Sanger reagent. In the other model the plakalbumin contains a free terminal amino group, in contradistinction to ovalbumin.

The stepwise dephosphorylation of ovalbumin has been confirmed by the electrophoretic isolation of the diphospho ovalbumin A_1, by partial dephosphorylation of ovalbumin with prostate phosphatase to yield the monophosphorus A_2, and by complete dephosphorylation of A_2 with intestinal phosphatase to give the phosphorus-free ovalbumin A_3.[150b] Except for phosphorus content and mobility, all three proteins A_1, A_2, and A_3 have similar properties. As in the ovalbumin–plakalbumin transformation, the mobility shifts which accompany the dephosphorylation can be used to estimate the change in net charge of the proteins. The results indicate that two ionizable hydrogens are involved in the removal of each phosphorus. The elucidation of the relationships of these three

(151e) K. U. Linderstrøm-Lang, *Stanford University Publications, Medical Sciences* Vol. VI (Lane Medical Lectures), (1952).

forms of ovalbumin aids in explaining the electrophoretic heterogeneity of freshly prepared solutions of this protein and the changes found on aging.

Prostate and intestinal phosphatase dephosphorylate plakalbumin in a manner similar to their action on ovalbumin, yielding P_2 and P_3 as indicated in the scheme of Fig. 1. Thus, by the proper use of three enzymes, five crystallizable modifications of ovalbumin are obtained; i.e., A_2, A_3, and the three plakalbumins. The properties of these proteins are summarized in Table II taken from Perlmann.[150b]

TABLE II

COMPARISON OF THE PROPERTIES OF PLAKALBUMINS AND OVALBUMINS[150b]

Electrophoresis was carried out in sodium phosphate buffer at pH 6.8 and 0.1 ionic strength.

Protein	Plakalbumins			Ovalbumins		
	P_1	P_2	P_3	A_1	A_2	A_3
Crystal form	Plates	Plates	Plates	Needles	Needles	Needles
Atoms phosphorus per mole of protein[a]	2	1	0	2	1	0
$\mu \times 10^5$ sq. cm./v./sec.	-5.5	-4.6	-3.8	-6.1	-5.2	-4.5
Isoelectric pH at 0.1 ionic strength	4.72	4.8		4.58	4.65	4.74

[a] Assuming a molecular weight of 44,000.

These interesting results suggest that proteins may be modified enzymatically to give new forms differing greatly in solubility and crystalline form, significantly in electrophoretic mobility, but not appreciably in molecular weight. They have great bearing on the question whether proteins exist in the same state in purified form as they do in their natural milieu and also suggest an explanation for the electrophoretic heterogeneity of many isolated proteins.

15. REMOVAL OF C-TERMINAL GROUPS BY CARBOXYPEPTIDASE

Carboxypeptidase also brings about an enzymatic transformation of proteins resulting in soluble products without detectable change in molecular weight and sometimes without loss of biological activity. This enzyme can liberate amino acids from some protein substrates, presumably at C-terminal positions which conform to its specific structural requirements. In the past two years carboxypeptidase has been investigated as a possible general means of bringing about controlled stepwise degradation of proteins and for the identification of the C-terminal acids.　This aspect has been described in Chaps. 2 and 3, but the advantages of carboxypeptidase for enzymatic modification of proteins should not be overlooked.　In a reinvestigation of the biological activity of insulin treated with carboxypeptidase, Harris and Li[151f] found, contrary to earlier reports, that the C-terminal alanine of the hormone was not essential for the hypoglycemic action although the C-terminal asparagine may be involved in this function.　Harris is also reported to have evidence that the C-terminal leucine of lysozyme is not essential for activity.[151g]　In a very interesting study of the action of carboxypeptidase on tobacco mosaic virus Harris and Knight[151g] observed that threonine is specifically released in an amount equal to about 7 per cent of the threonine content of the virus and corresponding to some 3400 residues per mole.　Apparently the C-terminal group is not essential for activity, for a virus preparation retained full infectivity after treatment until all the available threonine was liberated.　Moreover, the "dethreonized" virus yielded progeny containing C-terminal threonine just as acylated virus and polyglycine virus had produced progeny indistinguishable from the natural virus.

IV. Properties of Chemically Modified Proteins in Relation to Activity and Structure

The importance of collateral physical chemical studies must be stressed for any investigation of the effect of chemical modification of a protein in the elucidation of biological activity or protein structure and properties.　Such physical chemical studies give information on the homogeneity of the derivative, reveal whether any denaturation changes have supervened, and make known the existence of nonspecific structural changes which may affect activity, e.g., effects on the degree of ionization or alteration in net charge.　The goal of protein modification for investigation of structure and activity should be to produce derivatives as homogeneous as the natural material.　This has seldom been aspired to and more rarely realized.　On the one hand, the diminished solubility of many protein derivatives has hampered physical chemical investigation; on the other hand, the lack of specificity of reagents and of a means of controlling the extent of group coverage has discouraged such study. With the present accumulation of knowledge on the latter factors, one handicap has been overcome and we may hope for more frequent collateral physical chemical studies such as the recent work on the modification of human serum albumin[32,131,146] and insulin.[83,152]

(151f) J. I. Harris and C. H. Li, J. Am. Chem. Soc. **74**, 2945 (1952).
(151g) J. I. Harris and C. Knight, Nature **170**, 613 (1952).
(152) W. F. H. M. Mommaerts and H. Neurath, J. Biol. Chem. **186**, 815 (1950).

In this chapter much emphasis has been placed on the physicochemical characterization of chemical derivatives of proteins. In general, the expected distribution around a mean with regard to physicochemical homogeneity is realized whenever an appreciable number of groups are involved in a reaction. However, notable exceptions occur, for example, in the reduction and alkylation of the —S—S— bonds of lysozyme in urea.[73a] In contrast to most protein modifications, this is largely an all-or-none phenomenon. The partially reduced reaction mixtures consist of two well-defined fractions, which can be separated by means of solubility differences; the one is unreacted protein, the other is an almost completely reduced or alkylated product which is inactive and poorly soluble. Other instances of physicochemical heterogeneity, to be described shortly, result chiefly from aggregation or secondary reactions.

The following section will consider particularly the ultracentrifugal and electrophoretic evidence for homogeneity of protein derivatives and will illustrate the application of protein modification to the investigation of the relation between structure and activity. In passing, it is worth while to note the inadequacy of present criteria of protein purity and to draw attention to Bailey's suggestion that Sanger's DNP method may prove to be one of the most searching tests for protein purity if properly applied.[43] Some physical chemical properties of protein derivatives will be passed over briefly. Crystallizability is of little utility except as an aid in purification and as a criterion of the absence of degradative changes. The crystals of acetylpepsins appear all alike and are indistinguishable from those of the normal enzyme.[20] A variety of other protein derivatives have been crystallized including: iodinated horse serum albumin[31] and human serum albumin,[131] iodinated pepsin,[129] acetylinsulin,[33] mercaptalbumin,[32] guanidinated human serum albumin,[146] and the DFP derivative of chymotrypsin.[8] The crystalline derivative of ovalbumin and p-chloromercuribenzoate dissociates to yield native protein on dialysis against cysteine. Apart from light-scattering measurements on the mercaptalbumin equilibrium, no resort has been made to this procedure. Light-absorption spectra of many protein derivatives should be revealing and characteristic, but little advantage has been taken of this property. In several cases molecular weights of modified proteins have been determined by the osmotic-pressure method but without separate estimation of the homogeneity of the product. An interesting result of the use of DFP[32] has been the measurement of the minimum molecular weight for biological activity. In the case of chymotrypsin this corresponds to the actual molecular weight found by osmotic pressure or ultracentrifugation.

1. Solubility

One of the most obvious differences between a natural protein and its chemically modified counterpart is in solubility. This is to be expected since the general result of protein group reactions is the loss or gain of a charged residue, and since protein solubility is a function of the number of charged groups and their interaction with constituents of the medium.

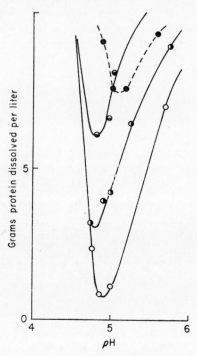

FIG. 2. Solubility of guanidinated serum albumins in acetate buffers at 25°; total protein concentration 10 g./l., dashed line, albumin with 32 amino groups guanidinated, ionic strength of 0.01; solid lines, 51 groups guanidinated; in order of decreasing solubility the ionic strength is 0.1, 0.05, and 0.01.[146]

In esterification and acylation, for example, large numbers of carboxyl or amino groups may be covered, and in deamination many amino groups are lost. Sulfation and phosphorylation completely change the solubility properties of proteins. Guanidination, though only exchanging a guanidyl group for an amino group, sharply decreases the solubility of serum albumin so that the product acts like a euglobulin. Plakalbumin, however, is 16 times as soluble as ovalbumin at pH 4.7 in 30 per cent ammonium sulfate.

The importance of solubility changes can sometimes be estimated by comparing derivatives; for instance, in the alkylation of sulfhydryl groups iodoacetate leaves a charged residue, whereas iodoacetamide does not. This leads to a remarkable difference in ease of thermal coagulation. Similarly, malonylation introduces a new polar carboxyl group into a protein with the possibility of dimerization of the derivative.

Since the isoelectric point of the derivative generally differs from that of the natural protein, comparison is difficult. This is particularly important in using altered solubility as a criterion of denaturation resulting from the chemical reaction. Since the derivatives are usually more insoluble at the altered isoelectric point, additional criteria of denaturation should be investigated.

Very few quantitative solubility studies of protein derivatives have been made. Clearly the solubility will depend upon the extent as well as the nature of modification. Typical behavior is illustrated in Fig. 2 for serum albumin having 32 and 51 amino groups guanidinated.

Since few purified proteins satisfy the rigorous phase-rule criterion of purity, it would be surprising to find any derivative that exhibited such ideal solubility behavior, and not more than one appears to have been obtained. Solubility tests indicated a high degree of homogeneity for iodinated pepsin.[129] The solubility curves of amorphous "100 per cent active" acetylpepsin (3–4 acetyl groups per pepsin molecule) and amorphous "60 per cent active" acetylpepsin (6–11 acetyl groups per molecule) were also investigated.[20,88] They indicated that both acetylpepsin preparations were solid solutions of similar proteins each consisting probably of several acetyl products although each preparation appeared to have constant composition and activity after repeated crystallization.

2. MOLECULAR KINETIC PROPERTIES

a. Ultracentrifugal Homogeneity

The dearth of ultracentrifugal studies of modified proteins is remarkable considering the potentialities of this instrument and its current availability. The analytical ultracentrifuge may be used to establish the homogeneity of a protein derivative, to determine its molecular weight and estimate its shape, and also to follow the course and extent of the reaction. Oncley, Ross, and Tracy[153] appear to have been the first to apply the ultracentrifuge to these problems. In a study of the malonylation of horse serum albumin they found evidence that malonylation may produce dimers supporting a concept based on the fact that carbon suboxide has two reactive foci. However, Herriott[18] mentions

(153) J. L. Oncley, W. F. Ross, and A. Tracy, *J. Biol. Chem.* **141**, 797 (1941).

unpublished results in which acetic anhydride-treated albumin showed similar ultracentrifugal patterns and suggests that denaturation might better explain the results.

A number of other sedimentation studies have been made: (1) For the soluble, partially deaminated fraction (B) of egg albumin "the patterns show a sharp sedimenting boundary indicative of a monodisperse system."[123] However, the insoluble, more highly deaminated fraction (A) sedimented as aggregates with patterns more like those of denatured egg albumin. (2) Considerable amounts of iodine could be introduced into human serum albumin without detectable degradative changes, as judged by ultracentrifugal analysis,[131] but highly iodinated preparations contained two sedimenting components. One of these corresponded to iodinated albumin; the other moved faster but was apparently not a dimer. (3) Sedimentation diagrams were used to confirm the hypothesis that on the addition of the stoichiometric amount of mercuric chloride, mercaptalbumin forms a dimer ($S_{20} = 6.5$) replacing the normal component ($S_{20} = 4.6$).[32] Further study showed that the dimer dissociates slowly on standing. (4) Crystallizable guanidinated human serum albumin is as homogeneous in the ultracentrifuge as the original unmodified protein; both contain about 5 per cent of a somewhat faster sedimenting component. No significant change was observed in the rate of boundary spreading for any of the preparations. Thus, with the possible exception of certain pepsin derivatives, guanidinated serum albumin appears to be the most homogeneous protein derivative yet obtained—at least the one most rigorously tested for homogeneity. Serum albumin esterified by diazoacetic acid derivatives also undergoes no change in size or shape detectable by ultracentrifugal or viscosity studies.[41a]

The best example of the use of the ultracentrifuge to observe the modification of a protein is furnished by a study of the effect of esterification on the molecular aggregation of insulin. Mommaerts and Neurath[152] prepared insulin methyl ester by reaction with acid–methanol at 0 or 25° for various periods of time. The process of esterification was followed by ultracentrifugal analysis at pH 3.7 in solutions of 0.1 and 0.2 ionic strength. Unlike normal insulin, the esterified hormone exhibited two sedimenting boundaries. A slower-moving component (α) predominated for short reaction times; a component of higher sedimentation constant (β) increased progressively with esterification. However, the proportion of the β-component depended on the ionic strength as well as the degree of esterification. As shown in Fig. 3, the sedimentation rate of the α-component was a function of esterification, decreasing as the latter increased. This phenomenon was ascribed to a progressive dissociation of the insulin polymer into its monomeric units. It is analogous to the dissociation of insulin caused by acidification, which like esterification increases the net charge on the protein. The sedimentation constant of the β-component was unrelated to the methoxyl content, although the relative amount of this component increased with the degree of esterifica-

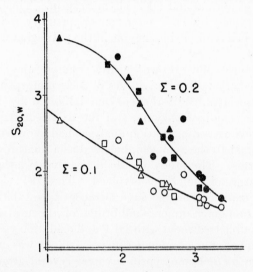

Fig. 3.   Sedimentation constants of the alpha component of esterified insulin, measured at pH 3.7 ± 0.1, plotted as a function of the methoxyl content.   Open symbols, 0.1 ionic strength; filled symbols, 0.2 ionic strength.   The conditions of esterification were as follows: (○,●), 0.1 N HCl-methanol, 25°; (△, ▲), 0.0125 N HCl-methanol, 25°; (□,■), 0.1 N HCl-methanol, 0°.   Taken from Mommaerts and Neurath.[152]

tion.   The formation of this material appeared to be due to a secondary aggregation process, possibly entailing a form of denaturation.

b. Molecular Weight and Shape

The chemical modification of a protein does not of itself necessarily alter the molecular weight beyond the experimental error of methods usually employed unless a large amount of a heavy atom or radical is introduced.   Thus, guanidinated serum albumin has a calculated molecular weight of 71,000 owing to introduction of 50 —$C(NH_2)_2^+$ groups compared to 69,000 for the original protein; it has the same S_{20}.[146]   The soluble deaminated B fraction of egg albumin has a slightly lower S_{20} and molecular weight than the natural substance.[123]   However, as expected, the sedimentation constant of iodinated serum albumin increased about 20 per cent when 34 iodine atoms per mole were introduced.[131]   Surprisingly little information is available on this question, for only occasionally have ultracentrifugal or osmotic-pressure measurements been made on the derivatives, and more rarely yet have combined sedimentation and diffusion methods been applied.

In unpublished experiments Snoke found no difference in the sedimentation patterns of normal and DFP–chymotrypsin. Thus, the inactivation of chymotrypsin by DFP offers an opportunity for study of the ultracentrifugal behavior of this enzyme in the pH region where autolysis usually occurs.

Recently Smith and Brown[153a] investigated the sedimentation behavior of three crystalline derivatives of α-chymotrypsin prepared by Jansen and associates:[8,26,141] the enzyme inhibited by reaction with DFP; the active, oxidized enzyme; and the oxidized enzyme inhibited with DFP. Previous sedimentation analyses had shown that α-chymotrypsin, in contrast to the zymogen, behaved as a mixture of monomeric and dimeric forms. The study of the derivatives was undertaken to ascertain the nature of the groups involved. The DFP–α-chymotrypsin and the active, oxidized enzyme gave ultracentrifugal diagrams characteristic of the monomer–dimer equilibrium of the untreated enzyme. However, the double treatment with DFP and oxidation yielded a derivative which sedimented as a monomer at pH 4.0. It was concluded that the dimerization of α-chymotrypsin involves several groupings, one of which must be ionic because of the pH dependence of the phenomenon. In contrast to this is the sedimentation behavior of the analogous modification of trypsin.[153b] At finite protein concentrations the sedimentation behavior of active trypsin, like that of active chymotrypsin and DFP-α-chymotrypsin, is characteristic of reversible aggregation which is dependent on concentration and pH. However, DFP-trypsin as well as trypsinogen[153c] sedimented under similar conditions as a single molecular species.

Although little change in molecular weight is to be anticipated as due simply to the introduction of reagent or the loss of protein groups, secondary processes may result in dimerization, aggregation, or dissociation. Some examples have already been described, e.g., (1) the effects of malonylation or mercaptide formation on serum albumin, and (2) the esterification of insulin with resulting dissociation and secondary aggregation. The polymerization of the relatively insoluble but highly deaminated fraction A of egg albumin should also be noted. In addition, intermolecular cross-linking of formaldehyde-treated serum albumin and

(153a) E. L. Smith and D. M. Brown, *J. Biol. Chem.* **195**, 525 (1952).

(153b) H. Neurath, L. W. Cunningham, Jr., F. Tietze, and N. M. Green, *Federation Proc.* **11**, 265 (1952).

(153c) F. Tietze, *J. Biol. Chem.* in press.

egg albumin has been demonstrated by osmotic-pressure measurements.[118] The relative absence of measurements of the molecular shape properties of protein derivatives also merits emphasis, particularly since change in asymmetry is one of the most revealing criteria of denaturation. In a careful comparison of guanidinated and normal serum albumin, Hughes and his associates found that the viscosity was unchanged for a preparation with 54 guanidinated amino groups. Doty and Edsall[154] mention that viscosity studies show that Alb—S—Hg—S—Alb is more asymmetric than Alb—SH, but shorter than two moles of Alb—SH joined end to end. This suggests that the two albumin molecules overlap for a considerable area. An example of a case where asymmetry measurements aided in distinguishing between native modified protein and denatured modified protein is offered by the case of deaminated egg albumin. Both the frictional ratio (calculated from sedimentation and diffusion constants) and the relative viscosity of the soluble, partially deaminated B fraction agreed within experimental error with the corresponding values for the native original protein. However, the increased frictional ratio and relative viscosity of the highly deaminated A fraction indicated an unfolding of the molecule comparable to that suffered in acid denaturation.[123]

The preceding remarks deal with the molecular kinetic properties of protein derivatives; conversely something may be learned about the relaxation time of rotation of proteins if they are coupled to a fluorescent dye and the depolarization of the fluorescence is studied by the method introduced by Weber.[154a] The latter has described the preparation of stable fluorescent conjugates of ovalbumin and bovine serum albumin with 1-dimethylaminonaphthalene-5-sulfonyl chloride. Only about 2 moles of naphthalene are introduced per mole of protein. The method has already been applied to a study of the denaturation of these proteins, and it has many foreseeable applications.

3. ELECTROCHEMICAL PROPERTIES

a. Titration Curves

The titration curve of a protein is necessarily altered whenever charged groups are removed, added, converted, or substituted during chemical modification. Indeed, this type of study serves as one of the chief methods for the identification of the nature of the ionizing groups. One difficulty is the insolubility of some protein derivatives. This leads to heterogeneous titration which is ambiguous. The effect of formaldehyde on the alkaline segment of the titration curves of proteins has been

(154) P. Doty and J. T. Edsall, *Advances in Protein Chem.* **6**, 37 (1951).
(154a) G. Weber, *Biochem. J.* **51**, 155 (1952).

mentioned above and has been described earlier in Chap. 6. The deamination of proteins converts the ε-amino group of lysine to an aliphatic hydroxyl which does not combine with acids and bases. In deaminized gelatin the resulting titration curve shows an almost complete loss of groups titrating between pH 8.5 and 12, an acidic shift in the isoelectric point, but no apparent effect on the carboxyl segment of the curve.[155,156] These results early led to conclusions important for the interpretation of protein titration curves.[157] It should likewise be possible to study the behavior of carboxyl groups by blocking them, using acid–methanol which gives complete and specific esterification. This procedure has been applied to insulin but unfortunately the unmodified hormone precipitates in the region of the pK's of the carboxyl groups. Nonetheless, Mommaerts and Neurath[84] found that a buffer capacity of zero, indicating a total absence of titratable carboxyl groups, was reached when the methoxyl content corresponded to the number of initially available carboxyl groups. Thus, titration data for modified proteins may be used to estimate the number as well as the identity of the ionizing groups in the original protein, or, conversely, the amount of a group-specific reagent introduced may be inferred from titration curves.

There are numerous other instances in which titration data have contributed to the study of chemically modified proteins. Examples include the treatment of hemoglobin and serum albumin with mustard gas,[90] the malonylation of serum albumin,[158] the phosphorylation of egg albumin,[47] the benzenesulfonation of gelatin,[108] and the reaction of chloropicrin with egg albumin.[92] One of the most fundamental investigations concerns the various derivatives of crystalline human serum albumin prepared by Hughes and his associates. Tanford[159] compared the titration curves of mercaptalbumin, guanidinated albumin, and iodinated albumin with that of the n-decanol crystallized protein. The titration curves of the mercaptalbumin and decanol preparations differed only slightly on the basic side. The guanidinated albumin offered an opportunity to study the effect of the conversion of some 55 amino groups per mole to more strongly basic guanidyl groups. As shown in Fig. 4, the titration curve of the modified protein was strikingly different from that of the normal protein (dashed curve) but accorded well with a theoretical curve computed on the assumption that all ε-amino groups were converted to

(155) D. I. Hitchcock, *J. Gen. Physiol.* **6**, 95 (1923/24).

(156) I. Lichtenstein, *Biochem. Z.* **303**, 22 (1940) (cited by Cohn and Edsall[157]).

(157) E. J. Cohn and J. T. Edsall, Proteins, Amino Acids and Peptides, Reinhold Publ. Corp., New York, 1943.

(158) W. F. Ross and H. N. Cristensen, *J. Biol. Chem.* **137**, 89 (1941).

(159) C. Tanford, *J. Am. Chem. Soc.* **72**, 441 (1950).

guanidinium groups. Unexpectedly, only a small difference was noted between the titration curves of the iodinated and unmodified albumin. This is surprising since iodination of tyrosine to give diiodotyrosine changes the pK value of the —OH from about 10 down to about 6.5. Moreover, Neuberger[160] had earlier shown considerable differences in the titration curves of zein and iodozein. When optical densities of iodinated serum albumin are plotted against pH, the dependence of absorption on

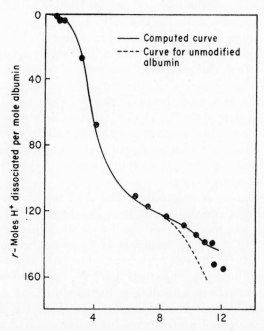

FIG. 4. Titration curve of guanidinated serum albumin at 25°, ionic strength, 0.15.[159]

pH closely resembles a titration curve. The midpoint is at pH 7.6, and Klotz and Urquhart[161] suggest this gives the pK of diiodotyrosine in the albumin.

b. Electrophoretic Analysis

(1) *Mobility and Isoelectric Point.* The possible changes just mentioned for titration curves of modified proteins will, of course, also be reflected in the electrophoretic mobility and isoelectric point of the proteins. The availability of the electrophoresis apparatus, the ease of detecting changes in ionizing groups through altered mobility, and, finally, the possibility of ascertaining homogeneity have made this one

(160) A. Neuberger, *Biochem. J.* **28**, 1982 (1934).
(161) I. M. Klotz and J. M. Urquhart, *J. Am. Chem. Soc.* **73**, 3182 (1951).

of the most commonly invoked methods for studying protein derivatives. When egg albumin is deaminated, the mobility curve is shifted as much as 1 pH unit toward the acid side, with a corresponding decrease in the isoelectric point.[123]   However, only small differences in mobility and isoelectric point are noted when the weak sulfhydryl groups combine with chloropicrin.[92]   A somewhat more acidic protein is formed when azlactones react with the amino groups of egg albumin.[109]   On the other hand, esterification of the carboxyl groups of this protein or of lacto-globulin with epoxides shifts the isoelectric point as much as 3 pH units toward the alkaline side.[42]   A similar shift is found when human serum albumin is esterified with diazoacetic acid.[41a]   Electrophoretic experiments indicate that the pituitary lactogenic hormone is also rendered more basic by esterification of the carboxyl groups.[83]   As expected, acetylation of the lactogenic hormone reduced the mobility on the acid side of the isoelectric point.[48]   The electrophoretic method, however, is too insensitive to be able to detect a change in mobility of chymotrypsin after reaction with only 1 mole of DFP per mole enzyme.   More complete investigation of the pH–mobility curves of protein derivatives would prove instructive.

(2) *Electrophoretic Homogeneity.*   The chief use of electrophoresis in the study of protein derivatives has been to ascertain their homogeneity. Too often, this test has been restricted to a single pH or a narrow pH range.   Generally speaking, modified proteins are remarkably homogeneous in the electrophoretic apparatus.   Guanidinated serum albumin was "completely homogeneous at pH 8.6."[146]   Esterified serum albumin exhibited some boundary spreading owing to statistical modification.[41a] At pH 2.9 where egg albumin is homogeneous both the A and B fractions of the deaminated protein were homogeneous, and they were less homogeneous at other pH values than was the unmodified protein.[123] Chloropicrin-treated egg albumin was quite homogeneous,[92] and the egg albumin–thiophene–2-azlactone compound[109] likewise migrated with a single boundary in the Tiselius apparatus at pH 7.5.   The more soluble epoxide derivatives of egg albumin and lactoglobulin showed the same degree of "purity" as the untreated proteins, but less soluble preparations were quite heterogeneous.[42]   Esterified pituitary lactogenic hormone was essentially homogeneous with regard to electrochemical properties and could readily be distinguished from the starting material when the two were mixed together before electrophoresis.[83]   The acetylated hormone was quite homogeneous but did not separate clearly from the untreated hormone at the single pH tested.[48]   The various acylated derivatives of tobacco mosaic virus possessed an electrophoretic homogeneity comparable to that of the normal virus.[30]   This is illustrated in Fig. 5 which

also demonstrates the sensitivity of the electrophoretic method for detecting small amounts of unreacted protein.

The apparent electrophoretic homogeneity of a variety of protein derivatives may be somewhat illusory. First, as mentioned above, the examination was usually done at only a single pH. Secondly, the mobility difference of the chemically modified and the untreated protein is often slight. Thus, within the compass of a single moving boundary might well be represented a whole family of derivatives varying progressively in the number of altered groups. Finally, electrophoretic analysis

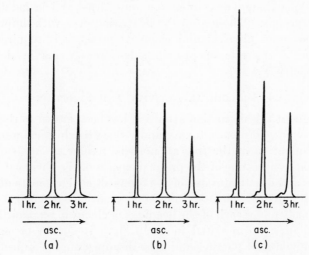

Fig. 5. Tracings of Longsworth scanning diagrams of ascending boundaries obtained during electrophoresis of (a) 0.2 per cent normal tobacco mosaic virus, (b) 0.2 per cent carbobenzoxy virus, (c) a mixture of 0.2 per cent carbobenzoxy virus and 0.01 per cent normal virus. The vertical arrows indicate starting positions of the boundaries.[30]

is restricted to the more soluble derivatives or often to a pH range away from the isoelectric point. Yet, the most searching test of electrophoretic homogeneity is made at the isoelectric point.

The first electrophoretic study of the kinetics of formation of a modified protein was made by Fischer and Lauffer.[45,119] The reaction between tobacco mosaic virus and formaldehyde at pH 7 results in an electrophoretically homogeneous preparation, regardless of the time of formaldehyde treatment; whereas, when the reaction is carried out at pH 4, the preparations are inhomogeneous and the patterns are anomalous. The shift in electrophoretic mobility increased with time of contact with formaldehyde and reached a maximum difference of 0.75 mobility units or only 10 per cent after 72 hr. The inactivation of the virus was a first-order process with a rate constant of 0.42/hr. or about 10 times the rate constant for the change in electrophoretic mobility. The increase in mobility is not associated in a simple manner with the decrease in free amino groups measured by the ninhydrin method. These results could be interpreted to mean either that inactivation was independent of the changes detected by physical and chemical methods or that loss of infectivity was due to the irreversible reaction of only the first one of several particular amino groups of one sort reacting irreversibly with formaldehyde. Fischer and Lauffer point out that at pH 7 there are about 8300 net charges on a tobacco mosaic virus particle and about 3400 free amino groups. These results indicate that even with simple proteins a combination of physical and chemical methods is required for the elucidation of the role of protein side-chain groups in determining biological activity.

4. Biological Activity and Function

Throughout this discussion attention has been drawn to the inactivation of enzymes, hormones, toxins, and viruses by chemical modification. The determination of the free amino acid residue groups essential for biological activity is one of the prime purposes of the chemical alteration of proteins and constitutes one of the foremost achievements of this type of research. In this chapter individual mention of classical examples has been made under each of the headings of chemical reactions. A complete tabulation is presented in Chap. 11. It should be emphasized again, however, that parallelism in the disappearance of a protein group and loss of activity is neither a necessary consequence nor a proof of an essential relation. The formaldehyde inactivation of tobacco mosaic virus, just mentioned above, is but one example of many which illustrate that only a fraction of one particular type of protein group is connected to biological activity. Moreover, for this virus there is evidence from studies with iodine, ketene, phenyl isocyanate, carbobenzoxy chloride, p-chlorobenzoyl chloride, benzenesulfonyl chloride, and dinitrofluorobenzene that not just some of the amino groups but also some of the phenolic and indolyl groups are responsible for infectivity. However, Knight[106] points out that despite these extensive studies in no case has it been possible to link a given type of grouping specifically or predominantly with the infectivity of this virus. Indeed, for nucleoproteins such as this the role of the nucleic acid moiety has been almost wholly neglected though it is known for at least one plant virus that a crystallizable protein occurs naturally having virtually all the physical properties but not the infectivity of its nucleoprotein counterpart.[162]

(162) R. Markham and K. M. Smith, *Parasitology* **39**, 330 (1949).

In the interests of precision it should not be stated that one type of group is essential for biological activity (for example, amino or phenolic groups, etc.) but rather that the group, or some critical fraction of one or more of these types of groups, is *involved in the structure responsible for biological activity*. It is on the aspect of specific structural relations that physical chemical evidence must be brought to bear. First, if it cannot be shown that biological activity is restored by unblocking the affected group, it must be demonstrated by physical criteria that denaturation has not occurred. Secondly, the molecular and electrochemical heterogeneity of the derivatives must be ascertained in relation to criteria of homogeneity of biological activity. Thirdly, consideration must be taken of possible nonspecific effects of modification on the physical structure of the protein. When a single mole of reagent is taken up per mole of protein to produce a completely inert compound, as in the case of DFP–chymotrypsin, it may be stated that a single but[141b] as yet unknown group or site is essential for activity. However, when extensive substitution or blocking only diminishes activity, it is possible that the effect is nonspecific and results either from an over-all alteration in net charge or a microscopic redistribution. Steric effects must likewise be considered. Fortunately, the variety of relatively specific chemical reagents now available allows a test for both electrostatic and steric effects. This can be done by treating with two reagents such as ketene and carbon suboxide, one of which produces a neutral group, the other transforming a basic group to an acidic one. Likewise, diazo compounds can be used to introduce either a positive or a negative charge at the same center and to investigate steric hindrance. Many similar combinations are available for this type of examination.

The retention of biological specificity in chemically modified enzymes and viruses is of as much importance as the abolition. The possibility of producing extremely acidic or basic proteins which retain physiological activity is conceivably both of theoretical and practical interest particularly in the case of insulin. It is significant that certain acylated derivatives of tobacco mosaic virus remain infective, and it is understandable that the chemical substitution is not a heritable characteristic. However, the fact that these derivatives elicit a disproportionate response from two hosts is a remarkable phenomenon that merits further investigation. Furthermore, the effect of chemical substitution should be compared for related strains of viruses or for similar enzymes and for hormones derived from different species. Although the dinitrophenyl derivatives of three strains of tobacco mosaic virus provoked the same relative response from two different hosts as did the normal virus, the susceptibility to treatment with FDNB varied for the three strains.

Another objective should be to determine the effect of chemical substitution on the *specificity* and not just on the over-all *activity* of an enzyme. The proteolytic enzymes are particularly suitable for this study because of the availability both of natural protein substrates and synthetic peptide substrates of highly defined structure and also because of their dual peptidase and esterase activity. The malonylation of pepsin is a case where there was no apparent difference in specificity of the normal and the chemically modified enzyme. Crystalline periodate-oxidized α-chymotrypsin at shifted pH optima possessed 65 per cent of the esterase activity but only 35 per cent of the proteinase activity of the unmodified enzyme. However, neither the DFP derivative of unaltered chymotrypsin nor of the oxidized enzyme had esterase or proteinase activity. It is noteworthy that though normal and malonylpepsin had the same specificity both attacked malonyl serum albumin more readily than the unmodified protein.

Every report of the preparation of a biologically active protein derivative should be accompanied by evidence of the biological stability of the linkage. This can be obtained by a search for specific enzymes, by tissue slice incubation with or without radioactive markers, and by comparison of the effect of several group-specific reagents.

From the above it should be clear that much judgment and much information are required in the interpretation of the biological effects of the chemical modification of proteins. Investigation with a single reagent and chemical tests alone are inadequate to reveal all the factors determining biological activity. Fortunately, a considerable body of data is available for a number of highly purified proteins such as pepsin, chymotrypsin, tobacco mosaic virus, insulin, and lysozyme. The modification of the last two proteins is discussed in some detail in Chap. 11. Immunological studies of modified proteins are taken up in Vol. II.

5. Chemical Modification of Proteins and Protein Structure

The chemical reactions of proteins give considerable evidence about their structure. The availability of virtually all the amino acid residues for chemical reactions analogous to those of amino acids supports the now widely accepted concept that the peptide linkage is the primary covalent bond in proteins. However, the presence of masked groups, revealed both by denaturation and chemical reactions, suggests that some of the phenol c groups, the sulfhydryl groups, and so forth are either combined in labile linkages susceptible to rupture by denaturation or are sterically inaccessible to chemical reagents unless the structure is deranged. The latter interpretation would be more attractive if further studies would reveal a dependence of group reactivity on molecular size of the reagent. The finding that only a fraction of the groups of a particular type are essential for biological activity emphasizes the topographical complexity of proteins. The different rates of reactivity of amino groups vs. phenolic groups in several proteins points up the individuality of protein structure. Indeed, the inability to make generalizations about the essentiality of protein groups for biological activity is evidence that a great deal more must be learned before detailed conclusions can be made about the nature of enzymatic activity or virus action. For example, in Olcott and Fraenkel-Conrat's tabulation (see Chap. 11 for modified table) phenolic groups were claimed as essential wherever investigated (except for amylase), carboxyl groups were deemed essential in 5 out of 5 cases listed, disulfide in 7 out of 11, and amino in 8 out of 22. Though the requirement for —SH groups has gained most prominence in the literature, sulfhydryls are absent in many proteins and not needed for the activity of others. In many proteins several types of groups have been found essential, for example, phenolic, carboxyl, and disulfide in insulin; both —SH and phenolic in papain; and all groups investigated in the case of crotoxin (amino, phenolic, carboxyl, aliphatic hydroxyl, imidazole, indolyl, amide, guanidyl and disulfide).[163] Such a multiple requirement is understandable for enzymes in which a two- or three-point type of enzyme substrate attachment has been demonstrated. Since enzymes are presumably monofunctional, all such groups must be present at the active center (or centers) and must cooperate to produce the specific electrostatic environment and steric structure. However, so little is known about the multiplication of viruses that no such simplified predictions can be made. It is puzzling that the nucleic acid moiety is involved in mutations but so little attention has been paid to its role in virus reproduction. The problem of toxins and hormones may be more analogous to that of enzymes since these proteins probably mediate enzymatic action, or in the case of toxins may actually be enzymes or enzyme inhibitors.

The elucidation of microscopic protein structure is clearly one of the problems for which chemical modification promises greater hope. In addition to the biological approach described above, the physical approach is now being actively pursued by Klotz and co-workers[96,161,164] who have studied the interaction of iodinated, guanidinated, and acetylated serum albumin in an attempt to discern the fine features of topography which must endow this protein with its characteristic affinity for ions. Gurd

(163) H. Fraenkel-Conrat and J. Fraenkel-Conrat, *Biochim. et Biophys. Acta* **5**, 98 (1950).

(164) I. M. Klotz, R. K. Burkhard, and J. M. Urquhart, *J. Am. Chem. Soc.* **74**, 202 (1952).

and Goodman[165] have used diazoesterified or guanidinated serum albumin in a study of the interaction with zinc ions. The quantitative study of the dye binding capacity or anion affinity of protein derivatives should be more vigorously pursued in the manner illustrated by the recent study of the binding of some neutral organic molecules by the guanidinated, methylated, acetylated, and iodinated derivatives of serum albumin.[166]

The most explicit and most important recent advances in protein structure have come through the use of chemical reagents to determine the terminal groups and the order and number of the peptide chains. This work derives from the first studies of chemically modified proteins such as the preparation of insulin compounds.   Its significance has been revealed in earlier chapters.

It would be difficult to exaggerate the extent to which immunological studies with azoproteins and other derivatives has influenced theories of antibody formation, protein synthesis, and protein structure. The whole concept of complementariness of structure is founded on the amazingly delicate delineation of serological specificity revealed by use of artifically modified antigens.   In turn, this supports the idea that templates are involved in the biosynthesis of proteins and that the specificity of proteins resides in spatio-chemical relationships.   However, it would be anticipatory to detail the development of these concepts which is described in Vol. II.

The possibilities inherent in further study of specifically modified proteins have been suggested throughout this discussion.   In conclusion, attention is directed to the chemical substitution of the polypeptide antibiotics and to prosthetic groups such as nucleic acid. Vast alterations in charge distribution and topography of proteins may little affect their activity, while quite subtle changes such as those due to denaturation or substitution of a single group may obliterate specificity.   The microscopic structure of active sites may be probed by the comparison of the effects of known reactions on prosthetic group vs. protein and of protein vs. polypeptide.   Collateral study of protein derivatives by physical, chemical, and biological methods gives greatest promise of revealing the intimate relation between structure and activity.

(165) F. R. N. Gurd and D. S. Goodman, *J. Am. Chem. Soc.* **74,** 670 (1952).
(166) I. M. Klotz and J. Ayers, *J. Am. Chem. Soc.* **74,** 6178 (1952).

CHAPTER 11

The Relation of Chemical Structure to the Biological Activity of the Proteins

BY R. R. PORTER

I. Introduction

The structural basis of biological activity in proteins is a problem whose importance in the understanding of biochemical processes is too obvious to need stressing. It is also apparent that as at present our knowledge of the detailed mechanism of any biological activity and our understanding of protein structure are slight, no satisfactory interpretation of one in terms of the other is yet possible. Much work, however, has been directed to the solution of this problem from many different points of view, and an attempt will be made in this chapter to summarize the results according to the methods used and to draw such limited conclusions as appear to be justifiable.

Antibodies, antigens, enzymes, some hormones, toxins, viruses, and genes are all believed to be simple or conjugated proteins. In addition to these substances whose biological role has long been recognized, there have recently been discovered proteins with a highly specific activity in biological systems whose significance is not understood. Examples of such proteins are the trypsin inhibitors which are found in such diverse places as lima beans, soybeans and egg white, as well as in the pancreas. The biotin-binding power of avidin and the iron-binding capacity of conalbumin are further examples of specific activities whose purpose is not apparent. The common characteristic feature of the activities of all these proteins is the high degree of specificity which they show, and it is perhaps irrelevant to the present chapter to consider what teleological purpose they may serve.

Twenty years ago the part played by proteins in biological systems was still in dispute. Many leading biochemists, particularly in Germany, believed that proteins were the inert colloidal carriers of a small active compound which was neither protein nor carbohydrate. In 1926 urease[1] was crystallized, followed by insulin[2] in 1927, pepsin[3] in 1930, trypsin[4] in 1931, and chymotrypsin[5] in 1933. All appeared to be simple proteins whose biological activity was destroyed by hydrolysis, by denaturation, or by chemical reaction. This was clearly strong evidence in favor of the view that the proteins themselves were responsible for the activity, but then, as now, the difficulty in deciding when in fact a protein is pure, prolonged the controversy. Since amino acid analysis has become more accurate, it has been possible to account within 1 or 2 per cent for the elementary analysis of several active proteins in terms of their constituent amino acids, making it most probable that biological activity can be an intrinsic property of a protein molecule. Many active proteins are conjugated with nucleic acid, heme, flavin, and other compounds, the activity displayed being dependent on the conjugation and neither part retaining it to any significant extent when split. Considerable progress has been made in elucidating the part played by the nonprotein component, particularly with the heme proteins. However, no

(1) J. B. Sumner, *J. Biol. Chem.* **69,** 435 (1926).
(2) J. J. Abel, E. M. K. Geiling, C. A. Rouiller, F. K. Bell, and O. Wintersteiner, *J. Pharmacol. Exptl. Therap.* **31,** 65 (1927).
(3) J. H. Northrop, *J. Gen. Physiol.* **13,** 739 (1930).
(4) J. H. Northrop and M. Kunitz, *Science* **73,** 262 (1931).
(5) M. Kunitz and J. H. Northrop, *Science* **78,** 558 (1933).

more is known of the role of protein in the heme proteins than is known in some unconjugated enzymes and antibodies, perhaps even less. It is primarily with the part played by the protein moiety that we shall be concerned throughout.

Most proteins have recognizable specific activity as antigens, though their antigenicity may be due to structural characteristics distinct from those responsible for any other biological function which they may perform. Thus, antibodies against pneumococcus polysaccharide when injected into a different species, give rise to *anti*-antibodies. It is immaterial whether for injection or testing the immune serum, free antibody, or the specific precipitate is used. This shows that the molecular surface responsible for their behavior as antibodies must be distinct from that controlling their antigenic specificity. Again, an enzyme when combined with the homologous antienzyme may or may not be inhibited by the combination, showing that in some cases enzymic and antigenic activity must depend on different parts of the molecule. From this and much other evidence to be discussed later, it has become accepted that only a part of the protein molecule, referred to as the active center, is responsible for any particular biological activity. In certain cases such as urease where the molecular weight of the enzyme is nearly ten thousand times greater than that of the substrate, it is clear that the active center or centers must be relatively very small. As from a study of the inhibition of urease by silver ions,[6] it appears that there are no more than three or four active centers per molecule, a very large part of the protein cannot be directly involved in the enzyme–substrate reaction. It does not follow that such active parts would retain their activity if they could be split from the remainder, as the essential structure of an active center may be dependent on the primary and secondary valencies which join it to the bulk of the molecule.

A further point in present ideas of the mode of action of active proteins is that actual combination occurs between the protein and the other reactant although these views are largely based on *in vitro* studies of only two types of biological activity, viz., enzymatic and immunological. An essential feature of such a combination is that it is reversible and is dependent primarily on the relative concentration of the reactants. This has been experimentally demonstrated with enzymes and antibodies. With such substances as hormones and toxins the second reactant is unknown and hence the mode of action uncertain.

Attempts to relate any biological activity with gross chemical or physical properties have failed. Thus enzymes may be of any size from

(6) J. F. Ambrose, G. B. Kistiakowsky, and A. G. Kridl, *J. Am. Chem. Soc.* **73**, 1232 (1951).

ribonuclease with a molecular weight of 15,000 to urease with a molecular weight of nearly 600,000. Hormones and toxins show a similar wide scatter in size, and even antibodies, which are always serum globulins and would be expected to be more uniform, may have a molecular weight from 150,000 to 900,000. Only with antigens has the suggestion ever been made that size is important in determining activity and this has been shown to be untenable. Now that association and dissociation of protein molecules is becoming recognized as a general phenomenon,[7] the recorded values of molecular weight may, however, have less significance.

Shape is equally no criterion for biological activity. Most active proteins are in fact globular, but myosin, a typical fibrous protein, is thought to be an enzyme and can combine specifically with actin, both reactions being associated with muscular contraction.

Electrophoretic mobility under various conditions may distinguish species differences in otherwise identical proteins, in the hemoglobins[8] as a class or in the cytochromes.[9] This property, however, which depends primarily on the net surface charge in given conditions, has never been correlated with the antigenic specificity of the same series of proteins from different species, nor with any other type of activity. Electrophoretic mobility has been used also by Velick[10] to detect a specific binding of phosphate ions by triosephosphate dehydrogenase. He found the dissociation constant too low to be explained by simple electrostatic attraction with the implication that the binding might be related to the binding of the substrate, which is a phosphate ester, to the enzyme.

Even solubility does not appear to be a property necessary for biological activity in proteins. Several enzyme systems, cytochrome oxidase for example, which can be demonstrated in suspensions of cell residue have rarely been obtained in true solution.[11] By careful ethanol denaturation, urease may be rendered insoluble and yet remain enzymatically active.[12] Insoluble particulate antigens may also combine successfully with their antibodies. As all probably are surface reactions these observations are not unexpected. Of the gross chemical characteristics of proteins, neither elementary analysis nor amino acid analysis can be related to the presence or absence of biological activity.

It follows from the foregoing that certain types of information will

(7) K. O. Pedersen, *Cold Spring Harbor Symposia Quant. Biol.* **14,** 140 (1949).
(8) K. Landsteiner, L. G. Longsworth and J. Van der Scheer, *Science* **88,** 83 (1938).
(9) H. Tint and W. Reiss, *J. Biol. Chem.* **182,** 385 (1950).
(10) S. F. Velick, *J. Phys. & Colloid Chem.* **53,** 135 (1949).
(11) K. G. Paul, in Sumner and Myrbäck, The Enzymes, Vol. 2, Part 1, Academic Press Inc., New York, 1951.
(12) J. B. Sumner, *Science* **108,** 410 (1948).

be necessary to solve the problem of the structural basis of activity. Clearly, the detailed nature of the activity studied must be known, whether it occurs in one or more steps, and what are the intermediates, if any. The precise degree of specificity has to be found in order that information as to the function of the active center can be deduced. In the last resort, knowledge of the complete spatial structure of the protein may be needed although more limited information as to the composition and structure of the active centers and their relation to each other may, in some cases, be sufficient. Much information of this type has been accumulated, though never have all the possible means of study been explored for one protein. None of the work has yet permitted more than very general conclusions to be drawn. Hence it has seemed preferable to discuss this unsolved problem according to the methods of investigation employed rather than by the results and conclusions obtained for proteins showing particular types of biological activity.

II. Methods of Investigation

1. Activity and General Structural Features

A perpetual difficulty in studying protein structure, or indeed most properties of proteins, is the lack of any final criterion as to purity. Solubility studies, the rate of sedimentation in the ultracentrifuge, electrophoretic mobility, and antigenic behavior are the four generally accepted tests of purity at present. Chromatography of proteins and countercurrent methods, which seem likely to be developed in the near future, offer other tests with different and perhaps higher resolving powers, but it remains implicit in all work with proteins that improvements in technique or developments of new methods may reveal unsuspected heterogeneity and necessitate revision of the interpretation of earlier work.

a. Amino Acid Analysis

It is only in recent years that the rapid development of microanalytical techniques has made it possible to obtain complete figures for the amino acid composition of proteins. Sufficient time has not yet elapsed for accumulation of the extensive data necessary in any attempted correlation with biological activity. It seems likely that much information may be obtainable particularly from comparative studies such as the amino acid analysis of an enzyme from widely differing sources or an analytical comparison of closely related enzymes in the same species.

At present, complete analyses are available for several enzymes, hormones, toxins, and viruses. Tables giving the analytical data for these biologically active proteins and many others, can be found in Chap. 3. From the data it is apparent that no particular pattern of amino acid content is associated with any class of biological activity; and estimation of the amino acid content of antibodies has shown it to be equally improbable that their specificity is directly related to the analytical figures. Bailey[13] has expressed the amino acid composition of 20 proteins in the form of histograms, which emphasize the general patterns and the exceptions to them (see also Chap. 3). It enabled him to conclude tentatively that in complex soluble proteins there were upper and lower limits, both to the total charge and to the number of polar groups. The upper limit implied that lipophilic side chains may be as important as the hydrophilic in determining specific interaction. Another rather obvious connection seems to be between a high cystine content and strong resistance to all forms of denaturation except by alkali. Insulin, ribonuclease, and lysozyme with cystine contents of 12 per cent,[14] 7 per cent[15] and 8 per cent[16] respectively, are all relatively stable proteins. As the disulfide linkage is the only known covalent interchain bond and as it is stable under most of the conditions of denaturation except in alkali, such a correlation is to be expected. These proteins lose their biological activity when the disulfide bonds are reduced.

It has been suggested that the presence of aromatic amino acids is necessary for a protein to be a good antigen. Thus gelatin, which is nonantigenic, becomes so on coupling with o-β-glucosidotyrosine.[17] However, insulin, which is a very poor antigen in spite of a high tyrosine content, also becomes more antigenic when similarly treated,[17] and the combination of phenyl isocyanate with gelatin fails to improve its antigenic power.[18] Polysaccharides which contain no amino acid residues may be powerful antigens in certain species, and the protein fraction of yellow turnip mosaic virus, which is of unknown amino acid composition, is nonantigenic unless coupled to its nucleic acid, when it becomes an extremely powerful antigen.[19] It is evident that antigenic power need not be related to amino acid composition.

An obvious feature revealed by amino acid analysis is the constancy

(13) K. Bailey, *Chemistry and Industry* **1950**, 243.
(14) A. C. Chibnall, *J. Intern. Soc. Leather Trades Chemists* **30**, 1 (1946).
(15) E. Brand, quoted by J. H. Northrop, M. Kunitz, and R. M. Herriott, Crystalline Enzymes, Columbia University Press, New York, 1948.
(16) C. Fromageot and M. Privat de Garille, *Biochim. et Biophys. Acta* **3**, 82 (1949).
(17) R. F. Clutton, C. R. Harington, and M. E. Yuill, *Biochem. J.* **32**, 1111, 1119 (1938).
(18) S. J. Hopkins and A. Wormall, *Biochem. J.* **27**, 1706 (1933).
(19) R. Markham, R. E. F. Matthews, and K. M. Smith, *Nature* **162**, 88 (1948).

TABLE I
COMPOSITION OF SEED GLOBULINS[20]
(All data in per cent)

Amino acid	Edestin	Pumpkin	Squash	Watermelon	Cucumber	Tobacco
Arginine	16.7	16.2	16.2	17.9	15.8	16.1
Histidine	2.52	2.22	2.18	2.20	2.28	2.22
Lysine	2.35	2.76	3.01	2.93	2.94	1.58
Threonine	3.14	2.58	2.77	2.95	3.59	4.17
Leucine	7.4	8.0	8.0	7.5	9.1	10.5
Isoleucine	6.2	5.1	5.5	5.7	5.5	6.3
Valine	6.6	6.5	6.5	6.4	7.0	6.7
Tyrosine	4.34	4.36	4.36	4.57	4.60	4.07
Tryptophan	1.23	1.74	1.74	1.86	1.93	1.47
Phenylalanine	5.45	7.2	6.8	7.7	6.5	5.7
Methionine	2.22	2.31	2.31	2.77	2.51	2.18
Cystine/2	1.32	1.12	1.11	1.10	1.06	1.11
Total S	0.88	0.99	0.95	1.06	1.04	1.03
Missing S	0.05	0.19	0.15	0.17	0.22	0.26

of composition of given proteins from a variety of sources. Owing to the poverty of data on other systems, an example is shown from proteins which do not possess any obvious biological activity, viz., the seed globulins from related and unrelated species (see also Chap. 3). Analysis of silk fibroins[21,22] and collagens[23] shows a similar constancy of composition (see Table I[20]).

Older analyses of hemoglobin from several species suggested that while the content of basic amino acids was remarkably constant, the cystine figures differed widely.[24,25] However, the values then quoted for horse hemoglobin are only one-half that of a more recent and reliable value,[26] so that the reality of the variation is doubtful.

It is not certain whether pure preparations of the same protein from the same species will always have a constant composition. The diet of a hen can influence the amino acid content of the egg white,[27] but in this

(20) E. L. Smith and R. D. Greene, J. Biol. Chem. 167, 833 (1947).
(21) J. Roche, R. Michel and M. B. Tichadou, Compt. rend. soc. biol. 144, 100 (1950).
(22) L. B. Rockland and M. S. Dunn, J. Am. Chem. Soc. 71, 4121 (1949).
(23) R. E. Neuman, Arch. Biochem. 24, 289 (1949).
(24) M. Bergmann and C. Niemann, J. Biol. Chem. 118, 301 (1937).
(25) H. B. Vickery and A. White, Proc. Soc. Exptl. Biol. Med. 31, 6 (1933).
(26) G. R. Tristram, Haemoglobin, Butterworths Scientific Publications, London, 1949.
(27) F. A. Csonka, C. A. Denton, and S. J. Ringel, J. Biol. Chem. 169, 259 (1947).

case no evidence has been offered to show that the composition of a purified protein has been changed. Small but significant differences have been observed in the composition of crystalline β-lactoglobulin, prepared in the same laboratory by similar methods but with an interval of several years between preparations.[28]

Knight[29] has carried out an interesting study of the amino acid composition of a series of plant viruses related to tobacco mosaic virus. The results found are shown in Table II.

TABLE II
AMINO ACID CONTENT[a] OF HIGHLY PURIFIED PREPARATIONS OF SOME STRAINS OF TOBACCO MOSAIC VIRUS[29]

Amino acid	Strain							
	TMV	M	J14D1	GA	YA	HR	CV3	CV4
Alanine	5.1	5.2	4.8	5.1	5.1	**6.4**		**6.1**
Arginine	9.8	9.9	10.0	**11.1**	**11.2**	9.9	**9.3**	**9.3**
Aspartic acid	13.5	13.5	13.4	13.7	13.8	**12.6**		13.1
Cysteine	0.69	0.67	0.64	0.60	0.60	0.70	0	0
Cystine	0		0		0	0		0
Glutamic acid	11.3	11.5	**10.4**	11.5	11.3	**15.5**	**6.4**	**6.5**
Glycine	1.9	1.7	1.9	1.9	1.8	**1.3**	**1.2**	**1.5**
Histidine	0	0	0	0	0	**0.72**	0	0
Isoleucine	6.6	6.7	6.6	**5.7**	**5.7**	**5.9**	**5.4**	**4.6**
Leucine	9.3	9.3	9.4	9.2	9.4	9.0	9.3	9.4
Lysine	1.47	1.49	**1.95**	1.45	1.47	1.51	**2.55**	**2.43**
Methionine	0	0	0	0	0	**2.2**	0	0
Phenylalanine	8.4	8.4	8.4	8.3	8.4	**5.4**	**9.9**	**9.8**
Proline	5.8	5.9	5.5	5.8	5.7	5.5		5.7
Serine	7.2	7.0	6.8	7.0	7.1	**5.7**	**9.3**	**9.4**
Threonine	9.9	10.1	10.0	10.4	10.1	**8.2**	**6.9**	**7.0**
Tryptophan	2.1	2.2	2.2	2.1	2.1	**1.4**	**0.5**	**0.5**
Tyrosine	3.8	3.8	3.9	3.7	3.7	**6.8**	3.8	3.7
Valine	9.2	9.0	8.9	8.8	9.1	**6.2**	8.8	8.9

[a] The values given in the table represent percentages of the indicated amino acids. In order to facilitate comparison, the values which are considered to differ significantly from those of TMV are in bold-faced type.

From these data he concluded that biological relationships ran parallel with the amino acid content. Thus, the closely related pairs of strains TMV and M, and again GA and YA (see Table II) are chemically identical, within the experimental errors of the methods used. Holmes rib

(28) C. F. Jacobsen, Compt. rend. trav. lab. Carlsberg. Sér. chim. 26, 455 (1949).
(29) C. A. Knight, J. Biol. Chem. 171, 297 (1947).

grass virus, the strain biologically most distantly related to tobacco mosaic virus, has a distinctly different amino acid composition. This suggests that the composition may be related to the biological specificity, but more definite interpretation is difficult as these viruses are nucleo-proteins and variation in the structure of the nucleic acid may occur in these strains. It is known to occur in other plant viruses[30] and may be more important than the amino acid content.

In contrast to these results with viruses are the analytical figures for antibodies. Unfortunately, no complete modern data are available, but such as there are suggest that purified antibodies are probably analytically indistinguishable from inert globulins with which they are associated.[31-34] Full analysis of carefully purified antibodies from the same species would be of great interest, but the tentative conclusion at present seems to be that globulins may display their tremendous range of specificity without their amino acid content being significantly different. Rather similar findings have been reported for the licheniformins[35] which are antibiotic polypeptides produced under certain conditions by *Bacillus licheniformis*. Thus, licheniformins *a* and *b* have the same molecular weight of about 4000 and amino acid compositions which are identical within the limits of error of the methods of analysis employed, and yet they differ markedly in antibiotic activity and in their toxicity to mice. It has been suggested that the differences in activity may arise from differences in amino acid sequence though no evidence to support this has been obtained as yet.

The conclusion from this analytical work would seem to be that, except for occasional suggestions to the contrary, there is at present no good evidence that either the specificity or the mechanism of activity of a protein bears any direct relation to its gross amino acid composition.

b. Denaturation and the Importance of Configuration in Biological Activity

It has been known for some time that comparatively mild treat-ment of proteins in solution results in dramatic changes in solubility and other physical properties. These changes are usually irreversible and are associated with the loss of any specific biological activity which the proteins may have possessed. This phenomenon is known as denatura-

(30) R. Markham and J. D. Smith, *Biochem. J.* **46**, 513 (1950).
(31) H. O. Calvery, *J. Biol. Chem.* **112**, 167 (1935).
(32) E. L. Smith, *J. Biol. Chem.* **164**, 345 (1946).
(33) E. L. Smith, R. D. Green, and E. Bartner, *J. Biol. Chem.* **164**, 359 (1946).
(34) L. Velluz, *Compt. rend. soc. biol.* **116**, 981 (1934).
(35) R. K. Callow and T. S. Work, *Biochem. J.* **51**, 558 (1952).

tion and by definition is limited to conditions where no detectable breaking or formation of covalent bonds occurs (see Chap. 9). It follows, therefore, that changes in the secondary valence forces, such as hydrogen bonds and salt linkages, are largely responsible for the loss of biological properties and change in physical behavior. These bonds are believed to be largely responsible in determining the native configuration of a protein.[36,36a] It has been concluded, therefore, that the activity of a protein must be dependent on the particular configuration and charge distribution of part or all of the polypeptide chains of which the molecule is built. It is not known whether of the many possible configurations which could exist only one or several possess biological activity. Since denaturation is of general occurrence, it is apparent that in most cases the active forms are relatively unstable. The degree of instability, or the susceptibility to denaturation, varies widely. Stable proteins such as insulin and ribonuclease withstand strongly acid solutions and high concentrations of detergents, and they may be boiled for several minutes at pH 3 without loss of activity. In contrast, diphtheria toxin loses its toxicity if allowed to stand at pH 5 for short periods at room temperature, and pepsin is equally labile above pH 5. Many proteins lose their biological activity if allowed to stand at room temperature in very dilute solution.

Loss of activity on denaturation could arise in three ways:

(1) The breaking of several key bonds might disrupt the entire structure of the molecule including the part essential for activity. This would be more probable in the absence of extensive interchain bondings, stable under the conditions of denaturation. It would be expected to be irreversible and to be associated with gross changes in physical properties.

(2) Local disorientation could occur in limited parts of the molecule. This might result in loss of biological properties without appreciable change in physical behavior or, conversely, loss of solubility might occur without loss of activity. This could be expected if covalent bonds are utilized to maintain the basic structure or if there are such differences in the strength of the labile bonds that some survive the destruction of others. It is also conceivable that conditions such as change in pH might affect certain parts of the molecular surface only and produce this type of effect. In such a case, loss of biological activity might be associated with only slight changes in physical properties and, under suitable conditions, the changes are likely to be reversible.

(3) The association of protein molecules by labile bondings may change the physical properties and may also result in loss of activity owing

(36) A. E. Mirsky and L. Pauling, *Proc. Natl. Acad. Sci. U. S.* **22**, 439 (1936).
(36a) L. Pauling and R. B. Corey, *Proc. Natl. Acad. Sci. U. S.* **37**, 251 (1951).

to the blocking of the active centers in the association, while leaving the intramolecular structure unchanged. The heat precipitation of acid insulin appears to be an example of this type (see, however, Chap. 9, p. 881). Waugh[37] has shown that long-chain polymers are formed, and Porter[38] found that in this instance denaturation had caused the blocking of two of the four imidazole rings in the submolecule. This is in contrast to all other types of denaturation which are always associated with an increased reactivity of chemical groups that may have been quite unreactive in the native protein.[39] The heat precipitation of insulin, which is so far unique, can be reversed with complete recovery of the original physical properties and biological reactivity.

The loss of biological activity by certain proteins under such conditions as heating and the subsequent slow recovery on cooling has been demonstrated for trypsin,[40] chymotrypsin,[41] and several other enzymes. The reversibility of denaturation in certain instances would therefore appear to be established, but it is a matter of dispute as to whether the reversal is complete in that all the original properties are regained. A somewhat similar phenomenon of reversible inactivation, on standing in solution, has been reported for the L-amino acid oxidase from snake venoms.[41a] This matter is fully discussed in a previous chapter (Chap. 9), and its significance here lies only in the suggestion that the active center of an enzyme may be reversibly altered under certain conditions. It is suggested that these cases of reversible inactivation may be examples of local disorientation, denaturation type 2, while the completely irreversible effects which are most common, are examples of type 1.

The complexity of the phenomenon is emphasized by recent reports that the gentle heating which denatures many proteins may reactivate enzymes whose activity has been lost on standing in solution at low temperatures. Hofstee[42] has reported the reactivation of urease by heating for 5 min. at 60°, and Rapkine, Shugar, and Siminovitch[43] found that triosephosphate dehydrogenase was reactivated by heating under similar conditions. In the case of urease it was suggested that inactivation had occurred by the blocking of the active centers on association of the molecules, i.e., denaturation type 3, and that heat treatment caused dissociation. The French authors on the other hand, suggested that loss

(37) D. F. Waugh, *J. Am. Chem. Soc.* **70**, 1850 (1948).
(38) R. R. Porter, *Biochem. J.* **46**, 304 (1950).
(39) M. L. Anson, *Advances in Protein Chem.* **2**, 361 (1945).
(40) J. H. Northrop, *J. Gen. Physiol.* **16**, 323 (1932).
(41) M. Kunitz and J. H. Northrop, *J. Gen. Physiol.* **18**, 433 (1935).
(41a) E. B. Kearney and T. P. Singer, *Arch. Biochem. and Biophys.* **33**, 337 (1951).
(42) B. J. H. Hofstee, *J. Gen. Physiol.* **32**, 339 (1949).
(43) L. Rapkine, D. Shugar, and L. Siminovitch, *Arch. Biochem.* **26**, 33 (1950).

of activity and reactivation are dependent on the effect of temperature on the equilibrium between sulfhydryl and disulfide bonds. If this interpretation is correct, the breaking and re-formation of these covalent bonds would exclude us from considering the phenomenon as denaturation according to our definition.

Another unusual finding of considerable interest is the observation of Erickson and Neurath[44] that the antibody of horse pneumococcal antisera could be completely denatured, as judged by solubility and other physical criteria, and yet when brought into solution with sodium thiocyanate, almost completely retained its power to combine specifically with antigen, though in altered proportions. This would seem to imply that small but essential parts of the globulin molecule were able to retain their specific configuration while that of the remainder underwent gross changes. A similar phenomenon has been reported for urease. Sumner[12] showed that in certain conditions this enzyme could be denatured with ethanol in a manner such that its solubility was lost irreversibly although it still retained much of its enzymatic activity. Both these cases appear to be examples of denaturation type 2.

Working with surface films, it has been found that some globular biologically active proteins may be spread in monomolecular layers without losing their activity. These include proteolytic enzymes[45] and urease[46] and some antigens such as ovalbumin and serum albumin,[47] though with the former some decrease in ability to combine with antisera was observed. Three-dimensional configuration must be destroyed by such spreading, but some two-dimensional structure may remain intact. These observations are difficult to understand in the light of the dominant role ascribed, generally with full justification, to the intact three-dimensional molecular configuration.

In conclusion, it may be said that the phenomenon of denaturation suggests that the biological activity of a protein depends upon the configuration of all or part of the molecule. The resistance of proteins to denaturation is extremely variable and, in certain cases, biological activity may survive gross changes in physical properties. In the latter cases, however, different or more drastic conditions usually result in total loss of activity. Some of the very stable proteins may have their configuration entirely determined by covalent bonds and hence be incapable of denaturation.

(44) J. O. Erickson and H. Neurath, *J. Gen. Physiol.* **28,** 421 (1944).
(45) E. Gorter, *Nature* **142,** 1024 (1938).
(46) I. Langmuir and V. J. Schaefer, *J. Am. Chem. Soc.* **60,** 1351 (1938).
(47) A. Rothen, *J. Biol. Chem.* **168,** 75 (1947).

2. COMPARATIVE STUDIES OF STRUCTURE AND ACTIVITY

This type of comparative work can be directed to the study of structural features of chemically very similar proteins with diverse biological properties, such as the different antibodies from one species, with a view to detecting differences referable to activity.   Or it could take the form of an examination of proteins with identical biological properties from different species, in order that any characteristics which vary significantly could reasonably be excluded as being connected with activity. If, as with an antigen from a variety of sources, some structural property varied in a systematic manner paralleling the variation in biological activity, again a connection could be inferred.   The weakness of such an approach is that it is rarely, if ever, possible to test the conclusion by experimental change of the structure in order to produce an expected change in activity.   Nevertheless, some interesting data have been collected.

Antigens were the first proteins used for comparative studies.   At the beginning of this century, Nuttall[48] investigated the formation of precipitins in animals when the latter were injected with serum proteins of many different species.   He found a systematic variation in the antigenic specificity of these proteins which paralleled their zoological relationship.   Ten years later, Wells and Osborne,[49] in a series of papers, described a similar variation in the seed globulins from a number of plants.   These authors used crystalline proteins and carried out simultaneous chemical investigations in an attempt to relate structural differences to antigenic specificity.   The analytical methods available at that time were limited, but they did enable Wells and Osborne[49] to draw the important conclusion that "since chemically similar proteins from seeds of different genera react anaphylactically with one another, while chemically dissimilar proteins from the same seeds fail to do so, we must conclude that the specificity of the anaphylaxis reaction depends on the chemical structure of the proteins."   Ehrlich had put forward a similar view earlier but with little or no experimental evidence to support it.

Because of their availability and ease of purification, the hemoglobins have been a frequent choice for comparative studies of many kinds. Variation in the properties according to the species of origin have usually been found whether physical, physiological, or chemical techniques have been used.   A systematic variation related to zoological classification was

(48) G. H. F. Nuttall, Blood Immunity and Blood Relationship, Cambridge University Press, Cambridge, England, 1904.

(49) H. G. Wells and T. B. Osborne, *J. Infectious Diseases* **19**, 183 (1916).

again found in the antigenic specificities,[50–52] although other properties
did not show a similar systematic change until the free amino groups
were estimated.[53] This estimation by the method of Sanger enables the
N-terminal amino acids of open polypeptide chains to be identified and
estimated (see Chaps. 2 and 3).   Table III gives the results.

It is apparent that there is a systematic variation which runs parallel
with the zoological relationship and with the changes in antigenic specificity.   This correlation in a small number of species could, however, be
coincidental; or what is perhaps more likely, is that both the antigenic
specificity and these structural features may be related to the zoological
classification without being dependent on each other.   As mentioned
earlier the crucial test of the effect of altering the number of chains and
terminal acids on specificity is not possible.

TABLE III
TERMINAL RESIDUES OF HEMOGLOBINS[53]

Hemoglobin	Assumed mol. wt.	Terminal residues	Free lysine ε-amino groups
Horse	66,000	6 valine	41
Donkey	66,000	6 valine	41
Human adult	66,000	5 valine	43
Human fetal	66,000	2.6 valine	47
Cow	66,000	2 valine, 2 methionine	47
Sheep	66,000	2 valine, 2 methionine	47
Goat	66,000	2 valine, 2 methionine	48
Horse myoglobin	17,000	1 glycine	20

An interesting point in connection with antigens is the apparently
lower antigenic power of fetal proteins in comparison with the same
proteins from an adult animal.   This is suggested by the much greater
tolerance for fetal tissue grafts.[54]   Very little structural work has been
carried out in this field, but if the recapitulation theory of embryonic
development were true, comparative studies at different stages might
give rather interesting results.

Insulin from a variety of species has been crystallized and appeared

(50) M. Heidelberger and K. Landsteiner, *J. Exptl. Med.* **38**, 561 (1923).
(51) L. Hektoen and K. Schulhof, *J. Infectious Diseases* **33**, 224 (1924).
(52) L. Hektoen and A. K. Boor, *J. Infectious Diseases* **49**, 29 (1931).
(53) R. R. Porter and F. Sanger, *Biochem. J.* **42**, 287 (1948).
(54) J. Needham, Biochemistry and Morphogenesis, Cambridge University Press, Cambridge, England, 1942.

at first to be identical in chemical structure and biological activity.[55]   Its very poor antigenic power is in conformity with the close chemical similarity of insulins from different sources, which would make it difficult for the injected animal to "recognize" it as a foreign protein.   Wasserman and Mirsky[56] were, however, able to cause sensitization of guinea pigs to anaphylactic shock by injecting a variety of insulins.   Again, no species differences could be demonstrated, using this very sensitive technique.   Insulin of cow, sheep, and pig similarly had the same terminal amino acids when examined by the dinitrophenyl (DNP) technique[57] and presumably, therefore, have a similar four-peptide chain structure. In further investigation, Sanger[58] found that the amino acid composition of the polypeptide chains with glycyl terminal residues was different. Those from pig contained threonine but little alanine, while those from cow and sheep contained more alanine but not threonine, establishing that insulin could have identical physiological properties associated with significant differences in structure.

The adrenocorticotropic hormones from pig[59] and sheep[60] pituitaries were reported to have very similar chemical and physical properties, though some doubt now exists as to the identity of the protein isolated with the active principle.   Thyroglobin is a poor antigen and it seems to be generally true that the species variation common to most proteins is much less marked in the protein hormones.

Crystalline pepsins have been prepared from several animals[3,61] and fish,[62,63] and slight differences in solubility and biological specificity were noted.   No simultaneous chemical investigations were, however, made.

Further opportunity for comparative work is now possible from the resolution of apparently pure compounds into different components, all possessing the original activity.   Gramicidin appeared homogeneous by diffusion and adsorption but was resolved by Craig, using countercurrent techniques, into three and possibly four active components.[64]   The same

(55) D. A. Scott and A. M. Fisher, *Trans. Roy. Soc. Can.* **34**, (V), 137 (1940).

(56) P. Wasserman and I. A. Mirsky, *Endocrinology* **31**, 115 (1942).

(57) R. R. Porter and F. Sanger, Haemoglobin, Butterworths Scientific Publications, London, 1949.

(58) F. Sanger, *Nature* **164**, 529 (1949).

(59) C. H. Li, M. E. Simpson, and H. M. Evans, *J. Biol. Chem.* **149**, 413 (1943).

(60) G. Sayers, A. White, and C. N. H. Long, *J. Biol. Chem.* **149**, 425 (1943).

(61) J. H. Northrop, *J. Gen. Physiol.* **16**, 615 (1933).

(62) E. R. Norris and D. W. Elam, *J. Biol. Chem.* **134**, 443 (1940).

(63) G. P. Sprissler, An Investigation of the Proteinase of the Gastric Mucosa of Shark, The Catholic University of America Press, Washington, D. C., 1942.

(64) J. D. Gregory and L. C. Craig, *J. Biol. Chem.* **172**, 839 (1948).

technique has also achieved a partial resolution of insulin into two components, but both seem to have less activity than the original.[65,65a] Ribonuclease has also been resolved by the use of chromatographic methods into two components both of which possesses enzymatic activity.[66,67] Martin and Porter gave evidence that the enzyme existed in the beef pancreas in the two forms, but the chemical differences responsible for the different chromatographic behaviors are not known.[67a] The possibility of the existence of several forms of one and the same enzyme had been suggested by solubility studies of pig pepsin.[68] No differences in pH optima or Michaelis constants have been reported.

3. BLOCKING OF REACTIVE GROUPS

Studies of the influence of chemical modification on the biological behavior of proteins have been carried out over many years, originating perhaps in the work of Obermayer and Pick[69] who investigated the effect of nitration and iodination of serum proteins on their antigenic specificity. This work was developed with great success by Landsteiner[70] into a study of the influence on specificity of small molecules coupled to an antigen through the azo linkage.   The influence of the nature of the substituent is, however, distinct from the effects of the actual blocking of the various polar groups in a protein and is of sufficient importance to be considered separately.

Interpretation of all the work to be described here is based on the assumption that the activity of the protein is localized in an active center and that by finding the type of groups whose blocking causes loss of activity, the nature of this active center can be deduced.   It is implicit that the chemical reactions used are specific for one or two types of polar groups and that no secondary effects, such as denaturation, occur.   Both conditions are difficult to establish and demand that the reagent used and the protein group involved may be estimated quantitatively.   It is also

(65) E. F. Harfenist and L. C. Craig, *J. Am. Chem. Soc.* **73**, 877 (1951).
(65a) E. F. Harfenist and L. C. Craig, *J. Am. Chem. Soc.* **74**, 3083 (1952).
(66) C. H. W. Hirs, W. H. Stein, and S. Moore, *J. Am. Chem. Soc.* **73**, 1893 (1951).
(67) A. J. P. Martin and R. R. Porter, *Biochem. J.* **49**, 215 (1951).
(67a) For further development of the chromatographic technique see also R. R. Porter, *Biochem. J.* **53**, 320 (1953).   C. H. W. Hirs, S. Moore, and W. H. Stein, *J. Biol. Chem.* **200**, 493 (1953).   H. H. Tallan, and W. H. Stein, *J. Biol. Chem.* **200**, 507 (1953).
(68) V. Desreux and R. M. Herriott, *Nature* **144**, 287 (1939).
(69) F. Obermayer and E. P. Pick, *Wien. klin. Wochschr.* **16**, 569 (1903); *ibid.* **17**, 265 (1904); *ibid.* **19**, 327 (1906).
(70) K. Landsteiner and H. Lampl, *Biochem. Z.* **86**, 343 (1917).

necessary that the biological activity is again manifest following reversal of the substitution, showing that denaturation cannot have occurred, unless this is reversible under the same conditions.   A further condition for successful interpretation of the results should be that the substituent is small in order that its primary effect will be the blocking of the group with which it reacts, and not of preventing the access of larger molecules to adjacent groups by steric hindrance.   These conditions are difficult to realize and the validity of conclusions based on this type of work is correspondingly reduced.   The chemical aspects of the substitution of proteins have been reviewed by Herriott[71] and, with particular reference to the present problem, by Olcott and Fraenkel-Conrat.[72]   They are discussed in greater detail in Chap. 10.   Table IV, which collects most of the data obtained with these methods, is based on that given by Olcott and Fraenkel-Conrat.[72]

Insulin and lysozyme can be taken as two typical examples.   The latter is an enzyme from egg white which causes rapid lysis of certain bacteria, probably by depolymerization of mucopolysaccharides in the cell wall.   Both are proteins of small molecular weight obtainable as crystals of high purity.   They are exceptionally resistant to conventional methods of denaturation and hence the effects of substitution particularly in acid or neutral media are not likely to be complicated by secondary effects.   It can be seen from Table IV that only the phenolic, carboxylic, and disulfide groupings are necessary for the activity of insulin.   By contrast, lysozyme appears to require amino, carboxylic, amide, guanidyl hydroxylic, and disulfide groups.   Owing to the lack of absolute group specificity in some of the reagents used, it is not possible to be quite definite that all the groups are necessary, but the use of several reagents of overlapping specificity gives support to the essential nature of the groups mentioned.

The importance of the disulfide bonds is a common feature in proteins with a high cystine content as they must play a predominant part in determining the configuration of the molecule.   Indeed, Rudall[72a] in x-ray studies found that insulin could not be induced to give the β-pattern typical of stretched denatured protein unless the disulfide bonds were first reduced.   It remains to be determined whether so many polar groups of different types which appear to be present in the lysozyme active center mean that this latter is also of greater size.   In insulin it has been shown that partial reaction of the phenolic groups can occur with only slight loss of activity.[100]   Similarly, two-thirds of the carboxyl groups may be

(71) R. M. Herriott, *Advances in Protein Chem.* **3,** 170 (1947).

(72) H. S. Olcott and H. Fraenkel-Conrat, *Chem. Revs.* **41,** 151 (1947).

(72a) K. M. Rudall, Fibrous Proteins, Soc. Dyers and Colourists, London, 1946.

TABLE IV
Requirement of Protein Groups for Biological Activity
(After Olcott and Fraenkel-Conrat)[72]

Protein	Essential groups	Unessential groups
Antibodies		
Rabbit antiovalbumin		Disulfide[73]
Horse antiovalbumin	Amino[74,75]	
Horse antipneumococcus polysaccharide	Amino[76]	
Antigens		
Ovalbumin	Phenolic[78]	Sulfhydryl[77]
Serum albumin		Phenolic[78]
Enzymes		
Amylase (pancreas)	Amino[79]	Phenolic, sulfhydryl, disulfide[79,80]
β-Amylase (barley)	Phenolic, disulfide[81]	Amino[81]
Chymotrypsin	Phenolic, disulfide[82]	Amino[82]
Lysozyme	Amino, carboxyl, amide, guanidyl, hydroxyl, disulfide[83]	
Papain	Phenolic,[84] sulfhydryl[85]	Amino[84]
Pepsin	Phenolic[86]	Amino[86]
Phosphatase	Amino[87]	
Ribonuclease	Amino[88]	
Solanine	Phenolic[89]	Amino, sulfhydryl[78]
Trypsin	Indolyl, amide[90]	Amino, phenolic, disulfide, carboxyl, imidazole[79]
Hormones		
Adrenocorticotropic (pituitary)	Amino, phenolic[91]	
Follicle-stimulating	Amino,[92] disulfide[93]	
Interstitial cell-stimulating	Amino,[92] disulfide[94]	
Prolan	Phenolic[92]	Amino[92]
Pregnant mare serum	Amino,[92] disulfide[94]	
Insulin	Phenolic,[95] disulfide,[96] carboxylic[97]	Amino,[98] hydroxyl,[99] amide,[100] guanidyl[100]
Lactogenic	Amino,[92] disulfide[94]	
Parathyroid	Amino,[101] carboxyl[102]	Disulfide[103]
Pitocin		Disulfide[104]
Virus		
Tobacco mosaic	Phenolic[105]	Amino[105]
Toxins		
Diphtheria	Amino[106]	
Scarlet fever	Phenolic[107]	
Crotoxin	Amino, phenolic, disulfide, hydroxyl, carboxyl[108]	
Miscellaneous		
Ovomucoid (trypsin inhibitor)	Carboxyl, phenolic, guanidyl[90]	Amino[90]

esterified before activity disappears.[109]   In lysozyme the loss of activity on esterification is gradual, suggesting that if the molecules react uniformly, some carboxyl groups may not be essential.[83]   The next step, the accurate determination of the number of different groups in an active

(73) R. R. Porter, *Biochem. J.* **46,** 473 (1950).

(74) H. Eagle, *J. Exptl. Med.* **67,** 495 (1938).

(75) S. Mudd and E. W. Joffe, *J. Gen. Physiol.* **16,** 947 (1933).

(76) B. F. Chow and W. F. Goebel, *J. Exptl. Med.* **62,** 179 (1935).

(77) D. Blumenthal, *J. Biol. Chem.* **113,** 433 (1936).

(78) E. A. Kabat and M. Heidelberger, *J. Exptl. Med.* **66,** 229 (1937).

(79) J. E. Little and M. L. Caldwell, *J. Biol. Chem.* **142,** 585 (1942).

(80) J. E. Little and M. L. Caldwell, *J. Biol. Chem.* **147,** 229 (1943).

(81) C. E. Weill and M. L. Caldwell, *J. Am. Chem. Soc.* **67,** 212 (1945).

(82) C. E. Weill and M. L. Caldwell, *J. Am. Chem. Soc.* **67,** 214 (1945).

(83) H. Fraenkel-Conrat, *Arch. Biochem.* **27,** 109 (1950).

(84) A. K. Balls and H. Lineweaver, *J. Biol. Chem.* **130,** 669 (1939).

(85) A. K. Balls and H. Lineweaver, *Nature* **144,** 513 (1939).

(86) R. M. Herriott, *J. Gen. Physiol.* **19,** 283 (1935).

(87) V. Baccari and G. Auricchio, *Boll. soc. ital. biol. sper.* **21,** 49 (1946).

(88) C. A. Zittle, *J. Franklin Inst.* **246,** 266 (1948).

(89) D. M. Greenberg and T. Winnick, *J. Biol. Chem.* **135,** 761 (1940).

(90) H. Fraenkel-Conrat, R. S. Bean, and H. Lineweaver, *J. Biol. Chem.* **177,** 385 (1949).

(91) C. H. Li, M. E. Simpson, and H. M. Evans, *Arch. Biochem.* **9,** 259 (1946).

(92) C. H. Li, M. E. Simpson, and H. M. Evans, *Science* **90,** 140 (1939).

(93) W. H. McShan and R. K. Meyer, *J. Biol. Chem.* **135,** 473 (1940).

(94) H. Fraenkel-Conrat, M. E. Simpson, and H. M. Evans, *Science* **91,** 363 (1940).

(95) C. R. Harington and A. Neuberger, *Biochem. J.* **30,** 809 (1936).

(96) V. du Vigneaud, A. Fitch, E. Pekarek, and W. W. Lockwood, *J. Biol. Chem.* **94,** 233 (1931).

(97) F. H. Carr, K. Culhane, A. T. Fuller, and S. W. F. Underhill, *Biochem. J.* **23,** 1010 (1929).

(98) K. G. Stern and A. White, *J. Biol. Chem.* **122,** 371 (1938).

(99) M. B. Glendening, D. M. Greenberg, and H. Fraenkel-Conrat, *J. Biol. Chem.* **167,** 125 (1947).

(100) J. Fraenkel-Conrat and H. Fraenkel-Conrat, *Biochim. et Biophys. Acta* **5,** 89 (1950).

(101) T. R. Wood and W. F. Ross, *J. Biol. Chem.* **146,** 59 (1942).

(102) W. R. Tweedy and M. Torigoe, *J. Biol. Chem.* **99,** 155 (1932).

(103) W. R. Tweedy, W. P. Bell, and C. Vicens-Rois, *J. Biol. Chem.* **108,** 105 (1935).

(104) R. R. Sealock and V. du Vigneaud, *J. Pharmacol.* **54,** 433 (1935).

(105) G. Schramm and H. Müller, *Z. physiol. Chem.* **266,** 43 (1940).

(106) A. M. Pappenheimer, Jr., *J. Biol. Chem.* **125,** 201 (1938).

(107) E. S. G. Barron, G. F. Dick, and C. M. Lyman, *J. Biol. Chem.* **137,** 267 (1941).

(108) H. Fraenkel-Conrat and J. Fraenkel-Conrat, *Biochim. et Biophys. Acta* **5,** 98 (1950).

(109) W. F. H. M. Mommaerts and H. Neurath, *J. Biol. Chem.* **185,** 909 (1950).

center has hardly been attempted, though in some cases it may not be difficult. A method of approach is to be found in the work of Hopkins, Lutwak-Mann, and Morgan[110] who showed that succinic dehydrogenase was protected from the inactivation which follows blocking of the sulfhydryl groups by the presence of excess substrate (succinic acid), the end product (fumaric acid), or the competitive inhibitor (malonic acid). This work has been confirmed,[110a] and it is probable that in such a case, where a nonprotein competitive inhibitor is available, estimation of the reactive groupings in the presence and absence of the inhibitor should give directly the number of groupings involved in the actual center. These however, may be only a small proportion of the total groups present in the molecule, and the significance of figures obtained by difference will depend upon the accuracy of the estimation.

The sulfhydryl groups have a special place in this work on the blocking of active groups, as they were the first to be fully investigated; indeed, very many enzymes are found to be inactivated when the —SH groups are oxidized or blocked.[111,111a] The —SH group also shows varying degrees of reactivity, the numbers estimated in a protein depending on the reagent used and on whether the protein is native or denatured. As a consequence of this, the sulfhydryl groups of any one protein can often be divided into different categories according to their reactivity toward one reagent or another; and in different proteins, the —SH groups essential for enzyme activity may also belong to different categories (see Chap. 9). Thus in urease, Hellerman[112] distinguished three classes of sulfhydryl group: (a) one class which reacted readily; (b) one class which was less reactive; and (c) two or three which failed to react with any reagent unless the protein was denatured. Blocking of group (a) did not reduce enzymic activity, whereas the blocking of group (b) destroyed it completely. This work was extended by Desnuelle and Rovery[113] using for the most part phenyl isocyanate as reagent. They confirmed that one sulfhydryl group could be blocked without loss of activity and that on prolonging the reaction, the activity had fallen to zero before a second group had completely reacted. These facts were interpreted, however, as suggesting that group (b) was only able to react after the rupture of labile bonds and that a local denaturation rather than

(110) F. G. Hopkins, E. J. Morgan, and C. Lutwak-Mann, *Biochem. J.* **32**, 1829 (1938).

(110a) V. R. Potter and K. P. Dubois, *J. Gen. Physiol.* **26**, 391 (1943).

(111) T. P. Singer, *Brewers Digest* **20**, 85T (1945).

(111a) E. S. G. Barron, *Advances in Enzymol.* **11**, 201 (1951).

(112) L. Hellerman, F. P. Chinard, and V. R. Deitz, *J. Biol. Chem.* **147**, 443 (1943).

(113) P. Desnuelle and M. Rovery, *Biochim. et Biophys. Acta* **3**, 26 (1949).

chemical reaction was the primary cause of loss of activity. Heller-man,[112] on the other hand, could show that if group (a) was eliminated by dilute porphyrindin, activity was then lost on addition of one molecule of p-chloromercuribenzoate and that this effect could be reversed by the addition of excess cysteine. Earlier in the section, the reversibility of the reaction accompanied by reactivation was given as a criterion of the primary significance of the condensation, but the simultaneous reversal of a local denaturation is also possible, and as the French authors point out, the direct importance of a relatively unavailable group seems unlikely, particularly when the substrate and the reagent are of com-parable size. Further, Hellerman's figures suggest that more than 40 sulfhydryl groups must be blocked per molecule before urease activity is destroyed, while Ambrose[6] et al. investigating the inhibition by silver ions, found that the combination of only three or four ions with one molecule of enzyme caused inactivation. If, as appears most probable, the silver is reacting with sulfhydryl groups, these results are difficult to reconcile with each other. A similar disparity in the reactivity and activity requirements of the sulfhydryl groups is shown by myosin, both in its adenosinetriphosphatase (ATPase) and actin-combining properties.[114]

These phenomena have been discussed in some detail as they are a particularly clear example of the equivocal nature of the results which may be obtained even when a variety of apparently ideal reagents are available. The interpretation of negative results such as the complete blocking of the insulin amino groups without destruction of activity is not of course open to such doubts.

A recent finding of great interest in studies of the active centers of proteins is the inactivating effect of diisopropyl fluorophosphate (DFP), on several esterases and other proteins.[115-118] In the reaction with chy-motrypsin, 1 mole of DFP condenses with 1 mole of chymotrypsin,[118,119] with the formation of 1 mole of hydrofluoric acid. Several analogs of DFP behave similarly. DFP will not, however, react under the same conditions with chymotrypsinogen, nor with denatured chymotrypsin,[118a] nor with any of the constituent amino acids, nor with a hydrolyzate of the enzyme. The inactive DFP–chymotrypsin compound may be

(114) K. Bailey and S. V. Perry, Biochim. et Biophys. Acta 1, 506 (1947).
(115) A. Mazur and O. Bodansky, J. Biol. Chem. 163, 261 (1946).
(116) K. P. Dubois and G. Mangun, Proc. Soc. Exptl. Biol. Med. 64, 137 (1947).
(117) E. F. Jansen, M. D. F. Nutting, and A. K. Balls, J. Biol. Chem. 175, 975 (1948).
(118) E. F. Jansen, M. D. F. Nutting, and A. K. Balls, J. Biol. Chem. 179, 201 (1949).
(118a) A. K. Balls and E. F. Jansen, Adv. Enzym. 13, 321 (1952).

crystallized and has the same electrophoretic mobility, amino acid content,[119] and sedimentation rate as the original protein.

This suggests that DFP is reacting with some group which exists only when the protein possesses its native configuration. The firmness of the binding and the small size of the reagent lead to the conclusion that neither simple electrostatic attraction nor hydrogen bonding nor any of the labile forces which are usually postulated as endowing the native molecule with its specific properties, are involved in the condensation. DFP and its analogs which also inhibit esterases are themselves esters, so that it is possible though not probable that steric factors facilitate their approach to the vulnerable key grouping, and that condensation follows. Alternatively, it may be that some new group not present in the constituent amino acids exists in the enzyme and is responsible for the reaction with DFP. It has been recently suggested that DFP or its analogs is a substrate for the enzyme, inhibition being caused by irreversible binding of organic phosphate.[119a]   Whatever the explanation, the part of the molecule involved in the reaction must be closely associated with the active center and there appear to be prospects of elucidating some of the unusual properties of this part of the protein surface.

4. The Substitution of Known Groups in Proteins and the Variation of the Nonprotein Reactant

a. Antigens

The combination of antigens with small organic compounds of widely different structures was effected through the azo linkage by Landsteiner.[120] The substituted proteins retained their antigenic power if the coupling was not too extensive and the specificity of the antibodies produced was directed almost entirely to the small substituent rather than to the original protein.   The technique was simplified by the finding that the substituent molecules themselves could inhibit the precipitation of the antigen by its antisera.   Such molecules are called haptenes and their inhibitory power confirmed that antibody specificity was directed primarily toward the substituent.   With the aid of this reaction, Landsteiner and others[120] were able to explore the tremendous range of antibody specificity and by analogy to elucidate the type of groupings which might be expected to play a prominent part in natural antigens.   The

(119) E. F. Jansen, M. D. F. Nutting, R. Jang, and A. K. Balls, *J. Biol. Chem.* **185,** 209 (1950).

(119a) B. S. Hartley and B. A. Kilby, *Biochem. J.* **50,** 672 (1952).

(120) K. Landsteiner, The Specificity of Serological Reactions, Harvard University Press, Cambridge, Mass., 1945.

specificity of antibodies could be directed toward a large variety of organic chemical groupings, and there was no suggestion that naturally occurring compounds were more effective than artificial ones.

The extension of the work in an attempt to solve the specificity-determining groups in a natural antigen was successful with pneumococcal polysaccharide. Thus, Goebel[121] showed that antisera prepared against cellobiuronic acid coupled to proteins could react both with the disaccharide and the constituent hexoses. It also reacted with the capsular polysaccharide of pneumococcus types III and VII of which cellobiuronic acid appears to be the principal recurring unit. Further, this antigen could be used to immunize and protect mice against infection with these types of pneumococcus,[122] thus giving convincing proof that cellobiuronic acid was the chief determinant of antigenic specificity in these capsular polysaccharides.

It was not surprising that this work was less successful when directed to the elucidation of the combining centers of protein antigens. Difficulties immediately arose because the specificity of a native protein *usually* differs greatly from that of a denatured protein. Though complex configurational phenomena play an important part, some relevant data were obtained with antigens made by coupling amino acids and peptides to proteins by the diazo linkage. Using leucyl and glycyl peptides, Landsteiner[123-125] found that in a peptide the C-terminal amino acid played a more important role in controlling specificity than did the *endo*-amino acids. Using the haptene technique he also studied the inhibitory effects of partial hydrolysis products of a protein, the results of which will be discussed later.

This type of work has been greatly extended by Pauling and his collaborators, who have studied the production of antibodies against proteins substituted with organic compounds and the inhibitory effect of related haptenes on the antibody–antigen reaction. From quantitative studies of the degree of inhibition an attempt has been made to map out the combining center of the antibody and to decide which are the important structural features and what types of bonding between antibody and haptene occur. A recent paper[126] may be quoted to illustrate this approach. Antiserum was produced against sheep serum protein substituted with 4-azophthalate, and the inhibition of combination between

(121) W. F. Goebel, *J. Exptl. Med.* **68**, 469 (1938).
(122) W. F. Goebel, *J. Exptl. Med.* **69**, 353 (1939).
(123) K. Landsteiner and J. Van der Scheer, *J. Exptl. Med.* **55**, 781 (1932).
(124) K. Landsteiner and J. Van der Scheer, *J. Exptl. Med.* **59**, 769 (1934).
(125) K. Landsteiner and J. Van der Scheer, *J. Exptl. Med.* **69**, 705 (1939).
(126) D. Pressman and L. Pauling, *J. Am. Chem. Soc.* **71**, 2893 (1949).

antiserum and azophthalate-substituted ovalbumin (**I**) was studied. The substituent was coupled to a different protein for testing purposes,

$$\text{ovalbumin}-N{=}N \underset{\text{COOH}}{\overset{\text{COOH}}{\bigcirc}}$$

(**I**)

in order that any influence of the protein part of the antigen be eliminated. Tetrahalogenated phthalate was found to be a more effective inhibitor than phthalate. This makes it unlikely that steric factors were playing any part in the combination, for were this so, the much greater bulk of the halogenated molecule would diminish its inhibitory power. The increase was attributed to the stronger van der Waals' attraction of the halogen atoms. o-Sulfobenzoate combined with antibody as readily as phthalate but o-nitrobenzoate much less, indicating that the presence of two charged groups was important but that the nature of charged groups was much less significant. Interpretation of these and other results in terms of the antibody-combining center led to the conclusion that it had one or two positive charges which combined with the negative charges of the haptene. The fit of this haptene was much looser than most of the other haptenes which have been studied by this group of investigators. The significance of the quantitative aspects of this work are uncertain, as it is known that these dyes polymerize in solution[126a] and that they are bound by serum albumin[126b] as well as by the specific antibody.

Such work may give information about the antibody-combining center which cannot at present be obtained by other techniques; but detailed structural knowledge will also be needed before it can be interpreted more exactly and the conclusions tested.

b. Enzymes

Bergmann and collaborators[127] synthesized a considerable number of peptides and used them to investigate the specificities of the proteases which had been crystallized earlier by Northrop. This use of small synthetic substrates and inhibitors to explore enzyme specificity was in some ways analogous to Landsteiner's use of haptenes to study antibody specificity. The later extension of Bergmann's work in several laboratories with the object of widening the knowledge of enzyme specificity and at the same time trying to deduce the mode of action of the enzyme,

(126a) A. B. Pardee and S. M. Swingle, J. Am. Chem. Soc. **71**, 148 (1949).

(126b) F. Karush, J. Am. Chem. Soc. **72**, 2705 (1950).

(127) M. Bergmann and J. S. Fruton, Advances in Enzymol. **1**, 63 (1941).

runs parallel with the work of Pauling which has been described.   It will therefore be considered.

Neurath and Schwert[128] have summarized the results obtained with trypsin, chymotrypsin, and carboxypeptidase. Perhaps the most unexpected result was the finding that these enzymes split ester, hydrazide and hydroxyamide as well as peptide and amide linkages.[129-131a]   There is good evidence that the hydrolyses of these different types of bond are all effected by the same grouping in the enzymes.   The rates of hydrolysis of, or alternatively the inhibition of hydrolysis by, a large number of peptides and their analogs and derivatives have been studied and the results have enabled the specificity requirements for enzymatic activity to be worked out in great detail.

This work has also produced evidence for multiple attachment of enzyme and its substrate.   The following suggestions as to the mode of action of these enzymes have been made:[128]

(1) Further interaction of the enzyme with previously unadsorbed parts of the substrate causes sufficient deformation of the hydrolyzable bonds to make them liable to attack by water.

(2) Activation may not cause gross change of configuration in the enzyme–substrate complex but may produce extensive polarization of the susceptible bond, facilitating approach of the hydrogen or hydroxyl ion.

(3) The enzyme may concentrate hydrogen or hydroxyl ions at the hydrolyzable bond so that cleavage follows proton or hydroxyl-ion transfer.   Further deductions in terms of the active center were not made.

Somewhat similar work on the specificities of several exopeptidases has been carried out by Smith and collaborators,[132-134] but, in this case, particular emphasis was placed on the importance of metal ions in the reaction.   It has been postulated that the metal ion is bound both to the protein and to the substrate in the enzyme–substrate complex.   The binding of the metal to the enzyme is presumably not by salt linkages as this is a slow process.   Theories as to the mode of enzyme action have

(128) H. Neurath and G. W. Schwert, *Chem. Revs.* **46,** 69 (1950).
(129) G. W. Schwert, H. Neurath, S. Kaufman, and J. E. Snoke, *J. Biol. Chem.* **172,** 221 (1948).
(130) J. E. Snoke and H. Neurath, *Arch. Biochem.* **21,** 351 (1949).
(131) J. E. Snoke, G. W. Schwert, and H. Neurath, *J. Biol. Chem.* **175,** 7 (1948).
(131a) R. V. MacAllister and C. Niemann, *J. Am. Chem. Soc.* **71,** 3855 (1949).
(132) E. L. Smith, *Federation Proc.* **8,** 581 (1949).
(133) E. L. Smith, *Proc. Natl. Acad. Sci. U. S.* **35,** 80 (1949).
(134) E. L. Smith and R. Lumry, *Cold Spring Harbor Symposia Quant. Biol.* **14,** 168 (1949).

been elaborated, and carboxypeptidase has been chosen as one example to illustrate the mechanism. Neurath and De Maria,[135] however, have criticized the evidence from which the metal protein character of this enzyme was inferred. Until this essential point is established, any general application of the chelation theories must remain in doubt, but their relevance to the mode of action of many peptidases seems fairly probable. A systematic attempt to map out the form of the active center of cholinesterase has been made in a series of papers by Wilson and collaborators.[136–140] Again, quantitative inhibition studies using competitive and irreversible inhibitors have been made. Careful study of the effect of pH, using ionizable and non-ionizable substrates and inhibitors, has helped to elucidate the relative positions of the charged groups in the active center. This has led to the postulation of an arrangement of the type shown. In addition to the electrostatic bond between the anionic site and the nitrogen atom, bonds between a nucleophilic group G_1 and the ester carbon, and a further bond between an electrophilic group G_2 and one of the oxygen atoms are suggested from physicochemical data on the acid and base catalysis of ester hydrolysis. From an interpretation of the relation between pH and enzymatic activity, the pK values of two ionizing groups in the esteratic site were deduced. The reasoning from which these conclusions were reached necessarily involves some assumptions, but the experimental data have been interpreted in a convincing manner.

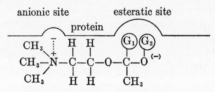

Kearney and Singer[41a] have arrived at some conclusions as to the nature of the active center of L-amino acid oxidase in snake venoms. The observations have arisen from a study of the reversible inactivation of this enzyme when in solution. The active and inactive forms exist together in equilibrium, the relative proportions of each depending on the nature of the ions present and on the pH of the solution; temperature

(135) H. Neurath and G. De Maria, *J. Biol. Chem.* **186**, 653 (1950).

(136) I. B. Wilson and F. Bergmann, *J. Biol. Chem.* **185**, 479 (1950).

(137) I. B. Wilson and F. Bergmann, *J. Biol. Chem.* **186**, 683 (1950).

(138) F. Bergmann, I. B. Wilson, and D. Nachmansohn, *J. Biol. Chem.* **186**, 693 (1950).

(139) I. B. Wilson, F. Bergmann, and D. Nachmansohn, *J. Biol. Chem.* **186**, 781 (1950).

(140) I. B. Wilson, *Biochim. et Biophys. Acta* **7**, 466 (1951).

changes influence the rate of conversion of one form to the other but not the final equilibrium. There is no detectable change, during inactivation, in the solubility at the isoelectric point, diffusion constant, sedimentation velocity, or electrophoretic mobility. The prosthetic group of the enzyme is also unaltered, and it is therefore concluded that inactivation is caused by a limited alteration of the configuration of a small part of the protein molecule. The pH–activity curve of the enzyme and the curve relating pH with equilibrium between active and inactive forms are similar. In both cases the important range is pH 6.5 ± 1 unit. It is assumed that the attraction of substrate to enzyme is electrostatic, and it is postulated that at pH 7.5 the positively and negatively charged groups of the amino acid are held by oppositely charged groups in the enzyme-active center. At pH 5.5 when the enzyme is inactive, the positive group on the enzyme remains charged while the negative group appears to have changed its sign, thus repelling the substrate. No amino acid polar group can, of course, change its sign, and in the range pH 7.5–5.5 the authors suggest that at the higher pH the imidazole group is sufficiently electronegative to attract the amino group of the substrate; at the lower pH limit, it is positively charged.

This extensive work with alternative substrates and inhibitors has greatly increased the knowledge of enzyme specificity. It has clarified somewhat our present ideas as to the mode of action of these enzymes and it has led to speculation as to the forms of the active centers. As with the similar work with antibodies it seems that only with more knowledge of the structure of these proteins will it be possible to put the speculations to adequate test.

5. Partial Hydrolysis of Proteins and the Search for Active Fragments

Hydrolysis of biologically active proteins and the testing of the products for activity has a long history originating in claims and counter claims of the nonprotein nature of enzymes and antibodies. Since that controversy was settled the work has been pursued in attempts to isolate protein fragments possessing the activity of the original protein, as this offers the most obvious short cut to the elucidation of the relation between structure and activity. Practical necessity prompted by the expense of extraction or shortage of raw material has given particular emphasis to this type of work, with insulin, and more recently with the adrenocorticotropic hormone (ACTH).

a. Hormones

Much published work seems to indicate that in insulin no covalent bonds, whether peptide or disulfide, can be split without complete loss of activity. It is a remarkable finding which serves to emphasize the complexity of the present problem.

With the adrenocorticotropic hormone the position is uncertain and no final conclusion can be reached until the very active work in progress all over the world is published. In 1943, Li, Evans, and Simpson,[59] and Sayers, White, and Long[60] reported the isolation of ACTH from sheep and pig pituitaries, respectively. The hormones were simple proteins, very similar in physical properties, and homogeneous when examined in the ultracentrifuge and by electrophoresis. The molecular weight was 20,000. In 1947, Li[141] quoted unpublished work showing that the sheep hormone could be digested either with pepsin or with hot acid to give active peptides which were dialyzable and not precipitated by trichloroacetic acid. The average number of amino acid residues in the peptides was stated to be about seven. The clinical value of ACTH in the treatment of rheumatic disease was reported in 1949, and since then much work has been carried out. The persistence of biological activity after acidic and after peptic but not tryptic digestion has been confirmed.[142,143] There has, however, also been confirmation[144,145] of earlier work by Tyslowitz[146] who in 1943 showed that dialyzable active substances not precipitable by trichloroacetic acid were present in the pituitary.

An extraction process which involves peptic digestion and results in the preparation of material at least 150 times more active than the original protein hormone has been developed by the Armour Laboratories.[147] This preparation is heterogeneous in the ultracentrifuge but has a molecular weight of several thousands. The activity per molecule is therefore more than fifteen times greater than the protein hormone and it is difficult to see what relation these preparations can bear to each other. Li[148] has recently reported the fractionation of a peptic digest of ACTH using adsorption chromatography on carbon, the purified material now appearing to have a molecular weight of about 2000.

(141) C. H. Li, *Ann. Rev. Biochem.* **16**, 291 (1947).
(142) C. H. Li, Conference on Metabolic Aspects of Convalescence, Josiah Macy Foundation, New York, 1948.
(143) N. G. Brink, M. A. P. Meisinger, and K. Folkers, *J. Am. Chem. Soc.* **72**, 1040 (1950).
(144) E. B. Astwood, A. P. Cleroun, R. W. Payne, and M. S. Ruben, *Bull. New England Medical Center* **12**, 2 (1950).
(145) B. Cortis-Jones, A. C. Crooke, A. A. Henly, P. Morris, and C. J. O. R. Morris, *Biochem. J.* **46**, 173 (1950).
(146) R. Tyslowitz, *Science* **98**, 225 (1943).
(147) J. B. Lesh, J. D. Fisher, I. M. Bunding, J. J. Kocsis, L. J. Walaszek, W. F. White, and E. E. Hays, *Science* **112**, 43 (1950).
(148) C. H. Li, A. Tiselius, K. O. Pedersen, L. Hagdahl, and H. Cartinsen, *J. Biol. Chem.* **190**, 317 (1951).

At present it seems probable that the pituitary contains a hormone of molecular weight less than 10,000 which is stable to acidic and peptic digestion. There is in addition a protein of molecular weight 20,000 which has some hormonal activity either as an intrinsic property or due to a firmly bound impurity. This activity also survives digestion. Interpretation of the data has become even more difficult since Stack-Dunne and Young[149] have reported that the maintenance of adrenal weight and depletion of the ascorbic acid content of the adrenals in hypophysectomized rats are functions of different hormones which have been almost completely separated. As both of these properties have been attributed to ACTH and are the basis of the most frequently used methods of assay, reconsideration of earlier data may be necessary (see Li, Vol. II).

b. Enzymes

No genuine example of the persistence of the enzymatic activity after hydrolysis has yet been described. Tsou[150] was able to obtain a partial hydrolysis product of cytochrome c by digesting with pepsin. From the iron content, the heme must have remained bound to a polypeptide of molecular weight 3000, i.e., less than one quarter that of the original protein. However, the specificity of the fragment had been lost as it was now autoxidizable and could not act as an intermediary in either succinic oxidase or cytochrome oxidase systems. As the chief function of the protein part of the heme proteins appears to be in controlling specificity, no conclusions as to the abilities of this enzyme to survive hydrolysis can be made.

There are several enzymes which exist in an inactive form and are converted into active enzymes by a hydrolytic process. Pepsinogen[151] and trypsinogen[152] are examples of these, both the precursor and enzyme having been obtained in a highly purified crystalline state. When chymotrypsinogen is activated the principal product is α-chymotrypsin,[153] but Kunitz[154] was able to crystallize from the mother liquor remaining after crystallization of the α-enzyme, two further enzymes, β- and

(149) M. Stack-Dunne and F. G. Young, *J. Endocrinol.* **7,** lxvi (1951).

(150) C. L. Tsou, *Nature* **164,** 1134 (1949).

(151) R. M. Herriott, *J. Gen. Physiol.* **22,** 65 (1938).

(152) M. Kunitz and J. H. Northrop, *J. Gen. Physiol.* **19,** 991 (1936).

(153) M. Kunitz and J. H. Northrop, *J. Gen. Physiol.* **18,** 433 (1935).

(153a) G. W. Schwert and S. Kaufman, *J. Biol. Chem.* **180,** 517 (1949).

(154) M. Kunitz, *J. Gen. Physiol.* **22,** 207 (1938).

(154a) G. W. Schwert, *J. Biol. Chem.* **190,** 799 (1951).

(154b) G. W. Schwert and S. Kaufman, *J. Biol. Chem.* **190,** 807 (1951).

(154c) E. L. Smith, D. M. Brown, and M. Laskowski, *J. Biol. Chem.* **191,** 639 (1951).

γ-chymotrypsins.   These three enzymes have similar activities but differ in crystalline form and in their stability to acid, alkali, and urea solution. Later, Jacobsen[155] followed the activation of chymotrypsinogen under different conditions, viz., 0° and higher trypsin concentration.   From a correlation of potential activity of the zymogen, the actual activity of the α-chymotrypsin produced, and the numbers of peptide bonds broken during hydrolysis, he postulated the intermediary formation of two more chymotrypsins.   π-Chymotrypsin, the first produced, has a specific activity 2–2.5 times greater than that of α-chymotrypsin; and δ-chymotrypsin has an activity about 1.5 times higher than the α-enzyme. Neither of these intermediates was isolated, though δ-chymotrypsin has been the subject of further study.[153a]   Of the three crystalline enzymes, α-chymotrypsin is rather more active than β- or γ-chymotrypsin.   In all these steps peptide bonds are broken and nonprotein nitrogen is produced, though its amount is small, being always less than 10 per cent of the zymogen nitrogen.   Earlier estimates of the molecular weight are doubtful as Kunitz[154] gives 41,000 as the value for α-chymotrypsin, while Jansen, Nutting, and Balls[118] give 27,000, and the most recent figure for the zymogen and several enzymes is 22,000.[154a,b,c]   It seems to be clear that only a small part of the precursor is split off during conversion to the enzyme.   Though final proof has not yet been obtained, it would appear that in this case a limited hydrolysis of an enzyme without destruction of its activity is possible.

c. Antigens

The specificity of artificially conjugated antigens has been shown to depend almost entirely on the hapten which is usually a comparatively small and simple molecule.   Antigens would thus be expected to be the most likely substances for the isolation of specifically active hydrolysis products.   Conclusive evidence from the isolation of peptides able to inhibit the combination of the whole antigen with its antisera is, however, still lacking, though evidence showing that it may be achieved has been obtained.   Landsteiner and Chase[156] prepared heteroalbumose from a 3-hr. peptic digest of serum protein and injected it into rabbits.   The antiserum produced could be inhibited in its reaction with the antigen by dialyzable fractions of the heteroalbumose.   Later, Landsteiner[157] prepared antisera against soluble silk fibroin which was adsorbed on charcoal.   He partially hydrolyzed the silk with sulfuric acid and obtained peptides able to inhibit the antisera.   The average molecular weight of

(155) C. F. Jacobsen, *Compt. rend. trav. lab. Carlsberg. Sér. chim.* **25**, 327 (1947).
(156) K. Landsteiner and M. W. Chase, *Proc. Soc. Exptl. Biol. Med.* **30**, 1413 (1933).
(157) K. Landsteiner, *J. Exptl. Med.* **75**, 269 (1942).

these peptide mixtures was estimated to be 600–1000. Holiday[158] and Kleczkowski[159] studied the peptic hydrolysis of crystalline serum albumin and found fractions able to precipitate and inhibit antiserum albumin. Porter[73] mentioned that papain digest of ovalbumin, which would no longer precipitate with its antisera, could still inhibit it. In no case, however, were the inhibitory fragments of a pure protein antigen isolated, characterized, and a satisfactory estimate of the size made. One great difficulty in all such work lies in the isolation of an active peptide from a complex mixture of other large peptides. This should be possible, however, as new methods of fractionation are continually being devised and advantage could be taken of the specific power of an inhibitory peptide to combine reversibly with the antibody.

There is no clear-cut evidence that a partially hydrolyzed protein can retain its power to stimulate antibody production when injected. The experiment of Landsteiner and Chase[156] with heteroalbumose suggests that it may be possible but, as no rigorous purification was attempted, the presence of some unhydrolyzed molecules cannot be excluded. The digestion of antisera, which will be discussed next, shows that in this case partially digested globulins are much poorer antigens than they were originally.

d. Antibodies

Antibodies are the only class of biologically active proteins which have been shown conclusively to retain their specific combining power after partial digestion. This work began in attempts to reduce the sensitization against horse serum proteins which often followed the use of diphtheria and other antisera. Parventjev[160] successfully digested diphtheria antitoxin with pepsin without loss of activity, and Pope[161] investigated the effect of several proteases on this antiserum. Peterman and Pappenheimer[162] purified the digestion product from a peptic hydrolyzate of the pseudoglobulin obtained from horse diphtheria antitoxin and found the molecular weight to be about one-half of that of the original: full antitoxin activity was retained. Digestion of the toxoid–antitoxin floccules gave a purer product of molecular weight 113,000. Symmetry estimations led to the suggestion that the original molecule had been split at right angles to its major axis. Northrop[163] dissolved

(158) E. Holiday, *Proc. Roy. Soc.* (London) **A170,** 79 (1939).
(159) A. Kleczkowski, *Brit. J. Exptl. Path.* **26,** 24 (1945).
(160) I. A. Parventjev, U. S. Patent 2,065,196 (1936).
(161) C. G. Pope, *Brit. J. Exptl. Path.* **20,** 132 (1939).
(162) M. L. Petermann and A. M. Pappenheimer, Jr., *J. Phys. Chem.* **45,** 1 (1941).
(163) J. H. Northrop, *J. Gen. Physiol.* **25,** 465 (1942).

diphtheria toxin–antitoxin floccules in acid, neutralized and digested with trypsin. About one-third of the activity was recovered in the supernatant fluid, and after many salt fractionations some active protein was crystallized. The crystals were unstable and were apparently denatured during attempts to recrystallize. They were not homogeneous when tested by solubility studies, but their molecular weight was estimated to be about 90,000, very considerably lower than the value before digestion. From this and other work it has been established that horse antidiphtheria globulin can be hydrolyzed to give molecules of little more than one-half of the original size, which still retain their power to flocculate with and neutralize the toxin. The neutralizing power of the half molecule is double that of the whole molecule on a weight basis[162,164] and hence the same on a molar basis. The combining centers of the antitoxin must therefore have been present only in one-half of the molecule. Porter[165] found that the γ-globulin of a rabbit immunized against ovalbumin, of which about one-third was precipitable by ovalbumin, could be hydrolyzed to give a fraction which, although it would no longer flocculate with the antigen, was able to inhibit precipitation. The inhibitory fraction could be further hydrolyzed with carboxypeptidase for some time before activity was lost. From end-group analysis after purification it was concluded that papain had produced an inhibitor of molecular weight about 40,000 and carboxypeptidase had reduced this to about 30,000 without destroying the activity. It seemed that the active fraction came from the end of the polypeptide chain which had a free terminal amino group and so the position of a combining center was roughly defined. In sufficient concentration relative to the antibody, the inhibitor could completely prevent flocculation, and both flocculation and inhibition could be reversed by changing the concentration of the reactants. No evidence of a second inhibitory fragment was found though this would be expected if an antibody has two combining centers as assumed in the lattice[166] theory of the antibody–antigen reaction.

From these hydrolysis studies it seems possible to split off parts of the antibody and probably of the antigen molecules which have all or part of the activity of the whole. This may also be possible with ACTH and perhaps with chymotrypsin though general success with hormones and enzymes seems less likely at present: the whole protein molecule is not necessarily involved in the specificity and the activity which are shown. Further generalizations are not possible, but the failure to obtain active

(164) C. G. Pope and M. Healey, *Brit. J. Exptl. Path.* **20**, 213 (1939).
(165) R. R. Porter, *Biochem. J.* **46**, 479 (1950).
(166) J. R. Marrack, Chemistry of Antigens and Antibodies, H. M. Stationery Office, London, 1938.

products after hydrolysis only proves that the methods used are ineffective.

6. INVESTIGATION OF THE MODE OF FORMATION OF ACTIVE PROTEINS

The mode of formation of biologically active proteins and the structural basis of their activity are interlinked problems, and it is evident that increased knowledge of either would be a mutual gain.   In so far as the method of formation involves complete protein synthesis there seems little prospect that it can provide useful data at present, but if it depends on partial synthesis or activation of an inactive precursor, valuable information may be obtainable.

a. Enzymes

In vitro activation seems to be a phenomenon peculiar to enzymes. They may fail to act as catalysts until coenzymes are added, these taking many forms of varying complexity, from metal ions to nucleotides.   In other cases, the formation of sulfhydryl groups by the addition of a reducing agent, or partial hydrolysis as with pepsinogen, may be necessary to activate the enzyme.

The distinction between an enzyme with a prosthetic group and an enzyme which is a simple protein requiring a coenzyme is frequently only a matter of degree, depending on the ease with which the protein is separated from the nonprotein component.   A conjugated enzyme is perhaps best defined as one in which the prosthetic group cannot be removed reversibly, that is without destruction of the protein.   The chemistry of many prosthetic groups and coenzymes is now understood as is also their function in catalysis.   There is, however, very little information as to how they are bound to proteins and no information as to how the protein confers specificity and a catalytic power many thousand times greater than any they may possess alone.   The activation of a prosthetic group or a coenzyme by a protein is probably a very similar phenomenon to the direct activation of a substrate, and advantage might perhaps be taken of their presence at a particular site to identify the peptide sequence immediately involved.

The formation of an enzyme by hydrolysis of an inactive precursor is quite a different type of activation from the others which have been mentioned.   The conversion of chymotrypsinogen into chymotrypsin has already been referred to.   The autocatalytic formation of pepsin from pepsinogen has the unusual feature that under certain conditions part of the nonprotein nitrogen split off can be isolated as a peptide of molecular weight about 5000.[167]   This large peptide can inhibit pepsin,

(167) R. M. Herriott, *J. Gen. Physiol.* **24**, 325 (1941).

though the inhibition is only demonstrable at about pH 5 because in more acid solutions pepsin hydrolyzes the inhibitor very rapidly. This is an unusual example of an inhibitor which under conditions more favorable for catalysis becomes a substrate. Whether the peptide plays any part in masking the potential active center in pepsinogen is unknown, but clearly some other stabilizing factor must also be present.

b. Antibodies and Adaptive Enzymes

Antibody and adaptive enzyme formation are two phenomena where the production *in vivo* of a specifically active protein may be stimulated at will. In the first case the new protein can be isolated and estimated as such. In the second its presence is inferred from the increase in enzymatic activity; no purified adaptive enzyme has yet been found homogeneous by all criteria,[168] though there is no reason to suppose that any peculiar difficulties should be encountered.

With antibody production in animals, there is little doubt that the formation of a protein with a new specificity has been initiated rather than just stimulated. The range of specificities which can be produced using artificially conjugated antigens is too great for any other interpretation. The formation of adaptive enzymes in microorganisms has not yet received the intensive study given to immunochemistry, but it would appear to be a stimulatory process rather than a synthesis *de novo*. Of the adaptive enzymes so far discovered, most have a basal level,[169-172] that is, they are detectable without addition of substrate to the growth medium, though sometimes only with difficulty. If this is true, adaptation must be a case of increased production and differs in an important characteristic from antibody formation. Other significant differences have been noted. Thus closely related strains of bacteria differ sharply in the range of adaptive enzymes which they can produce (for example, with respect to lactase[173] and tetrathionase[174] production within the coliform group of bacteria). The ability to adapt to a given substrate by formation of the specific enzyme is inherited like any other distinctive bacterial characteristic. On the other hand, although considerable variation in the response of animals of the same species to the same antigen

(168) M. Cohn and J. Monod, *Biochim. et Biophys. Acta* **7**, 153 (1951).
(169) G. S. Mirick, *J. Exptl. Med.* **78**, 255 (1943).
(170) M. R. Pollock, *Brit. J. Exptl. Path.* **27**, 419 (1946).
(171) M. R. Pollock, *Brit. J. Exptl. Path.* **31**, 739 (1950).
(172) S. D. Wainright, *Brit. J. Exptl. Path.* **31**, 495 (1950).
(173) J. Monod, Colloques Internationaux du C.R.N.S. VIII, Unités Biologiques Douées de Continuité Génétique, Paris, 1949.
(174) R. Knox, P. G. H. Gell, and M. R. Pollock, *J. Hyg.* **43**, 149 (1943).

is a common observation, no evidence that it is an inherited characteristic has yet been reported.

For the present purpose, however, the significance of these phenomena depends upon the provision that the new biological activity arises from a comparatively simple conversion of an inactive precursor: not that complex synthesis of a new protein from peptides or amino acids is required. The real answer is not known, but immunology has produced sufficient information for several rival theories of antibody production to be formulated.

Breinl and Haurowitz,[175] Alexander,[176] Mudd,[177] and Burnett[178] have put forward the view that an antigen causes antibody production by intervening in the synthesis of serum globulin, either directly by the formation of a template around which the synthesis proceeds, or indirectly by modification of the protein-synthezising system itself. Burnett[178] has collected evidence in favor of the latter view. None of these theories excludes the possibility of chemical differences between antibodies and normal γ-globulin. Pauling,[179] on the contrary, has suggested that formation of antibody is due to the refolding of preformed γ-globulin, in the presence of antigen. According to this theory the biological activity is dependent only on the configuration, and the suggestion that an almost infinite range of different specificities could be shown by essentially the same protein molecule is of considerable interest. Many of the details of Pauling's theory are incompatible with the experimental findings,[178] but the important suggestion that all antibodies and inert globulins are built up of the same amino acids arranged in the same sequence and held together by the same covalent bonds has not yet been disproved. The heterogeneity of the γ-globulins in an animal have been shown by electrophoretic mobility[180] and by ultracentrifugal[181] and salting-out studies.[182] In the horse, antiprotein antibodies appear in a new electrophoretic fraction,[183] and anticarbohydrate antibodies have a molecular weight

(175) F. Breinl and F. Haurowitz, *Z. physiol. Chem.* **192**, 45 (1930).
(176) J. Alexander, *Protoplasma* **14**, 296 (1932).
(177) S. Mudd, *J. Immunol.* **23**, 423 (1932).
(178) F. M. Burnet, The Production of Antibodies, Macmillan, Melbourne, Australia, 1941 and 1948.
(179) L. Pauling, *J. Am. Chem. Soc.* **62**, 2643 (1940).
(180) H. F. Deutsch, R. A. Alberty, and L. J. Gosting, *J. Biol. Chem.* **165**, 21 (1946).
(181) K. O. Pedersen, Ultracentrifuge Studies on Serum and Serum Function, Almquist and Wiksel, Uppsala, Sweden, 1945.
(182) Y. Derrien, *Svensk. Kem. Tid.* **59**, 139 (1947).
(183) N. Fell, K. G. Stern, and R. D. Coghill, *J. Immunol.* **39**, 223 (1940).

about five times greater than that of normal globulin,[184] but in both cases inert globulin is also associated with these new fractions. In no case has antibody activity been exclusively related to any particular chemical or physical property. Amino acid analysis, as far as it has gone, has not shown significant differences between antibodies and other globulin.[31–34] In rabbit antiovalbumin and the inert γ-globulin with which it is associated, only N-terminal residues of alanine can be identified, and in both the terminal peptide sequence appears to be alanyl-leucyl-valyl-aspartyl-glutamyl.[73] This suggests that rabbit γ-globulin, including that fraction precipitable by ovalbumin, may consist of a single long polypeptide chain with the same amino acid sequence along part at least of the length. From work with isotopically labeled amino acids,[185] the rate of turnover of antibodies and of other globulins appears to be the same. No marked differences have been observed between the antigenic specificities of different antibodies and the inert globulin from the same species.

Thus far, the complete failure to relate any chemical or physical characteristic of a globulin with its antibody function supports Pauling's theory that the biological activity depends only upon configuration properties which are controlled by labile bonding. This is, however, evidence of a negative kind and cannot be conclusive until more is known of the structure of γ-globulin. Two observations are difficult, though perhaps not impossible to interpret in terms of this theory. First, Erickson and Neurath[44] found that antipneumococcus antibody would survive denaturation with guanidine HCl and urea even though the denatured antiserum was insoluble in saline and had to be brought into solution in sodium thiocyanate for its activity to be demonstrable. Native and denatured normal globulin were found to be antigenically more closely related to each other than to native and denatured antibody globulin. Secondly, reduction of the disulfide bonds of rabbit antiovalbumin although delaying the rates of flocculation with antigen did not destroy its combining power.[73] In both cases, alteration of the configuration of the molecule must have occurred, but this may have been confined to a part of the molecule not containing the combining centers. This great diversity of specificity shown by otherwise indistinguishable proteins is unique to antibodies, since with enzymes, antigens, and hormones, physical and chemical differences are pronounced, though not yet correlated with activity. The explanation of this, on configurational grounds alone, may be possible in spite of seeming contradictions, but at present there is no prospect of direct proof.

(184) R. W. G. Wyckoff, *Science* **84**, 291 (1936).
(185) R. Schoenheimer, S. Ratner, D. Rittenberg, M. Heidelberger, and H. P. Tveffers, *J. Biol. Chem.* **144**, 541, 555 (1942).

7. INVESTIGATION OF THE NATURE OF BIOLOGICAL ACTIVITY

In attempting to relate protein structure and biological activity, it is apparent that the fullest information about the nature of the reactions which constitute that activity is necessary, and this is most likely to be gained by studying the activity in an isolated system *in vitro* with purified components. In his elegant study of the cytochrome system in living tissues such as bee's wings and yeast cells, Keilin[186] has shown that this is not altogether an essential provision, but here we have most probably an exceptional case. When antibody production or the effects of hormones or toxins are followed *in vivo* it is extremely difficult to decide which are primary and which are secondary effects. *In vitro* studies are of course open to the objection that the results obtained may not bear close relation to the behavior of the active protein in the organism. For the present purpose this does not seem to be a serious criticism as the interpretation of any kind of specific activity in terms of protein structure would be a major advance. It is further desirable in investigating biological activity that the methods used should permit rapid and continuous observations to be made. It is only with such techniques that it can be decided if the over-all result occurs in one or several stages.

a. Enzymes

Many studies of the mode of action of enzymes have been directed to intensive investigation of their specificity. This work has greatly widened our knowledge of their behavior and has led in some cases to interpretation of the results in terms of the structure of the active center. It is discussed elsewhere in this chapter. Kinetic investigations have been carried out based on the original Michaelis-Menten concept of an enzyme–substrate complex as the essential intermediary in catalysis. All this work has supported their idea, and the occurrence of such a complex is generally accepted. More recently, rapid observation of heme proteins during catalysis has enabled direct observation of such a complex. This was first observed by Keilin and Mann[187] in 1937 with peroxidase, and Chance[188] has subsequently developed techniques for the continuous recording of the reactions. He found that horse-radish peroxidase and hydrogen peroxide form two intermediary complexes as shown by the following equations:

$$FeOH + H_2O_2 \rightarrow FeOOH(I) + H_2O$$
$$FeOOH(I) \rightarrow FeOOH(II)$$
$$FeOOH(II) + AH_2 \rightarrow FeOH + H_2O$$

(186) D. Keilin, *Ergeb. Enzymforsch.* **2**, 239 (1933).
(187) D. Keilin and T. Mann, *Proc. Roy. Soc.* (London) **B122**, 119 (1937).
(188) B. Chance, *Arch. Biochem.* **22**, 224 (1949).

The primary complex **I** is green and rapidly changes to a pale-red complex **II,** which reacts with the acceptors oxidizing it and regenerating free peroxidase.   Alkyl hydrogen peroxides behave similarly.

With catalase, a similar green primary complex is formed which reacts with a second molecule of H_2O_2 with the formation of oxygen and regeneration of free catalase.[189]   This complex may also react with a number of compounds which it oxidizes in a manner similar to peroxidase, a reaction which is 10^4–10^5 times slower than that with a second molecule of H_2O_2.   With catalase, also a secondary red complex appears if the enzyme is left in contact with H_2O_2;[190] this is inactive and not an intermediary in the catalysis as is the red complex of peroxidase and H_2O_2. These papers and others relating to the mode of action of oxidizing enzymes have been well reviewed by Herbert.[191]   The results have not yet thrown any light on the function of the protein in these conjugated enzymes.

b. Antibody–Antigen Reactions

Antibody–antigen reactions *in vivo* may result in the neutralization of a toxic antigen and the agglutination, lysis, or increased phagocytosis of a cellular antigen; but from *in vitro* work it seems clear that the primary reaction is a combination of the two reactants.   The range of specificities of the reaction has been investigated, and the conclusion drawn from this work has already been discussed.   Using pure protein antigens, the influence has been examined of concentration of the reactants, temperature, and the presence of inhibitors on the rates of combination.   Light-scattering techniques[192] have been developed which enable changes in the size of large molecules to be followed continuously.   Two papers describing the application of this technique to the antibody–antigen system appeared simultaneously.   Goldberg and Campbell[193] followed the reaction between bovine serum albumin and its purified rabbit antibody.   Complex formation was detected immediately after mixing, and the size of the particles increased smoothly till precipitation occurred, no exceptional feature being associated with the appearance of visible turbidity.   Gitlin and Edelhoch[194] mixed human serum albumin with the homologous horse antibody.   In this system no precipitation occurs in the excess zone either of the antibody or of the antigen, but soluble

(189) B. Chance, *Acta Chem. Scand.* **1,** 236 (1947).

(190) B. Chance, *Biochem. J.* **46,** 387 (1950).

(191) D. Herbert, *Ann. Repts. on Progress Chem.* (Chem. Soc. London) **47,** 335 (1950).

(192) P. Doty and J. T. Edsall, *Advances in Protein Chem.* **6,** 37 (1951).

(193) R. J. Goldberg and D. H. Campbell, *J. Immunol.* **66,** 79 (1951).

(194) D. Gitlin and H. Edelhoch, *J. Immunol.* **66,** 67 (1951).

complexes increasing to a maximum size were observed, the final state being reached more rapidly in the zone of excess antigen. All the reactions were reversible, and the dissolution of the precipitate when antigen was added was also more rapid than when antibody was added.

It would be of interest to know the composition of the complexes as they increase in size, how uniform they are at any given time, whether their stability changes, and whether size or composition is more important in determining solubility. Such data, together with thermodynamical studies which Boyd[195] used in order to deduce the type of bond formation in the reactions, could give a clearer idea as to the actual mechanism of combination.

c. Long-Range Forces

The whole concept of the necessity of close contact between an enzyme and its substrate and between antibody and antigen has been questioned by Rothen's work with surface films. The novel suggestion that interaction between proteins may involve long-range forces has been the subject of prolonged controversy. Rothen[196] has recently summarized his views, and Singer[197] has critically tested the work. The experimental findings have been confirmed in several laboratories, but their interpretation has been rejected by most workers. The findings can be summarized as follows:

(1) Monomolecular films of certain proteins, notably beef serum albumin, retain their ability to combine specifically with homologous antibody as shown by increase in film thickness when brought into contact with antisera.

(2) When such layers are treated with a solution of trypsin their power to combine with antibody is lost, presumably because of proteolytic digestion.

(3) This immunological and enzymatic activity persists even when the original layers of serum albumin are protected from contact with antibody by inert barrier films of barium stearate, Formvar (polyvinyl methylal resin), and other polymers. The effects may be observed in some cases even though the barriers are several hundred angstroms thick.

(4) Screens of other substances such as metals or Parlodion (collodion) may prevent the activity when only 5–20 A. thick.

(5) The quantitative results in terms of thickness of antibody layer adsorbed or thickness of screen necessary to prevent the reaction are influenced by conditions such as the pH under which the initial protein

(195) W. C. Boyd, J. B. Conn, D. C. Gregg, G. B. Kistiakowsky, and R. M. Roberts, *J. Biol. Chem.* **139**, 787 (1941).

(196) A. Rothen, *Helv. Chim. Acta* **33**, 834 (1950).

(197) S. J. Singer, *J. Biol. Chem.* **182**, 189 (1950).

films are deposited and the nature of the buffer solution used to dissolve the antibody or trypsin.   When several superimposed layers of serum albumin are deposited on the slide, the antibody that it will hold and the thickness of the barrier necessary to prevent action are greater than with one layer.

Rothen has interpreted these findings as evidence for the existence of long-range forces operating at distances of 50–200 A.   The principal criticism is that irregularities in the layers of protein and screening material do not exclude the possibility of holes through which antibody or enzyme could diffuse to the antigen films.   It has been pointed out by Iball[198] that if only a very small number of holes existed originally, the subsequent antibody–antigen reaction taking place beneath the screen would disrupt the film further.   Trurnit[199,200] observed that phosphate buffers tend to dislodge the original film and suggested that antigen could diffuse to the outer surface.

Rothen rejects both these suggestions but the arguments for and against are too lengthy to be discussed here.   He believes that either specific long-range forces are operating through the screens or that these forces cause motivated diffusion of the reactants toward each other, in a manner that would not otherwise be possible.   In this second alternative the specific reaction would occur at short range.   The impression given by this work is that the surface-film technique has been stretched to its useful limit and that conclusive evidence for such new forces can only come from the use of other methods.   Evidence has indeed been given of long-range proteolysis in solution through a paper membrane impregnated with collodion and several polymers,[201] but confirmation is still awaited.

As conclusive evidence to the contrary is not available, it must at present be accepted that enzyme catalysis and immunological reactions depend on close contact between the reactants, probably over an appreciable surface area.   The high degree of specificity shown is common to all the biological activities of proteins, and it is probable that all will depend at some point on close contact with the active protein.   The number of such contacts in a given reaction, their duration, and the forces operating remain largely unknown.

III. Conclusions

The following summary is based on the experimental findings described.

(198) J. Iball, *Science* **109,** 18 (1949).
(199) H. J. Trurnit, *Science* **111,** 1 (1950).
(200) H. J. Trurnit, *Science* **112,** 329 (1950).
(201) M. Hanig, *Proc. Soc. Exptl. Biol. Med.* **73,** 381 (1950).

(1) The amino acid content of a protein bears no obvious relation either to the mechanism of its biological activity or to its specificity. Exceptions to this are not sufficiently certain to be stressed.

(2) The chemistry and mode of action of many coenzymes and prosthetic groups are understood, but little progress has been made in solving the influence of the protein on these compounds.

(3) No correlation between gross physical properties, such as size, shape, electrophoretic mobility, or solubility, on the one hand, and biological activity of proteins on the other, has yet been found.

(4) Denaturation of a protein usually destroys its specific biological activity, but with certain enzymes, the destruction may be reversible as judged by recovery of activity. The complexity of this phenomenon is such that clear interpretation is difficult.

(5) Proteins with widely differing specificities may have an extremely similar structure and proteins with almost identical biological activities may have different structures.

(6) Comparative studies have emphasized the dependence of biological activity on structure without revealing the basis of the correlation.

(7) Blocking of reactive groupings in proteins has proved that different types of polar groups may be essential for the activities displayed by different proteins. Technical difficulties demand that caution be used in interpreting positive findings. Very few quantitative data are available. The blocking of essential groups in some enzymes may be prevented by the substrate or inhibitor.

(8) The use of small molecules of known structure, such as haptens or enzyme substrates and inhibitors, has enabled the specificity requirements of some proteins to be worked out in great detail. It has been possible to deduce from the results some information as to the nature of the active centers, their mode of action, and the forces involved.

(9) Partial hydrolysis studies have proved that biological activity may survive in an isolated fragment of a protein though these fragments are often of considerable size. It seems unlikely at present that this can be a general phenomenon.

(10) Little information as to the relation of structure to activity has so far been obtained from studies of the mode of formation of active proteins.

(11) Enzymatic and immunological reactions probably proceed in several steps. Reversible combination of the reactants with the protein appears to occur.

From these observations it may be concluded that the biological activity of a protein is dependent upon the structure of a small part of its surface which combines reversibly with the other reactants. In certain cases the structure of the active center is independent of the integrity of the whole molecule, but in others this is probably not so. The observed characteristics of the active center are that it contains polar groups which in some proteins must be charged if their activity is to be apparent. The steric pattern is an important property and this may be dependent upon labile as well as covalent bonds in the molecule. Possibly slight changes in this pattern may occur without loss of activity.

For lack of evidence to the contrary, it has been assumed that the properties of an active center will eventually be explicable in terms of the known characteristics of the side chains of the constituent amino residues, which are joined together by peptide bonds and arranged in a particular three-dimensional pattern. There is, however, the possibility that these side chains may interact in an unexpected manner or be substituted by small groupings not yet recognized. That such a phenomenon could occur in molecules built only of amino acids is suggested by the peculiar chemistry of gramicidin.[202] The investigation of the condensation of diisopropyl fluorophosphate with chymotrypsin, though only in a preliminary stage, does hint that similar unexpected groupings may exist in proteins and be linked with their biological activity.

Theories as to the mode of action of the different classes of biological proteins have at times been advanced, and some have stimulated successful investigations. With enzymes, the part which the prosthetic groups or coenzymes play in their mode of action has, in some cases, been largely solved. Few theories have, however, attempted to explain the role of the protein in more than very general terms. Tests of these generalizations, even in isolated cases, have not been possible or have not been attempted, and it does not seem profitable at present to consider them further.

The combination of purified antigen with its antibody would appear to be the simplest example of specific biological activity, but, in fact, the reaction is a series of combinations which continue relatively slowly to give either an insoluble precipitate or large soluble complexes. These complexes may have widely differing compositions depending on the proportions of the reactants present. The number of combining centers in a native protein antigen or in an antibody has not been satisfactorily estimated. Again, the structural basis of these combinations has so far only been described in general terms, not capable of decisive test.

Studies of the mode of action of other proteins whose activities are only demonstrable *in vivo* have not led even to a discussion of the structural basis of their activity. Some toxins are poisonous because they are enzymes and catalyze the destruction of cells or tissues. The primary mode of action has not been elucidated for the protein hormones nor indeed

(202) R. L. M. Synge, *Cold Spring Harbor Symposia Quant. Biol.* **14**, 191 (1949).

for the chemically simpler hormones. With insulin there is evidence suggesting that it exerts its effect by intervening in one of the enzyme systems controlling carbohydrate metabolism. It is probable that the structural interpretation of the action of toxins and hormones must await a solution of the problem of enzymatic activity. Solution of this question with viruses and genes seems even more remote.

In future studies of these problems, progress would seem to depend on reducing them to their simplest terms. Enzymatic and immunological reactions can be simplified into a specific combination of a purified protein with a small molecule of known structure if inhibitors or haptens are used, though in such cases nonspecific absorption might be superimposed on the specific combination. If the protein can also be reduced in size without loss of activity, structural problems are correspondingly reduced. Sanger's remarkable investigation[203-205] of the chemistry of insulin has led to a knowledge of the entire sequence of amino acid residues in a protein for the first time. In this case it may be possible to build a complete model of the insulin molecule and still to be ignorant of the features responsible for biological activity. If such progress could be made with an enzyme or antibody, it is probable that simultaneous investigations of the specificity requirements, which have already led in certain cases to increased knowledge of the active centers, would enable the essential area to be located. Solution of the three-dimensional structure of a protein will probably be easier where the protein is exceptionally resistant to denaturation and its configuration, therefore, is largely determined by covalent bonds.

An understanding of the mechanism of a specific reversible combination of a small molecule with a protein would seem to be the first step in elucidating this question. As often happens, however, in problems of this magnitude the most important clues may well be given by work directed to quite different ends.

(203) F. Sanger and H. Tuppy, *Biochem. J.* **49,** 463 (1951).
(204) F. Sanger and H. Tuppy, *Biochem. J.* **49,** 481 (1951).
(205) F. Sanger and E. O. P. Thompson, *Biochem. J.* **53,** 353, 363 (1953).

Author Index

The numbers in parentheses are footnote numbers and are inserted here to indicate the reference when an author's work is cited but his name is not mentioned on the text page.

A

Abderhalden, E., 93, 101, 102, 106, 107, 118(106), 450
Abel, J. J., 45, 78(206), 974
Abitz, W., 275
Abraham, E. P., 79, 634(161), 645
Abrams, A., 84, 522
Abrams, R., 80
Abramson, H. A., 496, 505, 506, 547, 548
Acher, R., 115, 125(199, 263a), 126, 142, 163, 164(441)
Ackermann, W. W., 97
Acree, S. F., 465
Adair, G. S., 16, 17(76), 31(76), 73, 77, 164, 284, 300, 301, 352, 353(204), 403, 515, 568(14), 569, 592, 593, 594 (15, 19, 20, 22, 26), 597, 636(80), 642, 692, 720, 721, 800, 842
Adair, M. E., 73, 77, 300, 301, 352, 353 (204), 515, 568(14), 569, 594(15, 26), 636(80), 642, 842
Adams, E. Q., 465, 466(10), 752
Adams, M., 78
Adams, M. H., 84, 817, 827, 828(41)
Adams, R., 109, 131, 132(307)
Adkins, H., 104
Adolf, M., 735
Agatov, P., 897, 929
Agner, K., 66, 69(334), 75, 80, 743
Agren, G., 82, 119
Ahlström, L., 79
Akabori, S., 169, 175
Åkeson, Å., 75, 79, 487, 543
Albert, A., 117, 159, 169, 795
Alberty, R. A., 23, 24(143), 77, 480, 494, 496, 499, 504, 511, 512(53c), 514 (53c), 517, 519, 520, 525, 527(112), 528, 533, 534, 535(266), 536, 538, 540, 541, 558, 745, 780, 1007

Albrecht, G., 241, 261(17b), 361
Alderton, G., 45, 67, 79(205, 343), 85, 512, 594, 634(159), 645, 797, 815
Alexander, A. E., 547, 552, 628, 663, 694
Alexander, B., 481
Alexander, J., 359, 496, 770, 781, 802 (179), 1007
Alexander, P., 901
Allen, A. J., 431
Allen, D. W., 800
Allen, F. H., 913
Allen, T. H., 734
Allen, T. W., 564, 566
Almquist, H. J., 410
Alsberg, C. L., 83
Altschul, A. M., 80
Aman, G., 124
Amberson, W. R., 522
Ambrose, E. J., 241, 242, 261, 282, 323, 334, 376(24), 383, 416, 419, 423, 424(85), 425, 426, 427, 428(96), 429
Ambrose, J. F., 832, 975, 993
Anderegg, J. W., 576, 619, 621(66), 657 (66), 722
Anderson, A. K., 818
Anderson, E. A., 23, 24(143), 511, 536, 541, 558
Anderson, G. W., 174
Anderson, T. F., 574(5), 575, 639(142, 143), 644, 817
Andersson, K. J. I., 634(7, 14), 640
Andrus, E. C., 34, 56(180)
Anfinsen, C. B., 72, 138, 166(352a), 168, 334, 638(127), 644
Angelos, A., 793
Angier, R. B., 134
Anslow, G. A., 438, 449(124)
Anson, M. L., 81, 124, 195, 632, 743, 808, 812, 814, 824, 827(77), 831, 832, 833, 834, 835, 836, 869, 876, 879, 880

(3, 85), 882, 888, 900, 909(35), 922, 937, 940(35), 983

Antonin, S., 96, 118, 122, 910

Antweiler, H. J., 500

Aragona, C., 50, 79(242)

Archibald, R. M., 17

Archibald, W. J., 668

Armstrong, S. H., Jr., 7, 9(19), 17, 22(84), 37(19), 49(19), 56(19), 403, 404, 494, 518, 519, 535, 568, 638(117), 643, 655, 684, 734, 735(25), 774(25), 776 (25), 777(25), 778(25), 780(25), 786 (25), 796(25)

Arndt, U. W., 386

Arnold, V., 830, 899

Arnow, L. E., 445, 446, 818

Aronson, J. D., 84

Arrhenius, S., 636(179), 645, 811, 841, 864(13), 865(13)

Ash, L., 141

Ashworth, J. N., 34, 35, 53(181), 56(181), 58(181), 61(181), 816

Askonas, B. A., 57

Asselineau, J., 97

Astbury, W. T., 175, 239, 251, 254, 255, 256, 257, 258, 261, 263, 265, 266, 267, 268, 269, 270, 271, 272, 273, 274, 276, 279, 280, 281, 283, 284, 285, 294 (202c), 295, 323(9, 10), 362(29), 373 (68), 376(68), 383, 385, 841, 842 (138), 848, 854(138)

Astrup, T., 499

Astwood, E. B., 73, 1000

Atkin, W. R., 273

Atlas, S. M., 634(181), 645

Auer, P. L., 694

Auricchio, G., 990(87), 991

Ayers, J., 972

B

Baccari, V., 990(87), 991

Bach, S. J., 74

Bachman, C., 77

Backus, J. K., 686

Backus, R. C., 577, 578

Bacq, Z. M., 922

Baddiley, J., 105

Bader, R., 79

Badger, S. J., 84

Bailey, E. D., 21, 59(117), 663

Bailey, J. L., 173

Bailey, K., 13, 79, 84, 101, 102, 107, 133 (152), 134(152), 171, 185, 197, 200, 202, 210, 218, 225, 227, 228, 229, 232, 267, 269, 270(92), 280, 281, 283, 284, 285, 292(165), 492, 577, 637(93), 643, 692, 720, 721, 723, 842, 848, 901, 957(43), 978, 993

Bailey, O. T., 30, 67(161)

Bain, J. A., 75, 77, 521, 635(53), 642

Baker, C. G., 93

Baker, L. E., 168

Baker, W., 122

Bald, J. G., 505

Baldwin, R. L., 23, 540, 658

Balis, M. E., 793

Ball, C. D., 70, 828, 853(102)

Ball, E. G., 69

Ballantine, R. J., 83

Ballantyne, M., 296(202r), 297

Ballou, G. A., 35, 70(187, 188, 189), 530, 732, 738(12), 745, 746, 748, 778, 785, 805(12), 823, 828

Balls, A. K., 68, 73, 74, 81, 895, 897, 910, 943, 944, 945(56, 141), 946, 957(8), 962(8, 26, 141), 990(84, 85), 991, 993, 994

Bamann, E., 10, 11(36), 66

Bamford, C. H., 255, 271, 376(40), 384, 385(321), 415(82), 416, 423

Bancroft, W. D., 798

Banks, H., 131, 132(315)

Banks, T. E., 895, 923(5), 939(7)

Baranowski, T., 18, 19(98), 52(98, 99, 251), 53(98), 73(98), 75(99), 79

Barbour, H. G., 17

Barbu, E., 686, 848

Barcroft, J., 9, 37(29), 743

Barger, G., 108, 121

Barieau, R. E., 361

Barkdoll, A. E., 432

Barker, H. A., 411

Barnes, B. A., 12, 45(51), 53(51), 56(51), 58(51), 62(51)

Barnes, R. H., 84

Barnett, C. E., 798

Barre, R., 82

Barritt, J., 256

Barron, E. S. G., 123, 124, 194, 820, 832, 834(117), 857, 909, 915, 922(50), 990(107), 991, 992

Bjornesjo, K. B., 800]
Bjornstahl, Y., 679, 684
Black, E. S., 478, 480(51), 655, 740, 741, 742, 744, 792(50)
Black, S., 75
Blackburn, S., 128, 143, 164, 919
Blake, C. H., 276
Blaker, R. H., 608(5), 609
Blanchard, M., 73
Blanchard, M. H., 9, 37(29), 43(29), 47 (29), 49(29), 56(29), 78(29), 466, 474, 487, 488, 565, 887
Blanco, J. G., 108
Blix, G., 542
Block, H., 99
Block, K., 131, 132(306, 312)
Block, R. J., 125(262), 126, 201
Blodgett, K. B., 283
Bloor, W. R., 20
Blout, E. R., 420, 421(77), 422(77), 426, 454
Blum, A. E., 223
Blumenthal, D., 102, 990(77), 991
Bock, R. M., 520, 638(134), 644
Bodansky, O., 993
Boeder, P., 679, 681
Boehm, G., 267
Boettiger, E. G., 799
Boggs, S., 817
Bohr, C., 485
Boissonnas, R. A., 78, 142, 173
Bolhofer, W. A., 95, 96
Bolling, D., 201
Bond, A. C., 104
Bonjour, G., 107, 136, 157(154), 164, 168 (154), 170(154, 336)
Bonner, J., 522
Bonnichsen, R. K., 75
Boor, A. K., 986
Booth, V. H., 10
Boothe, J. H., 134
Borek, E., 180
Bormann, K., 93
Born, M., 754
Borsook, H., 124, 132(325), 133, 176
Bott, M. J., 414, 415
Bouchilloux, S., 80
Boulanger, P., 137, 138, 139(350), 142 (350)
Bourdillon, J., 80, 82, 597
Boursnell, J. C., 895, 923(5), 944

Bowen, W. J., 79
Bowman, K. L., 71
Bowman, R. E., 106, 146
Boyd, W. C., 947, 1011
Boyer, P. D., 35, 70(187, 188, 189), 530, 732, 738, 745, 746, 748, 778, 785, 805 (12), 823, 828
Boyes-Watson, J., 312, 321(227), 322 (227), 346(227), 347(227), 358(227), 359(227), 395, 637(176), 645, 654, 655, 720(176)
Bradfield, J. R. G., 456
Bradley, A. J., 293
Bradley, W., 784
Bragg, W. L., 242, 305, 340, 347, 348, 349, 350, 351, 352(267), 353(268), 354, 355, 357, 374, 375, 376, 377, 378, 385 (23), 387, 389, 390, 654, 691, 720
Brand, E., 16, 136, 186, 214, 413, 414, 490, 556, 568(17), 569, 570, 721(57), 722, 978
Brandon, B. A., 933
Brandt, W., 78
Branson, H. R., 230, 379, 388
Brattsten, I., 64, 138, 543, 545
Brauer, R. W., 945
Braun, E., 516
Brazier, M. A. B., 101
Breinl, F., 359, 781, 802(178), 1007
Brenner, M., 130, 178(514, 514a), 179
Bresler, S. E., 744, 799(73), 804(73)
Brewer, E., 66, 542
Brewster, J. F., 83, 93
Brewster, P., 90
Breyer, B., 736
Brice, B. A., 17, 18(87), 22(87, 89), 407, 608(6, 11), 609
Bridgman, W. B., 634(162), 645, 709
Briggs, D. R., 523, 531, 533, 547, 745, 800 (80), 841, 843(136), 844(136), 853, 862(136), 878(136)
Brill, R., 251
Brimley, R. C., 183
Brindley, C. O., 912
Brindley, G. W., 356
Brink, N. G., 144, 1000
Brinkman, H. C., 606
Brintzinger, H., 481
Brockmann, H., 106
Brodersen, R., 499

Brohult, S., 638(136), 644, 684, 803, 817, 819, 821(53), 844(53), 878
Bronfrenbrenner, J., 74
Bronk, D. W., 34, 56(180)
Brønsted, J. N., 463
Brosteaux, J., 403, 405, 407, 608(1), 609
Brown, A., 7, 285, 480, 554, 584, 589, 592 (78), 593, 594(21, 23), 595, 597, 606, 636(78), 637(118), 638(118), 655, 657, 658(12, 179), 684, 691, 692, 721 (78), 724(179)
Brown, D. M., 635(28, 29, 41), 636(70), 637(99), 641, 642, 643, 664, 962, 1001, 1002(154c)
Brown, H. V., 409
Brown, K. D., 81
Brown, L., 384, 385(321)
Brown, R. A., 23, 63, 538, 540, 545, 546, 637(100), 643
Brown, R. K., 12, 45(51), 53(51), 56(51), 58(51), 62(51)
Brown, W. G., 104, 198
Brown, W. L., 223
Browne, F. L., 3, 30(5), 46(5), 75(5)
Brownlee, G., 99
Bruckner, V., 99
Brumberg, E. M., 456
Brunings, K. J., 122
Brunish, R., 202, 211(74)
Bryan, W. R., 60, 85(285)
Buchanan, J. M., 72
Buchanan, T. J., 709, 716
Buchka, M., 155
Buchner, E., 10
Buchner, P., 679
Budka, M. J. E., 17, 22(84), 403, 404, 518, 519, 638(117), 643
Bücher, T., 608(4), 609
Buehler, H. J., 94, 638(126), 644
Buerger, M. J., 242
Buergermeister, E., 439
Bugarsky, S., 476, 789
Bull, H. B., 7, 16, 31(73), 151, 156(406), 162(406), 164, 255, 289, 300, 303, 358, 559, 560, 561, 594(13), 595, 597, 598, 623, 624, 747, 787(101), 798, 808, 812, 817, 841, 844, 851(21), 855, 856, 862, 889(159)
Bulliard, H., 269
Bunding, I. M., 73, 1000
Bunn, C. W., 242, 266

Burch, C. R., 457
Burger, M., 78
Burgers, J. M., 660, 688
Burk, D., 797
Burk, N. F., 553, 572(8), 594(20, 24, 25), 595, 596, 804, 830, 841, 842
Burkhard, R. K., 779, 781, 782(169, 177), 971
Burnet, F. M., 1007
Burris, R. H., 11, 33
Bursa, F., 134
Burton, I. F., 108
Buston, H. W., 101
Buswell, A. M., 426
Butler, A. M., 53
Butler, J. A. V., 24, 28(148), 64, 138, 150, 168(401), 169, 170, 177(460), 543

C

Cable, R. S., 205, 216(82)
Cady, L. C., 625, 626, 670
Cahill, W. M., 108
Cain, C. K., 77
Caldwell, M. L., 897, 935, 964(121), 990 (79, 80, 81, 82), 991
Calkins, E., 748
Callow, R. K., 981
Calvery, H. O., 16, 981, 1008(31)
Calvin, M., 76
Cameron, J. W., 78, 81(541)
Camien, M. N., 99
Cammarata, P. S., 77
Campanella, D. A., 796
Campbell, D. H., 63, 532, 546, 608(5), 609, 743, 770, 858, 891(46, 49), 1010
Campbell, E. D., 451
Campbell, G. F., 83
Canepa, F. G., 361
Cann, J. R., 23, 63, 529, 538, 540, 545, 546, 637(100), 643
Cannan, R. K., 23, 49, 73(234), 78(240), 109, 129, 139, 151(167), 154(418), 155, 183, 191(10), 196(10, 48), 478, 482, 484, 487, 490, 491, 506, 531, 537 (257), 745, 789, 791, 792, 800(79), 850, 872(172), 940, 952
Carlisle, C. H., 313, 315, 334, 335, 340, 378, 430
Carnelly, H. L., 862, 873(215)

Cogin, G. E., 776

Cohen, B., 78

Cohen, H. R., 818

Cohen, P. P., 522

Cohen, S. S., 46, 58(215), 896

Cohn, E. J., 3, 4, 7(9), 12(9), 19(30), 20
(33), 34, 35(33), 36(9), 37(19, 29, 30),
38(9b, 9c), 41, 42, 43(9c, 29), 45(51),
46(33), 47(29), 49(19, 29), 50(33), 53
(9, 12, 30, 51, 181), 56(12, 19, 29, 30,
51, 180, 181), 57(33), 58(12, 51, 181),
61(181), 62(12, 51), 73(33), 78(29),
239, 391, 464, 465(6), 468, 469(18),
470(18), 472, 477, 483, 487, 488, 514,
552, 563, 564, 565, 566, 568, 569, 633,
639, 648, 663, 680, 684, 689, 692, 700,
701, 702, 725, 764, 780, 791(137),
799, 805(277), 816, 828, 887, 964

Cohn, H., 128, 131, 132(308)

Cohn, M., 1006

Cole, A. G., 49, 73(233)

Cole, H. H., 77

Coleman, R. E., 83

Collier, W. A., 410, 748

Colowick, S. P., 35, 52(184), 70(184), 78
(184), 84

Combette, R., 76

Commoner, B., 65, 454, 456

Conn, J. B., 875, 1011

Conner, W. P., 701, 712

Connors, W. M., 76

Consden, R., 101, 125(264), 126, 127, 128
(264, 269), 138, 139, 142, 143(372),
146(372), 150(344), 183, 194, 541,
543, 919

Conway, E. J., 156

Cook, A. H., 111, 173

Cook, G. H., 500, 631

Cook, H. G., 107

Coolidge, T. B., 543, 732

Cooper, G. R., 314, 522, 537, 636(76, 77),
639(144, 147), 642, 644, 822, 823(66),
840, 841(66, 134), 843, 844(66, 134),
845, 852, 853(157), 890, 932

Cooper, M., 483, 746, 774(93)

Copley, M. J., 280, 281, 537, 854

Corcoran, A. C., 496

Corey, R. B., 60, 85(283), 230, 241, 252,
259, 261(17a, 17b, 17c, 17d), 263,
266, 274(21), 276, 277, 308(17d), 334,
335(20), 355, 361, 363(17a), 365, 369,

370(35), 371, 374, 375, 378, 379, 380,
381, 382, 383, 386, 387, 388, 389, 390,
789, 812, 849, 854, 885, 982

Cori, C. F., 18, 19(97), 34(103), 35(103),
52(97, 184), 70(103, 184), 75(97), 78
(184), 78, 80

Cori, G. T., 8, 9, 18, 19(97), 34(103), 35
(96, 103), 43(23, 96), 52(23, 96, 97),
53(96), 70(103), 73(96), 75(97),
80(23), 522, 638(112), 643

Cornforth, J. W., 102

Cornforth, R. H., 102

Corran, H. S., 76

Cortis-Jones, B., 1000

Corwin, A. H., 97, 124

Coryell, C. D., 474, 747, 770

Cosslett, V. E., 315, 574(3), 575

Costello, M., 517

Coulson, C. A., 260(50), 261, 628, 629,
630, 631

Coulson, E. J., 546

Coulter, C. B., 18, 433

Coulthard, C. E., 76

Courtois, J., 82

Cowan, J. C., 106

Cowan, P., 293, 316, 362, 372(302)

Cox, E. G., 308

Cox, J. T., 628 (156), 629, 630(156), 631
(156)

Craig, D., 571

Craig, L. C., 13, 24(58), 69(58), 144, 150,
204, 557, 570, 571, 719, 842, 987, 988

Crammer, J. L., 433, 837, 857, 899

Crampton, C. F., 939

Crane, E. J., 299

Creech, H. J., 928

Creeth, J. M., 170, 631, 634(163), 636
(85), 642, 645, 665, 721

Cremer, H. D., 63, 138, 544

Crick, F. H. C., 384, 386, 387, 389

Crocker, C., 125(263a), 126, 142

Crook, E. M., 285

Crooke, A. C., 1000

Crosby, B. L., 106

Crowfoot, D., 279, 292, 293, 294(202b),
295, 296(202p), 297, 311, 315, 318,
319(253b), 320, 321(190), 328, 329,
349, 362, 372(302), 717

Csonka, F. A., 82, 83, 979

Culhane, K., 990(97), 991

Cummings, A. G., 467

Cunha, R., 85
Cunningham, L. W., Jr., 635(32), 641, 962
Curl, A. L., 81, 818, 897, 910(26), 944, 962(26)
Curme, H. G., 771
Currie, B. T., 594, 597, 598
Cushing, J. E., Jr., 858
Custer, J. H., 45, 73, 205, 206, 237, 511, 512, 746, 896
Cuzin, J., 85
Czarnetsky, E. J., 101

D

D'Agostino, E., 489
Dahl, O., 637(88), 642
Dahlberg, A. C., 415
Dakin, H. D., 100, 116, 160
Dale, W. M., 820
Dalgliesh, C. E., 102, 111, 175, 271
Dalton, H. R., 84
Daly, M. M., 202, 211(75)
Damerel, C. I., 97
Damerell, V. R., 299
Damodaran, M., 82, 94
Dandliker, W. B., 76, 578, 602, 609(110), 612, 614, 615, 616(110), 639
Daniel, J., 566
Danielli, J. F., 787, 896
Daniels, F., 866
Danielsson, C. E., 82, 663
Dannenberg, H., 445, 456
Darmon, S. E., 175, 240, 271, 420, 421, 422
Darwin, C. G., 304
Dauphinee, J. A., 131
Davidson, E., 312, 321(227), 322(227), 346(227), 347(227), 358(227), 359(227), 395, 637(176), 645, 654, 655, 720(176)
Davie, E. W., 946
Davies, H. G., 456
Davies, M., 261, 260(50)
Davis, B. D., 7, 9(19), 37(19), 49(19), 56(19), 514, 522, 738, 776, 778, 780, 788, 804, 805(441), 853, 941
Davis, H. F., 164, 225
Davis, S., 636(84), 642, 798
Davis, S. B., 922, 923, 964(90)
Dawson, B., 361
Dawson, C. R., 84, 637(97), 643

Dawson, I. M., 318
Dayhoff, M. O., 564, 568(22), 569, 636 (62), 637(62), 642
De, S. S., 78
Deasy, C. L., 132(325), 133
Debye, P., 604, 606, 611, 671
de Duve, C., 50, 79(243)
Deitz, V. R., 67, 124, 195, 832, 833(118), 834(118), 835(118), 897, 992
Dekker, C. A., 130, 145, 168
Della Monica, E. S., 45, 206, 237, 746, 896
De Lollis, N. J., 465
De Maria, G., 998
de Montmollin, R., 74
Dempsey, M., 264
Dénes, K., 75
Dent, C. E., 115, 120
Denton, C. A., 979
Derksen, J. C., 268, 269, 273, 275(113)
de Rooy, A., 270
Derrien, Y., 50, 53, 79(241), 83, 1007
Dersuaux, G., 12, 45(51), 53(51), 56(51), 58(51), 62(51)
Dervichian, D. G., 618, 620, 621(135)
Desnuelle, P., 96, 107, 118, 122, 124, 131, 133(215), 136, 138, 142(353), 157 (154), 158(215), 162(353), 164(215), 168(154), 170(154, 336), 171, 185, 197, 910, 992
Desreux, V., 831, 886(112), 922, 923, 964 (92), 966(92), 988
Deutsch, H. F., 75, 77, 79, 511, 512, 517, 521, 537(169), 541, 568, 634(19), 635 (53), 637(101, 104), 641, 642, 643, 847, 863(161), 910, 1007
de Verdier, C. Henric, 119
Dewan, J. G., 76
Dewey, D. L., 106
Dewey, H. M., 806, 895, 923(5)
Dhéré, C., 77
Diamond, L. K., 913
Di Carlo, F. J., 73
Dick, G. F., 990(107), 991
Dickinson, S., 267, 280, 281, 848
Dickman, S., 820
Dickson, G. T., 121
Dieu, H. A., 855
Dill, D. B., 83
Dillon, J. F., 664
Dillon, R. T., 95, 106, 114
Di Moia, F., 863, 864(216b)

Eirich, F., 295, 553, 635(36), 641
Eisen, H. N., 430, 774, 781, 786(159), 895, 939(4)
Eisenberg, M. A., 862, 869, 871, 872(213), 882, 883(213)
Eitelman, E. S., 639(140), 644
Eklund, H. W., 84
Elam, D. W., 530, 745, 787(83), 987
Elkes, J., 787
Elkins, E., 81, 511, 635(42), 641
Elks, J., 121
Ellenbogen, E., 45, 203, 312, 328, 634 (174), 645, 718, 801
Elliot, H., 61
Elliott, A., 241, 242, 261, 282, 323, 334, 336, 376(24), 384, 385(321), 416, 419, 423, 424(85), 425, 426, 427, 428(96), 429, 430, 808
Elliott, D. F., 93, 119, 164
Elliott, W. H., 179
Ellis, D. A., 559
Elsden, S. R., 192
Emerson, K., 17
Emmens, C. W., 20
Enenkel, H. G., 63, 544
England, A., 128
Englard, S., 637(98), 643
Enoksson, B., 600
Epps, H. M. R., 105
Erbacher, O., 67
Erdos, T., 79, 284, 522, 638(165), 639 (169), 645, 665
Erickson, J. O., 70, 73, 194, 289, 522, 636 (77), 642, 808, 809(2), 812(2), 815(2), 822, 823, 826, 831(2), 832(2), 834 (2), 840, 841(2, 66, 68, 134), 844(66, 68, 134), 845, 852, 858, 860(73, 74), 877(68), 890, 909, 984, 1008
Eriksson, I. B., 638(133), 644
Eriksson-Quensel, I.-B., 150, 167(399), 634(18), 635(45, 46, 47), 636(57), 637(57, 110), 638(18, 46, 47, 110, 119, 121), 641, 642, 643, 725, 802
Erlanger, B. F., 413(59, 60, 61), 414
Erxleben, H., 98
v. Euler, H., 66
Evans, E. A., Jr., 919, 926, 927
Evans, H. M., 28, 73, 77, 80, 83, 594, 635 (21, 44), 641, 913, 987, 990(91, 92, 94), 991, 1000
Evans, M. G., 230, 512

Evans, R. S., 76
Evans, W. E., 131, 132(320)
Ewald, P. P., 351, 352
Ewart, R. H., 602, 606, 668(107)
Eyring, H., 290, 660, 812, 818, 860(22), 862(49), 865(22), 866(22), 868, 869 (22), 870, 872(49), 883(49), 885, 890, 891

F

Fabre, C., 107, 171, 910
Fahey, K. R., 692
Fåhraeus, R., 59, 568(15), 569
Falconer, J. S., 76
Fallon, L. D., 475
Fankuchen, I., 294(202a), 295, 296(202j), 297, 312, 313, 314, 318, 334, 356 (231), 574, 657, 725
Farah, A., 799, 805
Farber, E., 634(181), 645
Farley, D., 202, 211(74)
Farnsworth, J., 138, 166(352a), 334
Farr, A. L., 15, 16(64)
Farrant, J. L., 285
Fauré-Fremiet, E., 272
Fawaz, G., 805
Fearon, W. R., 96
Feeney, R. E., 797, 833, 834(120a), 915
Felix, K., 919
Fell, N., 1007
Feller, A. E., 85
Fellig, J., 33, 35(171)
Felton, L. D., 48, 72, 74
Fenichel, R. L., 500
Fennessey, J. F., 911, 912(64)
Feraud, K., 432
Ferguson, G. W., 104
Ferrel, R. E., 941, 942
Ferri, C., 276
Ferry, J. D., 76, 356, 608(13), 609, 638 (113, 115), 643, 686, 711, 712, 723
Ferry, R. M., 7, 37, 47, 78(222), 800
Fevold, H. L., 2, 3, 12(7), 36(7), 45, 67, 77(3), 79(205, 343), 85, 159, 512, 568, 594, 634(159), 645, 797, 798, 815, 834, 853
Fiala, S., 797
Fields, M., 131, 132(324)
Fieser, L. F., 730
Fiess, H. A., 793, 794(225), 797, 916

Filitti-Wurmser, S., 762
Findlay, D. M., 68
Finean, J. B., 787
Finholt, A. E., 104
Fink, K., 120
Fink, R. M., 120
Finkelstein, H., 60, 85
Finkelstein, P., 446, 447(142), 451, 452 (164), 453(164)
Finks, A. J., 82
Finogenov, P. A., 637(105), 643
Fischer, A. M., 78
Fischer, E., 117, 238
Fischer, E. H., 33, 35, 52(171), 73, 74, 78 (171)
Fischer, I., 942
Fischer, M. A., 902, 934, 967(45, 119), 968
Fisher, A. M., 74, 987
Fisher, J. D., 73, 1000
Fishman, J. B., 11, 57(49), 77(49), 636 (69, 70), 642, 664
Fishman, W. H., 77
Fitch, A., 990(96), 991
Fitzpatrick, T. B., 748
Fixl, J. O., 439, 445
Flavin, M., 138, 166(352a), 334
Fleisher, J. H., 945
Flexner, L. B., 124, 732
Florkin, M. J., 78
Flory, P. J., 356, 585
Flosdorf, E. W., 10, 11, 31
Fodor, P. J., 130
Förster, T., 713, 716
Folin, O., 15
Folkers, K., 144, 1000
Ford, O. E., 901
Ford, W. L., 566
Foreman, E. M., 125(263), 126
Foreman, F. W., 103
Forster, W., 84
Forsythe, R. H., 57, 521
Fort, M., 446
Fosdick, L. S., 144
Foster, G. L., 120, 183, 187, 190, 191(9), 488
Foster, J., 285
Foster, J. F., 57, 401, 452(15), 636(178, 180), 645, 683, 684, 685, 686, 848
Foster, J. H., 521
Fournet, G., 612, 618, 620(135), 621(135)

Fowler, R. H., 293
Fox, S. W., 146, 147(393), 895, 927(12)
Fraenkel-Conrat, H., 113, 130, 149, 154, 218, 483, 511, 746, 774(93), 797, 799, 802, 834, 836, 837(124), 896, 897, 899 (19), 900(19), 901, 902(19), 903, 907, 910(19), 911, 917, 919, 920, 921, 923, 924, 925, 926, 927, 931(19), 932, 933, 935, 936(19), 938, 939, 941, 942, 949, 950, 956, 957(73a), 963(118), 966 (42, 83), 971, 989, 990(83, 90, 94, 99, 100, 108), 991
Fraenkel-Conrat, H. L., 83, 84
Fraenkel-Conrat, J., 83, 149, 927, 941, 971, 990(100, 108), 991
Frampton, V. L., 637(109), 643
Francis, G. E., 895, 923(5), 939(7)
Franck, J., 452
Frank, F. C., 273
Frank, V. S., 172, 174
Frankel, M., 169, 174, 175
Frankel, S., 97
Franks, W. R., 928
Frampton, V. L., 66, 69(335), 75
Frantz, I. D., 131, 132(319)
Fraser, D., 11
Fraser, R. D. B., 278
Fredericq, E., 79, 170, 203, 231, 541, 634(9), 640, 686, 718, 744, 746, 786 (72), 787(72), 803, 804(72), 831, 842, 848, 881(156), 886(112, 166), 888, 923, 951, 964(92), 966(42)
Freedman, L. D., 124
French, D., 112, 474, 636(178), 645, 894, 931, 932, 934
Frenkel, S. Y., 609
Frensdorff, H. K., 411, 744, 823, 825 (71a), 829(71a), 830(71a), 857(71a), 862(71a), 877(71a), 887(71a), 889 (71a)
Freudenberg, K., 153
Frey, H. J., 559
Fried, M., 176, 178(505)
Frieden, E. H., 409, 474
Friedman, F. B., 546
Friend, J. A., 743, 824, 847(84a)
Fromageot, C., 105, 115, 125(199), 134, 136, 139, 140(360), 142, 147(131), 163, 164(441), 185, 197(26), 214, 432, 433(108), 899, 914, 978

Fruton, J. S., 81, 111, 130, 143, 145, 168, 172, 176, 177, 178, 238, 432, 996
Fürth, R., 711
Fugitt, C. H., 165, 492, 739, 740(46), 787(46)
Fuld, M., 73, 252
Fuller, A. T., 990 (97), 991
Fuoss, R. M., 709, 796

G

Gadd, J. O., Jr., 682, 683(236)
Gainsborough, H., 799
Gajdusek, D. C., 76
Gale, E. F., 96, 97, 105(53), 179, 182, 183(4, 5), 189
Galvin, J. A., 280, 296(202r), 297, 854
Gane, R., 753, 754
Gans, R., 672
Gard, S., 639(152), 644
Garden, G. A., Jr., 34, 56, 180
Gardiner, S., 32
Gardner, J. A., 799
Garen, A., 801, 806(293)
Garner, R. L., 10, 80, 81(41)
Garrault, H., 272
Garrod, M., 264
Gates, F. L., 452, 453(170)
Gaunt, W. E., 930
Gazzola, A. L., 134
Geddes, A. L., 21, 628, 737
Geiger, W., 110
Geiling, E. M. K., 974
Geissman, T. H., 230
Gelewitz, E. W., 788, 792(206)
Gell, P. G. H., 1006
Gellert, M., 718
Gellis, S. S., 34, 35(182), 70(182)
Gelotte, B., 79, 572
Gensler, R. L., 891
Gentile, P., 449
Gergely, J., 230
Germain, R. D., 84
German, B., 485, 486
Gerngross, O., 272, 275
Gerritsen, T., 72
Gersdorff, C. E. F., 82, 83
Gershbein, L. L., 82
Gersohn, H., 201
Geschwind, I. I., 125(263b), 126
Getman, F. H., 866

Gherardi, G., 818, 862(49), 872(49), 883 (49), 891(49)
Ghosh, J. C., 125
Gibbs, J. W., 5, 24
Gibbs, R. J., 815, 863, 872(27a, 216a), 873(216a), 874, 887
Gibson, D. M., 79
Gibson, S. T., 7, 30, 67(161)
Gies, W. J., 82
Giese, A. C., 447
Gigger, R. P., 99
Gilbert, G. A., 34, 770
Gilbert, J. B., 130
Gillespie, J. M., 12, 45(51), 53(51), 56 (51), 58(51), 62(51)
Gillis, J., 750, 766(117b)
Giroud, A., 269
Gisler, M., 104
Gitlin, D., 430, 634(174), 645, 718, 743, 801, 803, 1010
Gladner, J. A., 171, 784, 946
Glassman, H. N., 787, 791, 792(213)
Glasstone, S., 563, 580, 582, 864, 867 (219), 868(219)
Glendening, M. B., 897, 942(28), 990(99), 991
Glikena, M. V., 637(105), 643
Glassman, H. N., 84
Glenn, J. T., 84
Glomset, J., 119
Go, Y., 362
Goebel, W. F., 72, 990(76), 991, 995
Göksu, V., 826
Gofman, J. W., 61, 502, 724
Goiffon, R., 747
Goldbaum, L. R., 785
Goldberg, R. J., 606, 668, 743, 1010
Goldenberg, H., 451
Golder, R. H., 634(5), 635(5), 636(5), 639 (140), 640, 644, 659, 665(193)
Goldfarb, A. R., 857
Goldstein, A., 785, 791, 799(191), 804 (191), 805(191)
Goldstein, M., 427
Goldstein, R., 481
Goldwasser, E., 531, 745, 800(76), 801
Goldwater, W. H., 570
Goncalves, J. M., 521
Goodings, A. C., 568
Goodloe, M. B., 521
Goodman, D. S., 361, 794, 972

H

Haagen-Smit, A. J., 132(325), 133
Haarman, W., 915
Haas, A. R. C., 73
Haas, R., 450
Haas, W. J., 910, 911, 912(65), 913(65)
Hagdahl, L., 139, 141, 1000
Hagendorn, H. C., 45
Hagenguth, K., 736
Haggis, G. H., 709, 716
Haglund, H., 64, 544
Hahn, F., 746
Hahn, L., 63, 547
Hahn, M., 10
Hahn, W., 151, 156(406), 162(406), 164
Hakala, M., 177
Hakala, N. V., 511, 634(162), 635(35),
    641, 645
Halbert, S. P., 78
Haldane, J. S., 485, 743
Hale, W. S., 81
Halford, R. S., 427
Hall, C. E., 276, 277, 283, 285, 572, 573,
    574(9, 10, 11), 575, 576, 577
Halpern, P. E., 99, 102
Halwer, M., 17, 18(87), 22(87), 407, 608
    (6, 11), 609
Hamaguchi, K., 376
Hamer, D., 130, 202, 211(76, 77)
Hamer, W. J., 465
Hamilton, P., 114
Hamilton, P. B., 17, 113
Hamilton, W. F., 17
Hammarsten, E., 82, 796
Hammarsten, O., 76
Hammick, D. L., 792
Hamoir, G., 79, 84(569)
Hanby, W. E., 99, 134(80), 242, 255, 271,
    376(24, 40), 384, 385(321), 415(82),
    416, 423
Handler, P., 202, 211(76a)
Hanes, C. S., 180
Hanig, M., 166(456), 167, 1012]
Hanke, M. E., 77
Hankinson, C. L., 81
Hanning, K., 138
Hanson, E. M., 628, 630(152)
Hanson, H. T., 74, 81, 635(41), 641
Happey, F., 255, 263, 271, 376(40), 415
    (82), 423

Harding, V. J., 155
Hardt, C. R., 70, 828, 853(102)
Hardy, W. B., 32, 37, 40(194), 62, 479,
    495, 811
Harfenist, E. J., 13, 24(58), 69(58), 204,
    557, 571, 719, 842, 988
Harington, C. R., 100, 120, 121, 168, 897,
    914, 930(67), 931(67), 937, 939(67),
    978, 990(95), 991
Harker, D., 308, 391
Harned, H. S., 470, 472, 475
Harper, T. E. G., 207
Harrap, B. S., 743, 824, 847(84a)
Harrington, W. F., 660, 661, 662(198a)
Harris, D. L., 910
Harris, I. F., 37, 45(195)
Harris, J. I., 99, 956
Harris, L. J., 899
Harris, M., 282, 492, 548, 739, 740(46),
    787(46), 919
Harris, T. H., 81
Hart, E. B., 47
Harte, R. A., 79
Hartley, B. S., 994
Hartley, G. S., 633
Hartree, E. F., 68, 76, 84(488)
Haselbach, C. H., 73
Haskins, F. A., 68, 75(354), 143
Hasselbalch, K., 485
Hasson, M., 17, 22(84), 403, 404, 518,
    638(117), 643
Hasted, J. B., 709, 716
Hasting, S., 207
Hastings, A. B., 10, 47(35), 78(35), 95,
    730, 738
Hatschek, E., 694
Haugaard, G., 56, 112, 138, 167, 168
    (459), 544
Haugaard, M., 20, 36(108), 50(108), 73
    (108)
Haurowitz, F., 3, 30, 31(8), 33(8), 78
    (165), 134, 226, 288, 359, 559, 746,
    781, 799, 800, 802(89, 178), 808, 826,
    863, 864(216b), 919, 939, 1007
Hawn, C. V. Z., 285
Haynes, R., 78
Hays, E. E., 73, 1000
Healey, M., 84, 1004
Heathcote, J. G., 95, 106(27)
Hebb, M. H., 537, 539
Hedenius, A., 638(132), 644

Hegetschweiler, R., 395, 398

Heidelberger, M., 10, 28, 47(34), 72, 74, 78(34), 83, 84, 155, 504, 638(122), 643, 770, 841, 842(137), 843(137), 851, 859, 902, 935, 936, 940(47), 941, 960(123), 961(123), 964(47), 966 (123), 986, 990(78), 991, 1008

Heilbron, I., 111, 129(177), 173(177)

Heintz, E., 426

Hektoen, L., 49, 986

Hellerman, L., 124, 195, 832, 833(118), 834(118), 835, 897, 909, 992, 993

Hemingway, A., 131, 132(317)

Hempel, J., 477

Hems, B. A., 121

Hendee, E. D., 84

Henderson, L. J., 485, 587

Hendricks, S. B., 298

Hening, H. C., 415

Henly, A. A., 1000

Henze, M., 77

Hepp, O., 598

Heppel, W. A., 80

Herbert, D., 11, 13(47), 52(47), 69(47), 75, 78, 621, 1010

Herbst, R. M., 97, 180, 413

Heringa, G. C., 268, 269

Hermann, K., 275

Hermans, J. J., 606

Hermans, P. H., 399

Hernandez, A., 81

Herring, V., 61

Herriott, R. M., 6, 7(14), 15, 16, 23(14), 24(14), 25(14, 149), 27(14), 28(14), 30(14), 43(14), 51(14), 52(14), 57 (14), 68, 70(14), 72(14), 120, 169, 218, 815, 834, 837, 838(131), 875 (131), 882, 896, 897, 899(18), 900 (18), 903, 911, 919(18), 922, 924, 926, 928, 934, 937, 938, 942(18), 957(20, 129), 959(18, 20, 88, 129), 978, 988, 989, 990(86), 991, 1001, 1005

Hershey, A. D., 770

Herzog, R. O., 251, 267, 272, 647

Hess, E. L., 511, 512, 535, 537(169), 635 (30), 637(101), 641, 643

Hess, K., 272

Hess, W. C., 223, 834, 836(121)

Hettich, A., 352

Hewitt, J., 61

Hewitt, L. F., 50, 77(247), 409, 594(14), 595

Heyl, J. T., 30, 67(161)

Heymann, E., 848, 890(170)

Heymann, H., 730

Heyns, K., 101, 102, 118(106)

Heyroth, F. F., 464, 465(6)

Hier, S. W., 220

High, L. M., 914

Hill, R., 737, 743, 801(40)

Hill, T. L., 471

Hiller, A., 95, 96, 106, 118(36)

Hillmann, G., 103

Hilmoe, R. J., 80

Hink, J. H., Jr., 63

Hinshelwood, C. N., 372

Hipp, N. J., 205, 206(84), 293, 300(199), 410(52), 411, 511, 569, 655, 829, 873 (105), 878(105), 888(105)

Hirayama, K., 108

Hird, F. J., 180

Hirs, C. H. W., 24, 69(146), 143, 558, 998

Hirs, H. G., 77

Hirsch, J. S., 72

Hirschmann, D. J., 154, 218

Hirst, M. C., 260, 774

Hitchcock, D. I., 471, 734, 749, 964

Hoberman, H. D., 131, 132(305)

Hoch, H., 23, 517, 520, 529, 532, 536

Hoch-Ligeti, C., 520

Hocking, C. S., 684, 685

Hodgkin, D. C., 293, 294(202t), 297, 302, 314, 316, 317, 321, 362, 372(302)

Hoekstra, R. A., 799

Hoeprich, P. D., 84

Hofman, L., 411

Hofmann, A., 99

Hofmann, K., 175

Hofmeister, F., 238

Hofmeister, L., 49, 73(232)

Hofstee, B. J. H., 983

Hogden, C. G., 15, 778

Hogeboom, G. H., 12

Hogness, K. R., 517, 519

Hogness, T. R., 80

Holden, H. F., 737, 801(40), 879, 880 (230)

Holden, J. T., 99

Holiday, E. R., 18, 194, 430, 432, 433, 434, 436, 437(104, 116), 438, 520, 1003

J

Jaaback, G., 94
Jackson, S., 278
Jacob, J. J. C., 522
Jacobsen, C. F., 81, 154(417), 155, 156
(417), 290, 513, 514, 532, 541(182),
780, 798(175), 831, 886(111), 980,
1002
Jacoby, T. F., 850, 852(173)
Jacquot-Armond, Y., 762
Jaffe, W. G., 81
Jagannathan, V., 638(134), 644
Jaggi, M. P., 285
Jakus, M. A., 276, 277, 283, 572
James, A. T., 145
James, R. W., 249
James, W. A., 633
Jancke, W., 251, 267, 272
Jandorf, B. J., 945
Janeway, C. A., 30, 34, 35(182), 67(161),
70(182)
Jang, R., 910, 943, 945(56, 141), 962
(141), 993(119), 994
Jansen, E. F., 81, 818, 895, 897, 910, 943,
944, 945(56, 141), 946, 957(8), 962
(8, 26, 141), 993, 994
Jeannerat, J., 131
Jeffery, G. B., 681
Jenkins, L. T., 99
Jenness, R., 834, 862(125a), 878(125a)
Jennings, R. K., 531
Jenrette, W. V., 79, 746
Jensen, B. N., 45
Jensen, E. V., 811, 823, 827, 917
Jensen, H., 8, 47(22), 52(22), 919, 926,
927
Jette, E. R., 497
Jirgensons, B., 409, 411
Joel, N., 361
Joffe, E. W., 991
Johansen, G., 152, 826
Johns, C. O., 82, 83
Johns, R. G. S., 532
Johnson, A. H., 56
Johnson, F. H., 818, 862(49), 872(49),
883(49), 891(46, 47, 49)
Johnson, I., 616
Johnson, J. P., 594
Johnson, M. J., 81

Johnson, P., 501, 502, 531, 552, 609, 638
(166), 645, 663, 694, 722, 804
Johnson, P. H., 82
Johnson, T. B., 83
Johnston, J., 467
Johnston, J. P., 635(54), 636(54), 637
(54), 642, 660, 661
Johnston, R. B., 176, 178
Jollès, P., 134
Joly, M., 686, 848
Jones, A. V., 419, 421(69)
Jones, C. B., 822
Jones, C. O., 83, 100
Jones, D. B., 82, 83, 100, 159, 223
Jones, F., 34
Jones, F. T., 395
Jones, H. B., 132(327), 133
Jones, H. W., 175
Jones, M. E., 81
Jones, T. S. G., 97, 99, 143
Jope, E. M., 434, 436(116), 437(116)
Jope, H. M., 44, 49(204)
Jorpes, E., 82, 83
Joseph, N. R., 39, 734, 795, 844
Josephson, K., 66
Jukes, T. H., 474
Jullander, I., 600, 658
Jung, F., 84
Jutisz, M., 105, 115, 125(99), 136(131),
139, 140(360, 362), 142, 147(131),
158, 163, 164(441), 185, 197(26), 914

K

Kabat, E. A., 10, 15, 16, 18, 20(43), 22,
31(43), 84, 433, 517, 557, 637(102),
643, 684, 990(78), 991
Kaesberg, P., 318, 576, 618, 619, 620
(133), 621(66), 657(66)
Kahn, D. S., 628
Kahnt, F. W., 12, 45(51), 53(51), 56(51),
58(51), 62(51)
Kalauch, K., 480
Kalman, A., 903, 966(48)
Kalmanson, G., 74
Kalnitsky, G., 10
Kamin, H., 202, 211(76a)
Kaplan, E., 451
Kaplan, J., 432
Kaplan, N. O., 84, 179
Kar, B. C., 125

Knott, G., 352
Knox, R., 1006
Knox, W. E., 76
Kober, P. A., 30
Kocher, V., 130
Kocsis, J. J., 73, 1000
Kodama, S., 46, 76, 83
Koechlin, B. A., 83
Kögl, F., 98
Koehler, A., 454, 457, 459
Koelbl, W., 411
Koenig, V. L., 517, 519, 636(82, 83), 637 (82, 83, 103), 638(82, 83, 114), 642, 643, 659, 665, 684
Kohtes, L., 33, 35(171), 52(171), 78(171)
Kojiro, I., 636(172), 645
Kokes, E. L., 559, 798
Kolb, J. J., 122
Kolkmeyer, N. H., 242
Kolpak, H., 272
Kolthoff, I. M., 736
Konikova, A. S., 99
Korn, A. H., 559, 798, 929
Kossel, A., 800
Kotake, M., 102
Kraemer, E. O., 84, 635(34), 641, 653, 658, 668, 689, 819
Krarup, N. B., 45
Kratky, O., 263, 276, 439, 445, 612, 618
Kraut, H., 67
Krebs, E. G., 19, 52
Krebs, H. A., 182, 183(6), 189
Krebs, K. F., 426
Krejci, L. E., 84, 517, 531, 635(34), 641, 819
Kridl, A. G., 832, 975, 993(6)
Krigbaum, W. R., 585
Krishnamurti, K., 568(19), 569
Krishnan, P. S., 83
Krishnan, R., 406
Krishnaswamy, T. K., 83
Krogh, A., 485
Krom, C. J., 308
Kroner, T. D., 138, 544
Krop, S., 944
Krup, M., 82
Kubowitz, F., 52, 58(252), 75(252), 76, 77(520), 78
Kudar, H., 647
Kuhn, H., 679, 688, 694, 703
Kuhn, R., 80, 93, 103, 124, 824

Kuhn, W., 98, 152, 153, 688, 694, 703
Kunitz, M., 6, 7(14), 23(14), 24(14), 25 (14), 27(14), 28(14), 30(14), 43(14), 51(14), 52(14), 55, 57(14), 66, 67, 68, 70(14), 72(14), 76(248), 78(249), 81, 82, 84, 169, 218, 547, 594, 635(24), 637(94), 641, 643, 731, 795, 796(6), 802, 812, 815, 862, 869, 882, 922, 924 (88), 959(88), 974, 978, 983, 1001
Kunkel, H. G., 63, 544, 545
Kurtz, A. C., 117
Kylin, E., 736, 745(38), 804(38), 805(38)
Kylin, H., 80

L

Laaksonen, T., 177
Labhart, H., 500
Lackman, D. B., 811
Laidler, K. J., 863
Laki, E., 68, 77
Laki, K., 68, 76, 77, 608(8), 609, 638(116), 643
Lamanna, C. L., 84, 94, 568(18), 569, 638 (124, 126), 644
La Mer, V. K., 290, 616, 861, 866, 871
Lamm, O., 17, 18(85), 21(85), 22(85), 628, 629, 636(60), 637(60), 638(60), 642, 664
Lampl, H., 988
Landen, E. W., 447, 452(149), 453(149)
Landolt, H. R., 638(166), 645
Landsteiner, K., 28, 79, 495, 497, 781, 782, 783, 784(176), 802(176), 856, 859(199), 860, 947, 976, 986, 988, 994, 995, 1002, 1003
Lang, O., 83
Langmuir, I., 749, 984
Lansing, W. D., 653, 668, 689
Lanz, H., Jr., 17
La Rosa, W., 73
Lardy, H. A., 183
Larson, B. L., 834, 862(125a), 878(125a)
Larthe, N., 747
Laruonov, L. P., 456
Laskowski, M., 73, 75, 76, 81, 85, 635(28), 641, 684, 685, 1001, 1002(154c)
Lassettre, E. N., 261
Latimer, W. M., 261
Lauffer, M. A., 400, 401, 512, 537, 578, 639(12, 143, 151, 157), 640, 644, 653,

Lockwood, S. S., 34, 56(180)
Lockwood, W. W., 990(96), 991
Locquin, R., 93
Lodge, O., 495
Löfgren, N., 942
Loftfield, R. B., 131, 132(319)
Logan, M. A., 222
Lo Grippo, G. A., 85
Lomax, R., 272, 279, 280, 841, 842(138), 854(138)
Long, C. N. H., 73, 80, 635(23, 43), 641, 987, 1000
Long, E. R., 84
Longsworth, L. G., 17, 21, 22, 23(129), 404, 405, 479, 495, 496, 497, 498, 500, 501(96), 503, 504, 505, 506, 508, 509, 512(156), 513, 514, 515, 518, 520, 524, 525, 526, 527(160), 530, 531, 532, 536(145), 537(257), 541(182), 542(108), 628, 629, 630, 631, 636(65), 642, 663, 745, 780, 798(175), 800(75, 79), 851, 853(175), 952, 976
Lonsdale, K., 242
Lontie, R., 407, 590, 592(88), 606(88), 607(88), 608(2, 7), 609(88), 721, 743
Loo, Y. H., 118
Loofbourow, J. R., 910, 911, 912(65), 913 (65)
Loomis, E. C., 48, 68(231), 81(231)
Loos, W., 457, 459
Lorand, L., 171, 723
Loring, H. S., 85, 639(139), 644
Loshakoff, A., 154
Lotmar, R., 22, 407, 500
Lovelace, F. E., 81, 409, 415(33, 34)
Low, B. W., 300, 301, 302(210), 315, 316 (210), 317, 329, 330, 356(250), 357, 358, 378, 380, 381, 390, 395, 719, 721, 722
Lowry, O. H., 15, 16, 17
Lowther, A. G., 107, 128
Lowy, P. H., 132(325), 133
Luck, J. M., 35, 70(187, 188, 189), 202, 211(74), 530, 732, 738(12), 745, 746, 748, 774, 778, 780(160), 782, 785, 786(160), 788, 792(205), 805, 823, 828, 829
Ludes, H., 522
Ludewig, S., 732, 733, 772
Ludford, R. J., 460
Ludwig, W., 120, 937

Luebering, J., 80
Luetscher, J. A., Jr., 7, 9(19), 22, 37(19), 49(19), 56(19), 521, 536
Lugg, J. W. H., 82
Lum, F. G., 35, 70(187, 188), 748, 828
Lumry, R., 997
Lund, E., 477
Lundgren, H. P., 21, 59(115), 74, 175, 280, 281, 282, 289, 302, 530, 563, 628, 663, 744, 745, 787(83), 788, 826, 848, 859, 884, 914
Lutwak-Mann, C., 992
Lutz, J. G., 78
Lutz, O., 409
Lyman, C. M., 990(107), 991
Lynn, J., 517
Lyon, T. P., 61
Lyons, M. S., 630, 631
Lyons, W. R., 28, 80, 512, 594, 635(44), 641
Lyttleton, J. W., 66, 542

M

MacAllister, R. V., 997
MacArthur, I., 266, 384(77), 385(77)
McBain, J. W., 633
McCartney, J. R., 606
McClement, W. D., 85
McCullough, J. D., 361
McDermott, W., 805
MacDonald, E., 512
McDonald, H. J., 63, 544
McDonald, M. R., 52, 78(249), 81, 84, 637(94), 643
MacDonnell, L. R., 833, 834(120a), 915
McElroy, O. E., 84
McElroy, W. D., 884
MacEwan, D. M. C., 298
MacFadyen, D. A., 95, 96, 114, 116(196), 118(36)
McFarlane, A. S., 32, 314, 511, 639(141), 644
MacGillavry, C. H., 242
Macheboeuf, M. A., 78, 79(541a), 791, 792
MacInnes, D. A., 23, 463, 464, 465(6), 495, 496, 501(96), 503, 504(145), 524, 530, 531, 532, 536(145), 537(257), 564, 569, 636(62), 637(62), 642, 663, 745, 764, 800(75, 79), 952

Mercer, E. H., 264, 268(65), 285
Meyer, C. E., 108
Meyer, D., 105, 136(131), 147(131), 185, 197(26), 914
Meyer, F., 75, 77
Meyer, K., 637(89), 643
Meyer, K. H., 73, 74, 239, 251, 252, 265, 266, 362
Meyer, R. K., 990(93), 991
Meyerhof, O., 72
Michaelis, L., 74, 123, 124, 474, 495, 497, 748, 749, 762, 795, 917
Michaelis, R., 76
Micheel, F., 84
Michel, H. O., 944
Michel, K., 457, 459
Michel, M., 120
Michel, O., 121, 122(231a), 938
Michel, R., 83, 121, 122(231a), 213, 927, 936, 938, 979
Middlebrook, W. R., 723
Mie, G., 616
Miekeley, A., 103, 119(117)
Miller, G. L., 158, 576, 634(5, 7), 635(5), 636(5), 639(140, 177), 640, 644, 645, 659, 665(193), 837, 897, 900, 902(34), 926, 929, 930(30), 966(30), 967(30)
Miller, G. M., 811
Miller, H. K., 104
Miller, L., 15
Miller, S. G., 76
Miller, W. E., 450
Miller, W. W., 131, 132(319)
Milligan, W. O., 67
Mills, G. L., 107
Milnor, J. P., 793
Milstone, H., 70, 83
Mimms, V., 97
Mirick, G. S., 1006
Mirsky, A. E., 79, 195, 202, 211(75), 261, 289, 456, 743, 801, 812, 825, 831, 833, 835(17, 79), 836, 848(21),. 852, 869, 870, 879, 880(85), 882, 885, 982
Mirsky, I. A., 987
Misch, L., 265
Mitchell, H. K., 68, 75(354), 143
Mitchell, J. S., 447, 448
Mittelman, D., 12, 45(51), 53(51), 56(51), 58(51), 62(51)
Mittelmann, R., 117
Miwa, T., 102

Miyamoto, S., 796
Mizushima, S., 376
Mizutani, M., 474
Mohamed, M. S., 74, 76
Mohammad, A., 799, 917, 957(73a)
Molnar, D. M., 791
Moloney, P. J., 68
Molster, C. C., 153
Mommaerts, W. F. H. M., 48, 72, 79 (230), 638(130), 644, 665, 920, 956, 960, 961, 964, 990(109), 991
Monier, R., 128, 158
Monk, C. B., 795
Monobe, S., 97
Monod, J., 1006
Montgomery, H., 53, 77
Moody, L. S., 634(175), 645, 718, 803
Moore, B., 730
Moore, D. H., 62, 83, 496, 499, 500, 502, 517, 521, 531, 637(87), 638(129), 642, 644, 745, 800(77), 841, 842(137), 843 (137), 851(137), 935, 960(123), 961 (123), 966(123)
Moore, S., 24, 69(146), 106, 114, 115 (195), 126(268), 127, 128(268), 143, 144, 164, 183, 191(14, 15), 192, 193 (17a), 215(16), 216(15, 16), 217(16), 558, 568(12), 569, 570, 988
Moore, T. S., 260(51), 261
Moore, W. J., 164, 241, 261(19), 309, 362, 367(19), 368, 444, 449, 559, 664
Morawetz, H., 800
Morel, A., 122
Morgan, E. J., 992
Moring-Claesson, I., 141, 156(367), 167 (367)
Morris, C. J. O. R., 97, 100, 1000
Morris, M., 205, 216(82)
Morris, M. S., 628, 630
Morris, P., 1000
Morrison, D. B., 522
Morrison, K. C., 17, 22(84), 403, 404, 518, 519, 638(117), 643
Morrison, P. R., 76, 407, 590, 592(88), 606(88), 607(88), 608(7), 609(88), 721, 743
Morton, R. A., 194, 195(54), 436
Morton, R. K., 13, 36(54)
Moscowitz, M., 76
Moser, C. E., 566
Mosimann, W., 75, 80

Moss, A. R., 131, 132(304)
Mostafa, A., 116
Moubasher, R., 116
Mouette, M., 53
Moura-Goncalves, J., 84
Mourge, M., 832, 839
Mouton, R. F., 12, 45(51), 53(51), 56(51),
    58(51), 62(51)
Mowat, J. H., 134
Moyer, L. S., 496, 506, 508, 547, 851
Mudd, S., 31, 32(168), 49, 78(240), 359,
    781, 802(180), 990(75), 991, 1007
Müller, H., 990(105), 991
Müller, H. R., 178(514, 514a), 179
Mulford, D. J., 34, 53(181), 56(181), 58
    (181), 61(181), 816
Mulligan, W., 895, 939(7)
Munro, F. L., 512, 521
Munro, M. P., 512, 521
Muntz, J. A., 820
Murray, C. W., 79
Mutzenbecher, P., 937
Mycek, M. J., 178
Myrbäck, K., 10, 11(36), 20, 66, 976

N

Nachmansohn, D., 998
Nachod, V. R., 67
Nager, U., 97, 125(63)
Najjar, V. A., 6, 52(15), 71(15), 80(15)
Nanninga, L. B., 684, 692
Naora, H., 455
Needham, J., 686, 694, 986
Neefe, J. R., 34, 35(182), 70(182)
Negelein, E., 52, 75(253)
Neilands, J. B., 69, 558
Neimann, C., 206, 242
Nelson, J. M., 78, 84
Nesbitt, L. L., 82
Neuberger, A., 93, 94, 98, 99(17), 102, 108
    (7), 113, 117, 160, 161(7), 366, 409,
    433, 837, 857, 897, 899, 914(21), 924,
    965, 990(15), 991
Neufeld, E. F., 84
Neugebauer, T., 611
Neuhausen, B. S., 795
Neuman, R. E., 222, 979
Neurath, H., 17, 18(88), 21, 22(88), 23
    (118), 31, 70, 73, 81, 152, 168, 171,
    194, 203, 231, 254, 289, 303, 314, 358,

511, 522, 523, 530, 537, 561, 608(13),
    609, 625, 627, 628, 629, 634(9, 164),
    635(32, 33, 42), 636(76, 77), 639(144,
    147, 158), 640, 641, 642, 644, 645,
    718, 741, 744, 745, 746, 748, 777, 778,
    784, 786(72), 787(72), 788, 792(96a),
    803, 804, 808, 809(2), 812, 815(2),
    817, 822, 823, 824, 826, 829(80), 831
    (2), 832(2), 834(2), 840, 841(2, 66,
    68, 134), 842, 843, 844, 845, 852, 853,
    854, 855, 858, 860(73, 74), 862, 872,
    877(68), 881(156), 890, 891, 897, 909,
    920, 943, 946, 956, 960, 961, 962, 964,
    984, 990(109), 991, 997, 998, 1008
Newell, J. M., 9, 19(30), 37(30), 50(30),
    53(30), 56(30)
Newhouser, L. R., 30, 67(161)
Newman, E., 805
Newman, E. S., 37
Newman, M. S., 7
Nichol, J. C., 509, 512, 525, 533(241,
    243), 637(104), 643
Nichols, J. B., 21, 49, 59(117), 663
Nicholson, D. L., 420
Nicolet, B. H., 100, 118, 159, 188
Niederland, T. R., 18, 52(99), 75(99)
Nielsen, L. E., 63, 545
Niemann, C., 109, 131, 979, 997
Nier, A. O., 131, 132(317)
Nilsson, R., 10, 11(36)
Nitschmann, H., 531, 801, 802(288)
Nocito, V., 73, 77
Noelting, G., 73(418), 74
Noguchi, J., 175
Nolan, L. S., 47, 56, 82(225)
Nord, F., 816
Nord, F. F., 744, 791(68), 824, 863, 872
    (216a), 873(216a), 874(216a), 887,
    931, 966(109)
Norris, E. R., 987
North, A. C. T., 278
Northrup, J. H., 6, 7(14), 23(14), 24(14),
    25(14), 27(14), 28(14), 30(14), 43
    (14), 51(14), 52(14), 57(14), 66, 68,
    70(14), 72(14), 74, 75(270), 81, 169,
    218, 433, 547, 594, 632, 635(24, 49),
    637(91), 641, 643, 731, 795, 796(6),
    812, 815, 864, 882, 922, 924(20, 88),
    928, 957(20), 959(20, 88), 974, 978,
    983, 987(3), 1001, 1003

Norton, D. P., 945

Nuttall, G. H. F., 985

Nutting, G. C., 17, 18(87), 22(87), 280, 281, 407, 537, 608(6), 609, 854

Nutting, M. D. F., 895, 910, 943, 945(56, 141), 957(8), 962(8, 141), 993, 994

Nyman, M. A., 413

Nystrom, R. F., 104, 198

O

Oakley, H. B., 597

Obermayer, F., 988

O'Brien, J. L., 109

O'Brien, J. R. P., 44, 49(204)

O'Brien, M., 83

Ochoa, S., 75

O'Connell, R. A., 280, 530, 744, 745, 787 (83)

Ogston, A. G., 150, 194, 284, 436, 537, 594, 628(156), 629, 630(156), 631, 634(4), 635(50, 54, 55, 56), 636(54), 637(54, 93, 108), 639(138), 640, 641, 642, 643, 644, 660, 661, 665

Ohlmeyer, P., 72

Oinuma, S., 743

O'Konski, C. T., 400

Olcott, H. S., 80, 113, 799, 834, 836, 837 (124), 896, 897, 899(19), 900(19), 901, 902(19), 903, 907, 910(19), 919, 920(41), 924, 925, 926, 931(19), 932, 933, 935, 936(19), 941, 942, 971, 989

Olsen, N. S., 78, 131, 132(317)

Olson, J. A., 638(127), 644

O'Malley, E., 156

Oncley, J. L., 7, 8, 9(19), 19(30), 31(26), 32(26), 37(19, 30), 49(19), 50(30), 53(30), 56(19, 30), 61(26), 76, 78, 79 (26, 541), 81(541), 203, 285, 299, 312, 316, 328, 552, 554, 594(22, 23), 595, 634(174), 635(30), 636(78), 637(118), 638(118), 641, 642, 643, 645, 648, 655, 657, 658(12, 179), 667, 684, 689, 691, 692, 700, 701, 702, 703, 705, 706, 707, 708, 711, 712, 718, 721, 723, 724 (179, 317), 801, 817, 959

Onsager, L., 585, 630, 701

Oppenheimer, C., 66

Orahovats, P. D., 734

Ortiz, P. J., 113

Osborne, T. B., 9, 11(32), 12, 37, 40(32), 43(32), 45(195), 47(32), 56(32), 82, 83, 985

Osborne, W. A., 731

Oster, G., 285, 313, 314, 574(4), 575, 602, 608(9, 10), 609, 613, 616, 617(132), 621, 722, 792

Osteux, R., 128

Ostwald, R., 120, 131, 132(318)

Ostwald, W., 753

Othmer, D. F., 62

Ott, P., 52, 58(252), 75(252), 76, 78, 79

Ottesen, M., 8, 49(24), 143, 149, 170, 504, 636(58), 642, 951, 952, 953, 954

Otvos, J. W., 420

Oudin, J., 74

Overbeek, J. Th. G., 356

Overby, L. R., 129

Owen, B. B., 470, 471

Owen, R. D., 505

P

Pace, J., 453

Pacovska, E., 15, 794

Pacsu, E., 174

Page, I. H., 61

Page, L., 626

Paget, M., 743

Pakelen, T., 77

Paléus, S., 69, 558

Palitzsch, S., 477

Palmer, A. H., 48, 77(227), 154(418), 155, 482, 487, 490, 491, 506, 789, 791

Palmer, J. W., 637(89), 643

Palmer, K. J., 280, 296(202r), 297, 355, 854

Palmer, W. W., 83

Pankhurst, K. G. A., 743, 778(62), 787 (62)

Papkoff, H., 141

Pappenheimer, A. M., Jr., 71, 74, 637 (88), 642, 859, 901, 990(106), 991, 1003, 1004(162)

Pardee, A. B., 128, 142(273), 608(5), 609, 996

Parker, E. A., 276

Parrish, R. G., 48, 79(230), 638(130), 644, 665

Partington, J. R., 757

1042 AUTHOR INDEX

Partridge, S. M., 128, 129, 140, 156
(364a), 164, 183, 186(18), 225
Parventjev, I. A., 71, 1003
Passhina, T. S., 96
Passynskii, A. G., 634(160), 645, 799
Pasternak, R. A., 362
Patterson, A. L., 253, 307
Patterson, W. I., 97, 919
Patton, A. R., 125(263), 126
Paul, K.-G., 634(182), 645
Pauli, W., 63, 410, 411, 481, 495, 497
Pauling, L., 230, 241, 258, 261, 263, 274
(21), 278(45), 289, 334, 335(20), 359,
372, 374, 375, 378, 379, 380, 381, 382,
383, 386, 387, 388, 389, 390, 510, 512,
560, 735, 747, 762, 767, 769, 770, 781,
786, 789, 798, 800, 812, 831, 848(21),
849, 852, 854(25), 870, 885, 982, 995,
1007
Payne, R. W., 73, 1000
Peacock, A. C., 436, 838, 899
Pearson, H., 451
Pedersen, K. J., 795
Pedersen, K. O., 17, 21, 22(86, 114), 23
(114), 53, 59(114), 61(260), 76(260),
83, 242, 517, 563, 568(13, 16), 569,
634(14, 17, 171, 182), 635(17, 22, 47,
51), 636(61, 73, 79, 83, 171), 637(61,
83, 171), 638(47, 83, 122, 128), 640,
641, 642, 643, 645, 648, 650, 653,
655, 658(39), 659, 663, 664(39), 665,
667, 684, 718, 725(39), 804, 851, 852,
976, 1000, 1007
Pekarek, E., 990(96), 991
Pelser, H., 275
Pénasse, L., 105, 128, 136(131), 147(131),
185, 197(26), 914
Pennington, D., 74
Pennington, W. D., 919
Perkins, M. E., 78
Perlmann, G. E., 17, 22(83), 45, 49, 404,
405, 483, 504, 518, 519, 523, 564,
568(22), 569, 636(62), 637(62), 642,
746, 774(96), 853, 896, 952, 955
Perrin, F., 647, 670, 671, 702, 706, 713
Perrin, J., 671
Perrings, J. D., 519, 638(114), 643
Perry, S. V., 12, 13, 283, 993
Perutz, M. F., 204, 242, 292, 293, 295,
296(202k), 297, 302(198), 307, 309,
310, 312, 321(227), 322(227), 323,

324, 346(227), 347, 348, 349, 350,
351, 352, 353(192, 268), 354, 355,
357, 358, 359(227), 374, 375, 376,
377, 378, 384, 385, 386, 387, 389, 390,
395, 637(176), 645, 654, 655, 690,
691, 720
Pessotti, R. L., 945
Peterlin, A., 400, 401, 679, 681, 682, 688,
694
Petermann, M. L., 511, 635(35), 637(88),
641, 642, 1003, 1004(162)
Peters, E., 598
Peters, J. P., 17, 45(78)
Petersen, K. O., 150
Peterson, D. H., 97, 99(59)
Petre, A. W., 880
Pfankuch, E., 736
Pfeiffer, G., 117
Pfister, R. W., 178(514), 179
Phillips, D. M. P., 142, 150, 168(401),
169, 170, 177(460)
Phillips, H., 261, 264, 919
Phillips, R. A., 17
Philpot, J. St. L., 21, 122, 457, 497, 500,
628(156), 629, 630(156), 631(156),
635(45, 46), 641, 664, 934, 935, 946
(120)
Pickels, E. G., 59, 60(276), 61(276, 281),
639(137), 644, 656, 662, 663, 664
Pickett, M. J., 84
Picton, H., 495
Pierce, J. G., 145, 150(388), 158(388)
Piez, K. A., 144
Piguet, A., 73(418, 419), 74
Pihl, A., 76
Pilhorn, H. R., 730, 799(3)
Pillemer, L., 84
Pinching, G. D., 465
Pincus, S. N., 73
Pincusson, L., 453
Pinsent, J., 11, 13(47), 52(47), 69(47), 75
Pirie, N. W., 29, 85, 230, 313, 480, 574(8),
575, 880
Pitt-Rivers, R., 120, 121(224), 168, 937
Pivan, R. B., 731, 758, 774(5), 776(5)
Plane, R. A., 562
Plaskeyev, V., 634(160), 645
Plattner, P. A., 97, 125(63)
Plescia, O. J., 63, 532
Plimmer, R. H. A., 119
Polatnick, J., 413(59), 414

Volume I, Part A—Pages 1 to 548
Volume I, Part B—Pages 549 to 1015

1044 AUTHOR INDEX

Reindl, H., 919
Reinecke, L. M., 97, 99
Reiner, L., 521, 637(87), 642
Reiner, M., 500
Reinhart, R. W., 797
Reisman, J., 553
Reiss, W., 521, 976
Reith, W. S., 110
Reitstötter, J., 33
Reitz, H. C., 942
Reutner, F., 69
Rice, R. G., 35, 70(188), 748, 828
Rich, A., 420
Richards, F. M., 293, 300, 315, 357, 358, 561
Richards, M. M., 39
Richert, D. A., 78, 81(541)
Richter, M., 139
Richtmyer, N. K., 68, 78
Rideal, E. K., 437(123), 438, 446(123), 447, 448(150, 151), 449(123), 450 (123), 453(123), 531, 635(36), 641, 745, 770, 785
Riley, D. P., 292, 297, 311(190), 313, 318, 319, 321(190), 328(190), 386, 621, 722
Rimington, C., 77, 100, 256, 940
Ringel, S. J., 159, 979
Ringer, W. E., 795
Ris, H., 202, 211(75), 456
Riseman, J., 694
Rising, M. M., 794
Risley, E. A., 84
Ritland, H. N., 618, 619, 620
Rittenberg, D., 98, 131, 132(303, 305, 313), 1008
Ritthausen, H., 82, 83(667), 200, 210
Roaf, H. E., 730
Roberts, E., 97
Roberts, J. B., 517
Roberts, R., 437(123), 438, 446(123), 447 (123), 449(123), 450(123), 453(123)
Roberts, R. M., 167, 168(459), 813, 824 (26), 880(26), 1011
Roberts, S., 522
Robertson, J. M., 306
Robertson, T. B., 735, 737
Robinson, B. G., 709
Robinson, C., 282, 383, 414, 415
Robinson, D. S., 93
Robinson, E. S., 71

Robinson, G., 862
Robinson, H. W., 15, 778
Robinson, J. R., 687, 694
Robinson, K., 356
Robinson, M. E., 16, 17(76), 31(76), 403, 594(22), 595, 721
Robinson, R., 79
Robinson, R. A., 472, 798
Roche, A., 77, 594(26), 595
Roche, J., 50, 53, 74, 76, 77, 78, 79(241), 80, 83, 120, 121, 122(231a), 213, 594 (26), 595, 832, 839, 879, 927, 936, 938, 979
Rockland, L. B., 129, 154(282), 187, 189 (41a), 190, 979
Rodebush, W. H., 261, 426
Roess, L. C., 612
Roman, W., 410
Ronzoni, E., 19, 214, 218
Rose, W. C., 93
Rosebrough, N. J., 15, 16(64)
Rosenfeld, M., 60, 635(39), 641
Rosenheim, O., 101
Rosenthal, S. M., 732, 805(9)
Rosner, L., 195, 833
Ross, A. F., 85, 537, 897, 902, 928
Ross, E. C., 78
Ross, J. D., 664
Ross, W. F., 18, 80, 111, 432, 897, 902, 922, 923, 959, 964, 990(101), 991
Rossi, A., 50, 79(242)
Rotha, L. K., 82
Rothhaar, A., 481
Rothchild, S., 131, 132(324)
Rothen, A., 77, 82, 166(454), 167, 568, 634(11), 635(38, 40), 637(90, 92), 638(120), 640, 641, 643, 841, 855, 856, 859(199), 860, 984, 1011
Rothlin, E., 805
Roughton, F. J. W., 44, 554, 571(11), 720(11)
Rouiller, C. A., 974
Routh, J. I., 125(261), 126
Rovery, M., 107, 136, 157(154), 168(154), 170(154, 336), 171, 910, 992
Rowlands, I. W., 77
Roy, D. K., 73, 78(407)
Rozenfeld, E. L., 455, 456
Rozsa, G., 283, 572
Ruben, M. S., 1000

Rudall, K. M., 265, 266, 269, 270(92), 280(93), 281(93), 373, 989
Ruelius, H. W., 103
Rugo, H. J., 253, 555
Runnicles, D. F., 633
Ruska, H., 285, 313
Russell, J., 481
Russell, J. A., 11, 57(49), 77(49), 636(69), 642
Rusznyak, St., 736, 745(38), 804(38), 805 (38)
Rutenberg, A. M., 131, 132(315)
Rutherford, H. A., 919
Ryan, F. J., 570
Rydon, H. N., 99, 134(80)

S

Sachs, H., 413(59, 60), 414
Sadron, C., 685, 695
Saggers, L., 547
Sahyun, M., 78
Saidel, L. J., 556, 570
Saito, N., 694
Sakami, W., 118, 131, 132(320)
Sakan, T., 102
Salazar, W., 81, 82, 83(662)
Salomon, K., 80
Saltman, P., 74
Salton, M. R. J., 10, 12(40)
Saltzman, A., 805
Samsa, E. G., 686, 848
Samuel, L., 53
Sanger, F., 20, 107, 117(150), 125(259), 126, 128(150), 133, 136(329), 138 (329), 139(341), 140(329), 142(329, 341), 146(150, 341), 147(341), 149, 150(341), 151, 159, 162, 163(329), 165, 166, 170, 185, 196, 197, 204, 205, 217(25), 219, 225(99, 100), 231, 232, 240, 281(13), 331, 390, 554, 556, 571, 717, 720(11), 895, 917, 918, 927, 986, 987, 1015
Sanigar, E. B., 84, 517, 635(34), 641, 819
Sarkar, N. K., 77
Sarkar, N. M., 84
Saroff, H. A., 112, 736, 948, 949(146), 956 (146), 957(146), 958(146), 961(146), 966(146)
Sartori, L., 80
Sartori, M. F., 943
Saslow, G., 598

Saum, A. M., 639(158), 644, 844, 845, 891
Saunders, B. C., 107
Saunders, F., 82
Saunders, W. M., 23, 658
Sayers, G., 73, 635(23), 641, 987, 1000
Scallet, B. L., 56, 83(266b)
Scatchard, G., 7, 34, 35(182), 70(182), 285, 478, 480, 492, 494, 535, 554, 584, 586, 589, 590, 592, 593, 594(21, 23), 595, 597, 598, 599, 606, 636(78), 637(118), 638(118), 642, 643, 655, 657, 658(12, 179), 684, 691, 692, 721 (78), 724(179), 734, 735(25), 740, 741, 742, 744, 750, 765(118), 766, 774(25), 776(25), 777(25), 778(25), 780(25), 786(25), 789, 792(50), 796 (25)
Schaad, J. A., 276
Schachman, H. K., 636(72), 642, 652, 653, 656, 657, 659, 660, 661, 662 (198a), 726
Schack, J., 705, 711, 712
Schade, A. L., 83, 797
Schaefer, V. J., 984
Schaffer, N. K., 943, 969(141b)
Schales, O., 97
Schales, S. S., 97
Schantz, E. J., 94, 638(126), 644
Schauenstein, E., 439, 440(128), 442 (128), 443(128, 133), 445, 449(128)
Schayer, R. W., 131, 132(314)
Scheibling, G., 631
Scheinberg, H., 285, 401, 420, 680, 683, 685
Scheinberg, I. H., 494, 535, 655, 734, 735 (25), 774(25), 776(25), 777(25), 778 (25), 780(25), 786(25), 796(25)
Schellman, J., 411, 744, 823, 825(71a), 829(71a), 830(71a), 857(71a), 862 (71a), 877(71a), 887(71a), 889(71a)
Schenk, J. R., 131, 132(308)
Schepartz, B., 131, 132(322)
Scheraga, H. A., 400, 679, 682, 683, 684, 685, 686, 695, 891
Schiff, H., 473
Schiller, J., 927
Schlesinger, H. I., 104
Schmeiser, K., 117
Schmid, K., 12, 45(51), 50, 53(51), 56 (51), 58(51), 62(51), 77, 79(244), 196, 197(65), 215(65), 481

Speiser, R., 18, 22(89), 537, 608, 609
Sperry, W. M., 20
Spicer, S. S., 48, 79(229), 638(131), 644
Spiegel-Adolph, M., 446
Spiers, M., 340
Spies, J. R., 160, 546
Spiller, R. C., 293
Spinks, A., 806
Spitnik, P., 112, 175(186), 553, 750, 766 (117a)
Spooner, E. T. C., 85
Sprissler, G. P., 987
Squire, P. G., 23, 658
Stacey, M., 79
Stack-Dunne, M., 1001
Stadie, W. C., 78
Stahmann, M. A., 175, 176, 415, 950
Stair, R., 426
Stamm, A. J., 568(20), 569
Standfast, A. F. B., 76
Stanke, D., 439, 445
Stanley, W. M., 60, 61, 85, 285, 574(4, 5), 575, 639(142, 143, 151, 157), 644, 819, 842, 844(152), 897, 900, 902, 926 (38), 929, 930(30), 937, 966(30), 967 (30)
Stanly, P. G., 99
Staub, A., 74
Staub, H., 500
Staudinger, H., 275
Stauffer, J. F., 11, 33
Stauffer, R. E., 480, 481
Stearn, A. E., 290, 735, 812, 860, 865(22), 866(22, 207, 208), 868, 869(22, 207, 208), 870, 871, 885, 890
Steblay, R., 818, 862(49), 872(49), 883 (49), 891(49)
Stedman, E., 454
Stedman, E., 454
Steere, R. L., 574, 578, 725
Steiger, R. E., 161, 431
Stein, S. J., 407
Stein, W. H., 24, 69(146), 106, 114, 115 (195), 126(268), 127, 128(268), 139 (265c, 268), 143, 144, 164, 182, 183, 186, 191(14, 15), 192, 193(17a), 215 (16), 216(15, 16), 217(16), 558, 568 (12), 569, 570, 988
Steiner, R. F., 608(8), 609, 612, 613, 615, 616

Steinhardt, J., 165, 290, 291, 312, 488, 489, 492, 553, 567, 635(48), 641, 739, 740, 770(48), 785, 787(46), 792, 804, 812, 815, 821, 822(64), 823(64), 831, 838, 839, 842, 850, 851(113), 860(23), 861, 871, 872, 873, 875, 879(146)
Steinkopf, T., 736, 804(38)
Stelos, P., 816, 844(34)
Stenhagen, E., 531, 532(253), 745, 800 (74), 801(74)
Stephen, J. M. L., 64, 138, 150, 168(401), 169, 170, 177(460), 543
Stern, F., 108
Stern, J. R., 75
Stern, K. G., 80, 521, 522, 634(181), 636 (84), 642, 645, 742, 897, 903, 924 (33), 957(33), 990(98), 991, 1007
St. George, R. C. C., 800
Stetten, D., 131, 132(309)
Steudel, J., 124
Stevens, C. M., 99, 102, 108
Stevens, H., 546
Stevens, M. F., 117, 155
Steyne-Parvé, E. P., 72, 83
Stitt, F., 747
Stix, W., 107
Stock, A. H., 84, 635(34), 641
Stock, J. P. P., 457
Stocken, L. A., 916
Stockmayer, W. H., 356, 606
Stoddard, M. M., 409
Stöver, R., 285, 842, 854(148)
Stokes, A. R., 313
Stokes, J., 34, 35(182), 70(182)
Stokes, J. L., 189
Stokstad, E. L. R., 134
Stoll, A., 99
Stone, D., 145
Stone, F. M., 18, 433
Storm van Leeuwen, W., 804
Stosick, A. J., 361
Stott, E., 260, 264
Stotz, E., 76
Straessle, R., 721, 834, 939, 956(131), 957 (131), 960(131), 961(131)
Straub, F. B., 13, 68, 72(56a), 75(346), 283
Strauss, E., 410
Strecker, H. J., 75
Street, A., 239, 254, 255, 323(9)
Stricks, W., 736

Strisower, B., 61

Strong, L. E., 34, 35, 53(181), 56(181), 58(181), 61(181), 62, 70(182), 79, 83, 684, 816

Stroud, H. H., 106

Stuart, H. A., 400, 401, 679, 681, 682

Stumpf, P. K., 10, 73, 76, 80

Sturtevant, J. M., 176

SubbaRow, Y., 134

Sugita, T., 376

Sullivan, M. K., 223

Sullivan, M. X., 125, 834, 836(121)

Summerson, W. H., 748, 943, 945, 969 (141b)

Sumner, J. B., 2, 9(4), 11, 20, 33, 47, 49 (224), 57(172, 224), 66, 69(335), 72, 75(172, 268, 269), 75, 77, 80, 82, 84 (268), 636(57), 637(57, 107, 109), 638(121), 642, 643, 974, 976, 984

Surgenor, D. M., 4, 12, 45(51), 53(12, 51), 56(12, 51), 58(12, 51), 62(12, 51), 79, 83, 481

Suter, M., 104

Sutermeister, E., 3, 30(5), 46(5), 75(5)

Sutherland, E. W., 19, 78

Sutherland, G. B. B. M., 175, 240, 271, 417, 419, 421, 422

Suzutani, T., 736

Svedberg, T., 21, 22(114), 23(114), 49, 59(114, 275), 73, 242, 497, 517, 563, 568(15, 19, 20), 569, 634(1, 3, 15, 18), 635(37, 46, 47), 636(59, 61, 74), 637 (15, 61), 638(3, 18, 46, 47, 132, 133, 135), 640, 641, 642, 644, 648, 650, 653, 658(39), 663, 664(39), 667, 684, 725(39), 802

Svensson, H., 21, 22(121), 33, 62(121, 176), 63(176), 64(176), 65, 66, 137, 138, 496, 497, 499, 500, 514, 517, 518, 525, 529, 533(240), 542, 543, 545, 546(290), 631, 664, 796

Swain, T., 128

Swallow, A. S., 34

Swart, E. A., 97

Sweeny, L., 517

Swenson, T. L., 81

Swingle, S. M., 499, 996

Swoboda, T. J., 770

Swyngedauw, J., 137

Sykes, G., 76

Synge, R. L. M., 89, 95, 96, 99(38), 101, 102, 120, 125(265), 126, 137, 138, 141, 142, 143, 145, 150, 151, 163, 164 (378), 183, 192, 541, 1014

Szent-Györgyi, A., 13, 48(57), 79, 230, 268, 283, 572, 724, 806, 844

T

Takahashi, W. N., 574(2), 575

Tallan, H. H., 69, 81, 558, 988

Tanford, C., 436, 481, 482, 489, 490, 494, 567, 736, 789, 790, 964, 965(159)

Tang, Y-C., 296(202i), 297

Tani, H., 175

Tapley, D. F., 823, 827, 917

Tarpey, W., 121

Tarver, H., 131, 132(316, 326), 133

Taube, H., 562

Taubes, H., 81, 177

Taurog, A., 121

Taylor, A. C., 471

Taylor, A. R., 60, 74, 85, 537, 539, 639 (146, 147, 148, 153, 154), 644, 656

Taylor, B., 810

Taylor, D. B., 28, 76

Taylor, E. W., 459

Taylor, G. L., 73, 594(15), 595

Taylor, H. L., 34, 53(181), 56(181), 58 (181), 61(181), 79, 816

Taylor, H. S., 378

Taylor, J. F., 7, 10, 17, 18, 19, 22(82), 34 (21, 103), 35(96, 103), 43(16), 47(35), 52(96), 53(96), 60(21), 70(103), 71, 73(96), 78(35), 80, 522, 568, 636(86), 637(95), 642, 643, 659, 665

Taylor, T. W., 122

Teeters, W. O., 116

Tehen, P. K., 139

Tekman, S., 863, 864(216b)

Temple, R. B., 242, 376(24), 419, 427

Tennent, H. G., 634(162), 645

Tenow, M., 79

Teorell, T., 72, 531, 532(253), 745, 770, 800, 801(74)

Teresi, J. D., 774, 780(160), 785(160), 786(160), 788

Tereyama, H., 801

Terlouw, A. L., 454

Tesar, C., 131, 132(313)

Thalhimer, W., 31, 32(168), 49, 78(240)

Thaureaux, J., 142
Theis, E. R., 850, 852(173)
Theorell, H., 7, 50(18), 56(18), 62, 63, 75,
  76(302), 79(243), 80, 487, 495, 511,
  543, 634(13, 16), 640, 641, 743
Thiel, A., 787
Thoai, Ng.-V., 74, 80
Thomann, H., 104
Thomas, J. V., 630, 631
Thompson, A. R., 107
Thompson, E. O. P., 147, 162, 219, 225
  (100), 240, 390, 556, 717, 1015
Thompson, H. W., 420
Thompson, J. O., 602, 668(107)
Thompson, R., 637(89), 643
Thompson, R. E., 881
Thompson, R. H. S., 916
Thompson, R. R., 74, 81
Thudichum, J. L. W., 101
Tichadou, M. B., 979
Tietze, F., 17, 18(88), 22(88), 608(12),
  609, 634(164), 635(32, 33), 641, 645,
  718, 804, 962
Tillett, W. S., 10, 81(41)
Timasheff, S. N., 744, 791(68), 824, 931,
  966(109)
Timmis, G. M., 99
Tint, H., 521, 976
Tiselius, A., 21, 22, 23, 59, 62(120), 65,
  66, 68, 125(265), 126, 138, 139, 140,
  141(365), 150, 167(399), 191, 495,
  496, 497, 501(105), 502, 504(105),
  505, 514, 517, 525(101), 537(152),
  542, 544, 545, 546, 547, 629, 634(17),
  635(17), 637(88, 111), 638(111), 641,
  642, 643, 745, 1000
Todd, W., 78, 84
Toennies, G., 118, 122, 125(262), 126, 409
Tolbert, B. M., 131, 132(323)
Tompsett, R., 805
Tong, W., 121
Tooper, E. B., 144
Topol, L., 796
Torigoe, M., 990(102), 992
Toropoff, T., 480
Touster, O., 96
Townsend, F., 260
Tracy, A. H., 897, 902, 928, 959
Traube, J., 565
Trautman, R., 502
Travia, L., 50, 79(242)

Treffers, H. P., 500, 941
Treiber, E., 439, 443(133)
Treloar, L. R. G., 703
Tristram, G. R., 78, 82(533), 183, 186,
  188, 192, 198(38), 201, 204, 211(71),
  213(38), 215(38), 216(38), 217(38),
  218(38), 219(38), 220(38), 221(38),
  223(38), 227(38), 228, 231, 238, 252,
  568, 895, 979
Triwush, H., 825, 829(87), 847(87)
Trogus, C., 272
Trotter, I. F., 295, 384, 385(321)
Trueblood, K. N., 355, 361, 366(286)
Trurnit, H. J., 1012
Tsao, T.-C., 284, 692, 720
Tsou, C. L., 1001
Tsuboi, M., 376
Tsuchihashi, M., 71
Tudor, S. G., 128
Tullis, J. L., 723
Tumerman, L., 112
Tunca, M., 826
Tune, S., 800
Tupikova, N. A., 785, 802(189)
Tupper, R., 895, 923(5)
Tuppy, H., 138, 139(341), 142(341), 146
  (341), 149, 150(341), 159, 166, 170,
  219, 225(99), 240, 281(13), 390, 556,
  717, 1015
Turba, F., 63, 139, 544
Turl, L. H., 568
Turner, R. A., 144
Tutin, F., 108
Tveffers, H. P., 1008
Tweedy, W. R., 990(102, 103), 991
Tyslowitz, R., 1000

U

Udenfriend, S., 97, 109, 128, 144(168),
  146, 151(167, 387), 183, 191, 196,
  201, 204(65a), 940
Uhing, E. H., 106
Umbreit, W. W., 11, 33, 105
Underhill, S. W. F., 990(97), 991
Underkofler, L. A., 73, 78(407)
Urban, F., 446
Urbin, M. C., 63, 544
Uroma, E., 12, 45(51), 53(51), 56(51), 58
  (51), 62(51)

Urquhart, J. M., 371, 778, 779, 780, 781, 782(169, 177), 786(165), 787(167, 171), 788, 789, 792(206), 916, 965, 971

Utter, M. F., 10

V

Valko, E., 410, 753, 762, 770
Vandenbelt, J. M., 48, 68(231), 81(231)
van der Scheer, J., 522, 783, 853, 976, 995
Van Dyke, H. B., 77, 635(38, 40), 637(90), 641, 643, 785, 802(189)
van Heyningen, W. E., 84
Van Ormondt, J., 283
Van Slyke, D. D., 17, 45(78), 47, 95, 96, 106, 114, 118(36), 154, 474, 510
van Tamelen, E. E., 96
van Veen, A. G., 97
van Veersen, G. J., 98
van Vunakis, H., 722
Van Wazer, J. R., 796
Van Winkle, Q., 22
van Zyl, G., 96
Vassel, B., 82
Vaughan, J. R., 173
Vaughan, P., 363
Veis, A., 796
Velick, S. F., 19, 34(103), 35(103), 70 (103), 109, 144(168), 146, 196, 201, 204(65a), 206(103a), 207, 214, 218 (95, 98a), 508, 513, 786, 787, 806 (193), 940, 976
Velluz, L., 981, 1008(34)
Verwey, E. J. W., 356
Vicens-Rois, C., 990(103), 991
Vickerstaff, T., 770
Vickery, H. B., 47, 56, 82(225), 83, 89, 158, 200, 210, 232, 237, 570, 979
Vieil, H., 50, 79(241)
Vila, M., 77
Vilbrandt, C. F., 634(162), 645
Villee, C., 143, 953, 954
Virtanen, A. I., 177
Vittu, C., 743
Vles, F., 426, 454
Voet, A., 547
Volcani, B. E., 175
Volkin, E., 73, 530, 745, 787(88a), 823, 840(68), 841(68), 844(68), 877(68)
von Arnim, K., 115

von Bonsdorf, B., 77
Von Buzagh, A., 357
von Deseö, D., 18, 56(90)
von Magnus, P., 639(152), 644
von Muralt, A. L., 678, 686, 762, 825
von Mutzenbecher, L., 120

W

Waelsch, H., 104, 180
Wagley, P. F., 911, 913
Wagman, J., 819
Wagner, R. H., 597
Wainfan, E., 180
Wainright, S. D., 1006
Waitkoff, H. K., 220
Wakeman, A. J., 83
Walaszek, L. J., 73, 1000
Walden, M. K., 74
Waldron, N. M., 110
Waldschmidt-Leitz, E., 139, 155, 169
Wales, M., 602, 654, 668
Waley, S. G., 147
Walker, E., 836
Walker, F. M., 731, 758, 774(5), 776(5), 777, 779, 825, 829(87), 847(87)
Walker, H., Jr., 22
Walker, H. A., 785, 802(189)
Walker, P. B. M., 456
Wall, F. T., 770, 796
Waller, C. W., 134
Walti, A., 81
Walz, D. E., 131, 132(324)
Wanatabe, I., 636(172), 645
Wang, S. C., 131, 132(321)
Wang, Y. L., 35, 78
Warburg, O., 18, 30, 33, 46(95, 174), 52 (101, 160, 174), 58(95, 101, 174), 73 (160), 75(174), 76(101), 495
Ward, W. H., 21, 59(115), 67, 79(343), 302, 512, 563, 594, 628, 634(159), 645, 663, 797, 798, 815, 914
Warmbrand, H., 805
Warner, R. C., 46, 75(219), 158, 296 (202n), 297, 300, 318, 357, 504, 531 (146), 797, 798, 802(263)
Warren, W. J., 276
Waser, P., 104
Washburn, E. W., 502
Wassen, A. M., 75
Wasserman, P., 987

Winzler, R. J., 15, 79, 794
Wirth, L., 159
Wirtz, K., 440
Witkop, B., 99, 102(77)
Wittler, R., 84
Wodstrup, I., 45
Woiwood, A. J., 116, 117(203), 155(203)
Wolff, H., 108
Wollenberger, A., 149, 170(397b), 953
Wolter, H., 499
Wood, T. R., 80, 990(101), 991
Woodruff, L. M., 7, 30, 67(161)
Woods, H. J., 239, 254, 256, 257, 261, 264, 265, 323(10)
Woodward, J., 306
Woodward, R. B., 175, 553
Wooley, D. W., 221
Work, E., 97, 99, 106
Work, T. S., 981
Wormall, A., 806, 895, 918, 923(5), 926, 930, 939(7), 942
Wretlind, K. A. J., 130
Wright, B. A., 277
Wright, G. C., 818, 891(47)
Wright, G. G., 823, 859, 862(70), 884
Wright, L. D., 739
Wright, R. D., 81
Wrinch, D. M., 242, 267, 328
Wu, H., 15, 72, 74, 287, 312, 596, 812, 817, 841, 842
Wulff, H., 52, 75(253)
Wurmser, R., 762
Wycherley, V., 795
Wyckoff, R. W. G., 60, 85(283, 285), 266, 276, 277, 283, 313, 316, 454, 522, 572, 574(1, 6, 7), 725, 853, 1008
Wyman, J., Jr., 483, 484, 485, 486, 552, 554, 648, 666, 667, 674, 675, 690,

692, 699, 701, 707, 709, 711, 712, 743, 769, 800

Y

Yakel, H. L., Jr., 362, 390(299)
Yanafsky, C., 84
Yang, E. F., 312, 596, 841
Yang, P. S., 794
Young, F. G., 1001
Young, G. T., 172, 188
Young, J. L., 664
Young, R. W., 174
Yphantis, D. A., 60, 665
Yuill, M. E., 914, 930(67), 931(67), 939(67), 978

Z

Zahn, H., 255, 263, 274, 376
Zaiser, E. M., 291, 488, 489, 567, 739, 792, 831, 838, 839, 850, 851(113)
Zeile, K., 69
Zeisset, W., 93
Zerfas, L. G., 75
Zernike, F., 457, 459
Zervas, L., 103, 108, 109, 147(119)
Ziff, M., 531, 638(129), 644, 745, 800(77)
Zimm, B. H., 400, 585, 608(9), 609, 613, 614
Zinoffsky, O., 569
Zinsser, H. H., 797
Zittle, C. A., 990(88), 991
Zosa, M., 594(21), 595
Zürcher, H., 531, 801, 802(288)
Zuidema, G. D., 96
Zumstein, F., 93
Zussman, J., 361, 363, 366(285)
Zwanzig, R. W., 559

Subject Index

A

1054

Adenosine triphosphate, 940
  effect on actomyosin, 686
  role in peptide synthesis, 179
Adrenocorticotropic hormone, 73, 999, 1000
  amino acid composition, 213
  biological activity, of digestion products, 1000, 1004
    essential groups for, 990
  distribution of groups in, 203, 224
  molecular weight, 213, 635, 1000
  physical constants, 635
  possible species variations in active principle, 987
Adrenocorticotropin, see under Adrenocorticotropic hormone
Adsorbents, for proteins, 66–68
African porcupine quill tip,
  structure, α-helix as model for, 385
Agmatins,
  enzymatic formation, 105
Alanine,
  detection, 115
  determination, 114
  distribution in proteins, 211, 212, 213, 214, 215, 216, 217, 218, 219, 220, 221, 222, 223, 224, 225, 228, 910
  heat of ionization, 472
  molecular structure, 237, 360, 363, 364, 365, 369
  molecular weight, 91
  pK' values, 112, 472
  physical properties, 91
  polycondensation, 174
  resolution of DL-, 130
  separation of methionine and, 543
  in tobacco mosaic virus, 980
D-Alanine,
  molecular structure, 360, 361
  occurrence, 99
L-Alanine,
  butyl ester, reduction, 104
  preparation, 130, 131
α-Alanine,
  apparent molal heat capacity, 566
    molal volume, 566
  βielectric properties, 701
  pK' values, 469
  relaxation time, 701
d-Alanine,
  apparent molal heat capacity, 566

  molal volume, 566
  detection, 115
  occurrence, 97
  pK' values, 469
Alanine-d,
  preparation, 132
Alanine-1-C^{14},
  preparation, 132
Alanylalanine,
  formation in ovalbumin-plakalbumin conversion, 953, 954
  pK' values, 470
  from pyruvylalanine, 180
Alanylglycine,
  hydrolysis, 176
  pK' values, 112, 470
D-Alanylglycine,
  molecular structure, 362
Alanylglycylvalylaspartic acid,
  formation in ovalbumin-plakalbumin conversion, 953, 954
Alanylglycylvalylaspartylalanylalanine,
  effect of B. subtilis enzyme on, 954
  formation in ovalbumin-plakalbumin conversion, 953, 954
Alanyl peptides,
  preparation, 173
Alanylserine,
  separation, 143
Albumin,
  egg, see under Egg albumin, Egg white, Ovalbumin
  milk, 73
  plasma, 73, 516
    carbohydrate content, 19–20
    horse, homogeneity, 50
      isolation, 50
    human, isolation, 51
    isolation, 9, 50, 51, 57
    purification, 57
      of stabilized, 70
    stabilization, 35
    sulfate, 45
      effect of temperature on solubility, 43
  serum, 721–722
    amino acid composition, 215
      species variations in, 205
    binding of fluorescent dyes by, 716
    biological activity, essential groups for, 990

N-terminal, determination, 196–198

coupling to proteins, 950

crystal structure of molecule, 236–238, 240, 360–372

dielectric constants, 698

measurement, 711

diffusion constants, determination, 631, 633

dipolar ionic structure, 237, 699

dipole moments, 703

effect of ultraviolet irradiation on, 819

electrochemical properties, 461ff.

equilibria between, and peptides, 474

heavy metal salts, crystal structure, 361

hydroxy, determination, 188–189

infrared absorption, 420

ionization of, 462–476

acid dissociation constants, 463–464, 465

definition of pH, 464

effect of charged groups on, 475–476

entropy of, 472

equilibrium between dipolar ions and uncharged molecules, 466–467

formulation of, 463–467

heat of, 472–473, 483

isoelectric point, 471–472

natural, molecular structure, 237

optical rotation, 409

pK' values, 467–470, 472

thermodynamic, 470–471

photochemical reactions, 445, 453

Raman spectra, 420

reaction with formaldehyde, 932

separation, chromatographic, 192–193, 544

into groups, 546

by ionophoresis, 543

titration curves, effect of formaldehyde on, 473–474

of organic solvents on, 474–475

ultraviolet absorption spectra, 431

α-Amino acids, see also under Amino acids,

N-acetyl derivatives, 108

N-acyl, 108

anhydrides of, 109

racemization, 108

N-alkylation, 106

aromatic, iodination, 120

N-arylation, 106

aryl sulfonates of, 106

N-arylsulfonyl derivatives, 109

carboalkyloxy derivatives, 109

anhydrides of, 110

carboarylalkyloxy derivatives, 109

N-carboxy, 110

chemical properties, 1021–1025

chemical synthesis, 129

chemistry of, 88–132

commonly occurring, 90

radicals of, 92, 93

condensation with diazo compounds, 122

with keto acids, 180

cyclization, 109, 110, 111, 112, 113, 116, 119, 148, 174

deamination, 154

decarboxylation, 105

degradation, 158

detection, 115

determination, 109, 114, 117, 126, 144

in protein hydrolyzates, 157

diazotization, 122

diketopiperazines from, 116

N-dithiocarboxy derivatives, 110, 111

enzymatic resolution of racemic, 129

esters, preparation, 103

reduction, 104

flavianates, 106

N-formyl derivatives, 108

guanidylation, 111

hydroxy, acylation, 118

degradation during hydrolysis, 159

determination by oxidation, 118

etherification, 120

identification, 125

oxidation, 118

phosphoric acid esters, 119

reduction, 118

identification, 125

isolation of L-, from protein hydrolyzates, 237

isotopic, synthesis, 131

malonylation, 111

natural, 88

configuration, 90

occasional, 95

optical rotation, 409

partition chromatography of, 126

N-phosphorylation, 111

α-Amino acids (*continued*)
  picrates of, 106
  picrolonates, 100
  "pipsyl derivatives" of, 109, 128, 144
  racemization, 160
  reaction with aldehydes, 112
    with isatin, 115
    with isocyanates, 110
    with isothiocyanates, 110
    with metallic salts, 117
    with metals, 116, 155
    with ninhydrin, 114, 155
    with nitrosyl halides, 113
    with nitrous acid, 113
  reduction, 104
  resolution, 129
  salts of, 106
  structure of L-, 237, 238
  synthesis of, 129
    of isotopic, 131
D-Amino acids,
  in proteins, 98, 99
Aminoacetic acid, see under Glycine
Aminobenzoate,
  interaction with serum albumin, 782
α-(*N-p*-Aminobenzoyl) aminophenyl-
    acetic acid,
  antigens from, effect of optical isomer-
    ism on formation of antibodies to,
    783
α-Amino-n-butyric acid,
  heat of ionization, 473
  occurrence, 97
  pK' values, 469
    thermodynamic, 472
γ-Aminobutyric acid,
  enzymatic formation, 105
  occurrence, 97
ε-Aminocaproic acid,
  dielectric properties, 701
  relaxation time, 701
ε-Amino-n-caproic acid,
  pK' values, 469
α-Amino-β,β-dimethyl-γ-hydroxybutyric
    acid,
  occurrence, 97
α-Aminoglutaric acid, see under Glu-
    tamic acid
α-Amino-δ-guanidino-n-valeric acid,
  see under Arginine

α-Amino-γ-guanidinoxy-n-butyric acid,
  see under Canavanine
α-Amino-β-hydroxybutyric acid, see
  under Threonine
α-Amino-β-(*p*-hydroxyphenyl)propionic
  acid, see under Tyrosine
α-Amino-β-hydroxypropionic acid, see
  under Serine
α-Amino-5-imidazolepropionic acid, see
  under Histidine
α-Amino-3-indolepropionic acid, see
  under Tryptophan
α-Aminoisobutyric acid,
  heat of ionization, 472
  thermodynamic pK' values, 472
α-Aminoisocaproic acid, see under Leucine
α-Aminoisovaleric acid, see under Valine
α-Amino-γ-methylthiol-n-butyric acid, see
  under Methionine
α-Amino-β-methyl-n-valeric acid, see
  under Isoleucine
α-Amino-β-phenylpropionic acid, see
  under Phenylalanine
α-Aminopropionic acid, see under Alanine
Aminosuccinic acid, see under Aspartic
  acid
α-Amino-β-thiolpropionic acid, see under
  Cysteine
α-Amino-n-valeric acid, see under Norvaline
Ammonium sulfate,
  salting-out of proteins with, 42, 43, 49–
    56
Amylase,
  adsorbents for, 68
  pancreatic,
    biologic activity, essential groups for,
      990
    reaction with nitrous acid, 946
α-Amylase, 73
β-Amylase, 73
  barley,
    biological activity, essential groups
      for, 990
  sweet potato,
    molecular weight, 637
    physical constants, 637
    reaction with DFP, 946
Anaphylaxis reaction,
  specificity, protein structure and, 985

Anemia, sickle-cell,
effect on electrophoretic mobility of
human carbonylhemoglobin, 510
Antibiotics,
peptide structure of, 99
preservation of protein preparations
with, 34
Antibodies, 74
activity, essential groups for, 990
anticarbohydrate, 1007
to azoproteins, 948
combining centers in, 1014
destruction by freezing, 31
digestion products, immunological behavior, 1003–1004
films of, biological activity, 856
formation of, 1006, 1007–1008
following protein injection, 20
γ-globulin and, 1007
horse antiprotein, 1007
interaction of azo-coupled antigens
with, 736
isolation, 72
mode of action, 975
molecular weight, 976
protein nature, 974, 976
to proteins substituted with organic
compounds, 995, 996
specificity, 1008
amino acid composition and, 978, 981
studies on, 994–995
Antibody,
of horse pneumococcal antisera,
reversible denaturation, 984
to ovalbumin, 1004
γ-globulin nature, 1004
immunological behavior of digestion
products, 1004
Antibody-antigen reaction,
lattice theory, 1004
mechanism, 1010–1012, 1014
protein structure and, 359
Antibody globulin, horse,
molecular dimensions, 684
molecular weight, 684
Antibody, rabbit serum (anti-p-azo-
phenylarsonic)
molecular weight, derived from light
scattering, 608
Antigen-antibody precipitates, 729
analysis, 430

Antigen-antibody reaction, 746, 770,
1010, 1014
determination of protein homogeneity
by, 71
electrophoretic survey of, 532
in protein films, 860
role of "configurational complementariness" in, 781, 802, 948
of molecular size in, 784
of spatial configuration in, 783
selectivity of, 781, 782
study of, use of azoproteins in, 948
of labeled mustard gas sulfone
in, 923
use in purification of proteins, 71–72
Antigens,
activity,
effect of coupling with organic compounds on, 994
essential groups for, 990
antibody-combining centers in, 995–
996, 1014
artificially conjugated, 947–948
serological specificity, 948, 994–996,
1002, 1006
azo-coupled, interaction with antibodies, 736
denaturation, effect on immunological
properties, 859
films of, biological activity, 856, 984
hydrolysis products, biological activity,
1002–1003
production of antibodies by, 1007
protein nature, 974
specificity,
of artificially conjugated, 948, 994–
996, 1002, 1006
groups essential for, 995
molecular size and, 976
solubility and, 976
Antiovalbumin(s),
biological activity, essential groups
for, 990
rabbit, 1004, 1008
effect of denaturation on antigenic
activity of, 858
Antipneumococcal horse serum antibody
(type I),
antigenic activity, configuration and,
858
effect of denaturation on, 858

Antipneumococcus antibody,
   denatured, biological activity of, 1008
   isolation, 48
Antipneumococcus polysaccharide,
   horse, activity, essential groups for, 990
Anti-Rh agglutinins,
   biological activity, tyrosine and, 913
   inactivation, oxidative, 913
Antitoxin,
   inactivation, volume change in, 891
Antiurease, 74
Apoferritin, 74
   crystals, x-ray data, 294
   molecular weight, 638
   physical constants, 638
Apparent molal heat capacities, of
   amino acids, 566
Apparent molal volumes,
   of amino acids, 566
      covolume and, 565
      electrostriction and, 565, 566
Apyrase, 74
Arabic acid,
   reaction with potassium, 796
Arachin, 662, 722
   amino acid composition, 233
   dissociation into subunits, 659, 722
   electrophoresis, 531
   group distribution in, 208
   molecular size and shape, 722
   source, 722
Arginase, 74
   interaction with detergents, 825
      with guanidine hydrochloride on, 825
      with sodium salicylate on, 825
Arginine, 906
   conversion to ornithine, 143
   degradation, 159
   detection, 115
   enzymatic decarboxylation, 105
   flavianate, 106
   identification, 125
   ionizable group of, 462, 476, 477
      heat of ionization, 477
      pK' value, 469, 477
   molecular structure, 237
   physical properties, 91
   resolution of racemic, 130
   in seed globulins, 976
   in tobacco mosaic virus, 980

D-Arginine,
   preparation, 131
Arginine-N^{15},
   preparation, 132
Arsenicals,
   reaction with proteins, 914, 916
Asclepain, 81
Ascorbic acid oxidase,
   molecular weight, 637
   physical constants, 637
Asparagine, 886
   detection, 115
   molecular structure, 237, 361
   occurrence, 94
      in protein hydrolyzates, 89
   pK' values, 469
   solubility, effect of ions on, 38
   tetrahydro-6-hydroxy-4-pyrimidine-
      carboxylic acid from, 112
Aspartic acid,
   copper complexes, 117
   detection, 115
   distribution in proteins, 211, 212, 213,
      214, 215, 216, 217, 218, 219, 220,
      221, 222, 223, 225, 228
   enzymatic assay, 189
   ionizable group of, 462, 476, 477
      heat of ionization, 477
      pK' value, 469, 477
   molecular structure, 237
   physical properties, 91
   resolution of racemic, 130
   separation from glutamic acid, 543
   in tobacco mosaic virus, 980
L-Aspartic acid,
   molecular structure, 361
Aspartic acid-4-C^{14},
   preparation, 132
Aspartylaspartic acid,
   pK' values, 470
Aspartylglycine,
   pK' values, 470
Assay, microbial,
   of amino acid composition of proteins,
      189–190
      accuracy of, 199
   of biotin-binding activity of aridin, 739
Aucuba mosaic virus, 85
Aureomycin,
   excretion, plasma proteins and, 805

Avidin, 74, 230
  activity, biotin-binding, 974
    microbial assay of, 739
  amino acid composition, 219
  molecular weight, 219
Avogram, 299
"Azasuccinic" anhydrides, 110
Azides,
  reaction with proteins, 904, 931
Azlactones,
  in peptide synthesis, 172
  preparation, 109
  reaction with proteins, 931, 966
Azoproteins, 947
  immunological studies with, 948, 972
Azosulfathiazole,
  reaction with albumin, 777

B

BAL (British anti-lewisite, 2,3-dimer-
    capto-1-propanol),
  inactivation of metal-containing en-
    zymes by, 916
  reduction of disulfide bonds by, 904,
    913, 916
  therapeutic effect in lewisite vesication,
    916
  in metal poisoning, 917
Bacillus anthracis,
  peptide structure of, 134
Bacillus phlei protein,
  molecular weight, 634
  physical constants, 634
Bacillus subtilis,
  enzymes of, effect on alanylglycyl-
    valylaspartylalanylalanine, 954
  transformation of ovalbumin to
    plakalbumin by, 951, 952
  flagella, x-ray diffraction pattern, 271
Bacitracin,
  fractionation, 144
Bacteria,
  photochemical reactivation, 819
T_2-Bacteriophage,
  molecular weight, 639
  physical constants, 639
Bacteriophages, 74, 85
  effect of high pressure on, 818
    of ionizing radiation on, 821
    of sound waves on, 817

photochemical reactivation, 819
  stabilizers for, 827
Barbiturates,
  reaction with proteins, effect of sub-
    stituents on, 785
Barium salts, of proteins, solubility, 58
Bean mosaic virus, 85
Bean proteins, 82
Bence-Jones protein, 74
  denaturation, 844
    effect on electrical properties, 844,
      852
Benzene,
  reaction with albumins, 744
Benzenesulfonic acid,
  reaction with proteins, 930
Benzenesulfonyl chloride,
  reaction with proteins, 924
Benzoyl chloride,
  reaction with proteins, 904, 929–930
    mechanism, 930
Benzoylalanine,
  quantum yields, 449
Benzoylation, of proteins, 929
α-Benzoylhomoarginine,
  from α-benzoyllysine, 111
Benzoyltyrosylglycylamide,
  hydrolysis, 176
Benzylcetyldimethylammonium chloride,
  reaction with proteins, 791
Bergmann-Zervas degradation, 103, 147
Biotin,
  interaction with avidin, biological
    assay, 739
Birefringence,
  adsorption, 398
  form, 397
  of polypeptide chains, 397
  of protein fibers, 397
  streaming, see under Double refraction
    of flow
  structural, 397
  of tobacco mosaic virus, 667
Bisulfite,
  reaction with keratins, 914
Blood clotting,
  effect of iodide on, 748
    of thiocyanate on, 748
Blood proteins,
  molecular shape of, calculation from
    physical constants, 655

N-Carboxyamino acid anhydrides,
  reaction with proteins, 950
N-Carboxy-L-leucine,
  labeled, reaction with proteins, 950
Carboxypeptidase, 81, 729
  biological activity, 997
    mode of, 997, 998
  denaturation by freezing, 31
  determination of carboxyl groups with,
    908
  effect of DFP on, 946
    of ionizing radiation on, 820
    on proteins, 955–956
  isoelectric point, 511
  molecular weight, 635
  pancreatic, 147
  physical constants, 635
Cardiotoxin, 74, 84
Carnosinase, 74
Casein, 75
  absorption of water by, 798
  alkali metal salts, electrical properties,
    735
  alkaline earth salts, electrical proper-
    ties, 735
  amino acid composition, 216
  determination of tryptophan in, 195,
    437
    of tyrosine in, 195, 437
  drying of, 30
  fractions of, 46, 47, 205
  interaction between α- and β-, 802
    electrophoretic survey, 531
  iodinated, isolation of thyroxine from,
    937
  ionizing groups of, 476
  light scattering, depolarization ratios,
    407
  in milk, 2
  molecular structure, 941
  molecular weight, from osmotic pres-
    sure measurements, 596
  oxidation, with tyrosinase, 911
  reaction with calcium, 46, 47, 732, 733,
    772, 797
    with mandelic acid, 784
    with phenylisocyanate, 926
    with sodium, 796
  specific volume, 568
  x-ray diffraction pattern of denatured,
    280

α-Casein, 46
  amino acid composition, 205, 216
  distribution of groups in, 205, 224
  interaction with β-, 802
    electrophoretic survey, 531
  isoelectric point, 216, 511
  molecular weight, 216
  relative affinities for cupric ion, 798
  specific volume, 568
β-Casein, 46
  amino acid composition, 216
  distribution of groups in, 224
  interaction with α-, 802
    electrophoretic survey, 531
  isoelectric point, 211, 511
  relative affinities for cupric ion, 798
  specific volume, 568
γ-Casein,
  isoelectric point, 511
Catalase(s), 75
  bacterial,
    purification by partition chromatog-
      raphy, 69
  complex formation with hydrogen per-
    oxide, 1010
  horse erythrocyte, inactivation, order
    of, 863
  inhibition by polymeric anions, 801
  isolation, 11, 57, 66
  liver, removal of polysaccharide from,
    33
  molecular size and shape, electron
    microscope studies on, 572, 573,
    574
  molecular subunits, 573
  molecular weight, 573, 637
  physical constants, 637
  protective action on SH-groups, 820
  reaction with anions, spectrophoto-
    metric study, 743
Cathepsin, 81
Cathepsin C,
  synthesis of peptides by, 178
Cellobiuronic acid,
  role in antigenic specificity of capsular
    pneumococcal polysaccharides, 995
Cells,
  bacterial, microelectrophoretic studies
    on, 548
  extracts of, electrophoretic analysis,
    522

Cells (*continued*)
isolation of proteins from, 10–14
number of proteins in animal and microbial, 2
structure of, 457
Cellulose,
birefringence of fibers of, 399
Chicken sarcoma virus,
molecular weight, 639
physical constants, 639
Chloride,
reaction with serum albumin, 734–735, 744, 776
free energies of, 786
heat of reaction, 778
pH and, 780
p-Chlorobenzoyl chloride,
reaction with proteins, 924
Chloroform,
interaction with proteins, 730
p-Chloromercuribenzoate,
reaction with sulfhydryl groups, 835, 902, 904, 914–915
Chloropicrin,
reaction with proteins, 964, 966
Cholesterol,
reaction with serum proteins, 799
Cholinesterase, 50
active centers in, 998
inhibition by organic phosphates, 945
Chondroitin sulfate,
reaction with proteins, 801
Chromatography,
determination of amino acid composition of proteins by starch, 192–193, 199
by resins, 192, 193
partition, of pipsylamino acids, 128
in purification of proteins, 558
separation of peptides by, 138, 140, 142
of proteins by, 68–69
Chromium,
reaction with collagen, 794–795
Chymopapain, 81
Chymotrypsin, 81, 720
action on peptides, 238
biological activity, 943, 944, 997, 1002
configuration and, 944
essential groups for, 935, 969, 990
of hydrolysis products, 1005
mode of, 997ff.

chemical modification, biological effects, 970
crystalline, x-ray data of, 296
dissociation, 804
distribution of groups in, 207
effect of high pressure on, 818
of ionizing radiation on, 821
electrophoretic heterogeneity constants, 541
hydrolysis of peptides by, 168, 169, 170
inactivation, 910
reversible, 882, 983
isoelectric point, 511
molecular weight, 1002
from osmotic pressure measurements, 594
oxidation with tyrosinase, 911
quantum yield of photoinactivation, 451, 452, 453
reaction with *N*-carboxyglycine anhydride, 950
reaction with DFP, 943, 957, 962, 993, 1014
applications, 946
mechanism, 944
with nitrous acid, 935, 946
with phenyl isocyanate, 928
structure, 171
synthesis of peptides by, 178
ultraviolet absorption spectrum, 435
α-Chymotrypsin, 1001, 1002
biological activity, 1002
effect of periodate oxidation on, 970
inhibition by DFP and its analogs, 943, 944
by tetraethyl pyrophosphate, 945
isolation, 51
molecular weight, 635
oxidation with periodate, 910
effect on specificity, 970
physical constants, 635
N-terminal residues in, 910
β-Chymotrypsin, 1002
inhibition by DFP, 944
isolation, 51
γ-Chymotrypsin, 1002
crystalline, x-ray data on, 296
inhibition by DFP, 944
isolation, 51
δ-Chymotrypsin, 1002
molecular weight, 635

Crystals,
  geometry of, 242–245
  structure, 242–245
    analysis of, 300ff.
      Fourier-Series and, 305–307
      Patterson-Series and, 307–310
    unit cells of, 243, 244
    x-ray diffraction pattern, 245–249, 304ff.
      fiber photographs, 248–249
      powder photographs, 248–249
      single crystal photographs, 247–248
    x-ray scattering, intensity, 250–251
Cucumber mosaic viruses, 85
  molecular size and shape, electron microscope studies on, 574
Cucurbit seed globulins, 75, 209
  amino acid composition, 209
  distribution of groups in, 208
  isolation, 47
Cyanide,
  reaction with disulfide groups, 836, 904–905
Cypridina,
  luciferase of, reversible inactivation, 883–884
Cysteine, 886
  copper complexes, 117
  from cystine, 123
  destruction, 159
  determination in hydrolyzed proteins, 836
  distribution in proteins, 211, 212, 213, 215, 216, 217, 218, 219, 220, 221, 222, 223, 229
  in egg albumin, 834
  ionizable group of, 477
    heat of ionization, 477
    pK′ value, 477
  molecular structure, 237
  occurrence in protein hydrolyzates, 89
  oxidation to cystine, 123
  oxidation-reduction potential, 123
  properties, chemical, 124
    physical, 91
    sulfhydryl groups and, 9
  racemization, 160
  reduction of disulfide bonds by, 904, 913
  sulfhydryl groups of, 9
    reactivity of, 834

  4-thiazolidinecarboxylic acid from, 112
  in tobacco mosaic virus, 980
Cysteine-S^{35},
  preparation, 132
Cysteine peptides,
  identification, 125
Cysteinesulfinic acid,
  formation, 124, 125
Cysteinesulfonic acid,
  detection, 115
  formation, 124, 125
Cysteinylglycine,
  molecular structure, 364
    of sodium iodide of, 362, 363, 368-369, 370
Cystine,
  cysteic acid from, 125
  from cysteine, 123
  destruction, 158
  distribution in proteins, 211, 212, 213, 214, 215, 216, 217, 218, 219, 220, 221, 222, 223, 225, 228, 229
  ionizable groups of, 477
    heat of ionization, 477
    pK′ values, 469, 477
  photochemical decomposition to cysteine, 446
  properties, chemical, 124
    physical, 91
  reaction with sulfhydryl groups, 836
  reduction to cysteine, 123
  resolution of racemic, 130
  solubility, effect of ions on, 38
  stability of proteins and, 978
  structure, 90, 237, 238
  sulfur content of keratin and, 256
  in tobacco mosaic virus, 980
  ultraviolet spectrum, 431
D-Cystine,
  preparation, 131
L-Cystine,
  molecular structure, 360
Cystine/2,
  in seed globulins, 979
Cystine-cysteine system, 123
Cystine disulfoxide,
  formation, 125
Cytochrome(s), 75
  electrophoretic mobility, species differences in, 976

ionizing group of, 476
Cytochrome c, 80
  adsorption on kaolin, 69
  differential titration of ferro- and ferri-
    forms, 487
  hydrolysis products, biological activ-
    ity, 1001
  infrared spectrum, 426
  isoelectric point, 511, 513, 514
  molecular weight, 634
  physical constants, 634
  purification,
    chromatographic, 69
    ion-exchange resin for, 558
    by moving-boundary method, 543
  species differences, electrophoretic sur-
    vey, 521
Cytochrome oxidase,
  solubility, 976

D

DPF, see under Diisopropyl fluorophosphate
DPN, see under Diphosphopyridine nu-
  cleotide
Deamination, of proteins, 934–936
Decarboxylases, 75
  effect on amino acids, 105
  estimation of amino acids with, 189
  formation, 105
Decyl sulfate,
  reaction with serum albumin, 774
Dehydrogenases, 75
Dephosphorylase, 76
  thymonucleo, 76
Denaturation, of proteins, 807–890
  agents for, 814–826
  applications, 811
  chemical, as theory of protein structure,
    286–291, 810
  criteria of, 812–813
  definition, 809–810, 896
  degrees of, 291, 813–814
  effect on biological properties, 857–860
    on physical properties, 839–857
    on protein reactivity, 898
  elucidation of protein structure and,
    810–811
  kinetics of, 860ff., 866ff.
  liberation of chemically reactive groups
    in, 830–839

protection against, 826–830
  thermodynamics of, 863ff., 868ff., 875
Desoxyribonuclease,
  isolation, 51
Dexsoyribonucleoprotein, 76
Detergents,
  heat coagulation of proteins and, 827
  interaction with proteins, 289, 743, 744,
    788, 791, 847–848, 853, 888
    size of detergent molecule and, 785
    surface tension studies on, 747
    viscosity studies on, 746
  non-ionic,
    effect on proteins, 824
  synthetic,
    effect on proteins, 815, 817, 822ff.,
      830
    mechanism, 824, 825, 829
Dialysis,
  purification of protein solutions by, 33–
    34
α, γ-Diaminobutyric acid,
  occurrence, 97
L-α, γ-Diaminobutyric acid,
  from gliadin, 95
α, ϵ-Diamino-n-caproic acid, see under
  Lysine
α, ϵ-Diamino-γ-hydroxycaproic acid, see
  under Hydroxylysine
Di(α-aminopropionic acid)β-disulfide, see
  under Cystine
Diaminopimelic acid,
  decarboxylation, 106
meso-α, ϵ-Diaminopimelic acid,
  occurrence, 97
α, δ-Diamino-n-valeric acid, see under
  Ornithine
Diazo compounds,
  coupling of proteins with, 947–948
  applications, 947, 948
Diazoacetic acid,
  reaction of proteins with derivatives of,
    904, 920–921
Diazotization, of proteins, 935, 946–947
2,6-Dichlorophenolindophenol,
  reaction with sulfhydryl groups, 836
Dielectric constants,
  of amino acids, 698
  measurement, 710–712
  of peptides, 698
  of proteins, 698

molecular weight, 637
physical constants, 637
reactivity of amino groups in, 901
stability, 982
Dipole moments, 701
of amino acids, 700, 701, 703
of peptides, 701, 703
of proteins, 702, 707
Disulfide bonds,
protein configuration and, 989
Disulfide groups, of proteins,
reagents for, 836, 904–905
Djenkolic acid,
occurrence, 97
Dodecyl sulfate,
reaction with proteins, 746, 787, 792,
825, 830
with serum albumin, 743, 778, 786,
792
Dodecyl sodium sulfate,
effect on serum albumin, 824
reaction with β-lactoglobulin, 829
stabilizing effect on proteins, 828–829
Dodecylamine hydrochloride,
effect on proteins, 824
reaction with egg albumin, 791
Double refraction of flow, 677–687
optical anisotropy and, 399–402
in polydispersed systems, 685
relation to molecular shape of proteins,
679ff., 845, 848
to rotary diffusion constants, 682ff.
Drugs,
binding by proteins, 785
inhibition of bacterial luminescence by,
891
interaction with plasma proteins, 804,
805–806
Dyes,
reaction with proteins, 483, 735, 736
with serum albumin effect of optical
isomerism on, 783
with wool, 770

E

Edestin, 75, 82
amino acid composition, 217, 223
denaturation, effect on molecular
weight, 842
on x-ray diffraction pattern, 280,
281, 853–854

determination of tryptophan in, 437
determination of tyrosine in, 437
dielectric dispersion curve, 707
dissociation into subunits, 573, 596, 842
distribution of groups in, 224
hydration, 577
hydrolyzate, composition of, 94
isoelectric point, 217
isolation, 47
molecular size and shape, 707
electron microscope studies on, 573,
574, 577
molecular weight, 197, 217, 573, 577,
596
from light scattering, 608
from low-angle x-ray scattering, 618
from osmotic pressure measurements, 596
solubility, 39, 40
specific volume, 568
sulfhydryl groups of, 833
N-terminal residues of, 197, 217
Egg albumin, 73, see also under Egg
white, Ovalbumin
aged, electrophoretic homogeneity, 853
conversion to plakalbumin, 170, 895
deamination, 935–936
denaturation, 865, 877–878
acid, 872
activation energy, 866
effect on electrophoretic homogeneity, 853
on hydrodynamic properties, 844
on immunological properties, 859
on isoelectric point, 851
on molecular shape, 848
on molecular weight, 841, 843
entropy changes in, 890
ionizing steps, 887
liberation of SH groups during, 888
rate, 874
effect of pH on, 872
stages of, 889
surface, 817
thermal, kinetics of, 864
volume changes in, 891
dielectric properties, 702, 707
disulfide groups of, 836
effect of freezing on, 816
of guanidinium salts on, 823, 824
of inorganic electrolytes on, 825, 830

Electrostriction, 565, 566
  in calculation of specific molal volumes
    of amino acids, peptides and pro-
    teins, 565, 566, 567
  of solvent by charged groups in pro-
    teins, 653
Elinin, 76
Endopeptidases,
  hydrolysis of proteins by, 167
  specificity, 168
Enolase,
  isolation, 58
  molecular weight, 636
  physical constants, 636
  yeast,
    molecular weight, derived from light
      scattering, 608
Entropy,
  changes of, in egg albumin denatura-
    tion, 890
  of ionization, 472–473
Enzyme-substrate interactions, 806
Enzymes, see also under names of indi-
    vidual enzymes
  action on proteins, 8, 238, 826
  activation, *in vitro*, 1005
  adaptive, formation in microorganisms,
    1006
  bacterial, isolation, 817
  of beef pancreas,
    homogeneity, 52
    isolation, 51–52
  biological activity,
    effect of chemical modification on,
      897, 969
    essential groups, 233, 907, 909, 914,
      915, 928, 971, 990
    of hydrolysis products, 1001–1002
    mechanism of, 975, 1009, 1013, 1014
    specificity requirements, 997
  biological methods in study of, 748
  chemical modification, biological activ-
    ity and, 897
  conjugated, definition, 1005
  determination of amino acid composi-
    tion of proteins with, 189
    accuracy of, 199
  effect on globular proteins, 826
    of high pressure on, 818
    of ultraviolet irradiation on, 818
  formation of, 1005–1006

hydrolysis of peptides by, 165
  of proteins by, 165
inactivation, by freezing, 816
  by heat, 816
  by light, quantum yield, 451
  reversible, 983, 1013
inhibition by arsenicals, 916
  by DFP and analogs, 943–946
  by heavy metals, 916
  molecular size of inhibitor and, 784
isolation, 9, 58, 66
  source and, 9, 11, 12
metal, 729
  inactivation by BAL, 916
  modified, biological specificity of, 969
  nature of, 974
  oxidation of protein groups with, 910–
    913
  photochemistry, 451
  preparation, 811
  protein, amino acid composition, 230
    interactions of, effect on biological
      activity, 747–748
  proteolytic, 165
    biological activity,
      effect of tyrosinase on, 911
        of monomolecular layers of, 984
    effect on immune globulins, 951
      on proteins, 825–826
      of urea on, 823
    inactivation, 882
      reversible, 875, 882
    isolation of insulin and, 8
    specificity, effect of chemical modi-
      fication on, 970
    synthesis of peptides by, 176
  purification, 70
    criteria for, 230
  quantum yield of photoinactivation,
    451
  reaction with mustard gas, 922–923
  resolution of amino acids by, 129
  separation from mitochondria, 3
  specificity, 996–999
    chemical substitution and, 970
  stabilizers for, 70
  stability, 35
  sulfhydryl, effect of ionizing radiation
    on, 820
    protection against, 820
    inactivation by iodine, 937

Enzymes, sulfhydryl (*continued*)
 reaction of halogenated picrins with, 923
 synthesis of peptides by, 176
 proteins by, 176
 yellow, see under Yellow enzyme
Epidermin,
 molecular structure, 385
Epidermis, x-ray studies on, 268
Epoxides,
 reaction with proteins, 904, 921–922
 mechanism, 922
Equilibria, theory of multiple, in protein interactions, 748–770
 association, single, 748–753
 sites for, 748–758
  electrostatic interaction between, 753–754
  with independent intrinsic affinities, 766–769
  single set of, with cooperative interactions between them, 769–770
  with electrostatic interactions between them, equation for, 764–766
  with no interactions between them, reduced equation for, 763–766
 definition of equilibria, 758
 equilibrium constants, relationships in absence of interactions, 758–762
 general equations for extent of binding, 762
Equine encephalitis virus, 85
 molecular weight, 639
 physical constants, 639
Erythrocruorin, 76
 Gastrophilus,
  molecular weight, from osmotic pressure measurements, 594
 molecular weight, 634, 638
 physical constants, 634, 638
Erythrocytes,
 "ghosts," 10, 12
 isolation of hemoglobin from, 10
 mammalian,
  electrophoretic mobilities, 548
  hemoglobin content, 2
Escherichia coli, bacteriophages,
 effect of ionizing radiation on, 821

inactivation, reversible, 880
Esterase(s), 76
 inhibition by DFP, 943, 944, 945, 946, 993
 possible mechanism, 994
Esterification, of proteins, 918, 919–923
Ethanol,
 isolation of proteins with, 56, 57
Euglobulin(s), 36
 dielectric constants, determination, 699
 immune, isoelectric point, 511
 isolation, 47, 48, 49
 removal of ions from solutions of, 33
 serum, solubility, 39
 solubility, 37, 47
  effect of salt addition on, 37
Excelsin, 76, 82
 crystals, x-ray data, 294
 denaturation, effect on molecular weight, 842
  on x-ray diffraction pattern, 280
 molecular weight, derived from light scattering, 608
  from osmotic pressure measurements, 594
 sulfhydryl groups of, 833
Exopeptidases,
 specificity, 997

F

FDNB, see under 1-Fluoro-2,4-dinitrobenzene
FSH, see under Follicle-stimulating hormone
Fatty acids,
 hemolytic action, albumin and, 805
 interaction with proteins, 732, 746
 stabilizing effect on proteins, 748, 828, 829
Ferricyanide,
 reaction with sulfhydryl groups, 835, 903, 904
Ferritin, 76
 crystals, x-ray data, 294
Ferrohemoglobin,
 magnetic properties, 747
Fetuin, 76
Fibers,
 artificial, effect of chain length on tensile strength, 282

antibodies and, 1004, 1007, 1008

biological activity, configuration and, 1008

birefringence, 401

bovine, polar amino acid composition, 789

fractionation, by electrophoresis convection, 545

homogeneity, 559, 1007

electrophoretic survey, 537–538, 541, 545

human, amino acid composition, 215

distribution of groups in, 224

molecular size and shape, 692

molecular weight, 215

from amino acid analysis, 570

plasma, 516

effect of acute infections on, 522

refractive index, 403

serum, molecular size and shape, 684

molecular weight, 684

refractive index increment of, 404

specific, 518

viscosity, 692

isolation, 50, 57

rabbit, 1004

molecular weight of film of, 856

reaction with fluorodinitrobenzene, 900

with ketene, 900

structure, 1007

reaction with anions, 788

with cations, 792

with p-hydroxyphenylazophenyl-arsonate, 774

specificity, 786

with serum β-lipoprotein, 801

sedimentation studies on, 659, 661, 662

serum,

molecular weight, 637, 658

physical constants, 637, 658

stabilization of, 35

γ_1-Globulin(s),

homogeneity, electrophoretic survey, 536

isoelectric point, effect of buffer concentration on, 514

species differences in, 512

γ_2-Globulin(s),

isoelectric point, effect of buffer concentration on, 514

species differences in, 512

Glucoprotein, 50

Glucose,

reaction with proteins, 799

o-β-Glucosidotyrosine,

antigenic activity of gelatin on coupling with, 978

of insulin, 978

β-Glucuronidase, 77

Glutamic acid,

assay, enzymatic, 189

copolymer with lysine, 175

detection, 115

distribution in proteins, 211, 212, 213, 214, 215, 216, 217, 218, 219, 220, 221, 222, 223, 225, 228

enzymatic decarboxylation, 105

ionizable groups of, 462, 476, 477

heat of ionization, 477

pK' values, 469, 477

molecular structure, 237

physical properties, 91

resolution of DL-, 130

in tobacco mosaic virus, 980

Glutamic acid-d_2,

preparation, 132

separation from aspartic acid, 543

D-Glutamic acid,

in cancer tissues, 98

occurrence, 99

L-Glutamic acid,

crystal structure, 361

Glutamic acid dehydrogenase,

molecular weight, 638

physical constants, 638

Glutamine, 886

detection, 115

enzymatic synthesis, 179

occurrence, 94

in protein hydrolyzates, 89

molecular structure, 237

pK' values, 469

Glutathione,

enzymatic synthesis, 179

oxidation–reduction potential, 123

protective action on SH- groups, 820

reduction of disulfide bonds by, 904, 913

light scattering depolarization ratios, 407

low-angle x-ray studies on, 621

mammalian, iron content, 569, 593

  molecular lifetime, 551

  molecular weight, 569, 593

methylation, 919

molecular size and shape, 690, 691, 720

molecular structure, 355, 554, 698, 720

  α-helical, 384, 385, 386, 387, 389

  species differences in, 554

molecular weight, 197, 215, 554, 555, 720, 986

  from osmotic pressure measurements, 592, 594, 596

myoglobin and, 49, 204

oxygenation, 800

  acidic properties and, 485

physical constants, 688

properties, species differences in, 985–986

reaction with acetic anhydride, 925

  with hexadecyl sulfate, 787

  with sodium, 796

reduced, molecular structure, 295, 358

salting-out constants, 41

sedimentation, studies on, 662

sheep, isoelectric point, 515

solubility, 69

  in ammonium sulfate solutions, 42

  effect of prosthetic group on, 9

    of temperature on, 44

    species differences in, 47, 49

stability, 35

structure, infrared spectrum and, 430

terminal residues of, 197, 986

titration of, 487–489

Hemolysin(s), 78

  goat, thermal inactivation, 866, 868

Heparin,

  interaction with proteins, 46, 58

  with sodium, 796

Hepatocuprein, isolation, 20

Heteroalbumose,

  immunological behavior, 1002, 1003

Hexadecyl sulfate,

  reaction with hemoglobin, 787

Hexaethyl tetraphosphate, 945

  labeled, inhibition of human plasma cholinesterase by, 945

  molecular weight, 637

physical constants, 637

yeast, stabilization, 35

Hexokinase, 78

  isolation, 52

Hippuric acid,

  hydrolysis, 176

Hippurylglycine,

  hydrolysis, 176

Histamine,

  enzymatic formation, 105

Histidine, 90, 906

  copper complexes, 117

  detection, 115

  distribution in proteins, 211, 212, 213, 214, 215, 216, 217, 218, 219, 220, 221, 222, 223, 225, 228, 229

  enzymatic assay, 189

  decarboxylation, 105

  flavianate, 106

  identification, 125

  ionizable groups of, 462, 476, 477

    heat of ionization, 477

    pK' values, 469, 477

  molecular structure, 237

  physical properties, 91

  resolution of DL-, 130

  separation from lysine, 543

  4,5,6,7-tetrahydro-1H-imidazo[c]pyridine-6-carboxylic acid from, 113

  titration curves, 467, 468

  in tobacco mosaic virus, 980

  ultraviolet absorption spectrum, 431

Histidine-N^{15},

  preparation, 132

Histidylhistidine,

  pK' values, 470

  titration curves, 468

Histones, 78, 202–203

  amino acid composition, 202–203, 211, 212

  distribution of groups in, 202, 205, 224

  methyl esters of, 919

  molecular weight, 211

Holmes rib grass virus, 980

Hormones, see also under names of individual hormones

  biological activity,

    effect of chemical modification on, 897

    essential groups for, 914, 990

    mechanism of, 1014

Hormones (*continued*)
  chemical modification, effect on biological activity, 897
  effect of ultraviolet irradiation on, 818
  electrophoretic studies on, 546
  isolation, source and, 11
  pituitary,
    films, biological activity of, 856
    isolation of stable, 1000–1001
  protein, 203, 213, 974
    amino acid composition, 213
    distribution of groups in, 203
    molecular weights, 213
Hurain, 78, 81
Hydantoin,
  preparation, 110
Hydration, of protein molecules, 559–569, 647, 648, 653ff., 675, 690–693, 695ff.
  effect of denaturation on, 848–849
  from x-ray scattering, 617, 619
Hydrocarbons, carcinogenic, coupling of proteins to, 928
Hydrogen bonds, 241, 260–261
  energies of, 789
  protein configuration and, 596, 982
Hydrogen ion concentration,
  definition, 464–465
  role in protein denaturation, 815, 816, 818
Hydrogen peroxide,
  oxidation of proteins with, 904, 909, 910
Hydrogenation,
  catalytic, of substituted proteins, 914
Hydroxyamino acids, see under Amino acids, hydroxy, and under names of individual compounds
Hydroxyglutamic acid,
  occurrence, 100
β-Hydroxyglutamic acid,
  occurrence in protein hydrolyzates, 89
Hydroxyleucine,
  occurrence, 101
Hydroxylysine,
  detection, 115
  distribution in collagen and related proteins, 221
  occurrence, 95, 96
  oxidation, 118
  phosphoric ester, occurrence, 96

picrate, 106
  reduction, 118
  structure, 90, 95
p-(2-Hydroxy-5-methyl-phenylazo)benzoate,
  reaction with albumin, sites of, 776
Hydroxyphenylacetate,
  reaction with serum albumin, position of hydrogen donor substituent and, 782
p-Hydroxyphenylazophenylarsonic acid,
  reaction with γ-globulin, 774, 786
Hydroxyproline, 238
  detection, 115
  determination in protein hydrolyzates, 113
  diffusion constant, determination, 631
  distribution in collagen and related proteins, 95, 221
  in gelatin hydrolyzates, 95
  oxidation, 118
  pK′ values, 469
  physical properties, 91
  preparation, 93
  reaction with nitrous acid, 113
  structure, 90, 93, 237, 364
L-Hydroxyproline,
  molecular structure, 361, 363, 366, 371
  trans-configuration, 366
γ-Hydroxypyrrolidine-α-carboxylic acid,
  see under Hydroxyproline
Hydroxytryptophan,
  occurrence, 102
  synthesis, 102
β-Hydroxyvaline,
  occurrence, 101
Hyperglycemic-glycogenolytic factor, 78
$\gamma^1(\gamma^2)$-Hyperimmune proteins, isoelectric points, 511

I

Influenza virus, 85, 880
  composition, 657
  density of, 656
  molecular weight, derived from light scattering, 608
  PR8, molecular weight, 639
    physical constants, 639
Influenza A virus,
  destruction, order of, 862

Influenza A virus hemagglutinin,
destruction, effect of pH on, 873
Insulin, 78, 230, 662, 717–719, 989, 999
acetylation with ketene, 903
acid, 961
molecular weight, from light scattering, 608, 609
from osmotic pressure measurements, 594, 622–623
reversible denaturation, 983
amino acid composition, 213, 789
species differences in, 203, 225
antigenicity on coupling with o-β-
glucosidotyrosine, 978
biological activity,
chemical modification and, 969, 970
denaturation and, 814, 858
essential groups for, 233, 956, 989
esterification and, 920
hyperglycemic factor and, 19
mechanism, 1015
bovine, amino acid composition, 225
structure, 225
carboxyl groups of, 964
determination, 921
chemical modification, 956
biological effects of, 969, 970
composition, 213, 232
species variations in, 20, 203, 231
compound formation with zinc, see
under Zinc insulin
configuration, 282
"core," molecular weight of, 150
cystine content, 978
denaturation, reversible, 881
denatured, x-ray diffraction pattern of,
281–282
determination of amide groups in, 921
of carboxyl groups in, 921
of tryptophan in, 195, 437
of tyrosine in, 195, 437
dielectric properties, 702, 707, 708
dissociation, 659, 708, 718, 719, 803–
804, 842, 881, 882
distribution of groups in, 198, 203, 224
effect on blood clotting, 748
of permanganate on, 910
of tyrosinase on, 912, 913
electrophoresis, 530
fibrils, formation of, 285

films, 855–856
biological activity, 856, 858
molecular weight, 624
homogeneity, 24, 987
hydrolysis, acid, 162
alkaline, 159
enzymatic, 166, 168, 169
inactivation, surface, 817
iodinated, catalytic hydrogenation, 914
isoelectric point, 213
isolation, pancreatic enzymes and, 8
methyl ester, physical properties, 960–
961
methylation, 919, 920
molecular size and shape, 702, 708, 717,
718
molecular weight, 197, 203–204, 213,
634, 717, 718–719, 881
from amino acid analysis, 570
from low angle x-ray scattering, 618
osmotic pressure, determination, 597
peptides from, molecular weight of, 150
phenolic hydroxyl groups of, 913
physical constants, 634
polypeptide chains of, 556
species variations in amino acid
composition, 987
purification, by partition chromatography, 558
purity, investigation by counter-cur-
rent distribution, 557
reaction with acetic anhydride, 925
with aromatic isocyanates, 926
with carbobenzoxy chloride, 930
with thiocyanate, 744, 787
free energies of, 786
reduction, 914
relaxation time, 699, 702
salts of, 45
solubility, 559
effect of pH on, 47
stability, 881, 982, 989
cystine content and, 978
structure, 95, 146, 147, 149, 842, 987
infrared absorption spectrum and,
429, 430
molecular, 312, 327–328, 355, 390, 717
sulfhydryl groups, 833
terminal residues of,
N-, 197, 198, 204, 213
determination of, 196

Insulin, terminal residues of (*continued*)
  source and, 987
  β-transformation, disulfide bonds and,
    989
  tyrosine ionization in, 899
  ultraviolet absorption spectrum, 435,
    436
  wool keratin and, 227
  x-ray diffraction pattern, 854
Insulin-insulin complex, 729
Insulin sulfate,
  acid,
    crystals, structure, 327, 330–334
      x-ray studies on, 292, 297ff., 334,
        719
  biological activity of, 942
  solubility, effect of temperature on, 43
Interstitial cell-stimulating hormone,
  activity, essential groups for, 990
Invertase, 78
  inactivation, 910
    volume change in, 891
  yeast, oxidation by tyrosinase, 912
    removal of polysaccharide from, 32,
      35
    stabilization, 35
Iodide,
  effect on proteins, 825
Iodination, of proteins, 936–940
  mechanism, 938
Iodine,
  reaction with proteins, 904, 923, 937
    with sulfhydryl groups, 836, 903, 904
Iodoacetamide,
  reaction with proteins, 917, 959
Iodoacetate,
  reaction with proteins, 904, 917, 959
    with sulfhydryl groups, 835
Iodoacetic acid,
  heat coagulation of proteins and, 827
Iodohistidine,
  preparation, 122
p-Iodophenylsulfonyl chloride, labeled,
    determination of amino acids
      with, 191, 196
    of free amino groups with, 936–940
Iodoproteins, see also under names of
    individual compounds
  immunochemical behavior, 939
  2-iodotyrosine in, 937–938
  radioactive, preparation, 939

Iodosobenzoate,
  reaction with sulfhydryl groups, 835,
    902, 904
Iodotyrosine,
  detection, 115
2-Iodotyrosine,
  formation in biosynthesis of thyroxine,
    938
  occurrence in iodinated proteins, 937–
    938
3-Iodotyrosine,
  occurrence, 120
  synthesis, 120
Iodozein, 965
Ion-exchange resins,
  purification of proteins with, 480–481,
    557–558
  removal of ions from protein solutions
    with, 34
Ionization constants, of amino acids and
    peptides, 467–471
Ionophoresis, 541, 542, 544
  in filter paper strips, 544
  separation of amino acids and peptides
    by, 543
Iron,
  reaction with siderophilin, 797
Irradiation,
  effect on proteins, 909
  ionizing, biological effects, 819, 820
  ultrasonic, effect on proteins, 817
  ultraviolet, biological effects, 819
    effect on proteins, 818–819
Isatin,
  reaction with amino acids, 115
Isoagglutins, 78
Isoelectric point,
  of amino acids, 471–472
  definition, 477, 479
  of proteins, 478ff.
    effect of buffer solutions on, 512–515
Isoionic point,
  definition, 477–478
  of proteins, 478
Isoleucine,
  detection, 115
  distribution in proteins, 211, 212, 213,
    214, 215, 216, 217, 218, 219, 220,
    221, 222, 223, 225, 227, 229
  ionization, heat of, 472
  pK' values, 469, 472

physical properties, 91
preparation, 93
resolution of DL-, 130
in seed globulins, 979
structure, 90, 93
  molecular, 237
in tobacco mosaic virus, 980
Isotope dilution,
  in determination of protein composi-
    tion, 190–191, 199
Isotope swamping,
  in determination of protein composi-
    tion, 191

J

Jack bean meal,
  isolation of proteins from, 11
    of urease from, 57

K

Keratin(s),
  denatured, infrared spectra, 421
  dispersion of, disulfide groups and, 914
  feather, amino acid composition, 220
    infrared spectrum, 427
    x-ray studies on, 271
  infrared spectrum, 426, 427
  reaction with bisulfite, 914
  structure, 239, 251–266, 555
  sulfur content, 25
  supercontraction, 264
  α-β-transformation, 254–255
  wool, amino acid composition, 220
    distribution of groups, 224
      effect on properties, 208
    insulin and, 227
    titration of, 492
    ultraviolet absorption spectrum, 435
  x-ray diffraction pattern, 254ff.
α-Keratin,
  structure, 255, 327
    α-helical, 383–384, 385
  x-ray diffraction pattern, 254
β-Keratin, 254
  structure, 256, 257ff., 371, 387–389,
    423, 849
  x-ray diffraction pattern, 854, 855
Keratin-myosin-epidermis-fibrinogen
  group, of fibrous proteins, 251, 266–
  272

configuration, 286, 389
  denaturation and, 286
α-β-transformation, 271, 385
x-ray studies on, 266–272, 854
Ketene, 924
  reaction with proteins, 903, 904, 924–
    925, 928
Keto acids,
  condensation with amino acids, 180

L

Lactalbumin, 73, 78
  molecular weight, 634
  physical constants, 634
Lactamide,
  apparent molal heat capacity, 566
Lactase, 1006
Lactic dehydrogenase,
  hog heart, effect of concentration on
    sedimentation of, 660
  isolation, 58, 68
Lactogenic hormone, pituitary, see also
    under Prolactin
  acetylation with ketene, 903
  biological activity, essential groups for,
    920, 990
  esterified, electric properties, 966
  isoelectric point, 511
  reduction by thioglycolate, 913
Lactoglobulin, 77, 78, 906
  crystals, 318ff.
    x-ray data on, 296
  denaturation, effect of pH on rate, 873
    order of, 862
    reversible, mechanism, 884
    thermal, 836
  denatured, x-ray diffraction pattern, 854
  dielectric dispersion curve, 707
  hyperimmune, electrophoretic hetero-
    geneity constants of, 541
  immune, isoelectric point, 511
  inactivation, reversible, 875, 882
  modified, electric properties, 966
  stability, 888
β-Lactoglobulin, 303, 877, 878
  amino acid composition, 216, 217, 789
  amino groups of, 839
  crystals, binding of water by, 561
    structure, hydration and, 358
    stability of lattice, 357

β-Lactoglobulin (*continued*)
  denaturation, 841, 878
    activation of SH groups in, 888
    effect on hydrodynamic properties, 844
      on optical rotation, 857
    electrophoretic survey, 523
    rate, pH and, 888
    stages in, 889
    thermal, 843
  denatured, electrophoretic homogeneity, 853
    optical rotation, 411
  determination of tryptophan in, 437
    of tyrosine in, 437
  dielectric properties, 699, 702
  diffusion constants, determination, 631
  distribution of groups in, 204, 205
  dodecyl sulfate derivative, 746, 829, 896
  effect of trypsin on, 826
  electrophoresis, 532
  enzymatic hydrolysis, 167
  films of, 623, 856
    molecular weight, 624
  fractionation of crystallized, 237
  homogeneity, electrophoretic survey, 536
  of human serum albumin, refractive index increment, 404
  hydration, 619, 710
  imidazole groups of, 839
  interactions, 655
  ionizable groups in, 491, 791
  isoelectric point, 216, 217, 511
    effect of buffer on, 513, 514
  isolation, 47
  light scattering, depolarization ratios, 407
  masked groups in, 838
  molecular size and shape, 318–319, 320, 692, 702
    from low-angle x-ray scattering, 619
  molecular weight, 216, 217, 300, 491, 635
    from amino acid analysis, 570
    from light scattering, 608
    from osmotic pressure measurements, 594
    from solubility, 622
  optical rotation, 410

  ovalbumin and, 227, 238
  physical constants, 635
  reaction with methyl orange, 787
  refractive index increment, 404
    specific, 518
  relative affinities for cupric ion, 798
  relaxation time, 702
  salting-out constant, 41
  salts of, 45
  sedimentation studies on, 661, 665
  solubility, effect of ions on, 38, 39, 40
  specific volume, 568
  structure of, 291, 698
  N-terminal residues of, 197, 217
  titration curves, 850
    ionic strength and, 487
  x-ray diffraction pattern, 854
  viscosity, 692
  in whey, 47
β₁-Lactoglobulin, isoelectric point, 511
Lanthionine, 159
  destruction by hydrolysis, 159
  identification, 125
Leucine,
  in α-chymotrypsin, 910
  detection, 115
  distribution in proteins, 211, 212, 213, 214, 215, 216, 217, 218, 219, 220, 221, 222, 223, 225, 227, 229
  ionization, heat of, 472
    pK' values, 469, 472
  physical properties, 91
  resolution of DL-, 130
  in seed globulins, 979
  structure, 237
  in tobacco mosaic virus, 980
D-Leucine,
  occurrence, 99
L-Leucine,
  ethyl ester, reduction, 104
Leucine-d,
  preparation, 132
Leucine-3,4-d,
  preparation, 132
Leucine peptides,
  stability, 164
Leucylglycine,
  hydrolysis, 176
D-Leucylglycine,
  photohydrolysis, 450

DL-Leucylglycylglycine,
  photohydrolysis, 450
Lewisite [dichloro(2-chlorovinyl)arsine],
  vesicant action, dithiols as antidote
    against, 916
Licheniformins, 981
  biological activity, amino acid se-
    quence and, 981
Light scattering,
  evaluation of molecular size and shape
    of proteins from, 602–616, 845
    of molecular weight from, 605, 608,
      609–610, 613–615
  of solutions of small molecules, 602ff.
    effect of intermolecular interfer-
      ence on, 603, 610–616
    relation to osmotic pressure, 603ff.
  in study of protein interactions, 743
Lima beans,
  trypsin inhibitors in, 974
Limit dextrinase, 78
Linin, 78, 82
Lipase, 78
  of wheat germ, inhibition by p-chloro-
    mercuribenzoate, 915
Lipids,
  removal from protein solutions, 32
  in viruses, 657
Lipoprotein(s), 79
  denaturation, pH and, 815
  density, 61
  effect of freezing on, 817
    of lyophilization on, 817
  isolation of, 8
  partial specific volumes, 563
  sedimentation, 61
β-Lipoprotein,
  destruction by freezing, 31
  of human plasma, 723–724
    hydration, 655
    lipid content, 723
    partial specific volume, 655
  hydration, 724
  molecular size and shape, 724
  molecular weight, 724
  plasma, removal of lipid from, 32
  serum, γ-globulin derivative of, 801
    refractive index increment, 404
β₁-Lipoprotein,
  effect of freezing on, 816
  of plasma, human, 692

lipid content, 805
of serum, human,
  molecular weight, 638, 640
  physical constants, 638, 640
Lipoxidase, 79
Livetin,
  optical rotation, 410
Luciferase,
  denaturation, reversible, 883–884
    mechanism, 883
  inactivation, factors affecting, 818
Luciferin,
  denaturation, reversible, 883
Luminescence, bacterial,
  extinction, 872
    volume change in, 891
  inhibition by drugs, 891
  thermal destruction, order of, 862
Luteinizing hormone,
  molecular weight, 637
  physical constants, 637
Lyophilization, 31
  effect on lipoproteins, 817
Lysine,
  copolymer with glutamic acid, 175
  copper complexes, 117
  detection, 115
  distribution in proteins, 211, 212, 213,
    214, 215, 216, 217, 218, 219, 220,
    221, 222, 223, 225, 229
  enzymatic assay, 189
    decarboxylation, 105
  flavianate, 106
  ionizable groups of, 462, 476, 477
    heat of ionization, 477
    pK' values, 469, 477
  physical properties, 91
  picrate, 106
  resolution of DL-, 130
  in seed globulins, 979
  separation from histidine, 543
  structure, 237
  in tobacco mosaic virus, 980
Lysine-2-C¹⁴,
  preparation, 132
Lysine-6-C¹⁴,
  preparation, 132
ε-Lysine peptides, 134
Lysozyme, 11, 79, 989
  amino acid composition, 219

Lysozyme (*continued*)
biological activity,
  active centers, 989
  effect of chemical modification on, 970
  essential groups for, 956, 989, 990, 991
chemical modification, 957
  biological effects, 970
  effect on homogeneity, 957
chromatographic resolution, 69
cystine content, 978
distribution of groups in, 224
egg white, molecular weight, from osmotic pressure measurements, 594
hydration, 619, 710
inactivation, pH and, 815
infrared spectrum, 426
iodination, 938
isoelectric point, 511
isolation, 67
light scattering, depolarization ratios, 407
molecular shape, from low-angle x-ray scattering, 619
molecular weight, 219, 634
  from amino acid analysis, 570
  from light scattering, 608
physical constants, 634
purification with ion-exchange resins, 558
reaction with acetic anhydride, 925
  with benzylcetyldimethylammonium chloride, 791
  with iodine, 939
refractive index increments, 404
relative affinities for cupric ion, 798
salts of, 45
specific volume, 568
stability, 858, 989
  cystine content and, 978
structure, 149
tyrosine ionization in, 899
ultraviolet absorption spectrum, 435
x-ray scattering, 620, 621
Lysozyme chloride,
crystals, structure, 355
  x-ray data on, 296
optical properties, 396

Lysylglutamic acid,
dielectric properties, 701, 704
relaxation time, 701
Lysyllysine,
pK' values, 470

M

Magnesium,
reaction with proteins, affinity constants, 795
Malaprade's reaction, 118
Malonylation, of proteins, 928–929
Mandelic acid,
reaction with casein, 784
Mercaptalbumin, 236, 721, 744, 896
crystals, 957
  volume of, 302
interaction with mercuric ions, 744
mercury dimer, 721, 915–916
  dipole moment, 708
  human serum, crystals of, 292
    change in density on water uptake by, 561
    optical properties, 396
    structure, 316–318
  molecular shape, from low-angle x-ray scattering, 619
  molecular weight, 637
  physical constants, 637
molecular size and shape, 721–722, 963
serum, human,
  dielectric properties, 708–709
  molecular size and shape, 708
  relaxation times, 708
titration curves, 964
ultracentrifugal patetrn, 960
Mercaptans,
reduction of disulfide bonds by lower alkyl, 913
Mercurials,
interaction with proteins, 733, 743, 744, 904, 914–916
organic, preservation of human plasma with, 34
Mercuric ions,
dimerization of serum albumin in the presence of, 743
Mercury,
reaction with proteins, 793

viscosity, 692
L-Myosin,
molecular symmetry, 593, 595
Myosin, 197, 267–268, 492
amino acid composition, 218
cyclic peptide structure, 185, 197, 901
biological activity, 976
sulfhydryl groups and, 993
chemical modification of, availability
of groups for, 901
denaturation, 813, 847, 889
effect on molecular weight, 842
distribution of groups in, 207, 224
effect of guanidine on, 823–824
of urea on, 823–824
enzyme nature of, 976
fibers, birefringence of, 399
interaction with actin, 724
isoelectric point, 218
isolation, 48
light scattering, depolarization ratios,
407
molecular size and shape, 694, 724
electron microscope studies on, 572
molecular weight, 218, 238, 658, 724
from osmotic pressure measurements, 593, 594
physical constants, 238, 658
reaction with halogenated picrins, 923
sedimentation studies on, 665
solubility, effect of ions on, 39
sulfhydryl groups of, 833
viscosity, 694
x-ray studies on, 267–268

N

Naphthoquinones,
interaction with proteins, 730
"Nerve gases," chemistry, 943
Newcastle disease virus, 85
Ninhydrin,
reaction with amino acids, 114, 155
Nitrophenols,
reaction with proteins, pH and, 780
Nitration, of proteins, 904, 934–936, 946–
947
Nitrous acid,
reaction with proteins, 904, 934–936,
946–947

Norleucine,
ionization, heat of, 472
pK' values, 469, 472
occurrence, 101
in protein hydrolyzates, 89
Norvaline,
ionization, 472
occurrence, 101
Notatin, 76, 79
Nuclei, cellular,
isolation of, 12
Nucleic acid(s),
biological activity, 971
depolymerization of, 810
interaction with ovalbumin, electrophoretic survey, 530, 531, 532–533
with proteins, 46, 58, 800, 801
electrophoretic studies on, 530ff.,
745, 800, 801
role of viscosity in, 746
isolation, 811
phase microscopy, 459
reaction with organic cations, 793
reaction with sodium, 796
removal from protein solutions, 33
ultraviolet absorption, 18
ultraviolet microspectrophotometry,
454
Nucleohistone, 79
calf thymus, molecular shape, 659
sedimentation studies on, 659
ultraviolet absorption spectrum, 435
Nucleoprotamine, 79
Nucleoproteins, 79
biological activity, 974
nucleic acid moiety and, 968
ionizing groups of, 476
isolation of, 8
liver, sulfhydryl groups of, 833
Nucleotides, ultraviolet absorption, 18
Nucleotropomyosin, 79
Nylon,
infrared spectra, 425, 427
water adsorption of unstretched, 56

O

Octopine,
occurrence, 97
Oleic acid,
antibacterial action, albumin and, 805

Opsin-retinene complex, 729
see also under Rhodopsin
Optical rotation,
of amino acids, 409
of peptides, 411ff.
of proteins, 410–411, 857
in study of protein interactions, 743–744
Ornithine,
from arginine, 96, 143, 159
copper complexes, 117
detection, 115
enzymatic assay, 189
decarboxylation, 105
Ornithine-2-C^{14},
preparation, 132
Osmotic pressure, of proteins, 578–600
determination of, 597–600
of molecular weights from, 578ff., 592ff.
equations, 580–590
effect of activity constants of components on, 590–592
experimental data, 592–596
Gibbs-Donman effect, 579, 580, 586–589
relation of light scattering to, 603ff., 606–610
Ovalbumin, 73, 79
amino acid composition, 217, 219, 448
bacterial enzymes and, 8
binding of water by, 561, 798
biological activity,
essential groups for, 990
of monomolecular layers of, 984
composition, 36
conversion to plakalbumin, 149, 170, 951ff.
mechanism, 952–954
nature of peptides formed, 953
cyclic peptide structure, 133, 185
denaturation, 888
fluorescent depolarization method in study of, 716
by freezing, 31
order of, 862
steaming birefringence in study of, 686
denatured, optical rotation, 411
determination of tryptophan in, 195
of tyrosine in, 411

distribution of groups in, 224
effect of tyrosinase on, 912, 913
electrophoretic analysis, 529
electrophoretic mobilities, 505–506, 508, 952
buffer systems and, 509
effect of chemical modification on, 504–505
titration data and, 506
enzymatic dephosphorylation, 953, 954, 955
effect on electrophoretic mobility, 504
fibrils, formation of, 285
films of, 623
homogeneity, 49, 951
hydration, 561, 619, 798
immunological behavior,
of azophthalate substituted, 996
of digestion products, 1004
isoelectric point, 217
effect of buffer concentration on, 514
isolation, 49
β-lactoglobulin and, 227, 238
light scattering, depolarization ratios, 407
molecular size and shape, 692
from low-angle x-ray scattering, 619
molecular weight, 197, 217, 219
from amino acid analysis, 569
from light scattering, 608
from osmotic pressure measurements, 592, 594, 596
peptic hydrolyzates, molecular weight of, 150
phenolic hydroxyl groups of, 913
reaction with alkylbenzene sulfonates, 787
with dodecyl sulfate, 787
with nucleic acid, electrophoretic survey, 530ff.
refractive index increments, 404
relaxation times, measurement, 714, 715
salting-out constants, 41
salts of, 45
sedimentation studies on, 660, 665
solubility, 37, 38
temperature and, 44
specific volume, 568
stability, 887
anion-binding capacity and, 888

structure, 149, 902, 954
titration curve, ionic strength and, 487
viscosity, 692
x-ray scattering, 620, 621
Ovomucoid, 79
amino acid composition, 219
biological activity, essential groups for,
990
distribution of groups in, 224
homogeneity, electrophoretic survey,
537, 541
reaction with acetic anhydride, 925
molecular weight, 219
stability, 858
structure, 147
Ovoverdin, 80
2,5-Oxazolidinediones,
4-substituted, 110
Oxazoline derivatives,
from amino acids, 112
Oxazolones, 109
Oxidizing agents,
effect on proteins, 904, 909–910
L-β-Oxindolylalanine, see under
Hydroxytryptophan
Oxygen,
reaction with hemoglobin, 800
Oxyhemoglobin, see also under Hemoglobin, 800
differential titration, 485, 486
electrophoretic analysis, 520
homogeneity, electrophoretic survey,
536
horse, crystals, x-ray data on, 294, 295
ionization, heat of, 483, 485
reaction with mustard gas, 923
human, crystals, x-ray data on, 295
ionization, heat of, 484
isolation, 47
magnetic properties, 747
solubility, 47
temperature and, 44
Oxytocin, 80
analysis, 145
fractionation, 144
molecular weight, 150

P

Pancreas,
beef, isolation of enzymes from, 51–52

proteolytic enzymes of, effect on isolation of insulin, 8
trypsin inhibitor in, 974
Papain, 80, 81, 178
biological activity, essential groups for,
990
effect of DFP on crude, 946
hydrolysis of peptides by, 168
stability, 858
synthesis of peptides by, 177, 178
Parathyroid hormone, 80
biological activity, essential groups for,
990
Partial specific volumes,
of peptides, 565, 566, 567
of proteins in solution, 562–569, 651,
653
Partition chromatography,
of amino acids, 109, 126, 144
of peptides, 142
in study of protein interactions, 733
Patterson series,
determination of crystal structure and,
307–310
Peanut protein,
x-ray diffraction pattern of denatured,
280
Pectin,
homogeneity, electrophoretic survey,
537
Pectin esterase,
effect of DFP on, 946
Penicillin,
effect of plasma proteins on activity of,
805
on excretion of, 805
Pepsin, 80, 81, 988
acetylated, proteolytic activity of
crystalline, 89
action on peptides, 238
amino acid conposition, 218, 789
biological activity, effect of chemical
modification on, 970
essential groups for, 911, 929, 990
specificity of, 929
chemical modification, biological effects,
970
crystals, x-ray pattern of, 292, 296, 299
denaturation, effect of pH on rate of,
871–872
on sedimentation constant, 841–842

Periodic acid,
  oxidation of proteins with, 910
    application, 188–189, 199
Permanganate,
  oxidation of amino acids with, 910
    of proteins with, 910
Peroxidase(s), 80
  horse radish, complex formation with
    hydrogen peroxide, 1009–1010
  inactivation, of anti-Rh agglutinins by,
    913
  molecular weight, 635
  oxidation of proteins by, 913
  physical constants, 635
  purification, by moving boundary
    method, 543
Phase microscopy, 456
Phaseolin,
  amino acid composition, 223
Phenyl isocyanate,
  reaction with proteins, 904, 921, 926–
    928
Phenylacetate,
  reaction with serum albumin, free
    energies of, 786
Phenylacetylalanine,
  quantum yields, 449
Phenylalanine, 18
  in α-chymotrypsin, 910
  detection, 115
  diffusion constant, determination, 631
  distribution in proteins, 211, 212, 213,
    214, 215, 216, 217, 218, 219, 220,
    221, 222, 223, 225, 227, 229
  in insulin, 927
  pK′ values, 469
  physical properties, 91
  in seed globulins, 979
  structure, 237
  in tobacco mosaic virus, 980
  ultraviolet absorption spectrum, 431,
    435
D-Phenylalanine,
  crystals, structure of, 360
  occurrence, 99
Phenylalanine-d,
  preparation, 132
Phenylalanine-1,2-C^{14},
  preparation, 132
Phenylalanine-1,3,5-C^{14},
  preparation, 132

Phenylbutyrate,
  reaction with albumin, 774
    free energies of, 786
Phenylbutyrylalanine,
  quantum yields, 449
2-Phenyl-4-oxazolinecarboxylic acids,
  from β-hydroxy amino acids, 119
Phenylpropionylalanine,
  quantum yields, 449
Phenylthiohydantoin,
  derivatives, from peptides, 148
Phosphatase, 50, 80
  biological activity, essential groups for,
    990
  effect on ovalbumin, 953, 954, 955
    on plakalbumin, 953, 955
Phosphates, organic,
  toxic effects, mechanism of, 945
Phosphofructokinase, 80
Phosphogalactoisomerase, 80
Phosphoglucomutase, 80
Phosphoglyceraldehyde dehydrogenase,
  see also D-Glyceraldehyde-3-phos-
    phate dehydrogenase
  distribution of groups in, 224
Phosphohydroxylysine,
  occurrence, 119
Phosphokinases,
  sulfhydryl groups and activity of,
Phosphoproteins, stability, 941
Phosphorus pentoxide,
  reaction of aliphatic hydroxyl groups
    with, 904, 906
    with protein, 904, 941
Phosphorylase, 80, 206
  amino acid composition, 218
  distribution of polar groups in, 207
  molecular weight, 218
  muscle, isolation of, PR enzyme and,
    819
    solubility, effect of temperature on,
      43
  rabbit muscle, molecular weight, 638
    physical constants, 638
Phosphorylase b,
  isoelectric point, 511
Phosphorylation, of proteins, 940–941
Phosphoserine,
  occurrence, 119
Phosphothreonine,
  occurrence, 119

Phosphovitin, 80
Photobacterium phosphoreum, reversible inhibition of bacterial luminescence in, 883
Phycocyan, 80
  Ceramium, main component, molecular weight, 637
  physical constants, 637
Phycoerythrin, 80
  Ceramium, molecular weight, 638
  physical constants, 638
Picrin, halogenated, reaction with proteins, 923
Pipsylchloride, see under *p*-Iodophenyl sulfonyl chloride
Pitocin,
  activity, essential groups for, 990
Pituitary,
  extraction of stable hormonal substances from, 1001
Plakalbumin,
  components of, 504–505
  conversion of ovalbumin to, 149, 170, 895, 951–955
    mechanism of, 952–954
    nature of peptides formed in, 953
  electrophoretic mobility, 952
  enzymatic dephosphorylation, 953, 955
    properties of products formed, 955
  molecular weight, 636
    from osmotic pressure measurements, 594
    physical constants, 636
  relationship between ovalbumin and, 952–953
  solubility, 958
  structure, 954
Plant viruses, see also under names of individual viruses
  biological specificity,
    structure of nucleic acid component and, 980
  nucleoprotein nature of, 981
Plasma,
  albumins, see under Albumins, plasma
  bovine, electrophoretic analysis, 519
  components, 516
  electrophoretic analysis, 515ff.
    choice of buffer, 516
    effect of disease on, 522
    species differences in, 521

  human, electrophoretic analysis, 519
    preservation with organic mercurials, 34
    stabilizers for, 829
  isolation of proteins from, 56–57, 58
  lipoproteins of, 723, 724
  removal of calcium from, 34
  swine, electrophoretic analysis, 517
Plasmin, see under Fibrinolysin
Plasteins,
  formation, 177
Pneumococcus polysaccharide antibodies, antigenic specificity, 975
Poliomyelitis virus, 85
  molecular weight, 639
  physical constants, 639
Polyacrylic acids,
  reaction with alkali metals, 796
Polyamides,
  ultraviolet absorption spectra, 438
Polyamino acids, see also under names of individual compounds
  effect on bacteria, 175
Polyarginine,
  synthesis, 175
Polyaspartic acid,
  synthesis, 175
Poly-γ-benzyl L-glutamate,
  molecular structure, α-helical, 384, 385, 386
Polycysteine,
  synthesis, 175
Polycystine,
  synthesis, 175
Polyglycine,
  infrared spectra, 420
Polyhedral (silkworm) virus,
  molecular weight, 639
  physical constants, 639
Polymers,
  high, structure of, 553
  infrared spectra of, determination of structure by, 419
  synthetic, dielectric properties of long-chain, 709
Poly-γ-methyl L-glutamate,
  molecular structure, α-helical, 384, 385, 386
Polyornithine,
  guanylation, 112
  synthesis, 175

Polypeptidase, yeast, 81
Polypeptide chains,
  configurations of, 241, 242, 290–291, 372–389
    helical, 378–383
    non-helical, 376–378
  covalent cross bridges between, 886
  folded (coiled), 5, 239, 240, 241, 289
    in fibrous proteins, 286
    in globular proteins, 278, 279ff.
    in hemoglobin, 720
    in keratin, 239
    as model of protein structure, 326–327
    in myoglobin, 719
    structure, 290
    unfolding of, 278, 282
      during denaturation, 289
  salt linkages in, 260ff.
  sequence of amino acid residues in, as criterion of protein purity, 556
  structure, 242, 289, 356
  in zinc insulin crystals, 355
Polypeptides,
  basic, reaction with tobacco mosaic virus, 880
  birefringence, 397
  denaturation, 808
  infrared spectra, 421
  key frequencies and dichroic ratios, 426
  optical rotation, 411–416
  structure, 133
    infrared spectra and, 423, 429
  synthesis, 175
  synthetic, infrared spectra of, 424
  ultraviolet absorption spectrum, 436
Polypeptin sulfate,
  molecular weight, 150
Polysaccharides,
  antigenicity, 978
  pneumococcal,
    antigenic, 74
    isolation of antibody to, 72
  reaction with proteins, 800, 801
    electrophoretic survey, 531, 745
  removal from protein solutions, 32, 35
  role of cellubiuronic acid in antigenic specificity of, 995
Polytyrosine,
  synthesis, 175

Porphyrindin,
  reaction with sulfhydryl groups, 835, 903, 904
Potassium phosphate,
  as salting-out agent for proteins, 53
Potato latent mosaic virus,
  molecular weight, 639
  physical constants, 639
Pregnant mare serum hormone,
  activity, essential groups for, 990
Pressor hormone, oxytocic,
  molecular weight, 635
  physical constants, 635
Prolactin, see also under Lactogenic hormone
  amino acid composition, 213
  biological activity, essential groups for, 233
  distribution of groups in, 203, 224
  isoelectric point, 213
  molecular weight, 213, 635
    from osmotic pressure measurements, 594
  physical constants, 635
Prolamines, see also under Seed proteins, 83
  effect of alcohol on, 822
  isolation, 56
  solubility, 36, 56, 559
Prolan,
  activity, essential groups for, 990
Proline,
  detection, 115
  determination in protein hydrolyzates, 113
  diffusion constant, determination, 631
  distribution in proteins, 211, 212, 213, 214, 215, 216, 217, 218, 219, 220, 221, 222, 223, 225, 228, 229
  identification, 125
  pK' values, 469
  physical properties, 91
  reaction with nitrous acid, 113
  resolution of DL-, 130
  structure, 237
  in tobacco mosaic virus, 980
D-Proline,
  occurrence, 99

1098   SUBJECT INDEX

Propionylphenylalanine,
  quantum yields, 449
Prosthetic-removing (PR) enzyme,
  isolation of, effect of phosphorylase on, 9
Protamine-insulinate, 45
Protamines, see also under names of
    individual members, 80, 201
  amino acid composition, 211
  methyl esters of, 919
  reaction with proteins, role of con-
      figuration in, 802
Proteases, 81
Protein hormones,
  species variations in, 987
Proteinase(s),
  bacterial, 81, 83
    stabilization, 35
  pancreatic, thermal destruction, 868
Protein(s), see also under Peptides and
    under names of individual members
  acid- and base-binding capacities,
      determination of maximum, 481–
      483
  acidic and basic groups of, 476–477
  action of enzymes on, 8, 238
  acylation, 924–931
  aggregation, 843, 847, 848
  alkylation, 917, 918
  "all-or-none" proteolysis, 167
  amide groups of, determination, 921
    reagents for, 906
  amino acid composition, 181–233, 448
    biological activity and, 977–981, 1013
    classification based on, 227–229
    enzyme character and, 230
    methods of analysis, 183, 186–198
      assessment of accuracy and speci-
          ficity of, 198–210
    molecular weight and, 184
    properties and, 232–233, 238
    purity and, 184, 979–980
    source and, 978–979
  amino groups of, 839, 903
    biological activity and, 905
    determination, 934, 939
    reaction with FDNB, 904, 917–918
    reagents for, 839, 904, 905, 906
  antigenicity, see under biological activ-
      ity, antigenic
  apparent molal volumes, 563–564
    definition, 563

arylation, 917–918
asparaginyl residues in, 94
asymmetric,
  denaturation, effect on hydrody-
      namic properties, 844, 891
  structure, 844, 891
benzoylation, 929–930
  mechanism, 930
binding of water by, see also under hy-
    dration, 559–562, 690
  effect on density, 561
    on volume, 561, 562
  free energy of, 561
  groups participating in, 560–561
  vapor pressure of water and, 559, 560
biological activity, 974
  active centers for 975, 977, 989–994,
      1013, 1014
    determination of number of groups
        in, 991–992
  amino acid composition and, 977–
      981, 1013
  antigenic, 20, 975
    chemical basis, 947–948, 978
    of fetal, 986
  composition and, 976
  configuration and, 890, 976, 982ff.,
      1007, 1014
  denaturation and, 813, 981–984, 1013
  effect of chemical modification on,
      956–972
    of conjugation on, 974
  essential groups for, 898, 906, 968,
      969, 971, 978, 990, 1013
  esterification and, 920
  of hydrolysis products, 1013
  as intrinsic molecular property, 957,
      974
  nature of, 975, 1009–1012
  physical properties and, 982, 983,
      984, 1013
  solubility and, 976
  specificity of, 974, 975
    amino acid composition and, 981
    molecular configuration and, 976
    molecular weight and, 976
    structure and, 1013
  structure and, 901, 968, 973–1015
biosynthesis, 176
  structural aspects of, 972
birefringence, 395

Protein(s) (*continued*)
  imidazole groups, of proteins,
    reaction with zinc, 794
    reagents for, 904, 906
  immunological properties, 858
    effect of denaturation on, 858–860
    structure and, 860
  indolyl groups of, 837
    oxidation of, 909
    reagents for, 837, 904, 906
  infrared spectra, 416, 421, 426
  interactions, see also under Protein
      reactions, 609, 727–806
    anion-binding sites, 886
    binding data, graphical representa-
        tion, 771–773
    biological significance, 804–806
    electrophoretic survey, 531, 532
    immunological aspects, 804–806
    of insoluble, theories of, 770
    internal, 802–804
    long-range forces in, 1011
    methods of investigation,
      depending on interacting sub-
          stance, 736–739
        on changes in protein, 738–748
    nonabsorptive, with visible light,
        394–416
    with other molecules, 730–737
    pharmacological aspects, 804–806
    with proteins, 746, 800–802
      electrophoretic survey, 745
      role of electrostatic factors, 800,
          801
      structural aspects, 802
    with small anions, 773–789
      effect of anion concentration, 773–
          776
        of pH and buffer on, 778–780
        of temperature on, 776–777
      electrostatic interactions of suc-
          cessively bound anions, 776–777
      molecular structure of anion and,
          780–785
        of protein and, 788
      size of molecule and, 784–785
      specific, 785–787
    with small cations, 789–798
      with hydrogen ions, 789–791
      with metallic ions, 793–798
      with organic cations, 791–793

  with small neutral molecules, 798–
      800
  stoichiometry, 746
  structural aspects, 264
  theory of multiple equilibria, 748–
      771
    with ultraviolet light, 445
    with water, 798–799
  interconversion of groups in, 948–950
  intramolecular cross-linkages in, 288
  iodinated, preparation of labeled, 896
  iodination, 120, 936–940
  ionization of, 476–494
    heat of, 477, 483–484
    identification of ionizing groups, 473,
        483–484
    pK' values, 469, 477
  isoelectric points, 508–515, 959
    definition, 508
    determination, 508–512, 746
  isoionic points, 740–742
  isolation of, 1–85
    of cellular, 10–14
    choice of sources, 9
    general principles, 5–14
    methods, 14–28
      survey of, 13
    prevention of changes in protein
        structure during, 5–9
    by salting-out, 53ff.
    from yeast, 52
  light scattering by, 405–408
  linkage between amino acids in, 238
  linked groups of, 484
  macromolecules in, 239
  malonylation, 928–929, 959
  masked groups in, 837, 886, 898, 899
    determination, 832ff., 899
    structural significance, 831
    titratability, 850
  mercaptide formation, 914–916
  metal, magnetic properties, 747
  of milk, see also under Lactalbumin
    amino acid composition, 216
    distribution of groups in, 205, 224
    isoelectric point, 206
  mixtures, composition, 2
    electrophoretic survey of species
        differences in, 520ff.
    separation by chromatography, 66–
        68

1106 SUBJECT INDEX

Pyridoxal, phosphorylated, 105
Pyrophosphatase,
 molecular weight, 636
 physical constants, 636
Pyrrolidine-α-carboxylic acid, see under
 Proline
L-Pyrrolidonyl-L-glutamine,
 from *Pelvetia fastigiata*, 145
Pyruvic oxidase,
 molecular weight, 638
 physical constants, 638
Pyruvylalanine, alanylalanine from, 180

Q

Quill,
 infrared spectrum of porcupine, 427
 of swan, 427

R

Rabbit papilloma virus, 85
 composition, 657
 density, 656
 hydration, 656
 molecular weight, 639
 partial specific volume, 656
 physical constants, 639
 sedimentation, 60
Reduction, polarographic in study of protein complexes, 735
Refractrometry,
 in study of protein interactions, 743
Relaxation time,
 of amino acids, 701
 of proteins, 702, 707–710
  from dielectric dispersion, 694, 699
  from double refraction of flow, 699
  from polarization of fluorescence,
   712–716
  relation to dielectric dispersion,
   704–710
  to molecular size and shape, 697
  to rotary diffusion constants, 696
Rennin, 81
Resins, ion exchange,
 purification of proteins with, 480–481,
  557–558
 removal of ions from protein solutions
  with, 34
 separation of amino acids with, 139

of peptides with, 139
Rhodopsin, 729
Ribonuclease, 82
 amino acid composition, 211, 789
 chromatographic resolution, 69
 crystals, x-ray data on, 297
 cystine content, 978
 distribution of groups in, 224
 effect of ionizing radiation on, 820
 homogeneity, 24, 987
 inactivation, pH and, 815
  quantum yield of photo-, 451
 infrared spectrum, 430
 isoelectric point, 511
 isolation, 51
 molecular weight, 634, 976
  from amino acid analysis, 570
 physical constants, 634
 purification, 558
 reaction with tobacco mosaic virus, 880
 specific volume, 568
 stability, 858, 982
  cystine content and, 978
 structure, 166, 327, 334–341
Ricin, 84
 denaturation, 875
  ionizing steps in, 887
  order of, 862
  prototropic steps in, 873–874

S

SDS, see under Dodecyl sodium sulfate
Saccharase, films, biological activity, 858
Safranine,
 interaction with proteins, 58
Salicylates,
 reaction with proteins, 888
Salmine, 82
 amino acid composition, 211
 distribution of groups in, 224
 hydrolysis by trypsin, 169
 molecular weight, 197, 211
 structure, 146, 201
  species variations in, 201
 N-terminal residues in, 197, 211
Salt linkages, 241
 protein configuration and, 982
Sarcosine,
 pK′ values, 469

Scarlet fever toxin, 84
  biological activity, essential groups for,
    990
  molecular weight, 635
  physical constants, 635
Scleroproteins,
  iodinated, of invertebrates, 936
  solubility, 36
Secalin,
  dielectric properties, 702
  molecular size and shape, 702
  relaxation time, 702
  solubility, 559
Sedimentation, of proteins, 59–61
  effect of diffusion on diagrams, 652
  molecular weight and, 667–668
  studies in polydispersed systems, 65
Sedimentation constants,
  of proteins, 634–639, 652
    effect of protein concentration on,
      659–662
      solvation on, 653ff.
    frictional coefficient from, 652
    relation to molecular weight, 649
Seed globulins, 82, see also under Seed
    proteins and under names of individ-
    ual members
  amino acid composition, 976
  antigenic specificity, source and, 985
  isolation, 47
  physical constants, 663
  prunus, molecular weight from light-
    scattering, 608
  solubility, temperature and, 43
  sulfur content, 979
Seed proteins, see also under Prolamines,
    Seed globulins, 82–83, 200
  amino acid composition, 202, 223
    species variations in, 209
  distribution of groups in, 208, 224
  homogeneity, 209
  physiological importance of amides in,
    202
Sericin, 83
Serine, 886, 906
  crystals, structure, 361
  destruction, 158, 159
  detection, 115
  determination, 113

distribution in proteins, 211, 212, 213,
  214, 215, 216, 217, 218, 219, 220,
  221, 222, 223, 225, 228, 229
pK' values, 469
oxazoline ring formation from, 112
oxidation, 118
physical properties, 91
racemization, 160
resolution of DL-, 130
separation from glycine, 543
structure, 237
in tobacco mosaic virus, 980
L-Serine,
  structure, 90
Serine-1-C^{13},
  preparation, 132
Serum,
  bovine, proteins of, fractionation, 545
  conjugation with azo salts, 948
  denaturation, effect on electrical prop-
    erties, 853
  electrophoretic analysis, 517, 519, 520,
    545
    effect of disease on, 522
    of heating on, 522
    of light on, 522
  human, effect of acetic acid on, 523
  reaction with sodium, 795
    with sulfanilamide, 743
  Reagic, fractionation, 546
  stabilizers for, 828
Serum globulins,
  amino groups of, 839
    reactivity of, 901
  denaturation, effect on molecular
    weight, 841
    on specific viscosity, 844
    pressure and, 818
    volume change in thermal, 891
  horse, determination of tryptophan in,
    437
    of tyrosine in, 437
    refractive index, 403
  molecular dimensions, from light scat-
    tering, 615
  molecular weight, from osmotic pres-
    sure measurements, 596
  reaction with calcium, 797
  solubility, effect of salt addition on, 37
    ionic strength and, 40
  synthesis, effect of antigens on, 1007

Serum proteins,
  antigenicity, effect of amides on, 823
    species differences in, 985
  denaturation, effects of, 813
  effect on drug activity, 804, 805
    on excretion, 805
  heat coagulation, effect of iodoacetate
    on, 917
  horse, isolation of, 50
  reaction with calcium, 733, 735
    with guanidine, 799
    with steroid compounds, 799–800
    with urea, 799
    with urethan, 799
  sheep, substituted, production of anti-
    serum against, 995–996
  stabilizers for, 748
  unreactive groups in, 900
Serylalanine,
  separation, 143
Siderophilin, 83
  reaction with copper, 797
    with iron, 797
Silk,
  degummed suture, infrared spectrum,
    427
  electrophoretic properties, 548
  infrared spectrum, 427
    structure and, 423, 427
  structure, infrared spectra and, 423,
    425
  water adsorption of wet and dry, 560
  x-ray diffraction pattern, 253
Silk fibroin, 251–253
  amino acid composition, 220
    source and, 979
  distribution of groups in, 224
  fibers, birefringence, 398
  hydrolysis products, immunological
    behavior of, 1002
  molecular weight of, 1003
  infrared spectra, 420
  methylation, 919
  specific volume, 568
  structure, 251–253
  ultraviolet absorption spectrum, 438
  x-ray diffraction studies on, 239, 251–
    253, 855
Silver,
  reaction with proteins, 793
Snake venom toxin, 84

Snake venoms, species differences in,
  electrophoretic survey, 521
Sodium salicylate,
  effect on proteins, 822, 824–825
    mechanism, 824, 825
Solanine,
  biological activity, essential groups for,
    990
Solubility, of proteins,
  effect of denaturation on, 812, 813,
    816
Solvents, organic,
  effect on proteins, 815, 821, 822, 826,
    828, 849
    mechanism, 825, 829
    on titration curves of amino acids,
      474–475
  isolation of proteins with, 56–58
Sound waves,
  effect on proteins, 817
  in isolation of bacterial enzymes, 817
Southern bean mosaic virus,
  hydration, 576, 657
  isoelectric point, 511
  molecular size and shape, 657
    electron microscope studies on, 574,
      576
  molecular weight, 639
  physical constants, 639
Soybeans,
  trypsin inhibitor in, 974
Spectrophotometry, in study of protein
    interactions, 737–738, 742–743
Squash mosaic viruses,
  molecular size and shape, electron
    microscope studies on, 574
Staphylococcus antitoxin,
  inactivation, of equine, order of, 862
    pressure and, 818
Stearyl anilide,
  photolysis, 448
Steroids,
  interaction with proteins, 730, 799
Stromatin, 83
Subtilin,
  fractionation, 144
  structure, 159
Succinic dehydrogenase, 720
  biological activity, sulfhydryl groups
    and, 233, 992

Sucrose,
  measurement of diffusion constants for, 630
Sugars,
  reaction with proteins, 828, 934
Sulfadiazine,
  reaction with proteins, effect of substituents on, 785
  with serum, 743
Sulfation, of proteins, 942
Sulfhydryl groups,
  properties of cysteine and, 9
  of proteins, activation in denaturation, 888–889
    determination, 194, 195, 196, 832–836, 899
    reaction with metallic ions, 793
      with war gases, 922
    reactivity, 289, 902
    reagents for, 833, 834, 835, 902, 903, 904, 914–915
    role in biological activity of enzymes, 233, 907, 909, 990
      of proteins, 971, 992ff.
Sulfides,
  reduction of disulfide bonds by, 913
Sulfonamides,
  reaction with plasma proteins, 778
Supercontraction, of keratin, 264
Suramin, 805
  reaction with plasma proteins, 805
  stabilizing effect on serum proteins, 748

T

T globulin, 83
Tanning, 932
  possible mechanism, 933
  protein chemistry and, 894
Taurine,
  from cysteinesulfonic acid, 124
  pK' values, 469
Tendon,
  Achilles, 208
    amino acid composition, 221
    distribution of groups in, 224
  yellow, 208–209
    amino acid composition, 221
    distribution of groups in, 224
Tetanus toxin, 84

Tetraethyl pyrophosphate,
  inhibition of α-chymotrypsin by, 945
Tetraglycylglycine,
  synthesis, 173
Tetrahydro-6-hydroxy-4-pyrimidine-carboxylic acid,
  from asparagine, 112
4,5,6,7-Tetrahydro-1H-imidazo[c]pyridine-6-carboxylic acid,
  from histidine, 113
Tetrathionase, 1006
Tetrathionate,
  reaction with sulfhydryl reagents, 836
Thiaminokinase, 83
4-Thiazolidine carboxylic acid,
  from cysteine, 112
Thiocyanate,
  effect on blood clotting, 748
  effect on proteins, 825, 888
  reaction with insulin, 744, 787
    free energies of, 786
    with serum albumin, sites, 776
Thioglycollic acid,
  effect on proteins, 287
  reaction with disulfide groups, 836, 904, 913
Thiohydantoin,
  preparation, 110
Thiolhistidine,
  occurrence, 102
Thiolhistidine-N^{15},
  preparation, 132
Thiols,
  reaction with arsenical vesicants, 916
β-Thiolvaline,
  occurrence, 97
D-β-Thiolvaline,
  occurrence, 99
2-Thio-5-thiazolidone,
  4-substituted, 111
2-Thio-5-thiazolidone,
  derivatives, from peptides, 148
Threonine, 886, 906
  destruction, 158, 159
  distribution in proteins, 211, 212, 213, 214, 215, 216, 217, 218, 219, 220, 221, 222, 223, 225, 228, 229
  oxazoline ring formation from, 112
  oxidation, 118
  physical properties, 91
  in pig insulin, 20

Threonine (*continued*)
  preparation, 93
  racemization, 160
  reduction, 118
  resolution of DL-, 130
  in seed globulin, 979
  structure, 90, 93, 237, 364, 369
  in tobacco mosaic virus, 980
L-Threonine,
  configuration, 93
  structure, 361, 365–366, 371
Threonylproline,
  from insulin, 159
Thrombin, 83
  oxidation, by tyrosinase, 911
  reaction with fibrinogen, 723
Thrombokinase, 83
Thromboplastin, 83
Thymonucleic acid, 677
Thymus nucleate,
  heat coagulation of proteins and, 827
Thyroglobulin(s), 83, 936
  amino acid composition, 213
  denaturation, effect on electrophoretic
    mobility, 851
    reversible, mechanism of, 883, 884
  diiodotyrosine in, 89
  distribution of groups in, 203
  isoelectric point, 213
  molecular size and shape, 692
  molecular weight, 638
  physical constants, 638
  thyroxine in, 89
  viscosity, 692
Thyronine,
  from thyroxine, 121
Thyrotropin, 83
  labeled, biosynthesis, 939
Thyroxine, 937
  determination, 121
  from 3,5-diiodotyrosine, 120
  formation by iodination of peptides,
    121
    of proteins, 120
  isolation, 937
  occurrence in thyroglobulin, 89
  precursors, 938
  structure, 237
  synthesis, 121
  thyronine from, 121

L-Thyroxine,
  synthesis from L-tyrosine, 121
Tissues,
  electrophoretic analysis of, 522
Titration, of proteins, 194
  conductometric, 735
  differential, 485–487
Titration curves, of proteins, 477–494
  effect of interaction with ions on, 739–
    742
Tobacco disease viruses, 85
Tobacco mosaic virus, 725–726
  acylating agents for, 924, 929, 930
  amino acid composition of various
    strains of, 980
    biological relationships and, 980–981
  amino groups of, reactivity, 900
  biological activity, 968, 990
    of chemically modified, 929, 930, 956
    essential groups for, 956
  birefringence, 400, 667
  chemical modification, biological ef-
    fects, 970
    effect on infectivity, 969
      on stability, 902
  denaturation, 814, 842, 847, 900
    effect on hydrodynamic properties,
      844
    of pH on rate, 872
    kinetics, 865
  dissociation, 881
  effect of carboxypeptidase on, 956
    of high pressure on, 818, 891
    on sedimentation of bushy stunt
      virus, 662
    of ultraviolet irradiation on, 819
  electrophoretic mobility, strain differ-
    ences in, 505
  filaments, formation of, 285
  gels of, 356
  homogeneity, 676–677
    electrophoretic, of acetylated, 966–
      967, 968
  hydration, 657, 726
    effect of solvation on, 656–657, 658
  inactivation, 880–881
    by light, quantum yield, 451
  infectivity, essential groups for, 968
    of modified, 969
  light scattering, 407, 608, 613
    depolarization ratios, 407

Trypsin (*continued*)
films, biological activity, 856
  molecular weight in, 624
hydrolysis of peptides by, 168, 169,
  170, 238
inactivation, 882
  entropy changes in, 890
  heat of, 869, 875
  by light, quantum yield, 451, 453
  nature and number of bonds broken
    in, 871
  reversible, 869, 983
isolation, 51, 974
molecular weight, 635
  from osmotic pressure measure-
    ments, 594
oxidation, by tyrosinase, 911
physical constants, 635
quantum yield of photoinactivation,
  451, 453
reaction with acetic anhydride, 925
  with cations, 792
  with trypsin inhibitor, 802
stability, 70, 858
structure, 171
ultraviolet absorption spectrum, 435
Trypsin inhibitor, 81, see also under Ovomucoid
inactivation, 862
isolation, 51
occurrence, 974
reaction with trypsin, 802
  molecular weight, from osmotic
    pressure measurements, 594
  quantum yield of photoinactivation,
    451
reversible inactivation, 882
  kinetics, 869, 875
Trypsinogen, 81, 84
activation, 171
isolation, 51
structure, 171
Tryptophan, 906
destruction, 158
detection, 115
determination, 430
  in proteins, 194, 195, 437
    ultraviolet absorption spectrum
      and, 18, 436
diazo compound of, 122

diffusion constant, determination of,
  631
distribution in proteins, 211, 212, 213,
  214, 215, 216, 217, 218, 219, 220,
  221, 222, 223, 225, 227, 229
identification, 125
oxidation with permanganate, 910
pK' values, 469
physical properties, 91
protein properties and, 227
in seed globulins, 979
structure, 237
in tobacco mosaic virus, 980
ultraviolet absorption spectrum, 431,
  434, 435
  and determination of, 433
Tryptophan-N^{15},
preparation, 132
Tryptophan desmolase, 84
Tuberculin, 84
Tuberculosis bacillus protein,
human, molecular weight, 635
  physical constants, 635
Tumors,
malignant, ultraviolet microscopy of,
  460
Turnip yellow mosaic virus(es),
molecular size and shape, electron
  microscope studies on, 574
molecular weight, 315, 639
physical constants, 639
protein fraction, antigenicity of, 978
x-ray data on, 294, 315
Tyramine,
enzymatic formation, 105, 106
Tyrocidine,
analysis, 137, 141
fractionation, 144
optical rotation, 409
ornithine from, 96
polypeptide structure of, 133
Tyrosinase, 84
biological activity, source and, 912
effect of metal ions on, 912
oxidation of proteins by, 911–913
Tyrosine, 886
assay, enzymatic, 189
biological activity of, anti-Rh agglu-
  tinine and, 913
detection, 115

determination, 430
  in proteins, 194, 195, 437, 837
  ultraviolet absorption spectrum and,
    436
diazo compound of, 122, 946
distribution in proteins, 211, 212, 213,
    214, 215, 216, 217, 218, 219, 220,
    221, 222, 223, 225, 228, 229
in egg albumin, 837
enzymatic decarboxylation, 105
identification, 125
iodinated, determination, 121
  titration curves, 965
iodination, 937–938
  effect on ionization constants, 483
ionizable groups of, 462, 477
  heat of ionization, 477
  pK' value, 477
    iodination and, 483
oxidation with permanganate, 910
  with tyrosinase, 912–913
phenolic hydroxyl groups of, 907
physical properties, 91
role in biological activity of chymo-
    trypsin, 935
in seed globulins, 979
structure, 237
in tobacco mosaic virus, 980
ultraviolet absorption spectrum, 431,
    435, 839
  and determination of, 433, 436
L-Tyrosine,
  pK' values, 469
synthesis of L-thyroxine from, 121
Tyrosine-2-C¹⁴,
  preparation, 132
Tyrosine-3-C¹⁴,
  preparation, 132
Tyrosyltyrosine,
  pK' values of, 470
Tyrothricin,
  fractionation, 144

U

Ultracentrifugation, of protein com-
    plexes, 732–733
separation of proteins by, 59–62
Ultracentrifuges, for sedimentation
  studies on proteins, 664–665

Ultrafiltration, of protein complexes,
    731–732
Ultraviolet microspectrophotometry, 454
Urea,
  dissociation of proteins into molecu-
    lar subunits in solutions of, 596
  effect on proteins, 287, 799, 804, 822,
    823, 826, 841, 845
    denaturing, 841–842, 844ff.
  heat coagulation of proteins and, 827
Urease, 84
  biological activity,
    of monomolecular layers of, 858, 984
    number of active centers, 975
    solubility and, 976
    sulfhydryl groups and, 992–993
  effect of DFP on, 946
  films, biological activity, 858, 984
    of ultraviolet irradiation on, 819
  inactivation, quantum yield of photo-
    451, 452
    reversible, 983, 984
  isolation, 57, 66
    of crystalline, 974
    source and, 11
  molecular weight, 638, 976
  physical constants, 638
  sulfhydryl groups, 832, 833
δ-Ureidonorvaline, see under Citrulline
Urethan,
  reaction with proteins, 799, 822
Uricase, 84
Urogastrone, 84

V

Vaccines,
  preparation, 894, 932
Vaccinia virus,
  composition, 657
Valine,
  detection, 115
  distribution in proteins, 211, 212, 213,
    214, 215, 216, 217, 218, 219, 220,
    221, 222, 223, 225, 227, 229
  effect of solvation on size, shape and
    internal composition of, 656
  infrared absorption, 420
  ionization, heat of, 472
  pK' values, 469, 472
  physical properties, 91

Valine (continued)
  resolution of DL-, 130
  in seed globulins, 979
  structure, 237
  in tobacco mosaic virus, 980
D-Valine,
  occurrence, 99
Valine-3,4-d,
  preparation, 132
Valine peptides,
  stability, 164
Van Slyke method, for determination of
    amino groups, 934
Vasopressin,
  fractionation, 144
Vesicants, arsenical, see also under
    Lewisite
  effect of thiols on, 916
Vibrio phosphorescens, reversible inhibi-
    tion of bacterial luminescence in, 883
Virus proteins,
  molecular size and shape, from x-ray
    studies, 312–316
  removal from human serum albumin,
    34
Viruses, 85, see also under names of indi-
    vidual members
  animal, 85
    effect of high pressure on, 818
  bacterial, surface inactivation, 817
  biological activity, effect of chemical
    modification on, 897, 969
    essential groups for, 990
  chemical modification, biological activ-
    ity and, 897, 969
  effect of ultraviolet irradiation on, 818
    of urea on, 823
  hydration, 726
  interaction with heparin, 58
  isolation, 60
  molecular weights, 639
  physical constants, 639
  plant, 85
    inactivation, 880
    molecular size and shape, from elec-
      tron microscope studies, 572, 574
  protein nature, 974
  reaction with host cells, 801, 806
  reproduction, 971
  size of, 60
  stabilizers for, 827, 828

Viscometer,
  for measuring non-Newtonian flow, 694
Viscosity,
  definition, 693
  effect of molecular orientation on, 693–
    695
  non-Newtonian, 693
    measurement, 694
  relation to molecular shape, 686–698
    to translational diffusion constant,
      649
  of solutions containing large mole-
    cules, 686ff.
  structural, 693
Viscosity increment(s),
  of proteins, 692
  relation to molecular shape and hydra-
    tion, 689ff.
Visual purple,
  interconversion between visual yellow
    and, 891
Vitamin B₁₂,
  crystals, 293
    wet and dry stages, 293
Vitellin, 85
  structure, 941

W

War gases, see also under Mustard gas
    and under names of individual com-
    pounds
  effect on biological systems, 922
  mutagenic activity, 922
  reaction with SH groups of proteins,
    922
Water,
  interaction with proteins, 559–562,
    798–799
Whey proteins,
  species differences in, electrophoretic
    survey, 521
Witte peptone,
  insoluble proteins from, 177
Wool,
  chemical modification, availability of
    groups for, 901
  fibrils, formation of, 285
  interactions, 739, 740, 770, 785
    with dyes, 729, 770
    with optically active substances,
      783–784

methylation, 919
specific volume, 568
titration curves, 792
  effect of interaction with ions on, 739, 740
water absorption by, 798

X

Xanthine oxidase, 69, 76, 85
X-rays,
  diffraction, by crystals, 245–251
    fiber photographs, 248–249
    powder photographs, 247
    single crystal photographs, 247–248
    diffraction patterns,
      of denatured proteins, 279
      of native proteins, 279, 280
  scattering of,
    by crystals, intensity of, 250–251
    low-angle, by protein solutions, 616–621

Y

Yeast,
  extracts, fractionation, 57
  isolation of triosephosphate dehydrogenase from, 58
  isolation of proteins from, 52
  of zymase from, 10
Yellow enzyme, 76, 85
  respiratory, isolation of, 495
  purification by moving-boundary method, 543
Yellow fever virus,
  molecular weight, 639
  physical constants, 639

Z

Zein, 82, 85, 202
  amino acid composition, 209, 223, 448

birefringence, 401
denaturation, effect on molecular weight, 841
  on x-ray diffraction pattern, 280
determination of tryptophan in, 195, 437
  of tyrosine in, 195, 437
dielectric properties, 702
distribution of groups in, 208, 224
films of, 623
homogeneity, 559
hydrolyzate, composition of, 94
iodinated, titration curves, 965
isolation, 56
molecular size and shape, 684, 702
molecular weight, 635, 684
  effect of denaturation on, 841
physical constants, 636, 663
relaxation time, 702
solubility, 559
ultraviolet absorption spectrum, 438
Zein plasteins,
  molecular weight, 177
Zinc,
  insulin, crystals, hydration of, 292
    structure of, 312, 321, 323, 328–329
    x-ray data on, 297
    molecular weight of protein component, 311–312, 321
    specific volume, 568
  reaction with proteins, 735, 793, 794
    sites of, 794
  serum albumin complex, electrical properties, 735
Zinc salts, of proteins,
  solubility, 58
Zymase,
  isolation, 10
Zymogens,
  activation, 171
  of proteolytic enzymes, denaturation of, 882